# UPCO's

# Physical Setting

# Review

# EARTH SCIENCE

**Robert B. Sigda, Ph.D.**
Former Science Department Chairman
East Islip Schools
East Islip, New York

## UPCO-United Publishing Co., Inc.

21A Railroad Avenue
Albany, New York 12205

**Editor**

**Mary Bishop**
**Science Department Chairperson**
**Saugerties High School**
**Saugerties, New York**

Front Cover - view of Earth, taken on August 25, 1992 by the NOAA GOES-7 satellite.
NASA/JPL/Caltech and NOAA

Acknowledgments:
Special recognition for their contributions is accorded to:

**Ms. Jayne Humbert, M.S.**
**Earth Science Tutor**
**Syracuse, New York**

**Mr. Les Lowinger and his eighth grade students**
**Seaford Middle School**
**Seaford, New York**

**Mr. Peter Brusoe and his eighth grade students**
**Philip Livingston Magnet Academy**
**Albany, New York**

ISBN 0-937323-19-5

ESPHSE-0904

1 2 3 4 5 6 7 8 9 0

# CONTENTS

# CHAPTER 1
# PROLOGUE

## THE LOCAL ENVIRONMENT

### Observation

When you look at the stars or feel the force of the wind, you are making observations. An **observation** is an interaction of one or more of the senses – sight, hearing, touch, taste, or smell – with the environment or surroundings. The ability of the senses are limited. Therefore, instruments have been invented and developed to extend the powers of observation. **Instruments** improve our ability to observe and to make measurements that would otherwise be very inaccurate or even impossible to make. For example, a telescope allows us to take a closer look at the stars. A scale enables us to accurately determine how much we weigh by measuring the pull of Earth's gravity on our bodies, which is something our senses don't readily observe.

### Inference

An **inference** is an interpretation of one or more observations. The process of **inferring,** or making inferences, includes proposing explanations or reaching conclusions. When you examine scratches or grooves in exposed bedrock, you are observing. If you say that the scratches were caused by a glacier, you are making an inference. You are proposing an explanation for the presence of the scratches.

Some inferences are really predictions. A **prediction** is an inference based on observations that indicate what will happen in the future. For example, weather predictions are very common. By observing certain characteristics, such as cloud cover, wind speed and direction, and air pressure, people make predictions about upcoming weather.

### Classification

In order to make observations more meaningful, scientists often group different objects and events together on the basis of common properties or characteristics. Grouping of objects and events is called **classification,** and is based on observable properties. Samples of matter, for example, are usually classified by phase, that is, solid, liquid or gas (vapor). Almost everyone has, at one time or another, collected something–shells or rocks perhaps–and organized or classified the objects into various groups according to shape, color, or other similar properties.

# QUESTIONS

1. In order to make observations, an observer must use
   (1) experiments                 (2) the senses
   (3) proportions                  (4) mathematical calculations

2. A pebble found in a dry field has rounded edges. An instructor says that the pebble has been rolled over and over in a flowing stream. His comment can best be classified as
   (1) an inference      (2) a fact      (3) a description      (4) an observation

3. The general purpose of a scientific system of classification is to
   (1) make better interpretations    (2) organize for easier study
   (3) eliminate observations         (4) state theories

4. Which property was probably used to classify the substances below?
   (1) chemical composition           (2) specific heat
   (3) physical state (phase)         (4) abundance within Earth

| Group A | Group B | Group C |
|---------|---------|---------|
| water | aluminum | water vapor |
| gasoline | ice | air |
| alcohol | iron | oxygen |

5. Which descriptive term illustrates an inference?
   (1) transparent      (2) bitter      (3) younger      (4) smooth

6. The graph below shows the amount of noise pollution caused by factory machinery during a one-week period. Which inference is best supported by the graph?

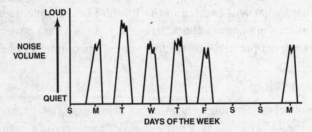

   (1) The machinery ran 24 hours a day.
   (2) The machinery was turned off on Saturday and Sunday.
   (3) The level of pollution remained constant during working hours.
   (4) The noise volume reached a peak on Friday.

**7.** A student recorded the times of three successive high tides at one location as:

9:12 a.m.
9:38 p.m.
10:04 a.m.

What is the approximate time of the next high tide?
(1) 10:12 p.m.　　　　(2) 10:30 p.m.　　　　(3) 10:38 p.m.　　　　(4) 11:04 p.m.

**8.** While on a field trip to a large lake in New York State, an observer recorded four statements about this lake. Which of these statements is most likely an inference?
(1) The lake was formed by glacial action.
(2) The water is clear enough to see the bottom of the lake.
(3) A log is floating in the lake.
(4) The surface temperature of the lake is 18.5°C.

# PROPERTIES OF THE ENVIRONMENT

## Measurement

　　Modern science requires that, for greater precision and accuracy, many observations be described through the use of numbers. A **measurement** is a means of describing observations using numbers. All measurements contain at least one of the three *basic dimensional quantities*–time, length, or mass. In order for a measurement to be understood, both the number of units and an appropriate label are usually needed.

　　Two different systems of measurement are in common use today. These are the metric system (now called the International System of Units, abbreviated SI) and the English system. The metric system is used exclusively in most countries throughout the world and in most scientific work in this country. However, some measurements relating to maps and weather are still made in the English system in the United States. Table 1-1 lists the basic dimensional units in both the metric and English systems.

| Unit | Metric | English |
|------|--------|---------|
| Time | second, minute, hour, day, year | second, minute, hour, day, year |
| Length | centimeter, meter, kilometer | inch, foot, mile |
| Mass | gram, kilogram | ounce, pound |

**TABLE 1-1:** MEASUREMENT SYSTEMS

　　**Time** is the instant at which something happens or the period during which a change occurs. To most people, the most familiar use of time is in keeping track of the "time of day." Change in the time of day is a scientific concept related to the apparent motion of the Sun in the sky.

**Length** is a measure of the distance between two points. Although distances are usually measured in the English system in the United States, some distances, such as 10K (kilometer) races, are measured in metric units.

**Mass** is the amount of matter in an object. Mass is often confused with *weight*. The two are frequently used interchangeably, but they are not the same. On Earth's surface, weight is a measure of the pull of Earth's gravity on a quantity of matter, such as your body. If you were to travel into space, beyond the influence of Earth's gravity, you would become "weightless." Yet, the mass of your body would remain unchanged, because your body would still contain the same amount of matter. Thus, the weight of a body may change with its location, but its mass never changes.

Some properties of matter are best described by using some mathematical combination of basic dimensional quantities. Volume, density, pressure, and speed are examples of properties that require such combinations.

*Volume* is the amount of space an object takes up. Volumes of solid objects are expressed as combinations of distance measurements. For example, the volume of a rectangular-shaped object combines three distance measurements:

$$\textbf{Volume} = \textbf{length} \times \textbf{width} \times \textbf{height}$$
$$\textbf{V} = \textbf{lwh}$$

Volume is usually expressed in cubic centimeters ($cm^3$).

*Density* is a property of matter that combines mass and volume.

$$\textbf{Density} = \frac{\textbf{mass}}{\textbf{volume}}$$

Density is usually expressed in grams per cubic centimeter ($g/cm^3$).

*Pressure* is a measure of force, or weight on a given area, and is expressed as newtons per square meter ($N/m^2$) or pounds per square inch ($lb/in^2$).

*Speed* is a measure of the rate of motion, and is often measured in meters per second (m/sec) or miles per hour.

Measurements of some properties of matter are made as direct comparisons with other standard units of measure. A **standard unit** is an accepted measurement against which other measurements can be compared. Some standard units include the second, the meter, and the gram. In order for a measurement to be precise, both the numerical value and the standard unit must be stated.

## Percent Deviation From Accepted Value

Although total accuracy is desired when measuring, most measurements are subject to error or inaccuracy. Errors may be caused by faulty measuring instruments, careless observations, or just plain human error.

The amount of error in a measurement can be determined by comparing the measurement with some standard or accepted value for that measurement. For example, suppose your weight was measured at 110 pounds on the school scale, which you knew to be accurate, and 121 pounds on your scale at home. You would know that this second measurement was in error. But *how* inaccurate is that scale? It is often useful to express the amount of error in a measurement as a percent. When expressed as a percent, it is called **percentage error,** or **percent deviation from accepted value.** To determine the percentage deviation, find the difference between the measured value and the accepted value. Divide this difference by the accepted value and multiply this result times 100%.

$$\text{Percentage deviation} = \frac{\text{difference between the measured value and the accepted value}}{\text{accepted value}} \times 100\%$$

The percentage deviation of the inaccurate scale can be calculated using this equation. The difference between the measured value and the accepted value provides us with the actual **amount of deviation** in the measurement. The difference between the measured value (the home scale) and the accepted value (the school scale) is 121 pounds–110 pounds, or 11 pounds. Using the above equation, the percentage deviation of measurements made on your home scale can be calculated:

$$\text{Percentage deviation} = \frac{121 \text{ pounds} - 110 \text{ pounds}}{110 \text{ pounds}} \times 100\%$$

$$= \frac{11 \text{ pounds}}{110 \text{ pounds}} \times 100\%$$

$$= .10 \times 100\%$$

$$= 10\%$$

The percentage deviation of measurements made on the home scale is 10%. This means that every measurement made on that home scale will be 10% too much. Every time you weigh yourself on that scale, you have to reduce the measurement by 10%.

# QUESTIONS

1. A student measures the volume of a rock sample to be 17 cubic centimeters. The student later finds that the actual volume of the rock is 20 cubic centimeters. Calculate the percent deviation of the student's measurement.
   (1) 15%          (2) 18%          (3) 3%          (4) 85%

2. Density is usually expressed in
   (1) $cm/in^2$          (2) $g/cm^3$          (3) km/hr          (4) $N/m^2$

3. The three basic dimensional qualities are
   (1) time, length, and shape          (2) density, mass, and volume
   (3) time, length, and mass          (4) density, volume, and weight

4. Two measurements often used interchangeably are
   (1) mass and length          (2) density and volume
   (3) length and shape          (4) weight and mass

5. A student determines the mass of a rock to be 196 grams, but the actual mass of the rock is 200 grams. The student's approximate percent deviation (percentage of error) is

   (1) 1.0%          (2) 2.0%          (3) 1.5%          (4) 4.0%

# DENSITY

## Density of Matter

**Density** is defined as the quantity of material contained in a certain amount of space. Something densely packed has a large quantity of material crowded into a small amount of space. For example, one hundred passengers jammed onto a 50-passenger bus would be densely packed. In scientific terms, density is defined as mass per unit volume, and is expressed by the equation

$$\text{Density} = \frac{\text{mass (m)}}{\text{volume (v)}}$$

The density of a substance is a physical property of that substance. No matter how large or small the sample, or what shape the sample, the density of a specific substance remains the same. For example, suppose you had a sample of clay in the shape of a perfect cube, having a volume of 40 $cm^3$ and a mass of 70 grams. The density of that clay would be 70 g/40 $cm^3$ = 1.75 $g/cm^3$. If you were to reshape the cube to form a ball, its volume would still be 40 $cm^3$ and its mass 70 grams. Thus, the density would still be 1.75 $g/cm^3$. If you were to cut the clay sample in half, both the mass and volume of each half-sample would be half the original values. The density of each half-sample would be 35 g/20 $cm^3$ = 1.75 $g/cm^3$.

The density of a substance can be represented graphically. As you have seen, the greater the mass of substance the greater its volume will be. On the graph below (Figure 1-1) mass and volume information for clay and water have been plotted. You can see the following data on the graph: 70 grams of clay occupy 40 cm³ of space, and 35 grams occupy 20 cm³. You can also see that 35 grams of water occupy 35 cm³ and 70 grams of water occupy 70 cm³.

If the graph is plotted with the mass on the Y axis (vertical) and volume on the X axis (horizontal) the mathematical slope of the line is equal to the density of the substance. The steeper the slope the more dense the substance. We could calculate the densities of clay and water easily, but it is easy to see from the graph that clay is more dense than water since its line is steeper.

We can also use our graph to determine the volume of clay (or water) if we know the mass, or the mass if we know the volume.

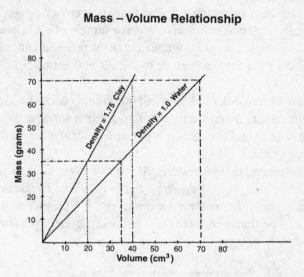

**Figure 1-1.** Graphing mass and volume gives a good visual representation of density. The steeper the slope the more dense the substance.

## Density and Phases of Matter

All matter is made up of individual particles–atoms and molecules. In general, the **phase (state)** in which a sample of matter is found depends on how closely packed these particles are. For most substances, particles are most closely packed in the solid phase of the substance. Thus, the solid phase is the most dense. As a substance undergoes a change of phase, its density changes. The density of most materials increases as they change from gas to liquid to solid. Water is an exception to this "rule."

Objects denser than water will sink in water, and objects less dense than water will float in water. Consider the fact that ice water in the solid phase–floats in liquid water. This fact indicates that the solid phase of water is *less* dense than the liquid phase.

As described earlier, the reason why the solid phase of most materials is the densest phase is because the particles are most closely packed in the solid phase. As a material cools, it contracts. That is, its particles move closer together. Thus, as a material cools, it becomes denser. This behavior is true for water, up to a point. As liquid water cools, it contracts and becomes denser until its temperature reaches 4°C. As water cools from 4°C to 0°C (the freezing point), water *expands*. It becomes less dense. Thus, water has its greatest density at 4°C, *while it is still liquid*. As water freezes, it continues to expand. The effect of this increasing volume is to *decrease* its density.

## Effect of Temperature and Pressure on the Density of Gases

As described earlier, a change in temperature does have an effect on the volume, and therefore the density, of a material. Pressure can also change the volume (and density) of a material. Because the particles of matter in the gas phase are widely separated, gases are affected by changes in temperature and pressure to a much greater extent than are liquids and solids. This fact is of particular importance in the study of weather.

Air is a gas (actually, a mixture of gases). When a sample of air is heated, it expands. Its molecules spread out to occupy a bigger volume, and the sample becomes less dense. Cooler, denser air moves in and forces the warmer air to rise. It is this principle that makes hot air balloons rise.

In the atmosphere, all movement of air, both horizontal (winds) and vertical (currents), are caused by unequal heating. When sunlight strikes Earth's surface, the air in contact with that surface heats up, expands, and becomes less dense. Cooler, denser air moves into the area, lifting the less dense air upward.

Air pressure is also related to temperature. Air pressure is actually a measure of the force or weight of the atmospheric air pushing down on Earth's surface. The denser, or "heavier" the air at a particular location, the greater the pressure it will exert. Since cold air is denser than warm air, it stands to reason that a cold air mass will exert greater pressure than a warm air mass.

## QUESTIONS

Base your answers to questions 1-3 on the diagram below. An ice cube and three other objects are placed in a container of water as shown.

1. Which object is most probably the ice cube?
   (1) A          (2) B          (3) C          (4) D

2. Which object probably has the same density as the liquid?
   (1) A          (2) B          (3) C          (4) D

3. Which choice lists the objects in the order of lowest density to highest density?
   (1) A, B, C, D       (2) A, D, C, B       (3) D, C, B, A       (4) C, B, A, D

4. At which temperature does water have its greatest density?
   (1) –7°C       (2) 0°C       (3) 96°C       (4) 4°C

Base your answer to question 5 on the *Earth Science Reference Tables*, your knowledge of Earth Science, and the data in the table below. The data represent mass and volume measurements of five mineral samples, A, B, C, D, and E. A column in the table is provided for you to record the density of each sample.

| Sample | Mass (g) | Volume (cm³) | Density |
|--------|----------|--------------|---------|
| A | 75.0 | 30.0 | |
| B | 60.0 | 20.0 | |
| C | 70.0 | 20.0 | |
| D | 60.0 | 30.0 | |
| E | 50.0 | 20.0 | |

5. Which two mineral samples have the same density?
   (1) A and D       (2) A and E       (3) C and D       (4) B and E

Base your answers to Questions 6 and 7 on the diagram below which represents a solid object with a mass of 120 grams.

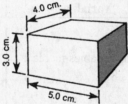

6. What is the density of the object?
   (1) 0.50 g/cm³       (2) 2.0 g/cm³       (3) 5.0 g/cm³       (4) 6.0 g/cm³

7. If the sample were cut in half, the density would be
   (1) twice as much       (2) half as much       (3) the same

8. As a volume of air expands due to heating, the density of this air will
   (1) decrease       (2) increase       (3) remain the same

9. In which phase (state) do most Earth materials have their greatest density?
   (1) solid       (2) liquid       (3) gas

10. What is the density of an irregularly shaped object that has a volume of 3.0 milliliters and a mass of 12 grams?
   (1) 1.0 g/mL       (2) 2.0 g/mL       (3) 3.0 g/mL       (4) 4.0 g/mL

# THE NATURE OF CHANGE

## Characteristics of Change

Observations of the environment around us show that change is occurring all the time. Changes can occur rapidly or slowly. For example, weather conditions often seem to change in a minute, while seasonal changes occur slowly throughout the year. Although most changes in Earth's surface occur slowly, earthquakes and volcanoes remind us that such changes can also occur very rapidly. In Earth Science, **change** can be described as the occurrence of an event. An **event** occurs when the properties of matter or a system are altered. For example, when lava hardens into rock, the properties of matter are altered. When a river becomes polluted, the properties of a system are altered.

## Frames of Reference

In order to study or describe a change, you must have some basis for comparison, or **frame of reference**. The frames of reference for studying change are time and space (or location). Consider landscape, for example. Over a period of time, the landscape at a given location can change dramatically, from a hilly, mountainous region to a flat plain. The time required for such change is in the millions of years.

On the other hand, in the space of a few miles, the landscape can change from a low, flat desert to high, snow-capped mountains.

| Types of Graph Relationships | Comparisons of Variables | Sample Graph |
|---|---|---|
| Direct | Both variables increase | |
| Indirect or Inverse | Independent variable increases, dependent variables decreases | |
| Cyclic | A repeating pattern | |
| Static | As the independent variable increases, the dependent variable remains the same | |

## Rate of Change

Change can also be described in terms of *how long* it takes to occur; that is, the **rate of change**. Some changes are very fast. A lightning flash, for example, can occur in a fraction of a second. Other changes, such as the wearing down of a mountain, are so slow that the rate of change is difficult to measure.

$$\text{Rate of change} = \frac{\text{change in field value}}{\text{change in time}}$$

## Cyclic Change

Some changes rarely ever repeat themselves exactly. For example, volcanoes and earthquakes are events that occur frequently, but do not seem to follow any regular pattern of occurrence. However, many events do seem to follow set patterns and repeat themselves on a regular basis. Such changes are **cyclic changes**. They include the water cycle, the rock cycle, the sunspot cycle, seasons, and many cycles that relate to the motions of objects in space (stars, Sun, planets, Moon). Most changes in the environment are cyclic to some degree.

## Predicting Change

If a change is cyclic, the amount and direction of the change are predictable. Some changes are more easily predicted than others. For example, astronomers can accurately predict events such as eclipses, or positions of objects in the sky such as the stars, Moon, and Sun. However, predicting weather changes involves a large number of variables, many of which do not change at a constant rate. Therefore, weather predictions are not always accurate.

## Energy and Change

During change, energy flows from one part of the environment, which loses energy, to another part of the environment which gains the energy the first part loses. For example, when wind blows through the trees, friction with the leaves causes the wind to slow down, or lose energy. The fluttering of the leaves is caused by the energy of the wind being transferred to the leaves. The change takes place along the boundaries of the moving air and the leaves. The boundary between different materials or systems is called an **interface**. In our environment, energy is usually exchanged across an interface.

# QUESTIONS

1. What always happens when a change occurs?
   (1) Pollution is produced.                    (2) The temperature of a system increases.
   (3) The properties of a system are altered.   (4) Dynamic equilibrium is reached.

2. A boundary between two regions of change is called a(n)
   (1) transition zone    (2) transfer zone    (3) interface    (4) cycle boundary

3. Over several years, the apparent size of the Sun as viewed by an observer on Earth will probably
   (1) vary in a cyclic manner          (2) decrease at a regular rate
   (3) increase at a regular rate       (4) vary in an unpredictable manner

4. Which graph represents the greatest rate of temperature change?

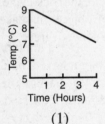
(1)

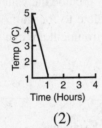
(2)

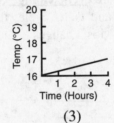
(3)

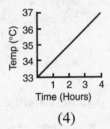
(4)

5. A student measures the distance from a bridge to a rock every day for a week. What is indicated by the graph of these measurements as shown below?

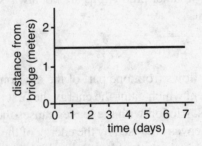

   (1) no change in time or distance took place
   (2) as distance decreased, time increased
   (3) as distance increased, time decreased
   (4) as time increased, distance remained the same

# ENVIRONMENTAL EQUILIBRIUM

## Equilibrium

A rock resting on the side of a hill is in a condition of balance between two opposite forces, the upward force exerted by the solid hill and the downward force of gravity. This condition of balance between opposite forces is **equilibrium**. If someone should push the rock a little, its condition of balance–its equilibrium–would be upset, and the rock would roll down the hill.

Things that are changing or in motion still can be in a condition of equilibrium. The ocean level remains constant, even though water is constantly evaporating from its surface and additional water is being added to it by streams and rivers and rainfall. When there is a balance between changes, it is called **dynamic equilibrium**.

**Environmental equilibrium** is a balance of changes within our environment. This equilibrium can easily be upset on a small scale, by animals digging holes in the ground, or by rain flooding a small area of farmland. Generally speaking, however, environmental equilibrium does not change too much on a larger scale. If it did, humans might have a hard time surviving. However, our present–day technology has enabled us to disrupt the equilibrium of large portions of our environment. One example is the strip–mining of the land, in which large shovels have gouged out huge holes in the ground and deposited large mountains of rocks beside the holes. These changes totally disrupt the environmental equilibrium of that area.

## Environmental Pollution

The environment is considered to be **polluted** when the concentration of any substance or form of energy reaches a proportion that adversely affects humans, their property, or the plant and animal life on which they depend. Pollution represents a disruption of the equilibrium of a region. Pollution can have natural causes, such as when volcanic gases and dust are in the air. Natural **pollutants** (things that pollute) can be either local or widespread. Ash and dust in the atmosphere from volcanic eruptions could cover the entire Earth, and even cut off light from the Sun, making the daylight period darker than normal.

Environmental pollutants include solids, liquids, gases and biologic organisms, as well as forms of energy, such as heat, sound, and nuclear radiation. As our society becomes more and more technological, pollutants are constantly being added to the environment through the activities of individuals, communities, and industrial processes.

# QUESTIONS

1. The data table below shows the average dust concentrations in the air over many years for selected cities of different populations.

| Population in Millions | Dust Particles/Meter$^3$ |
| --- | --- |
| less than 0.7 | 110 |
| between 0.7 and 1.0 | 150 |
| greater than 1.0 | 190 |

Based on this data table, which graph best represents the general relationship between population and concentration of dust particles?

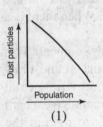
(1)

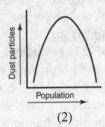
(2)

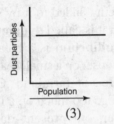
(3)

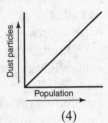
(4)

2. Which energy source listed below is most nearly pollution free?

   (1) nuclear　　　(2) solar　　　(3) coal　　　(4) natural gas

3. Which pollutant is *not* usually produced or added to the environment by human activities?

   (1) sound　　　(2) pollen　　　(3) radiation　　　(4) smoke

4. People who live close to major airports are most likely to complain about which form of pollution?

   (1) sound　　　(2) heat　　　(3) radioactivity　　　(4) particulates

5. Which condition exists when the rates of water flowing into and out of a lake are balanced so that the lake's depth appears to be constant?

   (1) equilibrium　　　(2) transpiration　　　(3) hydration　　　(4) saturation

Base your answer to questions 6 and 7 on your knowledge of Earth Science and on the graph below showing measurements of air pollutants recorded in a city during a two-day period.

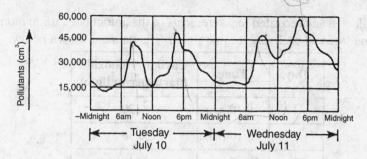

6. What is a likely cause for the increase in pollutants at 8 a.m. and 5 p.m. on the two days?

   (1) change in insolation          (2) occurrence of precipitation
   (3) high wind velocity            (4) heavy automobile traffic

7. On the basis of the trends indicated by the graph, at what time on Thursday, July 12, will the greatest amount of pollutants probably be observed?

   (1) 12 noon          (2) 5 p.m.          (3) 3 a.m.          (4) 8 a.m.

---

**PROLOGUE - CORE VOCABULARY**

| | | |
|---|---|---|
| change | inference | observation |
| classification | inferring | percent deviation |
| cyclic change | instruments | prediction |
| density | interface | rate of change |
| dynamic equilibrium | length | time |
| equilibrium | mass | |
| event | measurement | |

---

**HELPFUL VOCABULARY**

| | |
|---|---|
| environmental equilibrium | pollutants |
| frame of reference | polluted |
| percentage error | standard unit |
| phase (state) | |

## PRACTICE FOR CONSTRUCTED RESPONSE

1. A student collected and recorded measurements of the amount of carbon monoxide in the air at the same location each day for one week. The data are shown below.

| Day | Time | Carbon Monoxide (parts per million) |
|-----|------|-------------------------------------|
| 1 | 9:10 a.m. | 0.20 |
| 2 | 3:10 p.m. | 0.38 |
| 3 | 10:45 a.m. | 0.40 |
| 4 | 7:20 a.m. | 1.15 |
| 5 | 6:00 a.m. | 0.95 |
| 6 | 6:00 p.m. | 0.65 |
| 7 | 7:15 p.m. | 0.14 |

The student concluded that the amount of carbon monoxide in the air increased and then decreased during the week.

What is the major source of error in the student's investigation?

_____

_____

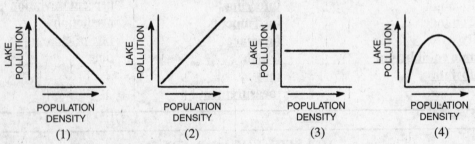

2. a. Which graph best represents the typical relationship between population density near a lake and pollution of the lake?

_____

   b. Why did you select this graph?

_____

_____

Base your answers to questions 11 through 15 on the data table below. The table shows the mass of three liquids, A, B, and C, each of which has a volume of 500 milliliters.

| Liquid | Volume (mL) | Mass (g) |
|--------|-------------|----------|
| A | 500. | 400. |
| B | 500. | 500. |
| C | 500. | 600. |

11. What is the density of liquid B? _____

12. If half of liquid A is removed from its container, how will the density of the remaining liquid compare to the original density?

_____

13. The accepted mass for liquid C is 600. grams, but a student measures the mass as 612 grams. What is the percent deviation (percent of error) of the student's measurement?

_____

14. The graph below shows the volume of liquid B as the temperature changes from 0°C to 10°C. According to the graph, at what temperature is the density of liquid B the greatest?

_____

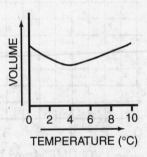

15. a. If the three liquids were placed in a cylinder, which would be on the top and which would be on the bottom?

_____

   b. How do you explain this?

_____

_____

Base your answers to questions 16 through 19 on your knowledge of Earth Science, the *Earth Science Reference Tables*, and the data in Tables I and II below. Table I and II show the volume and mass of three samples of mineral A and three samples of mineral B. Plot the data for each mineral on the graph below. Label each line.

### Table I: Mineral A

| Sample No. | Volume | Mass |
|---|---|---|
| 1 | 2.0 cm³ | 5.0 g |
| 2 | 5.0 cm³ | 12.5 g |
| 3 | 10.0 cm³ | 25.0 g |

### Table II: Mineral B

| Sample No. | Volume | Mass |
|---|---|---|
| 1 | 3.0 cm³ | 12.0 g |
| 2 | 5.0 cm³ | 20.0 g |
| 3 | 7.0 cm³ | 28.0 g |

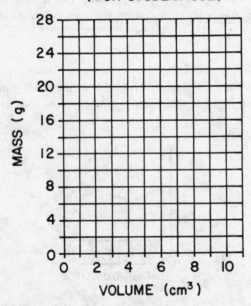

MASS v. VOLUME
( FOR STUDENT USE )

16. Sample 2 of mineral A and sample 2 of mineral B have the same _____

17. What is the density of sample 3 of mineral A? _____

18. Comparing the samples of mineral B in Table II shows that the sample with the smallest volume _____

**19.** One sample of mineral B is heated until it melts. Compared to the density of the original sample, the density of the melted sample most likely will be _____

Base your answers to questions 20 through 23 on the pH Scale of Adirondack Lakes below.

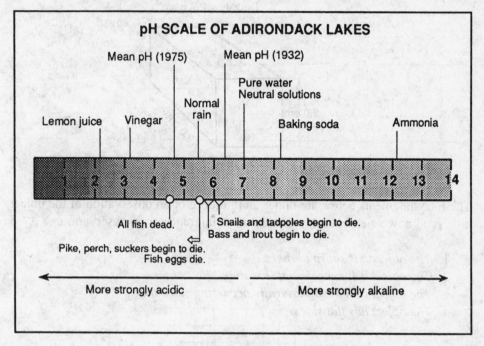

**20.** Which graph best shows the acidity (pH) of Adirondack lakes since 1930?

_____

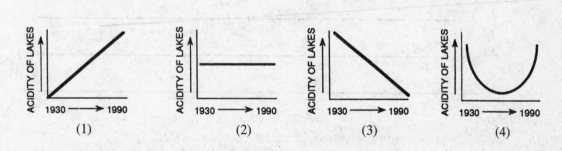

**21.** State the reasons for your choice: _____

**22.** In 1975 what had happened to the fish in the Adirondack Lakes? _____

**23.** Below which pH level would fish not survive in the Adirondack Lakes? _____

Base your answers to questions 24 through 28 on the *Earth Science Reference Tables*, the diagram below which represents a solid material of uniform composition, and your knowledge of Earth Science.

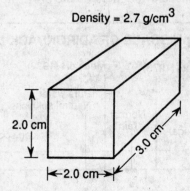

Density = 2.7 g/cm$^3$

2.0 cm

3.0 cm

2.0 cm

24. The four statements below are either an inference or an observation of the object. State how you know whether each statement is an inference or an observation.

    1. *The object has sharp corners.*
    2. *The object is longer than it is wide.*
    3. *The object is made of naturally occurring substance.*
    4. *The object has flat sides.*

1. _____

2. _____

3. _____

4. _____

25. The mass of this piece of material is approximately _____

**26.** How can you determine which graph below best represents the relationship between the mass and volume of various-sized pieces of this material?

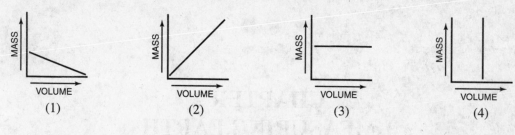

(1)  (2)  (3)  (4)

_____

_____

**27.** When this material is placed in a container of water, it sinks to the bottom of the container. Compared to the density of water, the density of this material is _____.

**28.** If this material is heated and expands (volume increases), the density of the material will

_____.

# CHAPTER 2
# MEASURING EARTH

## MODELS

It is not always possible to observe an entire system close up. Sometimes we must use observations to make **models**, which are smaller copies, or representations of the system. Then we use the models to help explain events. For example, it is impossible for us to step outside the Solar System and observe the planets. So, we develop models to explain the motions of the planets in space. The model of the Solar System we use today, with the Sun at the center, is not the same model people used over 2,000 years ago, with Earth at the center.

The major types of models include physical, mechanical, laboratory, mental, mathematical and graphic models. A **physical model** uses observations of sight to provide us with information. For example, a geographical globe is a physical model of Earth, built to scale. A model built to scale has all its parts in the same proportions (size and shape) as they are found in the original. Common physical models include cars, dolls, and planes. Some mechanical models, such as model electric trains, have moving parts.

### Laboratory Models

**Laboratory models** are used to simulate natural events. One of the most common laboratory models is the stream table. Stream tables can be used to study erosional and depositional characteristics of streams. Further, the slope of the stream, the type of stream bed material used, and the quantity and rate of water flow can all be changed as the experimenter wishes.

### Mental Models

**Mental models** represent ideas or images of something in your mind that you are trying to understand. For example, since you cannot go out into space to see the entire Solar System, the model you have of the Solar System is a mental model.

Formulas and equations used in science courses are **mathematical models.** Einstein's equation, $E = mc^2$, which explains his theory of relativity, is a well-known equation. A formula you have already learned in this course, $D = m/v$, is used to calculate density. Models which explain certain properties of a material or system are mathematical models. **Graphic models** use graphs to simplify certain relationships. For example, the graph (Figure 2-1) showing the relationship between the changing number of sunspots per year is a good example of a graphic model. This graph makes it easier to see that sunspots occur in 11 year cycles of maximums and minimums.

*Models are used to help us understand the real thing.*

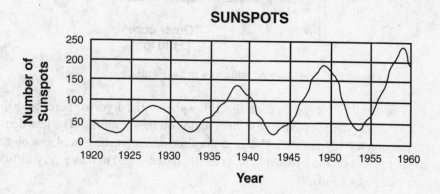

**Figure 2-1.** A graphic model of sunspot activity.

# SIZE OF EARTH

## Earth Dimensions

Today, accurate measurements of Earth's dimensions can be determined from space. Early astronomers were unable to travel into space, yet were able to make reasonably accurate measurements of Earth. Around the year 200 BC, a Greek mathematician, Eratosthenes, made a very accurate determination of Earth's **circumference** (distance around Earth). His value of over 39,000 km is close to the actual value. Knowing Earth's circumference and using various mathematical formulas, other Earth dimensions can be calculated.

## Earth's Structure

The solid Earth is divided into several parts, or "layers," as shown in Figure 2-2. The top layer, the <u>crust</u>, is about 10 km thick beneath the oceans and about 65 km thick beneath the continents. The next layer, the <u>mantle</u>, is about 2850 km thick. The <u>outer core</u> is about 2100 km thick, and the radius of the <u>inner core</u> is about 1400 km thick.

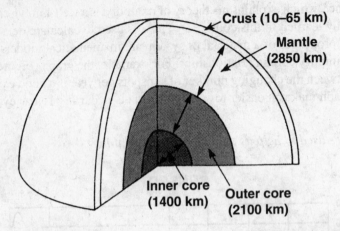

**Figure 2-2.** The "layered" structure of the Earth.

The outer part of Earth is composed of the lithosphere, the hydrosphere, and the atmosphere. The rocky lithosphere is the densest layer and is on the "bottom." The less dense liquid hydrosphere rests on the lithosphere. The gaseous atmosphere, resting in places on the lithosphere and in other places on the hydrosphere, is the least dense and makes a very diffuse interface with space (see Figure 2-3).

**Lithosphere.** The **lithosphere** is the rock near Earth's surface which forms a continuous solid shell around Earth (see Figure 2-3). Much of the lithosphere is covered by a layer of soil or loose rock.

**Hydrosphere.** The **hydrosphere** is the thin layer of water resting on the lithosphere (see Figure 2-3). It covers about 70% of Earth's surface. The oceans make up most of the hydrosphere, with lakes, rivers, and streams also included. The average thickness of the hydrosphere is less than 4 kilometers, almost too thin to show on a diagram in correct scale to both the lithosphere and the atmosphere.

**Atmosphere.** The **atmosphere** is a relatively thin shell of gases, held to Earth by gravity, that surrounds Earth. The atmosphere is about 78% nitrogen, 21% oxygen, with the remaining 1% mostly argon, carbon dioxide, helium and water vapor. The atmosphere extends into space from Earth's surface for several hundred kilometers, with most of its mass concentrated in the lower few kilometers. The moon, with no atmosphere, has a distinct (clear) interface with space. The atmosphere is stratified, or layered, with each layer possessing its own distinct characteristics of temperature and composition. Figure 2-3 shows the layers of the atmosphere. Even though the boundary between each layer is very diffuse, each change does occur within a small change in altitude.

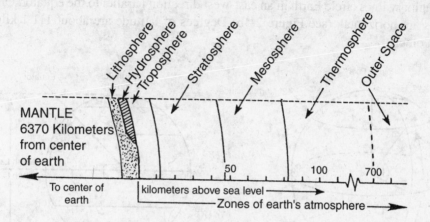

**Figure 2-3.** The lithosphere, hydrosphere, and atmosphere. All weather occurs in the troposphere.

# DETERMINING POSITIONS ON EARTH

## Coordinate Systems

In order to determine locations on Earth's surface, we must have some points of reference. Imagine for a moment that you live in a house surrounded by trees and your friend phones you and asks you to go outside and stand by "the tree." Would you know to what tree your friend was referring? No, you would need more information, such as "the tallest maple tree in the front of the house between the sidewalk and the driveway." That description would help. The information gives you a frame of reference. To help you determine the location of a point on Earth's surface, a **coordinate system** of imaginary lines has been developed. These lines form an Earth grid, like the grid-lines on a football field. The coordinate system used on Earth's surface is the latitude-longitude system with the equator and Prime Meridian as reference lines. It is based upon Earth's rotation and our observations of the Sun and stars. Earth's rotation determines the two poles and the equator.

## Latitude

**Latitude** is the distance, in degrees, north or south of the equator. The equator is 0° latitude, while the North Pole is 90°N latitude and the South Pole is 90°S latitude. The reference point for determining a person's latitude is the equator. If you draw a line from the equator to the center of Earth, and then from the center of Earth to where the person is, the angle between the two lines determines a person's latitude. For example, the angle formed between the line drawn from the equator to the center of Earth and the line from the center of Earth to a location in New York State could be 42°. That means that the latitude of that location in New York State is 42°N (see Figure 2-4a). All points that are the same angular distance from the equator have the same latitude and lie on circles called **parallels of latitude**.

These imaginary lines circle Earth in an east-west direction parallel to the equator. On a map, these lines are horizontal. (see Figure 2-4b) Degrees of latitude are about 111.1 kilometers from each other.

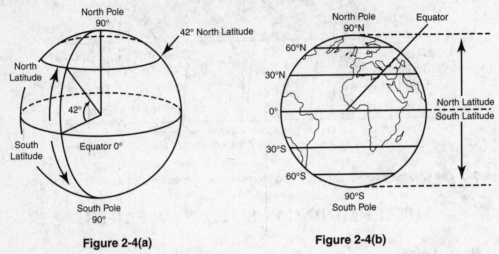

**Figure 2-4(a)**　　　　　　　**Figure 2-4(b)**

**Figure 2-4.** Determining parallels of latitude. Diagram 2-4(a) shows the parallel at 42°N, which is a circle, all points of which are at the same angular distance (42°) from the equator. Diagram 2-4(b) shows parallels of latitude on a map.

## Measuring Latitude

At night in the Northern Hemisphere, latitude can be determined by measuring the altitude of Polaris. The **altitude** of **Polaris** is equal to the observer's latitude. Polaris is not visible in the Southern Hemisphere, so altitudes of other stars must be measured to determine latitude.

During the day, latitude can be found by determining the altitude of the noon Sun and making calculations to account for the Sun's position. On March and September 22, when the Sun is directly overhead at the equator, the latitude of the observer equals 90° minus the altitude of the noon Sun. On days when the Sun is not directly overhead at the equator, calculations must be made to account for the different position of the Sun.

## Longitude

**Longitude** is the distance, in degrees, measured east or west of the Prime Meridian (0°). The reference line for longitude is the **Prime Meridian** which passes through Greenwich, England. **Meridians** are imaginary *semicircles* on Earth's surface which converge at the poles. As one travels east or west from the Prime Meridian (0° longitude), the longitude increases until it reaches a maximum of 180°. The **International Date Line,** which roughly follows the 180° meridian (with some deviations for the convenience of certain land areas), is a continuation of the prime meridian on the other side of the globe.

One hundred and eighty degrees is maximum longitude. If you travel west from the Prime Meridian, you are in the western hemisphere and have west longitude. If you travel east from the Prime Meridian, you are in the eastern hemisphere and have east longitude. The longitude of any point is the measure of the angle between a line drawn from the Prime Meridian to a line joining the poles (polar axis) and then back out to the point (see Figure 2-5). For example, a line drawn from the Prime Meridian to the polar axis and then out to a person in New York State could form an angle of 75°. This means that the longitude of that person is 75°. Since it is west of the Prime Meridian, it is 75°W. All points on a given meridian have the same longitude.

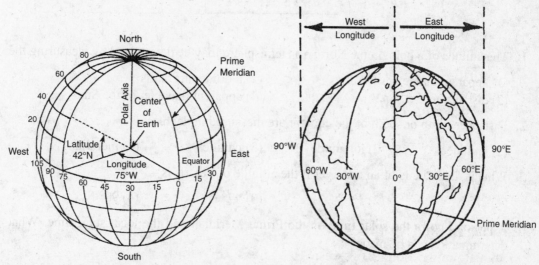

**Figure 2-5. Determining meridians of longitude.** (a) The cut-out section represents an angular distance of 75° measured west from the Prime Meridian (0° longitude). The dotted line leads to the point on Earth's surface whose location is 42°N latitude, 75°W longitude. (b) This shows meridians of longitude on the map.

## Measuring Longitude

The longitude of any location can be determined using a very accurate clock called a **chronometer** which keeps the time at the Prime Meridian (Greenwich Mean Time–G.M.T.) and the **solar time** (time by the Sun) at any other meridian. Sun time is most easily determined at **solar noon** when the Sun has its highest altitude.

Since it takes Earth 24 hours to rotate 360°, its rate of rotation is 15° per hour. In the western hemisphere, local time is *earlier* than Greenwich time; in the eastern hemisphere, local time is *later* than Greenwich time.

If it is 12:00 noon where you live and the chronometer reads 5:00 p.m. Greenwich time, then you are 5 hours away from Greenwich. Each hour's difference between local time and Greenwich time represents 15° of rotation. Thus, you must have rotated 5 times 15° for a total rotation of 75°. This means your longitude is 75°. Since local time is earlier than GMT, you must be in the western hemisphere. Your longitude is 75°W.

# Earth Rotation and Time

Earth rotates on an imaginary axis at a rate of 15 degrees per hour. To people on Earth, this turning of the planet makes it seem as though the Sun, the moon and stars are moving around Earth once a day. Rotation provides a basis for our system of local time. Meridians of longitude are the basis for the time zones.

## QUESTIONS

1. The latitude of a point in the Northern Hemisphere may be determined by measuring the

   (1) apparent diameter of Polaris     (2) altitude of Polaris
   (3) distance to the Sun     (4) apparent diameter of the Sun

2. Distances north or south of the equator are measured in degrees of

   (1) latitude     (2) longitude     (3) parallels     (4) meridians

3. What is the latitude of an observer if the altitude of Polaris is 43°?

   (1) 23° N.     (2) 43° N.     (3) 47° N.     (4) 90° N.

4. A person knows the solar time on the Prime Meridian and the local solar time. What determination can be made?

   (1) the date
   (2) the altitude of Polaris
   (3) the longitude at which the person is located
   (4) the latitude at which the person is located

5. Ship X and ship Y are sailing along the equator. The difference in local solar time between them is two hours. What is their difference in longitude?

   (1) 0°     (2) 15°     (3) 30°     (4) 45°

6. The diagram below represents a portion of a map of Earth's grid system. What is the approximate latitude and longitude of point A?

   (1) 15°N. 30°W.     (2) 15°S. 30°W.     (3) 15°N. 30°E.     (4) 15°S. 30°E.

**7.** According to the *Earth Science Reference Tables,* which city is located nearest to 43° North latitude and 76° West longitude?

    (1) Utica           (2) Niagara Falls     (3) Watertown     (4) Syracuse

**8.** The map below shows the location and diameter, in kilometers, of four meteorite impact craters, A, B, C, and D, found in the United States.

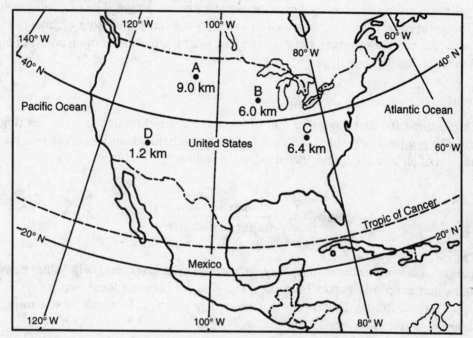

What is the approximate latitude and longitude of the largest crater?

    (1) 35° N 111° W     (2) 39° N 83° W     (3) 44° N 90° W     (4) 47° N 104° W

**9.** Upon what measurement is Earth's latitude and longitude system based?

    (1) star angles                     (2) gravity intensity
    (3) magnetism direction          (4) apparent solar diameter

**10.** As a ship crosses the Prime Meridian, the altitude of Polaris is 65°. What is the ship's location?

    (1) 0° longitude, 65° South latitude     (2) 0° longitude, 65° North latitude
    (3) 0° latitude, 65° West longitude      (4) 0° latitude, 65° East longitude

# MAPPING FIELDS

## Isolines

**Isolines** are lines connecting points of equal value on a map. For example, isolines joining points of equal barometric pressure on a weather map are called **isobars**; lines of equal temperature are called **isotherms**. On a topographic **field** (map), lines joining points of equal elevation are called **contour lines.**

## Gradient

One method for describing the rate of change for a field value is by measuring its gradient. The **gradient** or **slope** is the rate of change of a field quantity between two places. The gradient of an area can be calculated using the following formula:

$$\text{gradient} = \frac{\text{change in value}}{\text{change in distance}}$$

For example, if a topographic map shows that a stream drops 200 feet (field value) between two points that are 5 miles apart (distance), the gradient between these two points is 200 divided by 5, or 40 ft/mile. That means that every time you walk downstream one mile, you have dropped 40 feet in elevation.

# USING TOPOGRAPHIC MAPS

## Contour Maps

One of the most commonly used models in Earth Science is the **topographic map (contour map),** a two-dimensional model, which shows the elevations of various points on Earth's surface (see Figure 2-6).

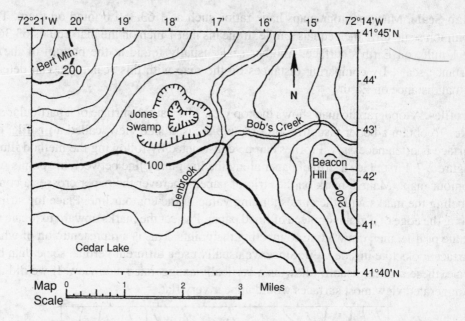

**Figure 2-6.** A portion of a contour map. The contour interval on this map is 20 feet. The elevation of the lake shoreline is 60 feet. Note that where contour lines cross the stream, they "bend" upstream. Jones swamp is a depression.

The topography of a map refers to the physical features of the land, such as hills, valleys, cliffs, and depressions. The isolines that connect points of equal elevation above sea level are called contour lines. The zero contour line is at sea level. The difference in value between two contour lines is the **contour interval**. Although contour lines are the most important information on a contour map, other features such as buildings, water, roads, and vegetation are also indicated.

## Map Features

**Depressions.** Many times, holes are dug into Earth's surface. To show these holes or depressions, *hachured* lines ⊥⊥⊥⊥⊥⊥⊥⊥⊥ are used. The first hachure line has the same value as the lowest of the contour lines between which it is found. Each additional hachure line inside the first (or outside) hachure has a lower value, equal to the contour interval.

**Finding Direction.** Most maps, including topographic maps, have some indication of direction. They are usually oriented so that north is at the top, with an arrow to indicate north. Most maps also indicate latitude and longitude along the margins of the map.

**Map Scale.** Many contour maps have ratios such as 1:63,360 printed on them. This is the common scale for 1 inch equals 1 mile. It means that 1 inch on the map equals 63,360 inches, or 1 mile, on Earth's surface. Another scale usually found at the bottom of the map is a distance scale. By comparing distances on the map with this scale, you can determine the actual distance on Earth.

**Profiles.** A topographic map shows the top view of what the surface of a particular area looks like. To obtain a better visualization of some areas, a side view, called a **profile**, of Earth's surface is often necessary. Profiles can be constructed by following the method illustrated in Figure 2-7. First place a strip of paper along the imaginary line between the points A-B on the contour map. Make a mark on the strip of paper wherever the paper crosses a contour line, labeling the marks with the corresponding value of the contour line. Place the strip of paper along the edge of a graph or piece of lined paper. Project the marks upward to locate the points of the profile, then draw a line connecting the points. This is a representation of what Earth's surface looks like in side view. Since we usually use a different vertical scale than horizontal scale, these profiles usually show us a vertically exaggerated side view. If we did not use an exaggerated view most surfaces would appear very flat.

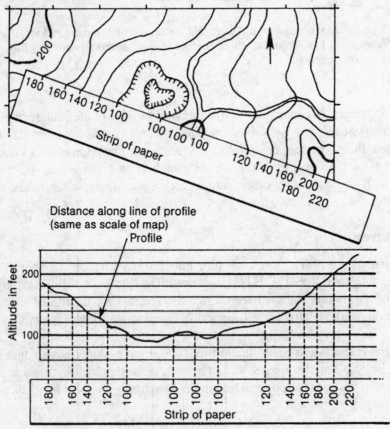

**Figure 2-7.** Constructing a profile from a contour map.

**Map Slope.** The slope, or gradient, on a map can be determined by comparing the rate of change in elevation between two points, as shown in the equation on page 32. The relative gradient can be determined by estimating the distance between contour lines. The closer the isolines, the steeper the slope; the farther apart the isolines, the gentler the slope. The contour lines on a steep mountain are very close to each other, while the contour lines on a very gentle hill are much farther apart.

**Direction of Stream Flow.** Streams always flow downhill. An easy way to determine the direction of stream flow is to examine the contour lines wherever a stream crosses them. The bends in the contour lines point upstream.

## QUESTIONS

1. Isolines on the map below show elevations above sea level, measured in meters.

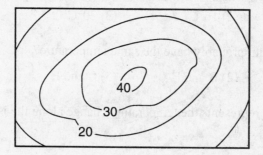

   What is the highest possible elevation represented on this map?
   (1) 39 m　　　　(2) 41 m　　　　(3) 49 m　　　　(4) 51 m

2. A stream has a source at an elevation of 1,000 meters. It ends in a lake that has an elevation of 300 meters. If the lake is 200 kilometers away from the source, what is the average gradient of the stream?

   (1) 1.5 m/km　　　　(2) 3.5 m/km　　　　(3) 10 m/km　　　　(4) 15 m/km

Base your answers to questions 3 through 5 on your knowledge of Earth Science and on the diagram below. The diagram represents a temperature field for a vertical cross section of a room from ceiling to floor with points A-H at different locations within the room.

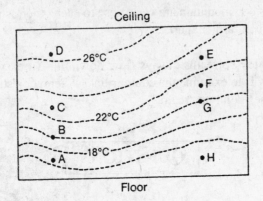

3. Which is the temperature at point B?

   (1) 10°C          (2) 16°C          (3) 20°C          (4) 28°C

4. Which points would probably have the same temperature?

   (1) A and H       (2) B and F       (3) C and E       (4) D and E

5. Which graph best represents the temperature change along the isotherm from point B to G?

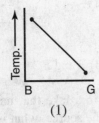   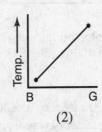   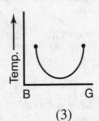   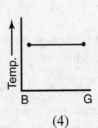

    (1)            (2)           (3)          (4)

6. A contour line that has tiny comblike marks along the inner edge indicates the presence of a
   (1) mountain                    (2) steep cliff
   (3) river valley                (4) depression in the ground

Base your answers to questions 7 through 10 on your knowledge of Earth Science and the diagram below which represents a temperature map of the air near the ceiling of a room. The letters represent points in the room.

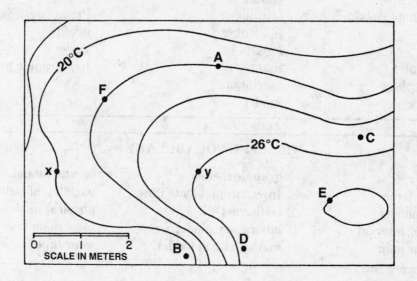

7. What is the air temperature at position A?

   (1) 18°C        (2) 21°C        (3) 22°C        (4) 24°C

8. The most likely direction of heat flow is from

   (1) F to A        (2) B to D        (3) C to E        (4) E to F

9. The greatest temperature gradient exists between

   (1) A and D        (2) B and D        (3) C and E        (4) E and F

10. The average temperature gradient between points x and y is closest to

   (1) 0.5 degree per meter        (2) 2.0 degrees per meter
   (3) 3.0 degrees per meter       (4) 1.5 degrees per meter

## CHAPTER 2 - CORE VOCABULARY

atmosphere
contour line
coordinate system
crust
field
gradient
hydrosphere
inner core

isobar
isoline
latitude
lithosphere
longitude
mantle
meridian
model

outer core
Polaris
Prime Meridian
profile
slope
topographic map

## HELPFUL VOCABULARY

altitude
circumference
chronometer
contour interval
contour map

graphic model
International Date Line
isotherms
laboratory model
mathematical model

mental model
parallel (of latitude)
physical model
solar noon
solar time

## PRACTICE FOR CONSTRUCTED RESPONSE

Base your answers to questions 1 through 4 on the diagram of Earth below, your knowledge of Earth Science and the *Earth Science Reference Tables*. Location A through H are on Earth's surface.

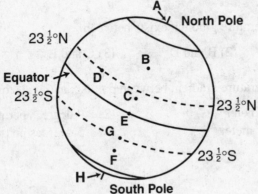

1. Describe what happens to the altitude of Polaris as a traveler moves from location C to location B.

_____

## MEASURING EARTH

**2.** Determine the lettered location where the altitude of Polaris is the greatest.

_____

**3. a.** What is the altitude of Polaris at location D?

_____

**b.** Explain how you determined this altitude.

_____

_____

**4.** If you calculated the actual circumference of Earth to be 30,000 km, and the actual circumference of Earth is approximately 40,000 km, calculate the percent deviation.

**a.** Write the equation for determining percent deviation.

**b.** Substitute data from the problem into the equation.

**c.** Calculate the percent deviation.

**d.** Label your answer with the proper units.

Base your answers to questions 5 through 7 on the diagram of Earth below, your knowledge of Earth Science and the *Earth Science Reference Tables*. Some of the latitude and longitude lines have been labeled. Points A through E represent locations on Earth's surface.

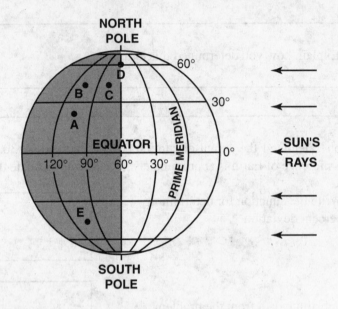

**5.** Determine the approximate latitude and longitude of location A.

_____

**6.** Describe what locations A, B, and E have in common.

_____

**7.** Which lettered locations have the same latitude?

_____

Base your answers to questions 8 to 11 on the topographic map below, your knowledge of Earth Science and on the *Earth Science Reference Tables*. The topographic map represents elevation in contour measured in meters.

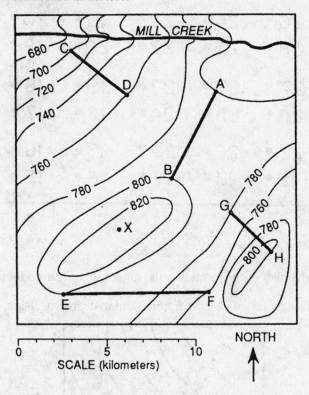

**8.** State the highest possible elevation of **X**. _____

**9.** State the direction in which Mill Creek is flowing. _____

**10.** Explain how the contour lines show the direction of stream flow.

_____

**11.** Compare the lines drawn from C-D, G-H, E-F. What is the gradient of C-D?

_____

**12.** The temperature data (in °C) shown on the map below were taken at the same elevation and time in a room. Letters A through D represent the corners of the room.

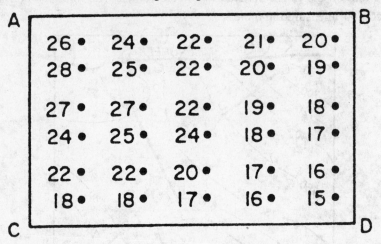

    **a.** Draw the isotherms.

    **b.** Identify in what part of the room was the highest temperature found? _____

**13.** The diagram below represents a temperature field in degrees Celsius.

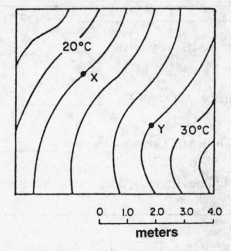

Calculate the temperature gradient between X and Y

    **a.** Write formula _____

    **b.** Substitute _____

    **c.** Calculate _____

**14.** The contour lines on the map below represent a hill.

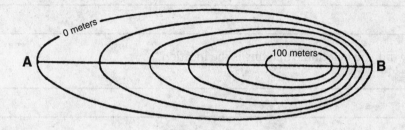

Construct a profile from A to B on the grid below.

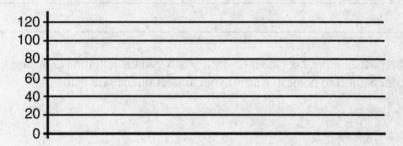

Base your answers to questions 15 and 16 on the diagram below, your knowledge of Earth Science and the *Earth Science Reference Tables*. The diagram represents the concentration of pollutants measured in particles/cm$^3$.

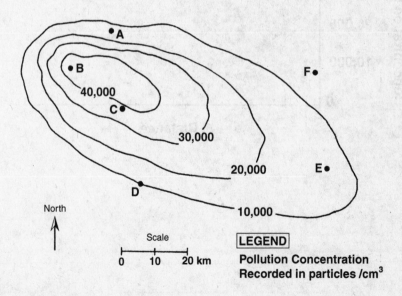

**15. a.** Describe the location of the major source of air pollution.

_____

_____

**b.** How did you determine that this is the location?

_____

_____

**c.** From which direction are the winds responsible for this air pollution pattern most likely blowing?

_____

_____

**16.** Draw a graph which represents the relationship between the pollution concentration and distance from point B to point E. Record your answer on the grid below.

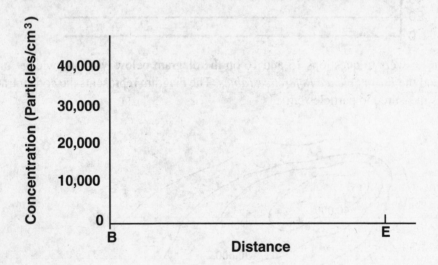

Base your answers to questions 17 and 18 on the temperature field map below. The map shows 25 measurements (in°C) that were made in a temperature field and recorded as shown. The dots represent the exact locations of the measurements. A and B are locations within the field.

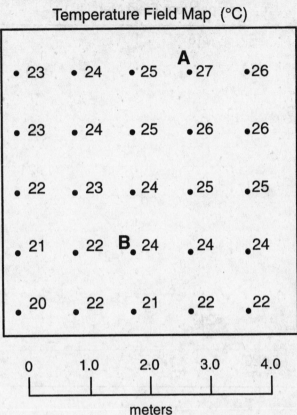

Temperature Field Map (°C)

17. On the temperature field map above, draw three isotherms: the 23°C isotherm, the 24°C isotherm, and the 25°C isotherm.

18. Calculate the temperature gradient between locations A and B on the temperature field map, following the directions below.

   a. Write the equation for gradient.

   b. Substitute data from the map into the equation.

   c. Calculate the gradient and label it with the proper units.

Base your answers to questions 19 through 21 on the temperature field map below. The map shows temperature readings (°C) recorded by students in a science classroom. The readings were taken at the same time at floor level. Temperature readings for points A and B are labeled on the map.

### Temperature Field Map (°C)

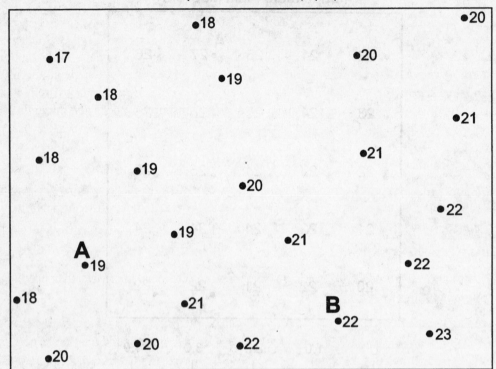

**19.** On the temperature field map provided, use solid lines to draw the 18°C, 20°C, and 22°C isotherms. Isotherms must extend to the boundry of the map. Label each isotherm to indicate its temperature.

**20.** Determine the temperature gradient from point A to point B by following the directions below.

    **a.** Write the equation used to determine the gradient.

    **b.** Substitute values from the field map into the equation.

    **c.** Solve the equation and label the answer with the proper units.

**21.** State temperature of point A in degrees Fahrenheit (°F). _____

# CHAPTER 3
# MINERALS AND ROCKS

Most of us have picked up a rock at some time and wondered, "Where did this come from?" Observations and classifications have helped us understand the great variety and complexity of Earth materials. This unit discusses the lithosphere, the solid portion of Earth's crust, and examines the origin, physical and chemical nature of rocks. The type of rock is a major factor in determining the landscape of an area. Rock type is also important in understanding the geologic history of an area. The natural resources of our planet help to determine the style and level of comfort of our lives. Some Earth resources can be renewed, but many cannot, so it is important to conserve our natural resources. Rocks and minerals are two resources which cannot be renewed.

## MINERALS

A **mineral** is a naturally occurring, solid, inorganic substance that has definite chemical composition and molecular structure. Naturally occurring means not produced artificially. Inorganic means that it is not now, nor has it ever been, alive.

### Mineral Characteristics

Minerals are classified on the basis of their physical and chemical properties, their chemical composition, and their structure.

**Physical and chemical properties.** Most minerals can be identified on the basis of well-defined **physical** and **chemical properties**. The **physical properties** of a mineral are due largely to the internal arrangement of their atoms. There are six key physical properties that can be seen, or easily tested. These properties, which are used to identify minerals in the field are: *color*, *streak*, *luster*, *hardness*, *cleavage*, and *fracture*. Less common physical properties useful in mineral identification are taste, crystal shape, magnetism, reactivity with acid, ability to bend light rays, and fluorescence.

### Distinguishing Characteristics of Minerals

*Color:* **Color** is the most visible property of a mineral. However, the use of color, alone for mineral identification is unreliable for two reasons: Many different minerals exhibit the same color, and many minerals are found in a variety of colors.

*Streak:* **Streak** is the color of a mineral in its powdered form. The color of a mineral's streak may be quite different from the color of the mineral itself. Streak is a reliable tool for mineral identification.

*Luster:* **Luster** is the way in which light is reflected from the surface of a mineral. Luster can be metallic or nonmetallic. Minerals with **metallic** luster shine like polished metals. Those with **nonmetallic** luster have no metallic shine. There are several different nonmetallic lusters such as glossy, pearly, greasy, dull, earthy, etc.

*Hardness:* The **hardness** of a mineral is its resistance to being scratched. The relative hardness of a mineral is determined by comparing it to the hardness of the ten "standard" minerals that make up the **Moh's Scale of Hardness** (see Table 3-1). Minerals are often compared to the hardness of glass which is 5.5.

### Moh's Scale of Hardness

**Table 3-1.**

| | |
|---|---|
| 1. Talc (softest) | 6. Feldspar |
| 2. Gypsum | 7. Quartz |
| 3. Calcite | 8. Topaz |
| 4. Fluorite | 9. Corundum |
| 5. Apatite | 10. Diamond (hardest) |

*Cleavage:* **Cleavage** is the tendency of a mineral to split along one or more smooth, flat surfaces, or planes. There are several common types of cleavage. Mica, for example, shows cleavage in one direction. It can be split into thin, flat sheets. Halite shows cleavage in three directions, and can splint into cubes.

*Fracture:* Minerals that do not show cleavage are said to **fracture** when they break. The fracture of most minerals is uneven, or rough.

Some other tests of physical properties include the following: a mineral may be magnetic; a mineral may react with dilute hydrochloric acid by bubbling, or effervescing; a mineral may have double refraction, causing light that passes through it to bend in two directions, producing a "ghost" image; a mineral may have a distinctive taste. (Note: Taste is a dangerous test, because many minerals are toxic.)

For hundreds of years, diamonds and other gemstones (all minerals) have been a symbol of power and wealth. Of all the minerals on Earth's crust, over 90% are combinations of the eight elements listed in Table 3-2.   The properties of Common Minerals are in Table 3-3.

### Composition of Earth's Crust

**Table 3-2.**

| Element | Symbol | Percent by Volume | Percent by Mass |
|---|---|---|---|
| Oxygen | O | 94.0 | 46.4 |
| Silicon | Si | 0.9 | 28.2 |
| Aluminum | Al | 0.5 | 8.2 |
| Iron | Fe | 0.5 | 5.6 |
| Calcium | Ca | 1.2 | 4.2 |
| Sodium | Na | 1.1 | 2.4 |
| Potassium | K | 1.4 | 2.1 |
| Magnesium | Mg | 0.3 | 2.3 |
| All Others | – | – | 0.6 |

## Properties of Common Minerals

| LUSTER | HARD-NESS | CLEAVAGE | FRACTURE | COMMON COLORS | DISTINGUISHING CHARACTERISTICS | USE(S) | MINERAL NAME | COMPOSITION* |
|---|---|---|---|---|---|---|---|---|
| **Metallic Luster** | 1–2 | ✔ | | silver to gray | black streak, greasy feel | pencil lead, lubricants | **Graphite** | C |
| | 2.5 | ✔ | | metallic silver | very dense (7.6 g/cm³), gray-black streak | ore of lead | **Galena** | PbS |
| | 5.5–6.5 | | ✔ | black to silver | attracted by magnet, black streak | ore of iron | **Magnetite** | $Fe_3O_4$ |
| | 6.5 | | ✔ | brassy yellow | green-black streak, cubic crystals | ore of sulfur | **Pyrite** | $FeS_2$ |
| **Either** | 1–6.5 | | ✔ | metallic silver or earthy red | red-brown streak | ore of iron | **Hematite** | $Fe_2O_3$ |
| **Nonmetallic Luster** | 1 | ✔ | | white to green | greasy feel | talcum powder, soapstone | **Talc** | $Mg_3Si_4O_{10}(OH)_2$ |
| | 2 | | ✔ | yellow to amber | easily melted, may smell | vulcanize rubber, sulfuric acid | **Sulfur** | S |
| | 2 | ✔ | | white to pink or gray | easily scratched by fingernail | plaster of paris and drywall | **Gypsum** (Selenite) | $CaSO_4 \cdot 2H_2O$ |
| | 2–2.5 | ✔ | | colorless to yellow | flexible in thin sheets | electrical insulator | **Muscovite Mica** | $KAl_3Si_3O_{10}(OH)_2$ |
| | 2.5 | ✔ | | colorless to white | cubic cleavage, salty taste | food additive, melts ice | **Halite** | NaCl |
| | 2.5–3 | ✔ | | black to dark brown | flexible in thin sheets | electrical insulator | **Biotite Mica** | $K(Mg,Fe)_3$ $AlSi_3O_{10}(OH)_2$ |
| | 3 | ✔ | | colorless or variable | bubbles with acid | cement, polarizing prisms | **Calcite** | $CaCO_3$ |
| | 3.5 | ✔ | | colorless or variable | bubbles with acid when powdered | source of magnesium | **Dolomite** | $CaMg(CO_3)_2$ |
| | 4 | ✔ | | colorless or variable | cleaves in 4 directions | hydrofluoric acid | **Fluorite** | $CaF_2$ |
| | 5–6 | ✔ | | black to dark green | cleaves in 2 directions at 90° | mineral collections | **Pyroxene** (commonly Augite) | $(Ca,Na)(Mg,Fe,Al)$ $(Si,Al)_2O_6$ |
| | 5.5 | ✔ | | black to dark green | cleaves at 56° and 124° | mineral collections | **Amphiboles** (commonly Hornblende) | $CaNa(Mg,Fe)_4(Al,Fe,Ti)_3$ $Si_6O_{22}(O,OH)_2$ |
| | 6 | ✔ | | white to pink | cleaves in 2 directions at 90° | ceramics and glass | **Potassium Feldspar** (Orthoclase) | $KAlSi_3O_8$ |
| | 6 | ✔ | | white to gray | cleaves in 2 directions, striations visible | ceramics and glass | **Plagioclase Feldspar** (Na-Ca Feldspar) | $(Na,Ca)AlSi_3O_8$ |
| | 6.5 | | ✔ | green to gray or brown | commonly light green and granular | furnace bricks and jewelry | **Olivine** | $(Fe,Mg)_2SiO_4$ |
| | 7 | | ✔ | colorless or variable | glassy luster, may form hexagonal crystals | glass, jewelry, and electronics | **Quartz** | $SiO_2$ |
| | 7 | | ✔ | dark red to green | glassy luster, often seen as red grains in NYS metamorphic rocks | jewelry and abrasives | **Garnet** (commonly Almandine) | $Fe_3Al_2Si_3O_{12}$ |

*Chemical Symbols:

| | | | | |
|---|---|---|---|---|
| Al = aluminum | Cl = chlorine | H = hydrogen | Na = sodium | S = sulfur |
| C = carbon | F = fluorine | K = potassium | O = oxygen | Si = silicon |
| Ca = calcium | Fe = iron | Mg = magnesium | Pb = lead | Ti = titanium |

✔ = dominant form of breakage

**Table 3-3.**

# The Formation of Minerals

There are three different occurrences in which minerals are found in rocks. They occur in loose cavities, attached to a wall of rock surrounding a cavity, or embedded in the rock. All minerals are **crystalline,** made of atoms arranged in a pattern. Many minerals occur as crystals. **Crystals** are minerals with geometric shapes and smooth flat surfaces called faces. Each kind of mineral has its own crystal shape. Any time a mineral has room to form without restrictions, it will develop individual crystals. There are 6 basic crystal systems (see Figure 3-1).

The origin of minerals in the crystal shape begins with a supersaturated solution. As the water evaporates, the molecules collect together or precipitate out. The speed of evaporation determines the size of the finished crystals. The slower the rate of evaporation, the larger the crystals will be.

Minerals also form as a result of cooling and solidification of magma or in the rearrangement of atoms in existing minerals subjected to conditions of high temperature and pressure.

**Figure 3-1.** The six basic crystal systems. The dashed lines on the crystal diagrams represent axes. The length and position of the axes relative to one another determine the system to which a crystal belongs.

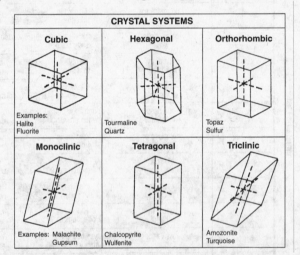

**Chemical Composition.** Minerals are grouped according to their **chemical composition**. All minerals are made of elements. Some minerals can be identified by their special chemical properties. For example, calcite usually fizzes in the presence of certain acids (HCl for example). Graphite and diamond are both composed of carbon atoms, yet they have very different properties. Graphite is very soft and diamond is extremely hard. Diamond is a network of carbon atoms with strong interlocking bonds. Graphite has layers of carbon atoms with weak bonds between the layers. Densities also differ. Tightly packed diamond has a density of 3.5 g/cm$^3$ while loosely packed graphite is only 2.3g/cm$^3$. The cleavage of a mineral is also due to the arrangement of its molecules. Minerals split along planes where the bonds between the layers are weak. Halite with weak bonds between layers splits into cubes. Quartz does not split because it has all strong bonds.

Some minerals are made up of just one element. Examples of such minerals are gold, copper, and sulfur. Most minerals are made up of *compounds,* two or more elements that are chemically combined.

The most abundant element in Earth's crust is oxygen. Oxygen makes up 94.0 percent of the volume of elements in the crust and 46.4 percent of the mass. Silicon, the second most abundant element in the crust makes up 28.2 percent of its mass (see Table 3-2, page 48). The most common minerals in the crust are compounds called **silicates,** which are combinations of silicon and oxygen with other elements. Silicates are the largest group of rock-forming minerals. Silicates include the minerals quartz, feldspar, mica and hornblende.

Minerals that contain a high percentage of some commercially valuable substance (usually a metal) are called **ores.** The metals iron, aluminum, copper, lead and uranium all come from ores.

Another mineral grouping is the **carbonates,** compounds of 1 carbon atom and 3 oxygen atoms. Calcite and dolomite are examples of carbonates. Another group are the **iron oxides** and the **sulfides.** In an oxide, the mineral iron combines with oxygen. In a sulfide, iron combines with sulfur. Magnetite, an ore of iron, is an oxide. Pyrite (fool's gold) is a sulfide.

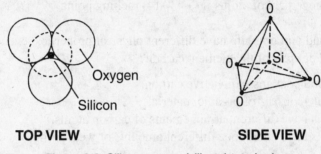

**TOP VIEW**                    **SIDE VIEW**

**Figure 3-2.** Silicon-oxygen (silicate) tetrahedron.

**Structure.** <u>Structure</u> refers to the arrangement of atoms in a mineral. Silicon and oxygen, the two most common elements in Earth's crust, combine chemically to form a structural unit in the shape of a tetrahedron. A **tetrahedron** is a four-sided solid, each side being a triangle (see Figure 3-2). Silicon-oxygen tetrahedrons can combine with other silicon-oxygen tetrahedrons or with other elements to form different structures. For example, in the mineral hornblende, the arrangement of the silicate tetrahedrons produces a chain structure (see Figure 3-3). In mica, the arrangement produces a sheet structure (Figure 3-3). The different structural arrangements and bonding account for differences in the physical properties of minerals.

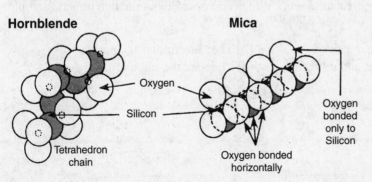

**Figure 3-3.** Arrangement of silicate tetrahedrons in the mineral hornblende (left) and mica (right). The arrangement in mica explains why that mineral splits into thin sheets.

# QUESTIONS

1. The physical properties of a mineral are largely due to its

   (1) volume
   (2) organic composition
   (3) internal arrangement of atoms
   (4) melting point

2. Why do diamond and graphite have different physical properties, even though they are both composed entirely of the element carbon?

   (1) Only diamond contains radioactive carbon.
   (2) Only graphite consists of organic material.
   (3) The minerals have different arrangements of carbon atoms.
   (4) The minerals have undergone different amounts of weathering.

3. According to the *Earth Science Reference Tables*, what are the four most abundant elements, by volume, in the Earth's crust?

   (1) oxygen, potassium, sodium and calcium
   (2) hydrogen, oxygen, nitrogen, and potassium
   (3) aluminum, iron, silicon, and magnesium
   (4) aluminum, calcium, hydrogen, and iron

4. Two mineral samples have different physical properties, but each contains silicate tetrahedrons as its basic structural unit. Which statement about the two mineral samples must be true?

   (1) They have the same density.
   (2) They are similar in appearance.
   (3) They contain silicon and oxygen.
   (4) They are the same mineral.

Base your answers to questions 5 through 8 on your knowledge of Earth Science, the *Earth Science Reference Tables*, and the table of minerals below. The table shows the physical properties of nine minerals.

| Mineral | Color | Luster | Streak | Hard-ness | Density (g/mL) | Chemical Composition |
|---|---|---|---|---|---|---|
| biotite mica | black | glassy | white | soft | 2.8 | $K(Mg,Fe)_3(AlSi_3O_{10})(OH_2)$ |
| diamond | varies | glassy | colorless | hard | 3.5 | $C$ |
| galena | gray | metallic | gray-black | soft | 7.5 | $PbS$ |
| graphite | black | dull | black | soft | 2.3 | $C$ |
| kaolinite | white | earthy | white | soft | 2.6 | $Al_4(Si_4O_{10})(OH)_8$ |
| magnetite | black | metallic | black | hard | 5.2 | $Fe_3O_4$ |
| olivine | green | glassy | white | hard | 3.4 | $(Fe,Mg)_2SiO_4$ |
| pyrite | brass yellow | metallic | greenish-black | hard | 5.0 | $FeS_2$ |
| quartz | varies | glassy | colorless | hard | 2.7 | $SiO_2$ |

**Definitions**
Luster: the way a mineral's surface reflects light
Streak: color of a powdered form of the mineral
Hardness: resistance of a mineral to being scratched
(soft – easily scratched;
hard – not easily scratched)

**Chemical Symbols**

| | | | |
|---|---|---|---|
| Al | – Aluminum | Pb | – Lead |
| C | – Carbon | Si | – Silicon |
| Fe | – Iron | K | – Potassium |
| H | – Hydrogen | S | – Sulfur |
| Mg | – Magnesium | | |
| O | – Oxygen | | |

5. Which mineral has a different color in its powdered form than in its original form?

   (1) pyrite      (2) graphite      (3) kaolinite      (4) magnetite

6. Which mineral contains iron, has a metallic luster, is hard, and has the same color and streak?

   (1) biotite mica      (2) galena      (3) kaolinite      (4) magnetite

7. Which mineral would most likely be weathered (broken up) the most after being placed in a container and shaken for 10 minutes?

   (1) pyrite      (2) quartz      ( 3) magnetite      (4) kaolinite

8. Which mineral is an ore of iron and has a characteristic reddish brown streak?

   (1) magnetite      (2) pyrite      (3) hematite      (4) olivine

# ROCKS

## Relation to Minerals

Most rocks are composed of one or more minerals. Rocks composed of only one mineral are said to be **monominerallic**. Limestone is a common monominerallic rock. Most rocks, however, are polyminerallic, that is, composed of more than one mineral. Granite, a polyminerallic rock is composed of the minerals quartz, feldspar, hornblende and mica. Pure coal and organic limestone are common rocks that do not contain minerals.

In identifying rocks, it is essential to know their mineral composition. Most rocks have a number of minerals in common. There are over 2,500 different minerals, and several minerals appear in numerous varieties. However, only ten to fifteen different minerals, called the **rock-forming minerals,** compose about 90% of all the rocks in Earth's crust.

## Types of Rocks

In order to make sense of them, rocks have been classified into three groups according to how they formed (igneous, sedimentary and metamorphic), texture, and mineral content. **Igneous rocks** form as a result of the solidification of molten rock material. **Sedimentary rocks** form as a result of the compaction and cementation of sediments. These sediments are usually eroded and deposited by the action of rivers, glaciers and wind. **Metamorphic rocks** form as the result of the recrystallization of existing rock material.

# IGNEOUS ROCKS

The formation of rocks must be inferred from their properties, because it is difficult to observe rocks directly as they form. Investigating the characteristics of a particular rock makes it possible to devise a model to explain how the rock formed. Rocks can be classified as either *igneous*, *sedimentary* or *metamorphic*, depending on their composition and the environment in which they formed.

## Formation of Igneous Rocks

**Igneous rocks** form due to the crystallization of molten rock material. Molten rock beneath Earth's surface is called **magma**. When the magma reaches the surface, it is called **lava.** When molten material solidifies, it crystallizes into igneous rock. Most igneous rocks are polyminerallic. Crystal size varies according to the period of time the crystals have to form, the temperature of the mineral when it solidifies, and the pressure under which the crystals form.

The **texture**, or grain appearance, of igneous rocks depends on both the size of the crystals and on their arrangement within the rock. The main reason for the differences in crystal size is the length of time available for the cooling to occur. Texture is dependent on the rate of cooling.

The longer the period of time the magma or lava has to cool and solidify, the larger the crystals that form. However, the period of time available for the molten material to cool depends on pressure and temperature of the surroundings. Pressure and temperature deep beneath Earth's surface are great, resulting in a very slow rate of cooling. Slow cooling results in rocks with large crystals. Coarse grained granite, with large intergrown crystals, is an igneous rock which cooled very slowly. Granite is one of the most common rocks found in mountain areas and underlies much of the continents.

At Earth's surface, temperature and pressure are much lower, resulting in a faster rate of cooling. Thus, rocks that form at or near the surface have small crystals. When lava pours out of a volcano, it cools quickly and the rocks that form have small crystals and are referred to as fine grained. Basalt is a fine grained igneous rock which cooled on or near the surface. When cooling takes place very quickly, no grains form and the rocks have a glassy texture. Obsidian is an igneous rock with a glassy texture.

Igneous rocks are grouped according to their mineral composition. Figure 3-4 shows the texture, color, density, and approximate composition used to identify most igneous rocks.

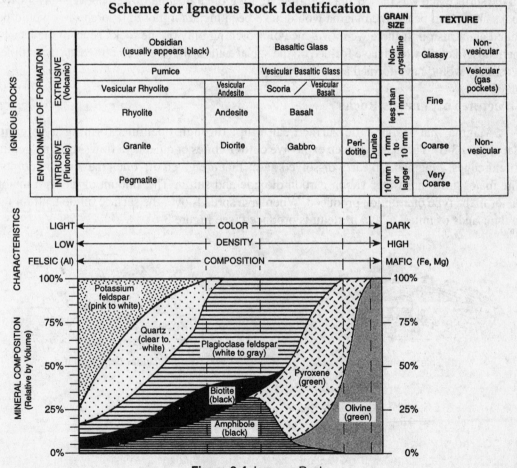

Figure 3-4. Igneous Rock.

## Features of Igneous Rocks

**Felsic** rocks are rich in potassium feldspar and quartz and are light in color. The granite family forms from felsic rocks. Felsic rocks are most common in the continents. Mafic rocks are rich in dark plagioclase feldspar and pyroxene. Mafic rocks form the gabbro family of igneous rocks. **Mafic** rocks are more common in the ocean basins. Those rocks with a composition and color between the granite and gabbro families form the diorite family.

Bodies of rock formed by the solidification of molten material beneath Earth's surface are called **intrusions.** Igneous rocks that form beneath the surface are called **intrusive igneous rocks**, or **plutonic rocks.** The core of many mountains are formed by intrusive rock. The most common intrusive rock is granite. Bodies of rock formed by the solidification of molten material at Earth's surface are called **extrusive igneous rocks,** or **volcanic rocks.** Basalt is a common extrusive rock.

Sometimes, basalt is covered by many layers of rocks. Geologists examine the rocks above and below the basalt to determine whether it formed between the rock layers or formed on the surface and was buried at a later time. If hot molten magma flowed between layers, the rocks above and below the magma would have been metamorphosed (scorched) it would be called an intrusion. If there were evidence of scorching only on the rocks beneath the basalt, then most likely it would have formed on the surface and will have been buried at a later time. It actually would have formed as an **extrusion**.

## Structures of Igneous Rocks

Magma that reaches the surface can erupt through openings forming a **volcano** (see Figure 3-5). They can be steep explosive **cinder cones** or quiet lava flows forming gentle **shield cones**. Magmas can carry dissolved gases that are given off when the volcano erupts. The major gases are water vapor, carbon dioxide and sulfur. The amount of gas is a major factor in the type of eruption produced. When lava spreads over the surface of the land for up to thousands of miles, a **lava plateau** is produced (see Figure 3-6).

(a) Shield volcano

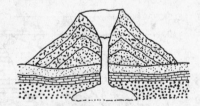
(b) Cinder cone volcano.

**Figure 3-5**. Shield and cinder cone volcanoes

When magma doesn't erupt and instead forces its way into rock fractures and hardens, it produces large masses of intrusive rock called **plutons.** Plutons are classified according to their size, shape and where they formed relative to the surrounding rocks (see Figure 3-6). **Sills** are slabs of igneous rock parallel to the rocks they intrude. The Palisades, on the New Jersey side of the Hudson River, is a large sill. **Dikes** are slabs of igneous rock that cut across the rock layers they intrude. A **laccollith** forms between two rock layers, bulging up to form domelike masses. A **batholith** is the largest of all intrusions. They form the cores of many mountain ranges. The Sierra Nevada Mountains in California are really an exposed batholith. When a volcano erodes, the harder **volcanic neck** is often left behind.

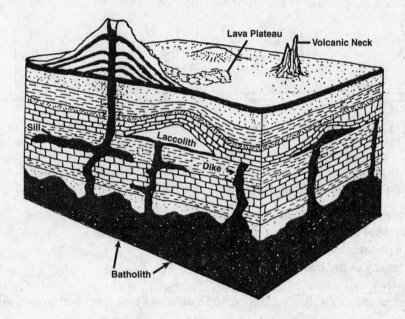

**Figure 3-6**. Intrusive formations and extrusive lava plateau

# QUESTIONS

1. Which observation about an igneous rock would support the inference that the rock cooled slowly underground?

    (1) The rock has well-defined layers.
    (2) The rock has large crystals.
    (3) The rock is about 50 percent feldspar.
    (4) The rock is light in color and low in density.

2. Most igneous rocks contain

   (1) recrystallized minerals      (2) intergrown crystals
   (3) sediments      (4) fossils

3. Most igneous rocks form by which processes?

   (1) melting and solidification      (2) heat and pressure
   (3) erosion and deposition      (4) compaction and cementation

4. Which graph best represents the relationship between the length of time molten magma takes to cool and the size of the crystals in the rock formed by the magma?

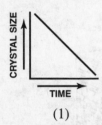 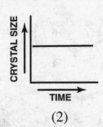 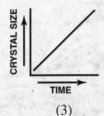 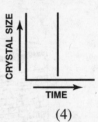

    (1)             (2)             (3)             (4)

5. What is the principal factor that determines the size of the crystals that will result when hot molten rock material (magma) cools to form igneous rock?

   (1) the rate at which the magma cools
   (2) the amount of aluminum in the magma
   (3) the percentage of feldspar in the magma
   (4) the density of the magma

6. The igneous rock Obsidian's glassy texture indicates that it formed from a magma that cooled

   (1) slowly, deep below Earth's surface      (2) slowly, on Earth's surface
   (3) quickly, deep below Earth's surface      (4) quickly, on Earth's surface

7. Which two igneous rocks could have the same mineral composition?

   (1) rhyolite and diorite      (2) pumice and scoria
   (3) peridotite and andesite      (4) gabbro and basalt

8. According to the *Earth Science Reference Tables,* which is a fine-grained igneous rock made up primarily of pyroxene and plagioclase feldspar?
   (1) gabbro      (2) basalt      (3) granite      (4) rhyolite

**9.** Sand collected at a beach contains a mixture of pyroxene, olivine, amphibole, and plagioclase feldspar. According to the *Earth Science Reference Tables,* the rock from which this mixture of sand came is best described as

(1) dark-colored with a mafic composition
(2) dark-colored with a felsic composition
(3) light-colored with a mafic composition
(4) light-colored with a felsic composition

**10.** According to the *Earth Science Reference Tables,* rhyolite and granite are alike in that they both are

(1) fine grained      (2) dark-colored      (3) mafic      (4) felsic

# SEDIMENTARY ROCKS

After transported sediments are deposited, they may be changed into solid units called **sedimentary rocks.** Most sediments are deposited in large bodies of water and tend to be rounded. Thus the presence of sedimentary rocks suggests the type of environment in which the rocks were formed. Figure 3-7 lists the common sedimentary rocks, their textures, their grain sizes, the materials from which they formed and their geologic symbols. Rocks that have formed chemically may not always be easy to identify because their textures do not readily show the characteristics of sedimentary rocks. Very fine grained rocks like shale may be composed entirely of cement. Sedimentary rocks are similar to the sediments from which they form.

## Compression and Cementation

Most sedimentary rocks form as a result of compression and cementation of broken rock material.

**Compression.** The pressure created by water and overlying sediments can sometimes be great enough to force particles of sediment close together, drive out any water present, and compact the sediments into a rock. A good example of rock formed in this way is shale, which can form from the compression of very small colloidal particles and clay. In most shales, some cementing usually takes place also.

**Cementation.** The addition of minerals, such as silica, lime, or iron oxide, tends to "glue" rock particles together to form solid rock. This process is called **cementation.** Sandstone and conglomerate are sedimentary rocks composed of particles of sand, pebbles, and small rock particles that have been cemented together as they were composed. Sandstones are primarily composed of uniformly sized particles of quartz. Conglomerates are formed from unsorted particles of many different materials. The color of a rock is often determined by the cementing agent.

## Scheme for Sedimentary Rock Identification

| INORGANIC LAND-DERIVED SEDIMENTARY ROCKS | | | | | |
|---|---|---|---|---|---|
| TEXTURE | GRAIN SIZE | COMPOSITION | COMMENTS | ROCK NAME | MAP SYMBOL |
| Clastic (fragmental) | Pebbles, cobbles, and/or boulders embedded in sand, silt, and/or clay | Mostly quartz, feldspar, and clay minerals; may contain fragments of other rocks and minerals | Rounded fragments | Conglomerate |  |
| | | | Angular fragments | Breccia |  |
| | Sand (0.2 to 0.006 cm) | | Fine to coarse | Sandstone |  |
| | Silt (0.006 to 0.0004 cm) | | Very fine grain | Siltstone | 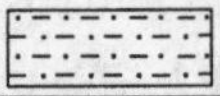 |
| | Clay (less than 0.0004 cm) | | Compact; may split easily | Shale | 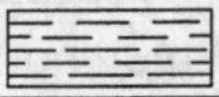 |

| CHEMICALLY AND/OR ORGANICALLY FORMED SEDIMENTARY ROCKS | | | | | |
|---|---|---|---|---|---|
| TEXTURE | GRAIN SIZE | COMPOSITION | COMMENTS | ROCK NAME | MAP SYMBOL |
| Crystalline | Varied | Halite | Crystals from chemical precipitates and evaporites | Rock Salt | 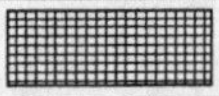 |
| | Varied | Gypsum | | Rock Gypsum |  |
| | Varied | Dolomite | | Dolostone | 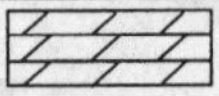 |
| Bioclastic | Microscopic to coarse | Calcite | Cemented shell fragments or precipitates of biologic origin | Limestone | 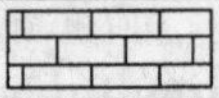 |
| | Varied | Carbon | From plant remains | Coal |  |

**Figure 3-7.** Sedimentary Rocks.

## Chemical Processes

Some sedimentary rocks form as a result of chemical processes, such as evaporation and precipitation. Sometimes water holding dissolved ionic minerals evaporates. The material that precipitates out as a result of this evaporation forms a mass of intergrown crystals. Rocks formed due to the evaporation of water–limestone, dolostone, rock salt, and rock gypsum–are called **evaporites.**

## Biological Processes

Some sedimentary rocks form as a result of processes acting on the remains of once living organisms. Coal, for example, forms as a result of the compression of dead plant materials that were deposited in shallow water. Corals and shellfish, which live in large bodies of water, use minerals such as calcite to form their shells. When the organisms die, the mineral fragments left behind can be compressed and cemented into the rock limestone.

Sedimentary rocks are generally found as a thin veneer, or layer, covering large areas of the continents. Over seventy-five percent of Earth's surface is covered with a veneer of sedimentary rocks. Sedimentary rocks are not found very deep within Earth because the processes that produce sedimentary rocks occur only on Earth's surface. Examine the *Bedrock Geology Map of New York State* in the *Earth Science Reference Tables* to note the wide distribution of sedimentary rocks over New York State.

The remains or impressions of plants and animals found in rocks are called **fossils**. Fossils are found almost exclusively in sedimentary rocks. As sediments collect, plants and animals that die in the area are buried. The formation of sedimentary rocks helps to make and preserve fossils.

## Features of Sedimentary Rocks

Sedimentary rocks are similar to the sediments from which they form, while nonsedimentary rocks are usually very different, with very little relationship to sediments.

**Kinds of Sediments.** There are three kinds of **sedimentary rocks**. Clastic sedimentary rocks form from the compaction and cementation of fragments of other rocks. Chemical sedimentary rocks form from mineral grains that precipitate out by evaporation or other chemical action. **Organic** sedimentary rocks form from the remains of plants and animals.

**Properties of Sedimentary Rocks.** The properties of rocks that are similar to sediments are discrete layers, fragmental particles, organic composition, a range of particle sizes or a predominance of one particle size. Rocks may have one or all of these properties at the same time.

*Discrete layers.* Layers formed when one layer of sediment settles on top of another and then the two layers harden into rock. The discrete (distinct or separate) layers remain in the rock. This layering can be seen in shale or sandstone (see Figure 3-8a). Such layers are often called **beds**, or **strata**.

*Fragmental particles.* Fragmental **particles**, or **clastics,** are rocks formed from sediments made up of rock fragments held together by cement. Conglomerate is a good example of a sedimentary rock composed of fragments (see Figure 3-8b) Fragmental sedimentary rocks are classified on the basis of grain size.

*Organic composition.* Some rocks are composed, either in part or totally, of the remains of plants or animals. Such remains are called **fossils**. Organic **bioclastic** and chemically formed sedimentary rocks are primarily identified through composition and texture. Since limestones are composed of the mineral calcite, they fizz in the presence of acid.

*Predominance of one particle size.* Many rocks are composed of sediment particles of the same size and type. This fact indicates that conditions under which the sediments were deposited remained unchanged for a long period of time.

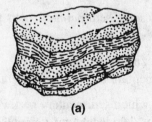

(a)

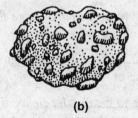

(b)

**Figure 3-8.** Sandstone. (a) often displays layering conglomerate. (b) is made of cemented rock fragments.

## Inferred Characteristics of Rock Types

The environment in which a sedimentary rock forms is often inferred from characteristics of the rock's composition, structure, and texture.

**Composition.** The presence of marine fossils in a rock indicates that it formed at or near Earth's surface from material deposited in a large body of water. If salt is the principal material in a rock, it was probably formed by the evaporation of water, leaving a salt precipitate behind. Limestone is another precipitate, the difference being that the dissolved material came from the shells of marine animals.

**Structure.** Sedimentary rocks tend to have a layered look. Rock layers showing ripple marks, cross bedding, and fossil shells indicate that these layers were formed from sediments deposited in a shallow sea. The presence of particles that have a large grain size in a sedimentary rock indicates that the sediments were deposited in shallow water near the shore rather than in deep water, where the sediments tend to be smaller. A massive sedimentary rock composed of uniformly small particles probably formed from the precipitation of material that was dissolved in sea water.

**Texture.** **Texture** is particularly important in determining the environment in which the rock was formed. The texture of sedimentary rocks is an important clue in helping determine the environment in which the sediments were deposited. Rock particles that have been transported by water for a brief period will be angular and rough, while those that have been transported over long distances for long periods of time will be rounded and smooth.

## QUESTIONS

1. According to the *Earth Science Reference Tables,* which characteristic determines whether a rock is classified as a shale, a siltstone, a sandstone, or a conglomerate?

   (1) the absolute age of the sediments within the rock
   (2) the mineral composition of the sediments within the rock
   (3) the particle size of the sediments within the rock
   (4) the density of the sediments within the rock

2. According to the *Earth Science Reference Tables,* some sedimentary rocks form as the direct results of the

   (1) solidification of molten magma      (2) freezing of material
   (3) melting of minerals                 (4) cementation of rock fragments

3. According to the *Earth Science Reference Tables,* which sedimentary rock is composed of fragmented skeletons and shells of sea organisms compacted and cemented together?

   (1) shale          (2) limestone          (3) sandstone          (4) gypsum

**4.** Which statement correctly describes the distribution of sedimentary rocks on Earth?

(1) Sedimentary rock layers are thickest in the middle of the oceans.
(2) Sedimentary rocks extend down into Earth's crust as far as the inner core.
(3) Sedimentary rocks are usually located in volcanic regions.
(4) Sedimentary rocks usually form a thin layer over large areas of the continents.

**5.** According to the *Earth Science Reference Tables,* which is a sedimentary rock that forms as a result of precipitation from seawater?

(1) conglomerate     (2) gypsum          (3) basalt          (4) shale

**6.** One similarity between a sand pile and sandstone is that they

(1) contain a cementing agent          (2) always contain fossils
(3) have crystalline structure          (4) are composed of sediments

**7.** Which property best describes a rock which has formed from sediments?

(1) crystalline structure          (2) distorted structure
(3) banding or zoning of minerals          (4) fragmented particles arranged in layers

**8.** Which rock is formed when rock fragments are deposited and cemented together?

(1) dolostone          (2) sandstone          (3) rhyolite          (4) gabbro

**9.** Which is most likely a nonsedimentary rock?

(1) a rock containing fossil shells
(2) a rock showing ripple marks and mud cracks
(3) a rock composed of layers of gravel cemented together
(4) a rock consisting of large intergrown crystals

**10.** Rock layers showing ripple marks, cross-bedding, and fossil shells indicate that these layers were formed

(1) from solidification of molten material
(2) from deposits left by a continental ice sheet
(3) by high temperature and pressure
(4) by deposition of sediments in a shallow sea

# METAMORPHIC ROCKS

## Formation of Metamorphic Rocks

Any kind of a rock can become a metamorphic rock (see Figure 3-9). **Metamorphic rocks** form as a result of the recrystallization of unmelted material under conditions of extremely high temperature and pressure over long periods of time. **Recrystallization** is a process in which rocks undergo change without true melting. As a result of heat and pressure, minerals in the rocks combine to form new, larger, denser crystalline structures. The crystals are often found in layer-like bands of alternating minerals, such as are found in gneiss. Other metamorphic rocks, such as marble and quartzite, have crystals that are larger than the crystals in the original rock from which they formed. While the original rocks may have been porous, metamorphic rocks are generally not porous. Metamorphic rocks are often found exposed in mountain areas where the covering rocks have been eroded away. Metamorphic rocks are classified according to their texture, grain size, and composition.

### Scheme for Metamorphic Rock Identification

| TEXTURE | | GRAIN SIZE | COMPOSITION | TYPE OF METAMORPHISM | COMMENTS | ROCK NAME | MAP SYMBOL |
|---|---|---|---|---|---|---|---|
| FOLIATED | MINERAL ALIGNMENT | Fine | MICA | Regional | Low-grade metamorphism of shale | Slate | 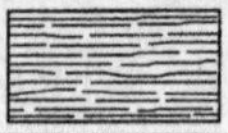 |
| FOLIATED | MINERAL ALIGNMENT | Fine to medium | MICA, QUARTZ, FELDSPAR, AMPHIBOLE, GARNET | (Heat and pressure increase with depth) ↓ | Foliation surfaces shiny from microscopic mica crystals | Phyllite | 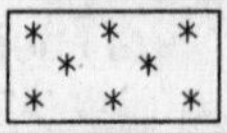 |
| FOLIATED | MINERAL ALIGNMENT | Fine to medium | MICA, QUARTZ, FELDSPAR, AMPHIBOLE, GARNET | | Platy mica crystals visible from metamorphism of clay or feldspars | Schist | 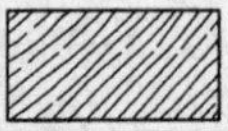 |
| FOLIATED | BANDING | Medium to coarse | MICA, QUARTZ, FELDSPAR, AMPHIBOLE, GARNET, PYROXENE | | High-grade metamorphism; some mica changed to feldspar; segregated by mineral type into bands | Gneiss | 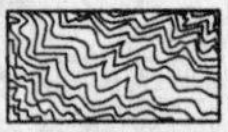 |
| NONFOLIATED | | Fine | Variable | Contact (Heat) | Various rocks changed by heat from nearby magma/lava | Hornfels | 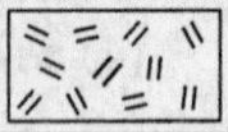 |
| NONFOLIATED | | Fine to coarse | Quartz | Regional or Contact | Metamorphism of quartz sandstone | Quartzite | 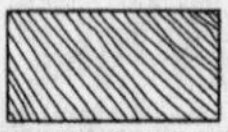 |
| NONFOLIATED | | Fine to coarse | Calcite and/or dolomite | Regional or Contact | Metamorphism of limestone or dolostone | Marble | 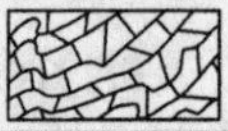 |
| NONFOLIATED | | Coarse | Various minerals in particles and matrix | Regional or Contact | Pebbles may be distorted or stretched | Metaconglomerate | 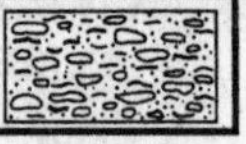 |

**Figure 3-9.** Metamorphic Rocks

**Classification of Metamorphic Rocks.** The characteristics of many metamorphic rocks are summarized in Figure 3-9. **Texture** refers to the appearance and mineral arrangement of metamorphic rocks. When the pressure aligns the minerals into layers that are easy to split, the rock is said to be **foliated.** Thin layers of alternating minerals found in metamorphic rocks (such as gneiss) is called **banding**. Grain size is in terms of fine, medium, or coarse. The composition of rocks shows that mica is in foliated rocks while pyroxene is only in gneiss and some schist. Figure 3-9 shows two types of Metamorphism–Regional or Contact Metamorphism.

## Parent Material

In many ways, metamorphic rocks are similar to their parent material. Parent material is the rock from which the metamorphic rocks formed. For example, the parent material for quartzite is sandstone. It is often possible to infer the parent rock of many metamorphic rocks from their mineral composition and structure. Quartzite is similar to quartz, the primary mineral in sandstone. Marbles are similar to some limestones. Slate has the layered look of shale. Gneiss displays the minerals of granite. Although similar in appearance to their parent material, metamorphic rocks are different rocks which have recrystallized under great heat and pressure. Metamorphic rocks occur on a continuum from little alteration to major changes. The same parent material can form different metamorphic rocks depending upon the type and degree of metamorphism.

## Types of Metamorphism

**Contact Metamorphism.** **Contact metamorphism** occurs when molten rock comes in contact with surrounding rocks. The heat from the magma alters the rock in contact with it. The temperature of the intruded magma determines how deep the metamorphism will occur. Under these conditions, a magma in contact with limestone will metamorphose into marble. The greatest metamorphism will take place next to the occurrence of magma and will diminish as the distance from the heat increases. The amount of metamorphic rock produced under these conditions is not great. Contact metamorphism is used to establish relative ages of rocks.

**Regional Metamorphism.** The greatest amount of metamorphism, **regional metamorphism,** occurs when large areas of rock are under intense heat and pressure. Regional metamorphism is generally associated with mountain building. Mountain building periods produce extreme pressures and heat. These ideas are related to deep Earth motions.

# QUESTIONS

1. Which diagram best represents a sample of the metamorphic rock gneiss?
   [Diagrams shown actual size]

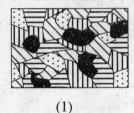 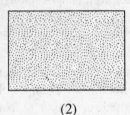 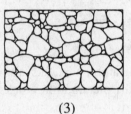 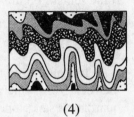

    (1)         (2)         (3)         (4)

2. The metamorphism of a sandstone rock will cause the rock

   (1) to be melted              (2) to contain more fossils
   (3) to become more dense     (4) to occupy a greater volume

3. Which properties are most often used to distinguish metamorphic rocks from other kinds
   of rocks?

   (1) organic composition and density     (3) mineral color and hardness
   (2) banding and distortion of structure   (4) layering and range of particle sizes

4. The recrystallization of unmelted material under high temperature and pressure results in

   (1) metamorphic rock         (2) sedimentary rock
   (3) igneous rock               (4) volcanic rock

5. Which characteristic of rocks tends to increase as the rocks are metamorphosed?

   (1) density                (2) volume
   (3) permeability           (4) number of fossils present

# THE ROCK CYCLE

It is believed that the earliest rocks formed on Earth were igneous. Those rocks were uplifted, weathered, and eroded. The weathered materials were deposited, buried, and compressed, and were eventually changed into sedimentary and metamorphic rocks. The **Rock Cycle** describes how rocks of all types can be constantly "recycled" or changed into other types of rocks. These changes are brought about by forces and processes that are constantly operating on and within Earth's crust. These forces and processes include weathering and erosion, deposition and burial, compression and cementation, folding, faulting, and volcanic activity. In this rock recycling process, any type of rock can be changed into any other type of rock (see Figure 3-10).

## Rock Cycle in Earth's Crust

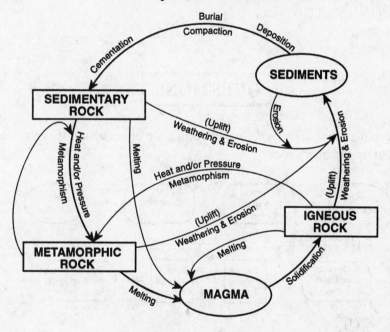

**Figure 3-10.** Rock Cycle

## Transition Zones

The process that creates a transition zone between rock types is contact metamorphism. When molten rock material comes in contact with existing rock, a transition zone of altered rock is often produced between the existing rock and the rock formed when the molten material solidifies. The rock in this transition zone may have characteristics of both rock types.

## Rock Composition

The **composition** of rocks often gives some hint as to the origin of the rocks. For example, some sedimentary rocks contain components of varied origin. This indicates that sediments from many different areas were transported to a single location and deposited. Some time later, these deposits were compressed and cemented into sedimentary rock.

The composition of some rocks indicates that the materials of the rock have undergone multiple transformations within the rock cycle. The model of the rock cycle (Figure 3-10) illustrates how these multiple transformations can occur. For example, original igneous rock can be weathered and eroded, and the transported particles deposited as sediments. Eventually, these sediments may become transformed into sedimentary rock. At some later time, heat and pressure may transform these rocks into metamorphic rocks. Still later, these rocks could be exposed to such conditions as to cause them to melt. Upon solidification, igneous rocks would form once again, perhaps totally different from the original igneous rocks at the "beginning" of this cycle.

## QUESTIONS

1. According to the *Earth Science Reference Tables,* which sequence of events occurs in the formation of sedimentary rock?

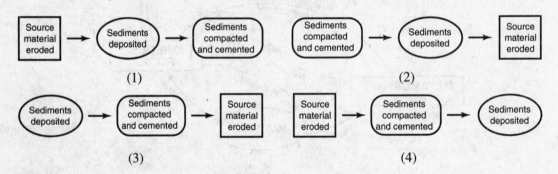

**2.** Why is the conglomerate rock shown below good evidence that rocks form from other rocks?

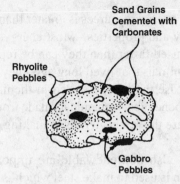

Sand Grains
Cemented with
Carbonates

Rhyolite
Pebbles

Gabbro
Pebbles

(1) The conglomerate contains some nonsedimentary rock fragments.
(2) The conglomerate was formed from material that was buried deep underground.
(3) The conglomerate's pebbles are all weathering at the same rate.
(4) The conglomerate was formed by the cooling of molten rock material.

**3.** Which statement is supported by information in the rock Cycle Diagram in the *Earth Science Reference Tables*?

(1) Metamorphic rock results directly from heat and/or pressure.
(2) Sedimentary rock can only be formed from igneous rock
(3) Igneous rock never results from melting and solidification.
(4) All sediments turn directly into sedimentary rock.

**4.** Most igneous rocks form by which process?

(1) melting and solidification      (2) heat and pressure
(3) erosion and deposition      (4) compaction and cementation

**5.** Some sedimentary rocks are composed of rock fragments which had different origins. Which statement best explains why this could occur?

(1) Fossils are often found in sedimentary rocks.
(2) Sedimentary rocks form from the weathered products of any type of rock.
(3) When molten lava solidifies to form sedimentary rock, it often contains foreign particles.
(4) Under high heat and pressure, recrystallization results in the formation of many minerals.

**6.** Which statement about the formation of a rock is best supported by the rock cycle?

(1) Magma must be weathered before it can change to metamorphic rock.
(2) Sediment must be compacted and cemented before it can change to sedimentary rock.
(3) Sedimentary rock must melt before it can change to metamorphic rock.
(4) Metamorphic rock must melt before it can change to sedimentary rock.

# MINERAL CONSERVATION

Today, the world's need for energy resources is greater than ever. Minerals are important to us because of their availability and properties. Most energy sources–coal, petroleum and natural gas–are **nonrenewable** (used faster than they can be replaced). Because they formed from the remains of plants and animals that lived long ago, they are called **<u>fossil fuels</u>.** When these fuels are burned, they release the energy stored in them. Fossil fuels are vital to our energy needs and a source of petrochemicals (chemicals made from oil) for the global economy. Both petroleum and natural gas are the raw materials in making plastics, dyes, medicines and fertilizers.

Other minerals which are also nonrenewable are important in our everyday lives. Copper is used to make wire. Iron is used to make steel which is essential for the construction of buildings, bridges, planes and a host of other items. Aluminum is used to make cans. Lead is used in storage batteries.

Alternative sources of energy are water power, wind power, solar energy and geothermal energy. These are renewable energy sources. Each of these energy sources is limited in some way–water power requires dams and rivers, wind power requires strong winds, solar energy varies with the time of day and seasons, and geothermal energy is created only where there is geothermal activity. The use and distribution of mineral resources have global political, financial and social implications. They must be used wisely. The fact that these resources are not available to everyone creates individual and national needs that cannot always be satisfied. Such unsatisfied needs may result in starvation or even cause wars.

## QUESTIONS

**1.** Which of the following is a renewable resource?

    (1) lead         (2) water power    (3) fossil fuels     (4) plastics

**2.** Which of the following items we use in our everyday life is obtained from a nonrenewable resource?

    (1) food          (2) gasoline      (3) oxygen       (4) wooden furniture

**3.** An energy source that would be difficult to use in place of a constant cloud cover is

    (1) water power    (2) wind power    (3) solar energy     (4) geothermal energy

**4.** Which natural resource is used to make plastics?

    (1) sun light      (2) oil          (3) iron        (4) lead

## CHAPTER 3 - CORE VOCABULARY

banding
cementation
chemical composition
chemical properties
classification
clastic
cleavage
color
composition
contact metamorphism
crystal
crystalline structure
evaporites
extrusion

extrusive ignous rock
features
felsic
foliated
fossil fuels
fossils
fracture
hardness
igneous rocks
intrusion
intrusive igneous rock
luster
mafic
magma

metallic
metamorphic rocks
mineral
nonmetallic
organic
particle
physical properties
regional metamorphism
rock cycle
sedimentary rock
streak
structure
texture
volcano

## HELPFUL VOCABULARY

batholith
bioclastic
carbonates
cinder cone
dike
iron oxides
laccolith
lava
lava plateau

Moh's scale of Hardness
monominerallic
nonrenewable
ore
pluton
plutonic rocks
recrystalization
rock-forming minerals
shield cone

silicates
sill
strata-beds
sulfides
tetrahedron
volcanic neck
volcanic rock

## PRACTICE FOR CONSTRUCTED RESPONSE

Use your knowledge of Earth Science and the *Earth Science Reference Tables* to answer questions 1 through 4.

Two students arrive at an uncharted island to study the types of materials there.

1. When they arrive, they notice large mineral samples. They note that the samples are soft and grayish silver in color. What test or tests could they use to determine the identity of the mineral?

   _____

   _____

2. They also see rocks that have fossils in them. Student A says that the rock is limestone. Student B says that the rock is sandstone.

   **a.** What test or tests could they use to determine the identity of the rock?

   _____

   _____

   **b.** What is the probable origin of the rocks?

   _____

3. When the students go further inland, they come across rock material that seems to form a layer on the surface. They note that it is vesicular and gray in color. It seems very light in weight and brittle. They know the rock is either scoria or pumice.

   **a.** What test or tests could they apply to determine the identity of the rock?

   _____

   _____

   **b.** What is the probable origin of that rock?

   _____

4. On the far side of the island, they find some rocks on the shore. They examine them and find that they are very hard and the minerals seem to be banded or aligned. Student A says he believes the rock to be schist, while student B believes the rock to be gneiss.

   **a.** What could the students look for in the rock to help them identify the rock?

   _____

   _____

   **b.** What is the probable origin of the rock, no matter what its identity?

   _____

   _____

Base your answers to questions 5 through 8 on the table of minerals below, your knowledge of Earth Science and the *Earth Science Reference Tables*.

| Mineral | Color | Streak | Hardness | Density (gm/L) |
|---|---|---|---|---|
| biotite mica | black | white | 2.5 | 2.8 |
| diamond | varies | colorless | 10 | 3.5 |
| galena | gray | gray-black | 2.5 | 7.5 |
| graphite | black | black | 1.2 | 2.3 |
| kaolinite | white | white | 2 | 2.6 |
| magnetite | black | black | 5.5 | 5.2 |
| olivine | green | white | 6.5 | 3.4 |
| pyrite | brass yellow | greenish-black | 6 | 5.0 |
| quartz | varies | colorless | 7 | 2.7 |

5. **a.** If there were equal masses of each mineral, how could you determine which one would occupy the least volume?

   _____

   _____

   **b.** Which one of the minerals in the table would occupy the least volume?

   _____

   _____

6. Explain how diamond and graphite can be composed of the same element, carbon, and have very different physical properties.

_____

_____

7. Describe why color and streak are useful properties in identifying pyrite.

_____

_____

8. **a.** If equal volumes of the mineral diamond, biotite and olivine were placed in a rotating tumbler, what evidence would be used to predict which mineral would be scratched the least?

_____

_____

**b.** Identify the mineral that would wear out the fastest.

_____

_____

Base your answers to questions 9 through 11 on the table below, your knowledge of Earth Science and the *Earth Science Reference Tables*. The table provides data about the texture and mineral composition of four different igneous rock samples having the same volume.

| Rock | Texture | Potassium Feldspar | Quartz | Plagioclase Feldspar | Biotite | Hornblende | Pyroxene |
|------|---------|--------------------|--------|----------------------|---------|------------|----------|
| A | coarse | 62% | 20% | 7% | 7% | 4% | 0% |
| B | coarse | 24% | 40% | 19% | 10% | 7% | 0% |
| C | fine | 6% | 16% | 41% | 14% | 23% | 0% |
| D | fine | 0% | 0% | 50% | 0% | 6% | 44% |

9. Describe how rocks A & B formed with a coarse texture while rocks C & D formed with a fine texture.

_____

_____

**10.** Describe the evidence that indicates that rock D is probably basalt.

_____

_____

**11.** Predict a name for Rock A. Use the *Earth Science Reference Tables* to support your choice. _____

Base your answers to questions 12 through 15 on the description of the different rock samples A through E, in the table below, your knowledge of Earth Science and the *Earth Science Reference Tables*.

| Rock Sample | Description |
|---|---|
| A | a gray rock consisting of particles of uniform size (0.05 cm in diameter) cemented together. |
| B | a light-colored felsic rock consisting of coarse-grained intergrown crystals (pink, white, and black) evenly distributed throughout the sample |
| C | a rock consisting of light and dark intergrown crystals with the crystals aligned in alternating light and dark wavy bands |
| D | a black mafic rock consisting of fine-grained dark, intergrown crystals evenly distributed throughout the sample |
| E | a soft white rock consisting of one uniform material containing fossil shells |

**12. a.** Describe the information which indicates the samples that are most likely sedimentary rocks.

_____

_____

**b.** Indicate the samples of sedimentary rocks.

_____

**13. a.** Describe the rock which was most likely formed from molten material that cooled and solidified deep within the Earth.

_____

**b.** Name the rock sample.

_____

14. Describe the environment in which the parent material for rock sample E was most likely formed.

_____

_____

15. Which part of the description of rock sample A can be used on the *Earth Science Reference Tables* to identify the sample?

_____

Use the *Earth Science Reference Tables* to answer the following questions:

16. A conglomerate contains pebbles of limestone, sandstone, and granite. Based on this information, which inference about the pebbles in the conglomerate is most accurate.

_____

17. Which igneous rock is composed of only one mineral? _____

18. Which igneous rocks can have the mineral quartz as part of their main component?

_____

_____

Base your answers to questions 19 through 22 on the diagram below, which represents a scheme for classifying rocks. The letters A, B, C and X, Y, Z represent missing labels.

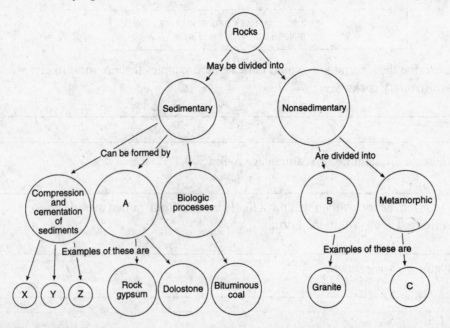

**19.** The classification of rocks into sedimentary or nonsedimentary groups is based primarily on the rocks' _____

**20.** Which processes would form the type of rock that is represented by circle B? _____

**21.** If the rock in circle C formed from limestone, it would be called _____

**22. a.** Which list below contains the rocks that best represents circles X, Y, and Z? _____
  1. shale, slate, and schist
  2. sandstone, shale, and siltstone
  3. anthracite coal, metaconlomerate, and rock salt
  4. breccia, gneiss, and rhyolite

  **b.** What prevents the other lists from representing X, Y, and Z? Be specific.

  _____

  _____

  _____

Base your answers to questions 23 and 24 on the data tables below, your knowledge of Earth Science and the *Earth Science Reference Tables*.

**DATA TABLE #1**

| Mineral | Composition |
|---|---|
| Mica | $KAl_3SiO_{10}$ |
| Olivine | $(FeMg)_2SiO_4$ |
| Orthoclase | $KAlSi_3O_8$ |
| Plagioclase | $NaAlSi_3O_8$ |
| Pyroxene | $CaMgSi_2O_6$ |
| Quartz | $SiO_2$ |

**DATA TABLE #2**

| Group A | Group B | Group C |
|---|---|---|
| basalt granite | sandstone shale | marble gneiss |

**23.** Data table #1 shows the composition of six common rockforming minerals. Describe what minerals have in common.

_____

_____

**24.** Data table #2 is a classification of six common rocks, based on how they were formed. Use the *Earth Science Reference Tables* to describe:
  **a.** What would be considered in placing a conglomerate rock in this classification.

_____

  **b.** Which group would the conglomerate rock be placed.

_____

# CHAPTER 4
# THE DYNAMIC CRUST

## MODEL OF EARTH'S CRUST AND INTERIOR

Properties of Earth's interior have been inferred primarily from the study of earthquake waves. Through these studies, the thickness, composition, density, temperature, and pressure of Earth's crust and interior zones have been determined. (see Figure 4-1) The continental crust is thicker and less dense than the oceanic crust.

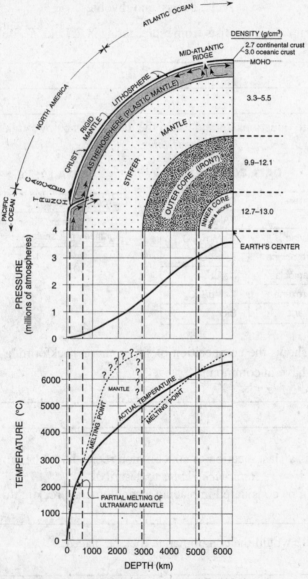

**Figure 4–1.** Inferred Properties of Earth's Interior

# EARTH'S CRUST AND INTERIOR

The **crust** is considered to be the solid outer rock zone of Earth. While the crust appears to be rigid, stable, and unchanging, there is considerable evidence that it is undergoing constant change. Some of this evidence is directly observable. Weathering and erosion, for example, are changes in the crustal rock. Earthquakes and volcanoes provide more dramatic evidence of change. However, much of the evidence for change is indirect or incomplete, making it difficult to evaluate the full extent of the change that the crust undergoes. **Tectonics** is the study of the movement of the solid rock of Earth's crust.

## Earthquake and Volcanic Distribution

Most earthquakes and volcanoes are concentrated in narrow geographic belts (see Figure 4-2), although some earthquakes have occurred in most parts of Earth. The most important concentration of earthquakes and volcanoes is the **circum-Pacific belt** which circles the rim of the Pacific Ocean. Another major concentration occurs along the Mediterranean-Himalayan Belt, which crosses the Mediterranean Sea, crosses the Mideast and extends beyond the Himalayas. Many other earthquakes occur along mid-ocean ridges and ocean trenches (see Figure 4-2)

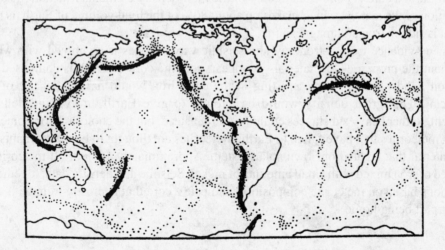

**Figure 4-2.** The dotted regions are the major earthquake zones, The solid lines are the major volcanic belts.

## Solid and Liquid Zones

Analysis of seismic data leads to the inference that three solid zones and a liquid zone exist within the Earth. The solid zones are the crust, mantle, and inner core, while the liquid zone is the outer core, (see Figure 4-1). The crust and uppermost part of the mantle are similar in composition and make up the rigid **lithosphere** (about, 100 kilometers thick). Under the lithosphere is the upper mantle, or **asthenosphere,** which behaves like a thick, plastic fluid. The part of the mantle under the asthenosphere is much stiffer. It has been observed that abrupt changes in the speed of P-waves occur between the mantle and the outer core and between the outer core and the inner core. These changes make interfaces between these zones easy to identify (see Figure 4-1). For example, using the patterns of earthquake waves, Andrija Mohorovicic discovered the location of the interface between the crust and the mantle. This interface has been named the **Mohorovicic discontinuity,** or **"Moho" Interface** in his honor. The fact that S-waves cannot travel through the outer core indicates that this zone is liquid.

Through the study of earthquake waves, geologists have determined the thickness, composition, density, temperature, and pressure of Earth's crust and interior (See Figure 4-1 or the *Inferred Properties of the Earth's Interior* chart in the *Earth Science Reference Tables)*. The density, temperature and pressure of Earth increase with depth.

## Interior Composition

Studies of seismic-wave patterns (and of some meteorites composed of iron and nickel) infer that Earth's core is composed mainly of the high-density elements iron and nickel. The composition of the mantle, which makes up about 80% of the total volume of Earth, is mainly rock that is rich in iron and magnesium.

When evidence from astronomy and seismic wave studies is combined with what we know about the properties of materials, it appears that the core of Earth is composed of the metal iron. Under the pressures existing in the core, iron would have a density of about 10 gm/cm$^3$. This great density would be enough to give Earth an average density of 5.5 gm/cm$^3$. Other heavy substances could be there instead, but the choice of iron comes from studying meteorites that have fallen to Earth. Meteorites are thought to be the remnants of the basic material that created our own solar system. Approximately 10% of all meteorites are composed of iron mixed with small amounts of nickel. Seismic and density data, together with assumptions based on meteorite composition, indicate a core that is mostly iron, with at least the outer part being liquid.

# QUESTIONS

Base you answers to questions 1 and 2 on the diagram below, which shows a cutaway view of Earth in which the interior layers are visible. The paths of earthquake waves generated at point X are shown. A, B, C, and D are locations of seismic stations on Earth's surface, and point E is located in Earth's interior.

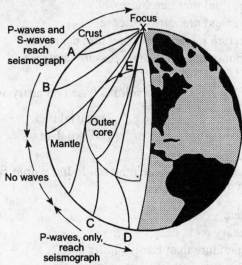

1. Both P-waves and S-waves were received at seismic stations A and B, but only P-waves were received at seismic stations C and D. Which statement best explains why this occurred?
   (1) S-waves are much weaker than P-waves.
   (2) S-waves travel faster than P-waves.
   (3) The liquid outer core prevents S-waves from traveling to seismic stations C and D.
   (4) The solid outer core prevents S-waves from traveling to seismic stations C and D.

2. According to the *Earth Science Reference Tables*, the actual rock temperature at point E is inferred to be approximately
   (1) 1,500°C      (2) 2,900°C      (3) 5,000°C      (4) 6,200°C

3. According to the *Earth Science Reference Tables*, which zone of Earth has the greatest density?
   (1) crust      (2) mantle      (3) outer core      (4) inner core

4. According to the *Earth Science Reference Tables,* approximately how far below Earth's surface is the interface between the mantle and the outer core?
   (1) 5 to 30 km                    (2) 700 to 900 km
   (3) 2,900 to 3,000 km            (4) 5,000 to 5,200 km

5. According to the *Earth Science Reference Tables,* the temperature at the center of Earth is estimated to be

   (1) 1,000°C          (2) 2,800°C          (3) 5,000°C          (4) 6,000°C

6. According to the *Earth Science Reference Tables,* as the depth within Earth's interior increases, the

   (1) density, temperature, and pressure increase
   (2) density, temperature, and pressure decrease
   (3) density and temperature increase, but pressure decreases
   (4) density increases, but temperature and pressure decrease

7. The inference that Earth's inner core is solid is based on analysis of

   (1) seismic data                    (2) crustal rock
   (3) radioactive data                (4) fossil data

8. Which statement is characteristic of the material found within Earth between a depth of 2,900 kilometers and 5,200 kilometers?

   (1) It is in the liquid state.
   (2) It contains sedimentary rock, only.
   (3) It has a higher temperature than Earth's inner core.
   (4) It is under a greater pressure than Earth's inner core.

9. The composition of Earth's core is thought to be the same as the composition of

   (1) certain meteorites              (2) most basalts
   (3) most granites                   (4) volcanic ash

10. Which of the following earthquake waves can travel through both solids and fluids?

    (1) S-waves, only     (2) P- waves, only     (3) S-waves and P-waves

# EARTHQUAKES

An **earthquake** is the vibration or shaking of Earth's crust caused by rapid movement of rocks in the lithosphere. Earthquakes usually occur along faults at or near Earth's surface, most frequently near the margins of tectonic plates.

The shaking of the ground during an earthquake is caused by the sudden release of energy in the rocks beneath Earth's surface. Forces deep within Earth put stress on the rocks, causing them to bend. When the stress on the rock causes it to break, waves of energy (seismic waves) are sent out through Earth. It is the seismic waves which cause the ground to tremble and shake during an earthquake.

Earthquakes generate three types of waves. **Compressional waves,** called **primary waves** or **P-waves**, are like sound waves. They cause particles of rock through which they travel to vibrate in a back-and-forth motion in the same direction as the wave is traveling. **Shear waves**, called **secondary waves** or **S-waves**, are similar to the waves produced in a rope when it is shaken vigorously. S-waves cause rock particles to vibrate at right angles to the direction in which the wave is traveling. **Long waves**, or **L-waves**, travel along Earth's surface at relatively slow speeds.

Two types of seismic waves radiate outward from the earthquake focus. P-waves and S-waves both travel through Earth. Surface waves, which travel along Earth's surface cause more damage than other waves because they produce more ground movement.

## Earthquake Waves

Scientists use an instrument called a **seismograph** to detect and record earthquakes. When an earthquake occurs, it generates energy waves, called **seismic waves**. These waves travel outward from the point in the crust where the earthquake originates. This point is called the **focus** of the earthquake (see Figure 4-3).

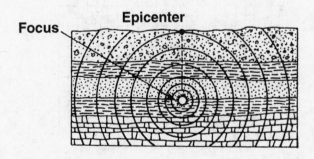

**Figure 4-3.** Focus and epicenter of an earthquake.

## Seismograms

Different types of seismic waves travel at different speeds, therefore they arrive at a seismograph station in a definite order (see Figure 4-4), first the P-waves, then the S-waves and finally the surface waves. By analyzing the **seismograms**, geologists determine a seismic wave's distance and size.

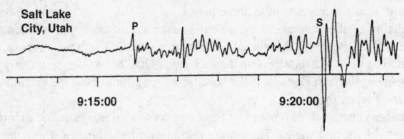

**Figure- 4-4.** P-waves arrive first, followed by S-waves.

## Locating the Epicenter of an Earthquake

The **epicenter** of an earthquake is the point on Earth's surface directly above the earthquake focus. As described earlier, P-waves travel faster than S-waves. Thus, P-waves arrive at a seismograph station ahead of the S-waves. The difference in travel time between P-waves and S-waves can be used to determine the distance from a seismograph station to the epicenter of a quake. The farther a station is from an epicenter, the greater the time interval between the arrival of P-waves and S-waves (see Figure 4-5) and the "Earthquake P-wave and S-wave Travel Time Graph" in the *Earth Science Reference Tables*.

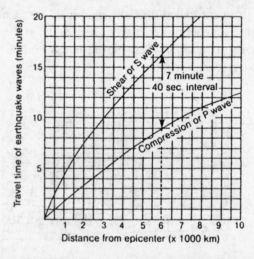

**Figure 4-5.** P- and S-wave travel times. The two curves show the time needed for P- and S-waves to travel a given distance from the epicenter of an earthquake. At a given seismograph station, the difference in arrival times for the two waves will be recorded. This difference can be used to determine the distance of the station from the epicenter. The example shows a difference of 7 minutes 40 seconds, which gives a distance of 6000 kilometers from the epicenter.

Determining the distance of an epicenter from a seismograph station does *not* determine the *location* of the epicenter. It simply places the epicenter on a circle having a radius equal to its distance from the recording station. In order to determine the *exact* location of an epicenter, its distance from three seismograph stations must be determined and three circles drawn. The epicenter is located at the point where all three circles intersect (see Figure 4-6)

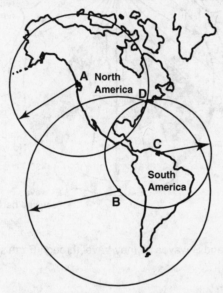

**Figure 4-6.** Locating the epicenter of an earthquake. The distance to the epicenter of an earthquake is plotted from three different stations A, B, and C. The epicenter is located at the point of intersection of the three plotted circles, at point D.

## Velocity of Earthquake Waves

When traveling through the same medium, P-waves travel faster than S-waves. Thus, P-waves are the first impulses to reach a seismograph located at some distance from the focus of the quake. S-waves move slower than P-waves and therefore lag behind the P-waves. On a seismograph recording, the greater the time difference between the arrival times of P-waves and S-waves, the greater the distance to the earthquake.

The velocity of seismic waves depends on the physical properties of the materials through which they travel. The denser the rock material, the greater the velocity of the waves. The density of rock material increases as you move deeper into Earth's interior. Thus, seismic wave velocity increases as the waves move toward Earth's center and decreases as the waves move toward the surface.

Seismic waves do not travel in straight lines. The waves are bent, or refracted, as they move from a medium of one density into a medium of a different density (see Figure 4-7).

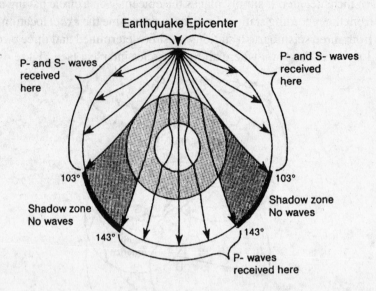

**Figure 4-7.** Pattern of P-waves and S-waves as they travel through Earth's interior.

The fact that S-waves will not travel through Earth's core combines with the refraction of seismic waves to produce a zone on Earth's surface where no seismic waves are received when an earthquake occurs. This zone, called the **shadow zone,** is located between 103° and 143° from the epicenter of the earthquake (see Figure 4-7).

## Earthquake Strength

The intensity of and energy of an earthquake is measured on two different scales. A measure of the amount of energy released during an earthquake is its **<u>magnitude.</u>** The **Richter scale** is a numerical scale of magnitudes starting from 0 to a high of any number (see Table 4-1). The higher numbers indicate larger earthquakes. Each step increase in magnitude represents an increase of 10 times the next lower number. For example, an earthquake with a magnitude of 6 is 10 times stronger than an earthquake with a magnitude of 5. An earthquake with a magnitude of 7 is 100 times stronger than an earthquake with a magnitude of 5. An earthquake with a magnitude of 8 is 1000 times stronger than an earthquake with a magitude of 5, etc.

## Richter Scale Magnitudes

| Effects of Earthquakes | Magnitude | Number of Earthquakes Per Year |
|---|---|---|
| Damage nearly total | 8.0 – | 1 – 2 |
| Great damage | 7.4 – 8.9 | 4 |
| Serious damage, rails bent | 7.0 – 7.3 | 15 |
| Considerable damage to buildings | 6.2 – 6.9 | 100 |
| Slight damage to buildings | 5.5 – 6.1 | 500 |
| Felt by all | 4.9 – 5.4 | 1,400 |
| Felt by many | 4.3 – 4.8 | 4,800 |
| Felt by some | 3.5 – 4.2 | 30,000 |
| Not felt, but recorded | 2.0 – 3.4 | 800,000 |

**Table 4-1.** Richter Scale Magnitudes

Another way to measure the strength of an earthquake is to determine the **intensity,** the measure of an earthquake's effect on people and buildings. The intensities are shown as Roman numerals from I to XII on the **modified Mercalli scale** (see Table 4-2 for abridged version). The higher numbers indicate greater damage. Because the Mercalli scale is based on descriptions of earthquake damage, problems can easily arise with this system. Damage estimates are subjective. Since damage generally diminishes with distance from the epicenter, different locations report different intensities for the same earthquake.

## Modified Mercalli Scale (Abridged)

| Intensity Value | Observed Effects |
|---|---|
| I | Usually detected only by instruments |
| II | Felt by a few persons at rest, especially on upper floors |
| III | Hanging objects swing; vibration like a passing truck; noticeable indoors |
| IV | Felt indoors by many, outdoors, by few; a sensation like a heavy truck striking a building; parked automobiles rock |
| V | Felt by nearly all; sleepers awakened; liquids disturbed; unstable objects overturned; some dishes and windows broken |
| VI | Felt by all; many frightened and run outdoors; some heavy furniture moved; glassware broken; books fall off shelves; damage slight |
| VII | Difficult to stand; noticed in moving automobiles; damage to some masonry; weak chimneys broken at roofline |
| VIII | Partial collapse of masonry; chimneys, factory stacks, columns fall; heavy furniture overturned; frame houses moved on foundations |

**Table 4-2.** Modified Mercalli Scale

The Richter Scale of earthquake magnitude is the most common in use throughout the world. There is a worldwide network of standard seismograph stations that determine magnitudes as a routine matter. The media reports earthquake magnitudes in Richter-Scale numbers.

## Earthquake Damage

Most earthquakes occur in the western part of the United States. They are generally uncommon and small in the east. These are not usually associated with crustal displacement.

The major effect of an earthquake is ground motion where trembling and shaking of the land cause buildings and bridges to vibrate and collapse. Fire is another serious problem right after an earthquake because of broken gas and water pipes and fallen electric lines. On the west coast, landslides can be triggered by the shaking of the ground. The land may be permanently displaced, tearing buildings, roads and pipes apart.

To prevent damage and the loss of life, building codes have been developed for both bridges and buildings. Most people injured or killed in an earthquake are hit by falling debris from buildings. Buildings must be located on hard rock rather than soft sediment.

## Volcanic Damage

Volcanoes can have a dramatic effect on humans that can be catastrophic, or sometimes, beneficial. Erupting volcanoes can bury the land, burn property and kill people. Three volcanoes on the island of Krakatoa erupted in 1883 with the force of several hydrogen bombs. The explosion was heard over 500 kilometers away and only one-third of the island remained. On nearby Java, tens of thousands of people died as a result of the giant sea waves (**tsunamis**) generated by undersea earthquakes associated with the volcanic explosions. People often die also as a result of the poisonous gases that are released during eruptions.

Volcanoes can also be beneficial. Hawaii, for example, would not exist if it were not for volcanoes. Also, the weathered ash makes excellent fertile soil. Volcanoes can be great attractions for both scientists and tourists. The heat from underground activity can be used to produce geothermal energy as it is done in Iceland.

## QUESTIONS

Base your answers to questions 1 and 2 on your knowledge of Earth Science, the *Earth Science Reference Tables,* and on the world map below. The dots on the map indicate the locations of epicenters of major earthquakes over a five-year period. Points A through G are locations on the map.

**WORLD MAP OF EARTHQUAKE EPICENTERS**

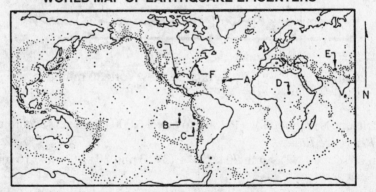

1. Where do most major earthquakes occur?

   (1) in the continental interiors
   (3) randomly over Earth's surface

   (2) at the mantle-core boundary
   (4) in specific earthquake belts within the crust

2. How would a map showing the locations of active volcanoes compare to the map showing the location of earthquake epicenters?
   (1) Only a small percentage of volcano locations would be in the same regions as the epicenters.
   (2) A large percentage of volcano locations would be in the same regions as the epicenters.
   (3) There would be no match between the locations of the volcanoes and the epicenters.
   (4) The location of the volcanoes and the epicenters would only match in the ocean regions.

3. Which is most helpful to a seismologist when determining the distance to the epicenter of an earthquake?
   (1) time of arrival of the P-wave
   (2) intensity of the P-wave
   (3) time interval between P-wave and S-wave arrival
   (4) S- wave characteristics on the seismogram

4. According to the seismogram below, approximately how far is Syracuse from this recorded earthquake? (Refer to *Earth Science Reference Tables*)
   (1) $7.0 \times 10^3$ km       (2) $2.0 \times 10^3$ km       (3) $5.4 \times 10^3$ km       (4) $4.0 \times 10^3$ km

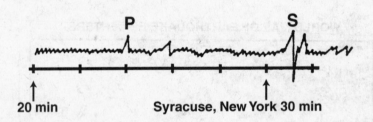

5. How much time is required for a P-wave to travel 6,000 kilometers according to the *Earth Science Reference Tables* ?
   (1) 6 min 00 sec       (2) 9 min 20 sec       (3) 10 min 30 sec       (4) 16 min 50 sec

6. A seismograph station records a difference in arrival time between the S-and P-wave of 4 minutes. About how far away is the earthquake epicenter? (Refer to the *Earth Science Reference Tables*)
   (1) 1,000 km       (2) 1,900 km       (3) 2,600 km       (4) 5,200 km

7. As the distance from the epicenter of an earthquake increases, the time between the arrival of the P-waves and S-waves on a seismograph will
   (1) decrease       (2) increase       (3) remain the same

Base your answers to questions 8 through 10 on your knowledge of Earth Science, the *Earth Science Reference Tables,* and the information and data table below.

An earthquake originated in New York State. The P-wave travel time for this earthquake was recorded in the data table below for four widely separated seismic stations, A, B, C, and D.

**DATA TABLE**

| Seismic Station | P-wave Travel Time |
|---|---|
| A | 8min 20sec |
| B | 0min 31sec |
| C | 12min 18sec |
| D | 3min 20sec |

**8.** Which of the four seismic stations is located farthest from the epicenter?

(1) A          (2) B          (3) C          (4) D

**9.** Which seismic station could be located in New York State?

(1) A          (2) B          (3) C          (4) D

**10.** What is the approximate distance between the earthquake's epicenter and station A?

(1) 1,130 km          (2) 2,400 km          (3) 5,100 km          (4) 7,500 km

# EVIDENCE FOR CRUSTAL MOVEMENT

Movement of Earth's crust can be divided into two classifications–major changes and minor changes. Minor changes are often part of a major change.

## Major Crustal Changes

Major crustal changes, such as continental drift, occur over very long periods of time. Evidence of such changes is obtained by observing "zones" of crustal activity–sediment basins, mid-ocean ridges, ocean trenches, and regions of frequent earthquake and volcanic activity.

## Zones of Crustal Activity

Zones, or belts, of frequent crustal activity can be located on Earth's surface (see Figure 4-8). Most earthquakes, volcanoes, sediment basins, mid-ocean ridges, deep sea trenches, and young continental mountains occur along these zones. The zones are located primarily along the margins of continents or in the middle of the ocean, separating the crustal plates that make up the Earth's surface. Today, most activity occurs along the Circum-Pacific Belt, located where the edge of the Pacific Ocean meets the land; along the mid-ocean ridges; and along the belt that runs through Southern Europe, the Middle East, and into Asia. All features of crustal activity are closely related and are often found together in the same locations.

## Tectonic Plates

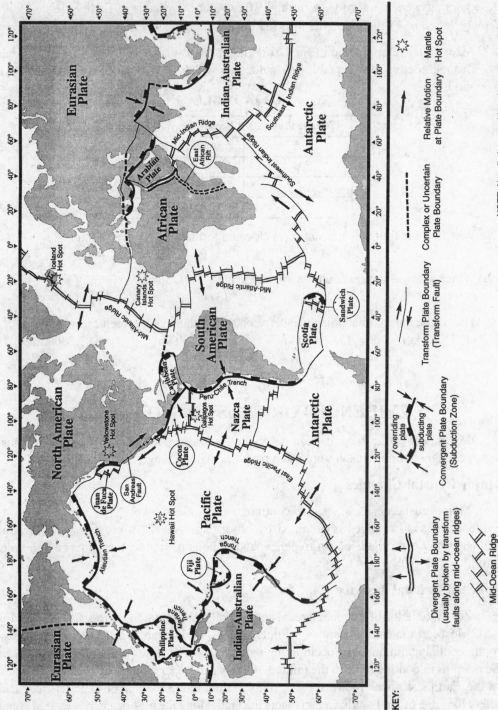

**Figure 4-8.** Major tectonic plates, ridges and trenches of Earth. Arrows show direction of plate movement. The large plates include both ocean and landmasses.

**Continental Drift**. In 1910, Alfred Wegener suggested that the coastlines of the continents on opposite sides of the Atlantic Ocean could be "fitted together" like pieces of a jigsaw puzzle. Thus was the theory of continental drift born. The concept of **continental drift** is that the continental land masses have been moving across Earth's surface for millions of years. Evidence in support of this theory is mainly the "fit" of continental coastal regions and the correlation of rock, mineral, and fossil evidence.

## Theories of Crustal Change

**Continental "Fit".** It is theorized that about 200 million years ago, all the continents were joined together in one giant supercontinent (see Figure 4-9 and the "Inferred Positions of the Earth Landmasses" in the *Earth Science Reference Tables*). Since that time, forces within Earth's interior have caused the continents to move apart to their present positions. Since these forces are still active, the continents are still moving and will continue to move in the future.

**Figure 4-9.** The continents around the Atlantic Ocean appear to "fit" together. The straight lines represent the latitude and longitude as they appear today.

**Rock, mineral, and fossil correlation.** Evidence for the idea that the continents were once joined together is the similarity of rock formations, minerals, and fossil remains found in widely separated locations along coastal regions of different continents (see Figure 4-10). By Richter Scale Magnitudes "fitting together" these continental boundaries, the rock, mineral, and fossil collections are also joined. Fossils of tropical plants found in Antarctica also support the idea of continental drift.

Studies show that rocks on continents now separated by an ocean matched in age and type. Plant fossils, hundreds of millions of years old, are found in matching locations on continents separated by an ocean. The fossil evidence, however, indicates that today's climates at these latitudes could not have produced the fossils found there–the plants and animals had to live in different climates. If the continents were brought together, and shifted south to warmer latitudes the fossils could have formed. The coal beds of North America, for example, were laid down in swampy, warm environments, yet they are mined in a colder, different climate zone. Evidence of glacial movements on the different continents in the Southern Hemisphere matches only if the countries were once together.

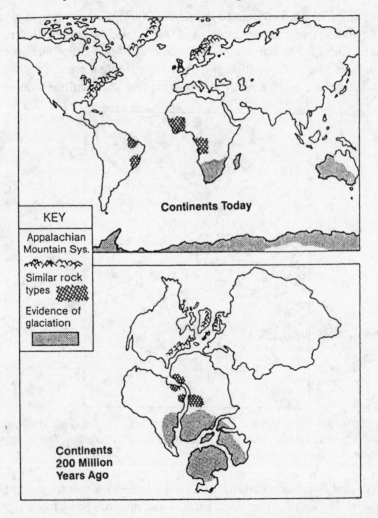

**Figure 4-10.** Evidence for the theory of continental drift. The apparent "fit" of some continental outlines led to the idea that all landmasses were part of a giant supercontinent (bottom). This idea would also explain the presence of similar rock formations, minerals, and fossils at widely scattered locations today (top). In the supercontinent, these different items were all close together.

## Plate Movements

The idea of drifting continents is not new. The similarities between the shapes of the Atlantic coastlines of South America and Africa was noticed in the 1600s. Later work showed even more similarities. But similarities are not proof. The concept of plate tectonics was born in the late 1960s by combining the ideas of continental drift and sea-floor spreading. Continental drift theorizes that continents move freely over Earth's surface, changing their positions relative to one another. Sea-floor spreading is a hypothesis that the sea floor forms out of the mid-ocean ridges and moves away from the ridge. On both sides, the sea floor moves like slow conveyor belts in opposite directions away from the ridge.

**Plate Tectonics.**  Although much evidence has been uncovered to support the concept of continental drift, a more expanded concept of large scale crustal movements, called **plate tectonics,** has been developed in recent years. This theory proposes that Earth's crust is divided into a number of large "plates." Some plates consist of just ocean floor, while others carry continental "blocks." The plates are moving across Earth's surface in such a manner that in different regions, plates are separating, colliding, or sliding past one another. Each plate is made up of crustal rock and the very upper part of the mantle. The combination of the crust and upper part of the mantle is rigid. This rigid material is called the lithosphere and it is about 100 kilometers thick. Lithospheric plates rest on the **asthenosphere,** the portion of the mantle that has the characteristics of a very thick liquid. This material is able to flow in slow, powerful convection cells (see Figure 4-11).  Although the effects of plate interactions are tremendous, the actual movement is generally less than a few centimenters a year.

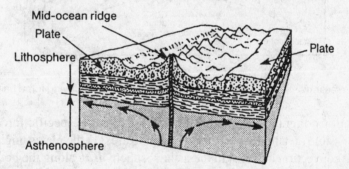

**Figure 4-11.** Huge, slow-moving convection currents in the asthenosphere are believed to be the driving force behind plate movements.

## Fact or Theory?

Although most geologists believe plate tectonics is an exciting theory and accept it as a working model of Earth, the theory may or may not be correct. Most geologists today believe that plates exist and move. But widespread belief in a theory does not make it true. Forty years ago, continental drift rated only a footnote in most introductory science textbooks. Objections have been raised to the concept of plate tectonics. The most important objection is that the geology of many regions does not fit into the theory. For example, the Rocky Mountains are difficult to explain by plate tectonics. Plate tectonics does not easily explain why the mountain building is younger in the Rockies than it is farther west in the mountains of California. Before you accept plate tectonics, you should know the data, testing and thinking involved in its development. You should be able to describe how plate tectonics can explain Earth features. Decide for yourself, "Is plate tectonics a hypothesis, a theory, or a fact?" Keep an open mind.

**Mantle Convection Cells**. Continental drift, high temperature heat flows where mid-ocean ridges and mountains are currently building, and low temperature heat flows where shallow basins are presently subsiding, all suggest that convection currents in the asthenosphere are the driving force behind plate movements in the lithosphere (see Figure 4-12). Convection currents in fluids are produced by the unequal heating of the fluids. Tremendous amounts of heat generated in the interior of Earth may supply the energy to produce these large convection cells in the asthenosphere. The separate plates of the lithosphere ride on the more fluid asthenosphere and more slowly to one another, creating convergent, divergent and transform plate boundaries.

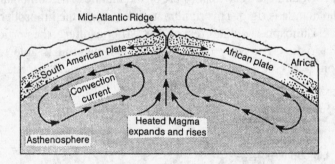

**Figure 4-12.** Convection currents in the mantle are believed to be the driving force behind plate tectonics.

The scientific community is not unified in accepting the specific forces that propel the plates. Three possible driving forces for plate motion are: (1) the plates might be *pushed* from the rear, (2) the convection currents in the asthenosphere *drag* along the bottom of plates and (3) the descending denser edge pulls the plate from the front as it sinks.

Hot spots, or Mantle Plumes, are areas of active volcanism in the lithosphere. Their cause is not clear, but they seem to remain in the same location as the lithospheric plates move above them. The result is a line of extinct volcanoes (seamounts or guyots) increasing in age away from the active area. The Hawaiian Islands appear to have formed at a hot spot. In the Hawaiian Islands, the only two active volcanoes arc on the southeastern islands (see Figure 4-13).

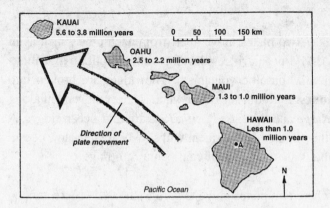

**Figure 4-13.** Movement over hot spot. The Hawaiian Island chain of volcanoes moving northwest. The island of Hawaii is an active volcano. The numbers show the bedrock age of some of the islands.

## Plate Boundaries

There are three basic types of plate interactions occurring at various locations on Earth's surface; divergent, convergent and transform (see Figure 4-14).

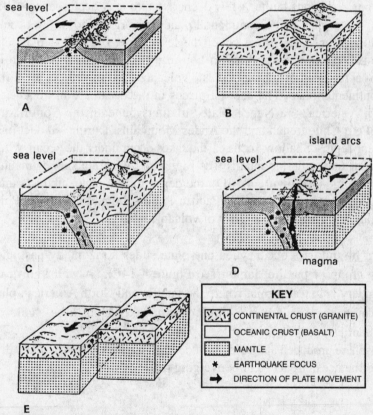

**Figure 4-14.** Three basic types of interactions among tectonic plates. *Diverging plates*: (A) two ocean plates are moving apart. *Converging plates*: (B) two continental plates are moving together, (C) an ocean plate and a continental plate move together, (D) two ocean plates are moving together. *Transform plates*: (E) two plates are sliding by each other.

**Diverging boundaries** occur where two plates move apart from each other, such as in mid-ocean ridges (see Figure 4-14A). Mid-ocean ridges develop valleys called **rift valleys** which are marked by high heat flow and basaltic volcanism. The ridges are broken into segments, by faults called **fracture zones.** Earthquakes occur when there is movement along the fracture zone. The *Mid-Atlantic Ridge* and the *East Pacific Rise* are mid-ocean ridges. A diverging plate boundary forming in the middle of a continent will slowly create a new ocean. The Red Sea and the African Rift Valleys are examples of continental splitting.

**Convergent boundaries** occur where two plates move toward each other. There are two types of convergent boundaries. When two continental plates meet, mountains are produced (see Figure 4-14B). The boundary between the two, continental plates is a **collision boundary.** The Himalayan Mountains are thought to have formed in this way, as India collided with the rest of Asia. The entire region of collision is marked by shallow-focus earthquakes along numerous faults. A few deeper quakes may occur beneath the mountains.

When an ocean plate and a continental plate converge **subduction** occurs, the denser ocean plate plunges or slides down under the less dense, overriding plate. The boundary between these two plates is a **subduction boundary** (see Figure 4-14C and D). An ocean trench develops at the point of subduction, and volcanoes and mountains are formed along the edge of the continental plate. The deepest places in the ocean are in trenches. On the west coast of South America, the Nazca Plate subducts beneath the South American plate producing the Peru-Chile trench and the Andes Mountains. During subduction, earthquakes occur at different depths. Shallow-focus earthquakes occur under the ocean, while deep-focus earthquakes occur under the mountains (see Figure 4-14C). In a similar manner, when two ocean plates converge (see Figure 4-14D), the denser ocean plate subducts under the other. Two ocean plates converge where the Pacific Plate subducts under the Philippine Plate forming the Marianas Trench and a chain of volcanic islands.

**Transform boundaries** occur when one plate slides horizontally past another along a single fault or group of parallel faults (see Figure 4-14E). A well known example of a transform boundary is in California, where the Pacific and North American plates slide past each other forming the *San Andreas Fault.* Earthquakes tend to be shallow-focus along transform boundaries.

The lithosphere produced at the ridges of diverging plates will eventually disappear when it subducts into the ocean trenches of converging plates.

## QUESTIONS

1. In the map below, location A is best described as an area that is

   (1) within a rift valley at a mid-ocean ridge
   (2) at the boundary between two diverging plates
   (3) within a deep-sea trench between two converging plates
   (4) above a mantle hot spot near the center of a crustal plate

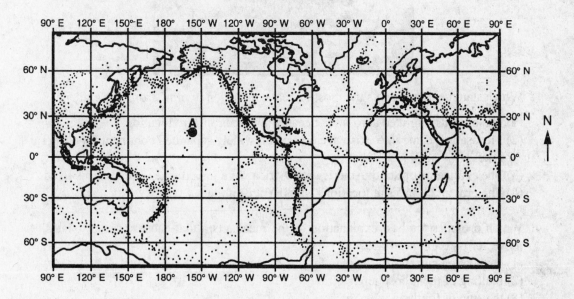

2. At the Aleutian Trench and the Peru-Chile Trench, tectonic plates are generally

   (1) moving along a transform boundary
   (2) moving over a mantle hot spot
   (3) diverging
   (4) converging

3. The map below shows the present-day locations of South America and Africa. Remains of Mesosaurus, an extinct freshwater reptile, have been found in similarly aged bedrock formed from lake sediments at locations X and Y.

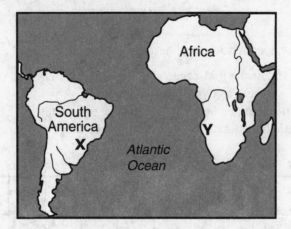

Which statement represents the most logical conclusion to draw from this evidence?

(1) Mesosaurus migrated across the ocean from location X to location Y.
(2) Mesosaurus came into existence on several widely separated continents at different times.
(3) The continents of South America and Africa were joined when Mesosaurus lived.
(4) The present climates at locations X and Y are similar.

4. Which provides the best explanation of the mechanism that causes crustal "plates" to move across Earth's surface?
(1) convection currents in the mantle
(2) faulting of the lithosphere
(3) the spin of Earth on its axis
(4) prevailing wind belts of the troposphere

5. Which observation is the best evidence to support the continental drift theory?
(1) the correlation of the rocks, minerals, and fossils of one continental with those of another continent.
(2) the changed benchmark elevations at the center of a continent.
(3) the presence of igneous intrusions at many locations.
(4) the subsidence of ocean basins causing very thick sediments.

Base your answers to questions 6 through 10 on your knowledge of Earth Science, the *Earth Science Reference Tables,* and the diagrams below. The diagrams represent geologic cross sections of the upper mantle and crust at four different Earth locations. In each diagram, the movement of the crustal sections (plates) is indicated by arrows and the locations of frequent earthquakes are indicated by symbols as shown in the key. Diagrams are not drawn to scale.

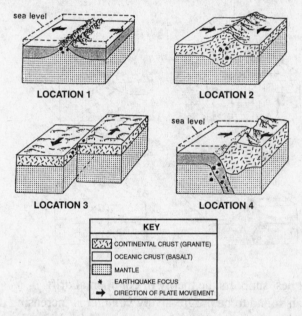

**KEY**

| | |
|---|---|
| ▨ | CONTINENTAL CRUST (GRANITE) |
| ☐ | OCEANIC CRUST (BASALT) |
| ▦ | MANTLE |
| ∗ | EARTHQUAKE FOCUS |
| → | DIRECTION OF PLATE MOVEMENT |

6. According to the diagrams, the most probable cause of the deep earthquakes at location 4 is the
   (1) collision of two oceanic plates
   (2) spreading of two oceanic plates
   (3) sinking of an oceanic plate under a continental plate
   (4) horizontal shifting of two continental plates

7. At which location is the collision of two continental crustal plates producing a mountain range?
   (1) location 1     (2) location 2     (3) location 3     (4) location 4

8. Which of the four locations most likely represents formation **x** in the profile shown below?

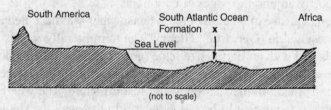

   (1) location 1     (2) location 2     (3) location 3     (4) location 4

9. Compared to the oceanic crust, the continental crust at location 4 is
   (1) thicker and less dense          (2) thicker and more dense
   (3) thinner and less dense          (4) thinner and more dense

10. Which diagram below best illustrates the theory of mantle convection current at location 1?

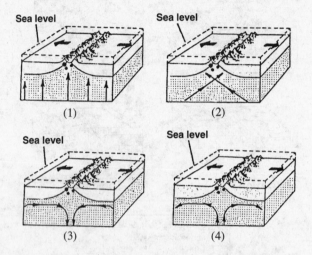

11. Which statement best supports the theory of continental drift?
    (1) Basaltic rock is found to be progressively younger at increasing distances from the mid-ocean ridge.
    (2) Marine fossils are often found in deep-well drill cores.
    (3) The present continents appear to fit together as pieces of a larger landmass.
    (4) Areas of shallow-water seas tend to accumulate sediment, which gradually sinks.

## Geosynclines

Most of the world's major land mountain chains consist of sedimentary rock layers often 40,000 to 50,000 feet thick. All these layers appear to have been deposited in shallow water. They are found mostly around the edges of continents.

The first attempt at an explanation of these facts, which was accepted until very recently, was called the **Geosyncline (Geocline) Theory**. The term literally means a basin (syncline) which can be measured with an Earth- size scale (geo-). Much of this theory is still accepted.

When the rivers and streams which erode the continents flow into the oceans they drop most of their sediment load in the shallow water just off shore. The weight of this sediment piled on the ocean crust causes it to bow downward. In this way the shallow water is never filled up but remains shallow as long as the crust can continue to sink.

After thousands of feet of sediment have been deposited, theory states, "some force" causes the whole pile of sediment to begin to uplift. This force causes extensive reverse faulting and much of the deep rock to become metamorphic or even igneous. The origin of such a force was not understood until the Plate Tectonic Theory was developed. It is now understood that continental collisions can provide the force necessary to build mountains and thereby increase the size of the continents.

## Crustal Thickness

Earth's crust, which is very thin in comparison to the other zones of Earth, is divided into two parts. The continental crust contains the continents; the oceanic crust is the part of the crust beneath the oceans (see Figure 4-15). The average thickness of the continental crust (20-40 km) is greater than the average thickness of the oceanic crust (10 km).

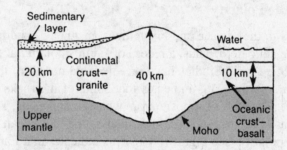

**Figure 4-15.** Variations In crustal thickness.

## Crustal Composition

The oceanic and continental crusts have different compositions, but both are rich in oxygen and silicon. The oceanic crust is composed mainly of high-density rocks, such as basalt, which are rich in iron and magnesium. The continental crust is composed mainly of low-density rocks, such as granite, which are rich in aluminum.

## Magnetic Poles

By studying the alignment of the magnetic materials in a rock, scientists can determine the positions of the magnetic north and south poles at the time the rock solidified. This rock "record" shows that Earth's magnetic poles have been located at widely varied locations throughout Earth history. This shifting of the magnetic poles is believed to be caused by the plates moving over the poles, causing the poles to appear to shift. This apparent shifting of the poles is another piece of evidence in support of the theory of plate tectonics.

## Ocean-Floor Spreading

Evidence of major crustal movement is found in the oceans, where the ocean floors appear to be spreading apart from the mid-ocean ridges. The two major pieces of evidence for this inference are the ages of the igneous rocks found along the ocean floors and the reversal of magnetic polarity found in these rocks.

## Ages of Igneous Rocks

The crust of the ocean floor is composed of basalt, an igneous rock. The basalt was formed from magma that rose to the surface at the mid-ocean ridges and solidified. Dating methods indicate that the basalt nearest the ridges is the youngest. That is, it formed most recently. The farther you travel from the ridge, the older the basalt becomes (see Figure 4-16). This indicates that as new basalt forms at a mid-ocean ridge, the previously formed basalt is moved farther from the ridge on both sides and the ocean floor widens.

## Reversal of Magnetic Polarity

As magma rises to the surface and crystallizes, magnetic materials in the magma are aligned by Earth's magnetic field. Thus, a record of Earth's polarity at that particular time is preserved in the solidified rock. Studies have revealed that not all of the rocks of the ocean crust exhibit the same polarity. This indicates that some of the rocks must have solidified when Earth's magnetic polarity was opposite from what it is at present. This is called **reversed polarity.** Parallel strips of basalt found on both sides of the mid-ocean ridges show periodic reversals of magnetic polarity (see Figure 4-16). This indicates that Earth's polarity reverses every several thousand years. Similarities of age and polarities of the strips of rock on either side of the ridge offers evidence of sea-floor spreading.

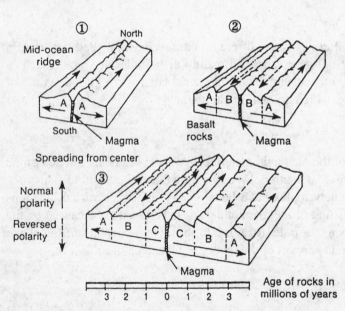

**Figure 4-16.** Ocean-floor spreading. As magma rises up through the mid-ocean ridge, it hardens and forms basaltic rock. In the upper left diagram (1), section A of the ocean floor has been formed. In the upper right diagram (2), a second younger section, B, has been formed. In the bottom diagram (3), section C has been added. The arrows indicate alternate reversals of polarity in the rocks. These reversals can be used to determine the ages of the rocks.

# QUESTIONS

1. In the diagram below, letters A and B represent locations near the edge of a continent.

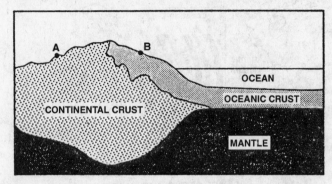

A geologist who compares nonsedimentary rock samples from locations A and B would probably find that the samples from location A contain

(1) more granite          (2) more basalt

(3) more fossils          (4) the same minerals and fossils

2. At which location would engineers have to drill the shortest distance through rock to reach Earth's mantle?

(1) the San Andreas fault east of Los Angeles, California
(2) the floor of the mid-Pacific Ocean
(3) the core of a recently cooled Hawaiian volcano
(4) the Atlantic Coastal Plain of the United States

3. A comparison of seismic graphs taken at a location in the ocean with those taken at the center of a continent would indicate that the crustal thickness under the oceans is probably

(1) less than that under the continents      (2) more than that under the continents
(3) equal to that under the continents

4. How does the composition of the oceanic crust compare with the composition of the continental crust?

(1) The oceanic crust is mainly limestone, while the continental crust is mainly sandstone.
(2) The oceanic crust is mainly limestone, while the continental crust is mainly granite.
(3) The oceanic crust is mainly basalt, while the continental crust is mainly sandstone.
(4) The oceanic crust is mainly basalt, while the continental crust is mainly granite.

Base your answers to questions 5 through 7 on your knowledge of Earth Science and on the diagram below. The diagram shows an enlargement of the mid-Atlantic ridge and surrounding area in its position with respect to the continents. Magnetic polarity bands of igneous rock parallel to the ridge are illustrated according to the key.

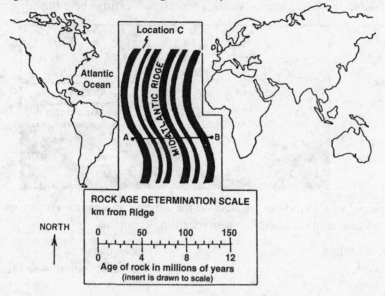

Polarity (indicated for only a portion of the Atlantic Ocean Basin)

☐ Normal — The magnetic minerals in these rocks indicate magnetic north as it is today.

■ Reverse — The magnetic minerals in these rocks indicate magnetic north where magnetic south is today.

5. Ocean floor rock found 20 kilometers west of the ocean ridge would have an approximate age of
   (1) 1.6 million years  (2) 2.0 million years  (3) 15 million years  (4) 30 million years

6. What are two characteristics of ocean floor rock found at location C?
   (1) normal polarity, continental composition
   (2) normal polarity, oceanic composition
   (3) reverse polarity, continental composition
   (4) reverse polarity, oceanic composition

7. Along the line from position A to position B, the comparative age of the rock
   (1) continuously decreases from A to B
   (2) continuously increases from A to B
   (3) decreases from A to the mid-Atlantic ridge and then increases to B
   (4) increases from A to the mid-Atlantic ridge and then decreases to B

**8.** To get sample material from the mantle, drilling will be done through the oceanic crust rather than through the continental crust because oceanic crust is

(1) more dense than continental crust     (2) softer than continental crust

(3) thinner than continental crust     (4) younger than continental crust

**9.** Two samples of ocean floor basaltic bedrock are found at equal distances from, and on opposite sides of, a mid-ocean ridge. The best evidence that both samples were formed at the ridge during the same time period would be that both samples also

(1) have the same density
(2) contain different crystal sizes
(3) are located at different depths below sea level
(4) have the same magnetic field orientation

**10.** Which statement best supports the theory of continental drift?

(1) Basaltic rock is found to be progressively younger at increasing distances from the mid-ocean ridge.
(2) Marine fossils are often found in deep-well drill cores.
(3) The present continents appear to fit together as pieces of a larger landmass.
(4) Areas of shallow-water seas tend to accumulate sediment, which gradually sinks.

## Minor Crustal Changes

The evidence that suggests minor changes in Earth's crust can be observed in exposed rock strata.

**Deformed Rock Strata.** Sedimentary rocks normally form in horizontal layers, or strata (see Figure 4-17). Thus, strata that is other than horizontal provides evidence of change. The most common changes evident in deformed strata are tilting, folding, and faulting.

**Normal Strata**

**Figure 4-17.** Normal sedimentary layers, or strata, are horizontal.

### Tilted Strata

**Figure 4-18.** Tilted strata is evidence that the once horizontal layers have changed by some crustal activity.

Tilted strata are once-horizontal layers of rock that are now tilted at an angle to Earth's surface (see Figure 4-18). Folded strata are rock layers that have been "bent" or "wrinkled" (see Figure 4-19). In folded rock strata, upward folded layers are called **anticlines;** downward folds are called **synclines**.

Fractures, or cracks, in a rock formation are called <u>**faults,**</u> Faults are zones of weakness along which the rock on either side may move.

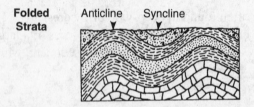

**Figure 4-19.** Folded strata indicate that strong "sideward" pressures were once exerted on horizontal rock layers, causing them to bend.

**Displaced Rock Strata.** The movement of rock along a fault is called an <u>**earthquake**</u>. Evidence of such movement is the displacement of strata. Along a **normal fault**, one section of rock moves *down* relative to the section on the other side of the fault (Figure 4-20A). Along **reverse faults**, one section moves *upward* relative to the other section (Figure 4-20B). Along **lateral faults** - also called **transform** or **strike-slip faults**-movement of the rock sections is *horizontal* (Figure 4-20C).

**Displaced Fossils.** Marine fossils are the remains of plants and animals that once lived in the sea. Such fossils are often found in sedimentary rock strata high up in mountains, thousands of meters above sea level. Since sea level has only varied a few hundred meters, it is unlikely that the sea was ever high enough to cover the mountains. Thus, the presence of marine fossils at elevations high above present sea levels suggests that the strata were uplifted to its present elevation.

Similarly, shallow-water fossils are sometimes found in strata at great ocean depths. This evidence suggests earlier subsidence, or sinking, of the fossil-containing strata.

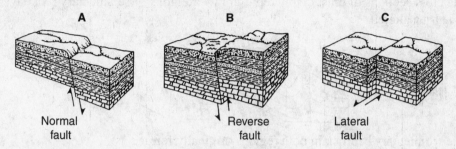

A        B        C

Normal        Reverse        Lateral
fault        fault        fault

**Figure 4-20.** Displaced rock strata. When strata is displaced, it may move vertically down (normal), or up (reverse), or it may move horizontally (lateral).

**Vertical Crustal Movements.** Bench marks are important indicators of vertical movement of the crust. A **bench mark** is a permanent marker set into the ground. Each bench mark has its exact elevation and date of placement stamped on it. Geologists determine change in elevation of a location by comparing the elevation of the bench mark at the time it was set into the ground with its elevation today. Changes in elevation indicate the amount of vertical movement of Earth's crust at that location.

Along the California coast, beaches of earlier shorelines can be found as much as 1,400 feet above present sea level. It is believed that the Coast Ranges have risen in a series of "pulses" separated by enough time to allow a series of beaches to develop. Altitudes of the raised beaches vary from place to place, indicating that the uplift was irregular.

Raised beaches are also found around the Great Lakes. These beaches were created as the continental ice sheet melted after the last ice age. As the weight of the ice was removed, the land uplifted, resulting in many raised beaches.

In other parts of the United States, such as in New England and Alaska, there is evidence of shorelines that have subsided below sea level.

All of these changes indicate that vertical movement has occurred over large portions of Earth's crust, and that these movements have occurred over very long periods of time.

# QUESTIONS

1. The cross sections of crust below represent two regions of sedimentary rock layers that have been altered.

The sedimentary bedrock in both regions originally formed as
(1) horizontal layers      (2) recrystallized layers
(3) faulted layers      (4) folded layers

2. The diagram below represents a geologic cross section of a portion of Earth's crust. Which geologic event that is shown in the diagram would suggest past crustal movement at that location?

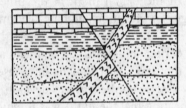

**KEY**

 Igneous Intrusion

Sedimentary Rocks

(1) deposition of sediments      (2) intrusion of molten material (magma)
(3) folding of rock layers      (4) faulting of rock layers

3. Folded sedimentary rock layers are usually caused by
(1) deposition of sediments in folded layers
(2) differences in sediment density during deposition
(3) a rise in sea level after deposition
(4) crustal movement occurring after deposition

4. As evidence accumulates, the support for the theory that the present continents were at one time a single, large landmass
(1) decreases      (2) increases      (3) remains the same

5. An observer discovers shallow-water marine fossils in rock strata at an elevation of 5,000 meters. What is the best explanation for this observation?
(1) The level of the ocean was once 5,000 meters higher.
(2) Violent earthquakes caused crustal subsidence.
(3) Marine organisms have evolved into land organisms.
(4) Crustal uplift has occurred in this area.

**6.** According to the concept of continental drift, the distance between two continents on opposite sides of a mid-oceanic ridge will generally

(1) decrease       (2) increase       (3) remain the same

**7.** Where does most present-day faulting of rock occur?

(1) in regions of glacial activity
(2) in the interior areas of continents
(3) at locations with many lakes
(4) at interfaces between moving parts of the crust

**8.** A sandstone layer is found tilted at an angle of 75° from the horizontal. What probably caused this 75° tilt?

(1) The sediments that formed this sandstone layer were originally deposited at a 75° tilt.
(2) This sandstone layer has changed position due to crustal movement.
(3) This sandstone layer has recrystallized due to contact metamorphism.
(4) Nearly all sandstone layers are formed from wind-deposited sands.

**9.** The diagrams below show cross sections of exposed bedrock. Which cross section shows the least evidence of crustal movement?

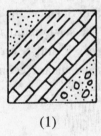   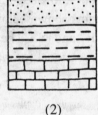      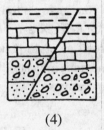

(1)        (2)        (3)        (4)

**10.** Fossils of organisms that lived in shallow water can be found in horizontal sedimentary rock layers at great ocean depths. This fact is generally interpreted by most Earth scientist as evidence that

(1) the cold water deep in the ocean kills shallow-water organisms
(2) sunlight once penetrated to the deepest parts of the ocean
(3) organisms that live in deep water evolved from species that once lived in shallow water
(4) sections of Earth's crust have changed their elevations relative to sea level

## CHAPTER 4 – CORE VOCABULARY

| | | |
|---|---|---|
| asthenosphere | focus | S-waves |
| convergent boundaries | lithosphere | seismic waves |
| crust | magnitude | subduction |
| divergent boundaries | P-waves | transform boundaries |
| earthquake | plate tectonics | transform (strike-slip) fault |
| epicenter | rift | tsunamis |

### HELPFUL VOCABULARY

| | | |
|---|---|---|
| anticlines | geosynclines (geocline) theory | reversed polarity |
| bench mark | intensity | Richter scale |
| Circum-Pacific Belt | lateral fault | rift valleys |
| collision boundary | long waves (L-waves) | secondary waves |
| compressional waves | modified Mercalli scale | seismograms |
| continental drift | Moho interface | seismograph |
| diastrophism | Mohorovicic discontinuity | shadow zone |
| faults | normal fault | shear waves |
| fracture zones | primary fault | synclines |
| | reverse fault | subduction boundary |

## PRACTICE FOR CONSTRUCTED RESPONSE

Base your answers to questions 1 through 3 on your knowledge of Earth Science, the *Earth Science Reference Tables*, and the three seismograms shown below. The seismograms were recorded at earthquake recording stations A, B, and C. The letters P and S on each seismogram indicate the arrival times of the compressional (primary) and shear (secondary) seismic waves.

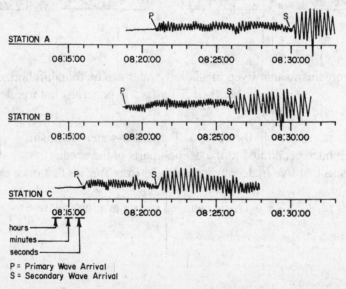

P = Primary Wave Arrival
S = Secondary Wave Arrival

1. The radius of each circle on the maps below represents the distance from each seismograph recording station to the epicenter. Which map correctly illustrates the position of the three recording stations relative to the location of the earthquake epicenter? _____

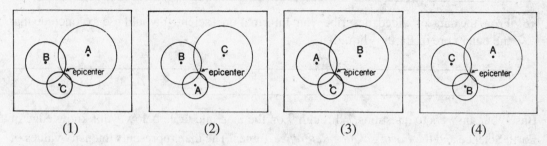

(1)             (2)             (3)             (4)

2. Approximately how far from station B is the earthquake epicenter located?

_____

3. A fifth station recorded the same earthquake, but reported that no S-waves arrived. The best explanation for the absence of S-waves is that they

_____

Base your answers to questions 4 through 6 on the diagram and data below, your knowledge of Earth Science and the *Earth Science Reference Tables*.

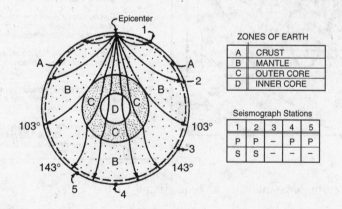

ZONES OF EARTH

| A | CRUST |
|---|---|
| B | MANTLE |
| C | OUTER CORE |
| D | INNER CORE |

Seismograph Stations

| 1 | 2 | 3 | 4 | 5 |
|---|---|---|---|---|
| P | P | – | P | P |
| S | S | – | – | – |

The diagram represents a cross-sectional view of Earth and the paths of some P-waves produced by an earthquake. Seismograph stations are numbered 1, 2, 3, 4, and 5. Letters A, B, C, and D represent specific zones within Earth. The table indicates the types of seismic waves that did arrive at each station.

4. Explain why station 4 received only P-waves.

_____

**5.** If you lived at station 3, describe what you would know about the earthquake.

_____

_____

**6.** From the data provided, describe what information a scientist would use to conclude that the outer core of Earth is liquid.

_____

_____

Base your answers to questions 7 through 9 on the map and table below, your knowledge of Earth Science and the *Earth Science Reference* Tables. The map represents intensity values of an earthquake according to the Modified Mercalli Scale of Earthquake Intensity.

**Modified Mercalli Scale of Earthquake Intensity**

| Intensity Value | Description of Effects |
|---|---|
| I | Usually detected only by instruments |
| II | Felt by a few persons at rest, especially on upper floors |
| III | Hanging objects swing; vibration like passing truck; noticeable indoors |
| IV | Felt indoors by many, outdoors by few; sensation like heavy truck striking building; parked automobiles rock |
| V | Felt by nearly everyone; sleepers awakened; liquids disturbed; unstable objects overturned; some dishes and windows broken |
| VI | Felt by all; many frightened and run outdoors; some heavy furniture moved; glassware broken; books off shelves; damage slight |
| VII | Difficult to stand; noticed in moving automobiles; damage to some masonry; weak chimneys broken at roofline |
| VIII | Partial collapse of masonry; chimneys, factory stacks, columns fall; heavy furniture overturned; frame houses moved on foundations |

**7.** Compare the earthquake intensity of zones II and VIII.

_____

_____

**8.** Describe how it is possible for a person in Zone III to have a different intensity from a person in zone VII.

_____

_____

**9.** The Richter Scale of earthquakes differs from the Mercalli Scale. The Richter Scale describes earthquake magnitude (the amount of energy released). Describe the major benefit of the Richter Scale over the Mercalli Scale.

_____

_____

Base your answers to questions 10 through 13 on the information and map below and your knowledge of Earth Science.

An earthquake occurred in the southwestern part of the United States. Mercalli-scale intensities were plotted for selected locations on a map, as shown below. (As the numerical value of Mercalli ratings increases, the damaging effects of the earthquake waves also increase.)

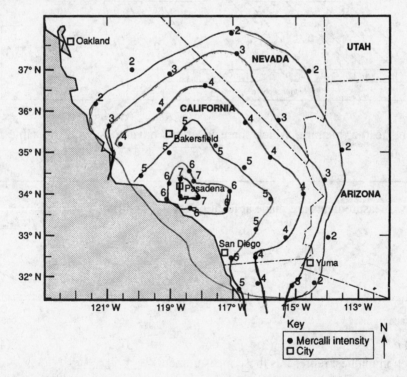

**10.** Using an interval of 2 Mercalli units and starting with an isoline representing 2 Mercalli units, draw an accurate isoline map of earthquake intensity.

**11.** State the name of the city that is closest to the earthquake epicenter.

_____

**12.** State the latitude and longitude of Bakersfield. _____

**13.** Using one or more complete sentences, identify the most likely cause of earthquakes that occur in the area shown on the map.

_____

_____

Base your answers to questions 14 through 18 on the diagram below. The diagram shows a portion of Earth's oceanic crust in the vicinity of the mid-Atlantic ridge. The stripes in the diagram represent magnetic bands of igneous rock formed in the oceanic crust. The orientation of Earth's magnetic field at the time of rock formation is shown by arrows within each band. Letters A, B, C, D, and E represent locations on the seafloor.

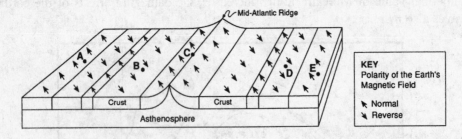

**14.** According to the diagram, which three locations have rock with the same magnetic orientation?

_____

**15.** Heat flow measurements are made at locations A through E.

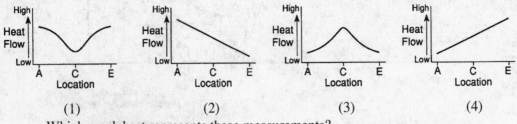

    (1)           (2)           (3)           (4)

  **a.** Which graph best represents these measurements? _____

  **b.** How do you know? _____

**16.** Rock samples taken from locations B would

  **a.** most likely be composed of _____

**b.** How do you know? _____

17. According to the theory of continental drift, the crust in this area is formed by convection currents in the asthenosphere below the mid-Atlantic ridge. Draw the cross-sectional diagram that best represents the currents that formed the ridge on the diagram below.

18. Along a line drawn from location A to location E, the relative age of the oceanic crust would most likely _____

19. The lines on the map below represent faults and fractures in the bedrock of New York State.

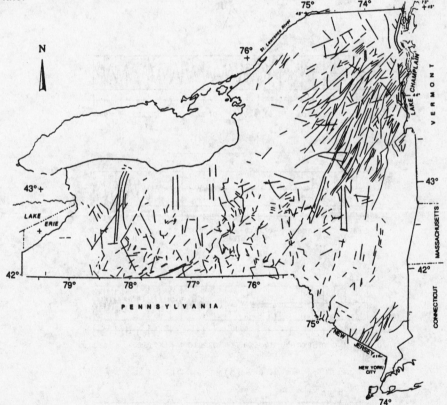

    **a.** At which location, latitude and longitude, on this map are earthquakes most likely to occur? _____

    **b.** How do you know? _____

Base your answers to question 20 on the map below. The map shows how the location of an earthquake epicenter could be determined using data from three seismic stations. Seismic station A is in Florida, seismic station B is in California, and seismic station C is in Illinois. Roman numerals I through IV represent locations in this area.

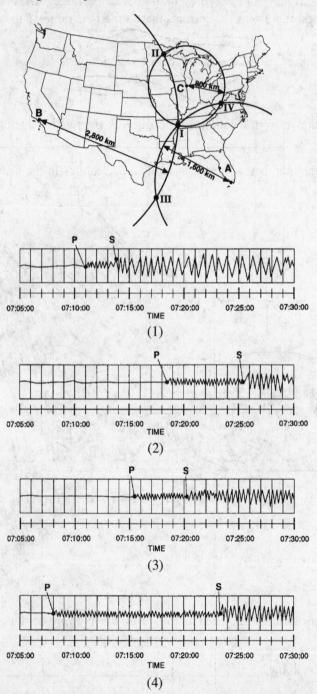

**20. a.** Which diagram best represents the seismogram recorded by seismic station A (in Florida) following the earthquake. _____

**b.** How do you know? _____

Base your answers to questions 21 through 25 on your knowledge of Earth Science, the *Earth Science Reference Tables*, and the diagram below. Diagram I is a map showing the location and bedrock age of some of the Hawaiian Islands. Diagram II is a cross section of an area of Earth illustrating a stationary magma source and the process that could have formed the islands.

DIAGRAM I

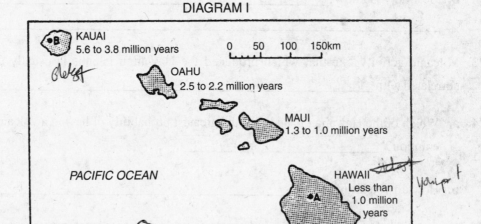

DIAGRAM II

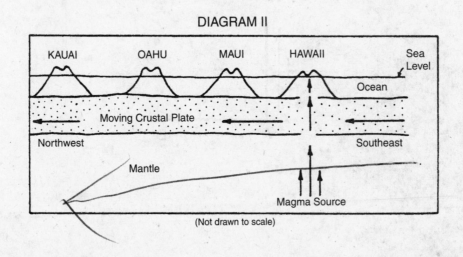

(Not drawn to scale)

21. **a.** If each island formed as the crustal plate moved over the magma source in the mantle as shown in diagram II, where would the next volcanic island most likely form?

_____

  **b.** How do you know? _____

_____

22. **a.** Compared to the continental crust of North America, the oceanic crust in the area of the Hawaiian Islands is probably _____

  **b.** How do you know? _____

_____

23. Volcanic activity like that which produced the Hawaiian Islands is usually closely correlated with _____

24. **a.** Which of the Hawaiian Islands has the greatest probability of having a volcanic eruption? _____

  **b.** How do you know? _____

25. On the grid below, construct the graphing relationship that best represents the ages of the Hawaiian Islands, comparing them from point A to point B.

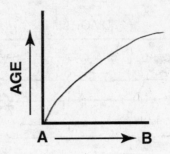

Base your answers to questions 26 and 27 on the map below, which shows a portion of California along the San Andreas Fault zone. The map gives the probability (percentage chance) that an earthquake strong enough to damage buildings and other structures will occur between the present time and the year 2024.

### Earthquake Damage Probability

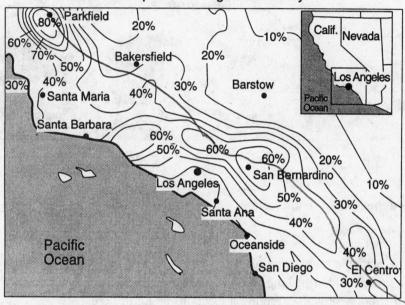

**26. a.** Which map represents the most likely location of the San Andreas Fault Line? _____

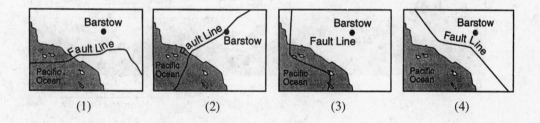

(1)  (2)  (3)  (4)

**b.** State the reason for your selection. _____

**27. a.** Which city has the greatest danger of damage from an earthquake? _____

**b.** State the reason for your selection. _____

**28. a.** Which map best represents the general pattern of magnetism in the oceanic bedrock near the mid-Atlantic Ridge? _____

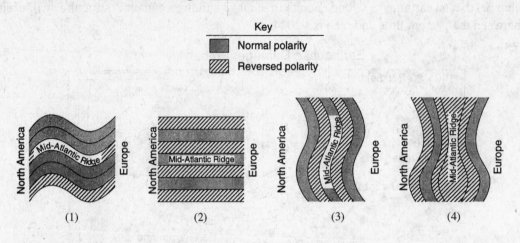

Key
Normal polarity
Reversed polarity

(1)    (2)    (3)    (4)

    **b.** State the reason for your selection. _____

Base your answers to questions 29 through 34 on the *Earth Science Reference Tables*, the diagram below, and your knowledge of Earth Science. The diagram is a cross section of the major surface features of Earth along the Tropic of Capricorn (23½°S) between 75°W and 15° E longitude. Letters A through G represent locations on Earth's crust.

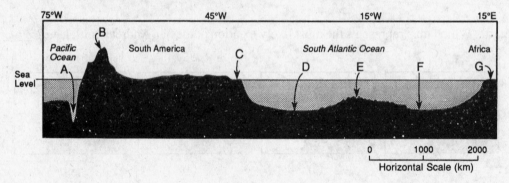

**29.** What is the approximate width of the Atlantic Ocean at this location? _____

**30.** A mid-ocean ridge is located near position _____

**31. a.** Which location is closest to the Prime Meridian (0° longitude)? _____

    **b.** How do you know? _____

**32. a.** Which two locations in the diagram have bedrock of approximately the same age, which has been separated by seafloor spreading? _____

  **b.** How do you know? _____

**33. a.** Which diagram shows the most probable direction of movement of the crustal plates and the inferred mantle convection currents under position A? _____

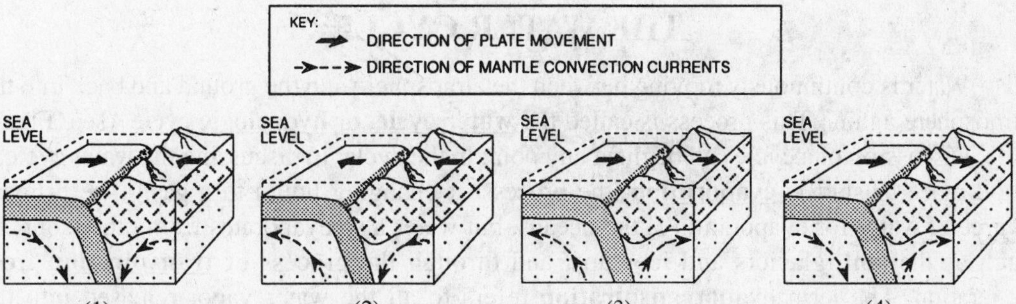

KEY:
→ DIRECTION OF PLATE MOVEMENT
→--► DIRECTION OF MANTLE CONVECTION CURRENTS

(1)        (2)        (3)        (4)

  **b.** State a reason you used to make your choice.

  _____

**34.** A student read an article in the local newspaper stating that a major earthquake can be expected to affect the region where the student lives within the next year. The student's family decides to help prepare her home and family for this expected earthquake.

State three specific actions the student could take to increase safety or reduce injury or damage from an earthquake,

  _____

  _____

  _____

# CHAPTER 5:  SECTION 1
# SURFACE  PROCESSES  AND  LANDSCAPES

## WATER AND THE GROUND

### THE WATER CYCLE

Water is continuously moving between the atmosphere and the ground and back into the atmosphere again.  This process is called the **water cycle**, or **hydrologic cycle**  (see  Figure 5-1). Discussion of a cycle can begin at any point in the cycle. In discussing the water cycle, a good place to start is **evaporation**; the process of changing liquid to a gas.  The primary source of water for evaporation is the oceans, but water also evaporates from other sources, such as the soil, glaciers and ice caps, and through the process of **transpiration** from vegetation. The term **evapotranspiration** refers to all the water vapor released into the atmosphere by both evaporation and transpiration.

Once in the air, water vapor is moved around by winds and currents until it condenses, forming clouds or fog. When water droplets grow large enough, they fall as rain or snow. Once on Earth's surface, the water can: (1) flow along the surface as **runoff**; (2) sink into the ground, or **infiltration**, and become part of the **ground water** supply; (3) remain on the surface as snow or ice; or (4) evapotranspire back into the atmosphere again, a process that keeps the cycle active.

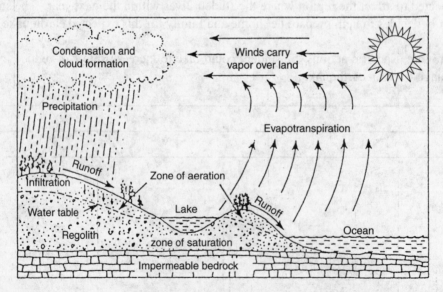

**Figure 5-1**. The water cycle. The level of the water table varies as the zone of saturation changes.

# GROUND WATER

## Infiltration

Most **precipitation** that reaches Earth's surface infiltrates the ground. **Infiltration** can occur only if the surface is **permeable** (allows water to pass through) and unsaturated. Bedrock, which is the hard, unbroken part of Earth's surface, allows very little infiltration. Most infiltration occurs in the **regolith**, the thin layer of rock, sand, gravel, and soil lying on top of the bedrock. The less saturated the regolith, the more the infiltration. Another factor that affects infiltration is the **slope**, or **gradient**, of the land. The steeper the slope, the less the infiltration. Infiltration is also affected by the shape of the particles that make up the regolith, by how tightly they are packed, and by the way they are sorted.

## Permeability

**Permeability**, is the ability of the regolith to allow water to pass through. The speed with which the water passes through is called the permeability rate. In order for the ground to be permeable, pore spaces between the loose material of the regolith must be interconnected to allow the water to pass through. Pumice, for example, is a very porous rock, but the pore spaces are not interconnected. Thus, pumice is not permeable. Sandstone, on the other hand, appears to be very hard but actually has many interconnected pore spaces. Sandstone is very permeable. Because larger particles have larger pore spaces, the permeability of loose material increases with increased particle size. (See Figure 5-2) Large particles, such as sand and gravel, are very permeable, while smaller particles, such as clay and silt, are less permeable. Material that does not allow water to pass through it is said to be **impermeable**. In winter the land becomes impermeable when water freezes in the spaces between particles.

As it rains, water infiltrates the regolith until it reaches an impermeable bedrock layer below the surface. The water cannot infiltrate further, so it fills in the pores above the impermeable layer with ground water, forming the **zone of saturation** (see Figure 5-1). The upper surface of the zone of saturation is called the **water table**. The zone above the water table is known as the **zone of aeration**, because the pore spaces are filled with air. Water passes downward through the zone of aeration until it reaches the water table. The depth of the water table depends primarily on the amount of water infiltrating the ground.

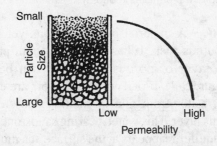

**Figure 5-2.** As the graph indicates, the permeability of a material is directly related to the particle size.

## Porosity

The **porosity** of a material is the amount of open pore space between particles. Porosity is usually presented as a percentage comparing the volume of open space in a material to the total volume of material. The porosity of loose material is largely dependent upon shape, packing, and the sorting (mixture of sizes) of the particles.

**Shape.** Particles that are rounded have a greater porosity than particles that are angular, because rounded particles do not fit together as well as angular particles (see Figure 5-3).

**Packing.** Particles that are tightly packed have a lower porosity than particles that are loosely packed (see Figure 5-3).

**Sorting.** When particles of a material are all about the same size, they are said to be well **sorted**. If the particles are of different sizes, they are **unsorted**. The porosity of a material with well sorted particles is high. Porosity of unsorted particles is low (see Figure 5-3 because the smaller particles fill in the larger spaces between the larger particles.)

**Size not a factor.** Size by itself does not affect porosity. Many people believe that larger particles have greater porosity because the pore spaces are larger, but this is not true. Although small particles have small pore spaces, there are more of them. If the factors of shape, packing, and sorting are about the same for materials of different sizes, the porosity of these materials will be about the same.

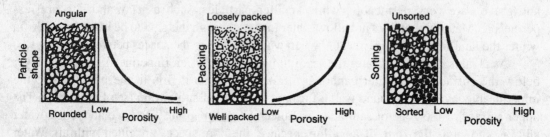

**Figure 5-3**. As the graphs show, the porosity of a material is directly related to the roundness of the particles (top), is inversely related to the degree of packing of the particles (center), and is directly related to the degree of sorting of the particles (bottom).

**Porosity and permeability.** A material may be porous yet relatively impermeable. For example, shale is a very porous rock. It has numerous small pore spaces but it is not very permeable. A permeable layer of porous sandstone can be found between layers of impermeable shale (see Figure 5-4). If parts of these layers are exposed to the atmosphere in regions of high elevation, water from rain or melting snow can infiltrate the permeable sandstone and flow down this layer. This water-bearing sandstone, which acts like a waterpipe, is called an **aquifer**. If the aquifer reappears at the surface at a much lower elevation, the water will rise to the surface, forming a well or spring.

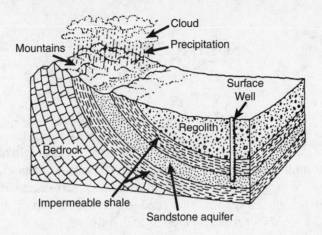

**Figure 5-4**. An aquifer is a natural "pipeline" through which water can move freely.

## Water Retained by Particles

Although the particle size of a material does not affect porosity, it does affect the amount of water retained. In two equal volumes of different-sized particles of the same material, the volume with the smaller particles will retain more water, because the smaller particles have a greater total surface area than the larger particles.

## Capillarity

Water can move *upward* through soil, much as water rises from the roots to the limbs of a tree. The ability of water to rise in small openings is called **capillarity**. In loose materials, the smaller the particle size, the greater the capillarity (see Figure 5-5).

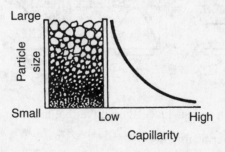

**Figure 5-5**. As the graph shows, the capillarity of a material is inversely proportional to the size.

# SURFACE WATER

## Runoff

There are a number of factors that affect runoff. If all the pore spaces in the ground are saturated, rainwater cannot sink into the ground, so it flows along the surface as runoff. Runoff occurs when rain falls faster than it can sink into the ground–when rainfall exceeds the permeability rate. Runoff always occurs on impermeable surfaces. Runoff will also occur if the slope of the surface is too steep to allow infiltration. When vegetation covers the soil, runoff is slowed. Plants, therefore, are often used to prevent the topsoil from being carried away by runoff. Most runoff is carried to streams and, ultimately, to the oceans.

## QUESTIONS

1. Rainfall is most likely to infiltrate into soil that is

   (1) permeable and saturated        (2) permeable and unsaturated
   (3) impermeable and saturated      (4) impermeable and unsaturated

2. Which graph best describes the relationship between the slope of the land and the amount of surface runoff during a period of heavy rainfall?

   (1)              (2)              (3)              (4)

3. When rain falls on a soil surface, flooding at that location would most likely occur if the

   (1) soil surface is permeable
   (2) soil surface is covered with vegetation
   (3) soil pore spaces are filled to capacity
   (4) infiltration rate exceeds the precipitation rate

Base your answers to questions 4 through 8 on your knowledge of Earth Science, the *Earth Science Reference Tables*, and the information and diagrams below which describe an investigation with soils.

Three similar tubes, each containing a specific soil of uniform particle size and shape were used to study the effect that different particle size has on porosity, capillarity, and permeability. A fourth tube containing soil which was a mixture of the same sizes found in the other tubes was also studied and its data are recorded in the table. (Assume that the soils were perfectly dry between each part of the investigation.)

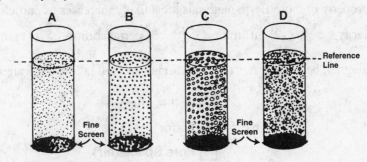

| Tube | Particle Size (diameter in cm) | Porosity (%) | Capillarity (mm) | Permeability (sec) |
|------|-------------------------------|--------------|-------------------|--------------------|
| A | Fine (0.025 cm) | 40 | 20 | 14 |
| B | Medium (0.1 cm) | 40 | 15 | 8 |
| C | Coarse (0.3 cm) | 40 | 7 | 6 |
| D | Mixed (0.025 to 0.3 cm) | 20 | 12 | 20 |

4. When water was poured into the top of each tube at the same time, which tube allowed the water to pass through most quickly?

   (1) A          (2) B          (3) C          (4) D

5. According to the *Earth Science Reference Tables*, the soil in tube C would be classified as

   (1) sand          (2) cobbles          (3) silt          (4) pebbles

6. Each tube was placed in a shallow pan of water. In which tube did the water rise the highest?

   (1) A          (2) B          (3) C          (4) D

7. The bottom of each tube was closed and water was slowly poured into each tube until the water level reached the dotted reference line. Which statement best describes the amount of water held by the tubes?

   (1) Tube D held more water than any other tube and tube A the least.
   (2) Tube C held more water than any other tube and tube D the least.
   (3) Tubes A and D held the same amount of water and twice as much as tubes B and C.
   (4) Tubes A, B, and C held the same amount of water and tube D half as much.

8. A handful of material from tube D was dropped into a fifth tube filled with water only. In which order would the particle sizes of this soil probably settle in the tube from the bottom of the tube upward?

   (1) fine on the bottom, then medium, then coarse
   (2) fine on the bottom, then coarse, then medium
   (3) coarse on the bottom, then medium, then fine
   (4) coarse on the bottom, then fine, then medium

9. Which property of loose Earth materials most likely increases as particle size decreases?

   (1) capillarity          (2) infiltration          (3) permeability          (4) porosity

10. Which diagram best illustrates the condition of the soil below the water table?

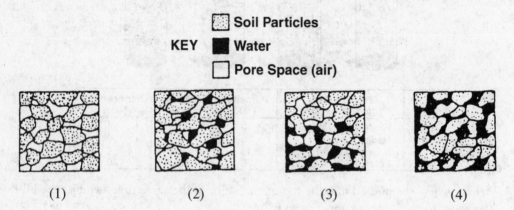

# WEATHERING

Weathering and erosion are often thought of as being the same thing, but are very different. Weathering is a *preparation* for erosion. **Weathering** is the chemical and physical *breakdown* of rocks on or at Earth's surface into smaller fragments. **Erosion**, on the other hand, is the *movement* of weathered material from one place to another. Weathering is a response to the effects of the environment on Earth's crust.

## Weathering Process

Weathering occurs when rocks are exposed to the hydrosphere, atmosphere, and other natural agents (plants and animals). These **weathering agents** change the physical and/or chemical characteristics of the rocks. Climate is the most important factor in the weathering process. The same rocks weather differently when exposed to different climates.

## Weathering Types

The two general types of weathering are physical and chemical.

**Physical Weathering. Physical weathering** occurs when rock is cracked, split, or broken into smaller pieces called **sediments** with no change in the rock composition. Sediments are classified by size as boulders, cobbles, pebbles, sand, silt, clay, colloids, and dissolved particles. There are several important types of physical weathering.

*Frost action* is the breakup of rocks caused by alternate freezing and thawing of water. Water condenses or seeps into the smallest cracks or spaces in rock as well as larger openings. When the water freezes, it expands, forcing the rock grains apart. When the ice melts the rock is more porous than before. Repeated freezing and expanding of water in these spaces will cause the rock to crumble into smaller pieces.

*Abrasion* is the physical wearing down of rocks as they rub or bounce against each other. Abrasion is most important in dry windy areas, under glaciers, or in stream channels.

*Exfoliation* is the peeling away of large sheets of loosened material at the surface of a rock.

Large shrubs and trees growing through cracks in boulders may break the rocks apart. Smaller plants that grow on rocks, such as lichens and mosses, wedge their tiny roots into pores and cracks, splitting the rock as they grow. Ants, earthworms and other burrowing animals digging holes in the soil break it down further.

**Chemical Weathering. Chemical weathering** occurs when rock is broken down by chemical action resulting in a change in the composition of the rock. The chief agents in chemical weathering are oxygen, rainwater, carbon dioxide, and acids produced by decaying plants and animals.

**Oxidation** occurs when oxygen unites chemically with minerals. For example, when oxygen combines with iron, rust (iron oxide) is formed.

**Hydration** occurs when water unites chemically with minerals. When certain minerals, such as hornblende and feldspar, unite with water, they crumble into small particles of clay.

**Carbonation** occurs when carbon dioxide unites chemically with minerals. When carbon dioxide is dissolved in water, it forms weak carbonic acid. Carbonic acid readily dissolves large masses of limestone, creating caves, caverns, and other structures in the bedrock. **Sink holes**–saucer-shaped holes on the surface of the land–are left when carbonic acid dissolves limestone in the ground. A limestone area pitted with sink holes is called **karst topography**. In caves, the carbonic acid solution containing the dissolved limestone drips from the roof of the cave. Evaporation leaves limestone deposits on the ceiling and floor. The icicle-like deposits that "grow down" from the ceiling are called **stalactites**. Those deposits which "grow up" from the ground are called **stalagmites**.

**Organic decay** occurs when acids, which are formed when plants and animals decay, dissolve in water. The acid solutions dissolve rock minerals much the same way as in carbonation.

## Climatic Conditions and Types of Weathering

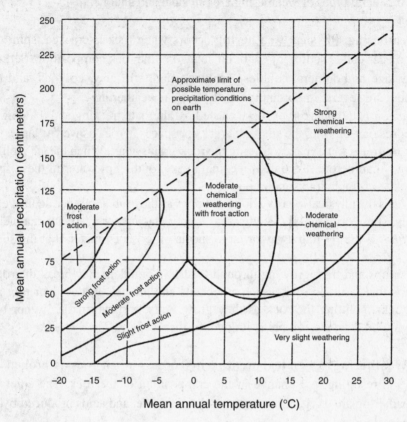

**Figure 5-6**. Climatic conditions and types of weathering. As an example, in a region with mean annual temperature of 10°C and 75 cm of precipitation, the dominant type of weathering will be moderate chemical weathering with frost action.

## Climate and Weathering

Physical and chemical weathering processes are both affected by climatic conditions of temperature and moisture (see Figure 5-6). Physical weathering is more pronounced in moist climates, where the wide range of temperatures cause alternate freezing and thawing. Chemical weathering is more intense in warm, moist climates. The amount of moisture available is the key factor in weathering. Usually, the more moisture available, the more weathering occurs.

## Weathering Rates

The rate of weathering of a particular rock depends on: (1) the particle size and the amount of surface area of the rock available, (2) mineral composition, and (3) climate.

**Particle size and surface area.** The weathering rate of rock material varies inversely with particle size. In equal quantities of the same rock, the smaller the particles, the greater the weathering rate - the faster the particles weather (see Figure 5-7). This rate difference occurs because the total surface area of the smaller particles is greater than the total surface area of the larger particles. Larger, solid pieces of rock weather more slowly than do smaller, loose pieces of the same rock.

**Mineral composition.** Rock particles weather at different rates depending on their mineral composition. Because the hardness of minerals differs, different minerals have different resistances to weathering. Hard rocks weather more slowly than soft rocks (see Figure 5-7).

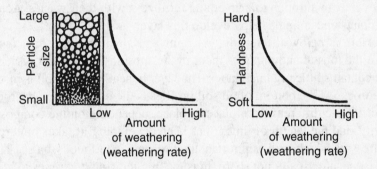

**Figure 5-7**. Relationship of particle size and hardness on rate of weathering. As the graphs show, the smaller the particles (left) and the softer the particles (right) the higher the rate of weathering.

**Climate.** Weathering of rocks occurs at a faster rate in humid climates than it does in dry climates. This is explained by the fact that most weathering agents–frost action, carbonation, organic decay, etc.–require, or are more effective in the presence of moisture.

# SOILS

One of the major products of weathering is soil. <u>Soil</u> is that part of the weathered regolith in which rooted plants will grow. It is composed primarily of particles of rocks, minerals, and organic matter, and consists of all three states of matter. Solid, sand and clay make up the bulk of the soil while minerals and decayed organic matter supply it with nutrients. Liquid water allows the chemical actions necessary to produce a mature soil. Air and the gases, oxygen and nitrogen, present mainly in solution, provide the soil with nutrients and increase the weathering processes in the soil.

# Soil Formation

Soil types depend on their place of origin. A soil formed by weathering of the bedrock found beneath it is called **residual soil**. A soil formed from rock that was moved to its present location before the soil was formed is called **transported soil**. The complex interrelationships of living organisms are significant factors in soil formation. Soils from the same kind of parent material (bedrock) differ, depending upon the climate in which they form.

**Soil profile.** As soils mature, they grow richer, developing a series of layers called a **soil profile**. Each layer of soil differs in texture, color, and composition (see Figure 5-8). Soil layers develop as a result of weathering processes and biologic activity.

The top layer of a mature soil is called the **topsoil**. This layer contains most of the organic matter (the leaves of plants, twigs and dead grass) and the most weathered rock. Topsoil is usually dark in color and is best for growing plants. Earthworms and insects aerate the soil as they burrow through this layer and fertilize it with their wastes. Acids released by the decay of plants and animals help develop this layer.

The **subsoil**, is below the topsoil. As rainwater sinks into Earth, it *leaches* (carries) minerals from the topsoil and deposits them in the subsoil. The subsoil is rich in clay-sized particles, but contains little organic matter. The layer beneath the subsoil is made up of partly weathered bedrock. At the bottom of all soil profiles is the unweathered bedrock.

Soil profiles are different from place to place, depending on the composition, climate, organic activity, and the length of time it has been developing. It takes hundreds of years to form a mature soil which will support plant life on a continuous basis. The boundaries between soil layers are usually not sharp, thus making it difficult at times to identify the type of soil.

**SOIL PROFILE**

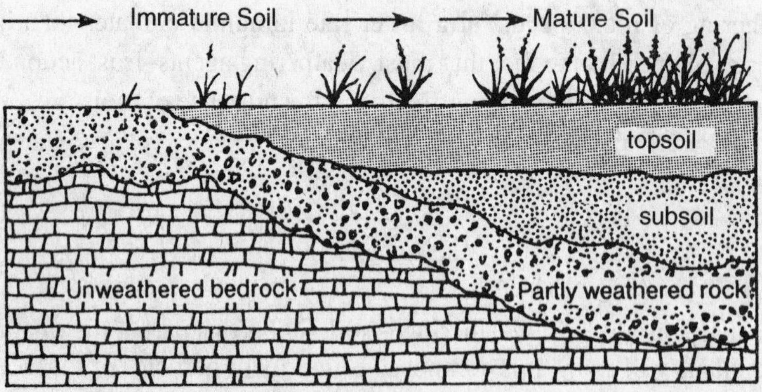

**Figure 5-8**. Soil profile. The soil in this profile shows an increasing maturity as you move from left to right. A fully developed soil is shown at the right of the profile.

## Soil Solution

The end product of weathering is a solution containing ionic materials present in all surface and ground water. As water seeps through the soil, it picks up ions of potassium, nitrate, calcium, iron, and phosphate. These ions are released by the chemical weathering of rocks. Groundwater containing these ions is called **soil solution**.

**Soil Conservation**. One third of Earth's surface is covered by land, but only a portion can be used for farming. An increasing population requires more food. So, Earth's soil must be used to its greatest potential. Farms must be made more productive. Soil that is now unusable for farming must be made fertile again. If the land is dry, it can be irrigated (water brought in from somewhere else). If the limited land resources are to be preserved, the use of the soil must be carefully planned and managed. It may take 100 to 400 years to form 1 centimeter of topsoil.

When one type of crop is grown on a soil for too long, depletion may occur. **Depletion** occurs when too many nutrients are removed from the soil for a crop to grow. To prevent depletion, crops must be alternated on the same soil each year. This type of farming is called **crop rotation.** Other good practices to follow are contour plowing and strip cropping. In **contour plowing,** crops are planted in rows parallel to the contours of the land. **Strip cropping** involves planting strips of low cover crops between strips of other crops.

Sometimes topsoil is carried down the slopes of a hill by water. To prevent this, the hill is **terraced** into a series of level steps. **Wind breaks** (belts of trees along the edge of farming areas) can also be set up to prevent the winds from carrying topsoil away. Sometimes, the soil can be left untilled so that the wind would not blow it away. Some land may be set aside as grazing land. If overgrazing occurs, the land can dry out and the area become a desert. This process is called **desertification.**

## QUESTIONS

1. Which is the best example of physical weathering?

   (1) the cracking of rock caused by the freezing and thawing of water
   (2) the transportation of sediment in a stream
   (3) the reaction of limestone with acid rainwater
   (4) the formation of a sandbar along the side of a stream

**2.** Two different kinds of minerals, A and B, were placed in the same container and shaken for 15 minutes. The diagrams below represent the size and shape of the various pieces of mineral before and after shaking. What caused the resulting differences in shapes and sizes of the minerals?

KEY
Mineral A
Mineral B

Container
before shaking

Container
after shaking

(1) Mineral B was shaken harder.
(2) Mineral B had a glossy luster.
(3) Mineral A was more resistent to abrasion.
(4) Mineral A consisted of smaller pieces before shaking began.

Base your answers to questions 3 through 7 on your knowledge of Earth Science, the *Earth Science Reference Tables*, and the graph below which was prepared from the results of a study of four different types of cemetery stones. The graph shows the relationship between the ages of four cemetery stones and the percentage of each stone which had weathered away.

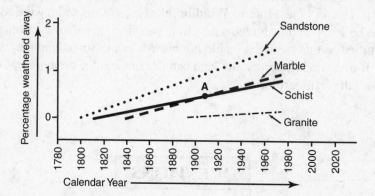

**3.** Which rock was found to have been exposed to weathering for the *least* number of years?

(1) granite          (2) schist          (3) marble          (4) sandstone

**4.** In this study, which rock was the most resistant to weathering?

(1) marble          (2) schist          (3) granite          (4) sandstone

**5.** What total percentage of the schist should have weathered away by the year 2020?

(1) 1.0%          (2) 2.0%          (3) 0.5%          (4) 1.5%

6. Point A on the diagram represents the time at which

   (1) industrial pollutants changed the weathering rates
   (2) the marble and schist weathered away at the same rate
   (3) climatic conditions changed the weathering rates
   (4) equal percentages of the marble and schist had weathered away

7. Studies have shown that pollutants added to the atmosphere in recent years are accumulating to cause an increase in the rate of weathering of marble. This factor should cause the line in the graph for marble in the future to

   (1) decrease in slope (curve downward)
   (2) increase in slope (curve upward)
   (3) remain at the same slope

8. Which property of water makes frost action a common and effective form of weathering?

   (1) Water dissolves many Earth materials.
   (2) Water expands when it freezes.
   (3) Water cools the surroundings when it evaporates.
   (4) Water loses 80 calories of heat per gram when it freezes.

9. Chemical weathering occurs most rapidly in climates which are

   (1) moist and warm    (2) moist and cold    (3) dry and cold    (4) dry and warm

10. Two tombstones, A and B, have each been standing in a cemetery for 100 years. The same style and size of lettering is clear on A but not on B. Which is the most probable reason for the difference?

    (1) B was more protected from the atmosphere than A.
    (2) A's minerals are more resistant to weathering than those of B.
    (3) A is more porous than B.
    (4) B is smaller than A.

# EROSION

Once rock material has been weathered, it is ready to be moved, or eroded. **Erosion** is the transportation of loose sediments or rocks produced by weathering. The major agents of erosion are gravity, running water, glaciers, wind, and waves.

# Evidence of Erosion

No matter what part of Earth's landscape is examined, it contains evidence of erosion. Some of the most spectacular displays of erosion on Earth's surface can be seen in the Grand Canyon and Yosemite Valley, where large valleys have been gorged into the land, and in the jagged skyline of the Rocky Mountains, which owe their shape to erosion.

## Types of Sediment

There are two types of sediment, transported and residual. **Transported sediment** is rock material that has been transported from its place of origin to another location. **Residual sediment** is rock material that has weathered and remained in its place of origin. Transported material is far more common than residual material. In fact, most of the United States is covered with a veneer of rock material that was transported from one place to another at least once. The entire surface of New York State is covered with a layer of rock material transported there by glaciers.

**Properties of transported materials.** Transported materials can usually be identified because they are unlike the rocks on which they have been deposited. Transported materials often possess distinctive properties that indicate the type of transporting medium.

For example, sediments carried by running water are usually rounded and smoothed by abrasion. **Abrasion** is the grinding and bumping of one rock against another. Sediments carried by wind are usually angular and, although smooth, they are not as smooth as those carried by running water. They are often pitted and frosted. Gravel and boulders carried directly by a glacier will be unsorted and have angular and scratched surfaces due to being scraped along the bedrock. Sediments carried by the meltwater of a glacier will be more rounded and smooth. Sometimes, gravity alone will pull a piece of weathered rock down the side of a steep slope or cliff. These angular deposits of broken rock along the base of a cliff are called **talus**.

## Factors Affecting Transportation

Gravity, water, wind and ice are the major forces, or agents, affecting the transportation of weathered material. These forces, which move sediments from one place to another, are called **transporting agents**. A transporting (erosion) system consists of the agents of erosion, the transported sediments, and the "driving forces"- gravity and the changing of potential to kinetic energy to move the sediments.

## Gravity

Earth materials move downslope (**mass movement**) under the influence of gravity. **Gravity** is the primary driving force behind all transporting (erosional) systems. Gravity may work alone, as when it pulls a rock down a slope, or with another agent, causing sediments to "flow" down-slope. When gravity acts with another erosional agent, such as running water, glaciers, or winds, to move sediment, it is gravity which causes the agent to move. Gravity provides the agent with enough kinetic energy to transport sediments.

# Running Water and Erosion

Running water is the primary agent of erosion on Earth. Most running water is found in streams or rivers. There are a number of factors that affect the movement of sediments in a stream.

Any running water forms a **stream**. Gradient, discharge, and channel shape influence a stream's velocity and the erosion and deposition of sediments. Sediments transported by streams tend to become rounded as a result of abrasion. Stream features include *V-shaped valleys*, *deltas*, *flood plains*, and *meanders*. A **watershed** is the area drained by a stream and its tributaries.

**Carrying power.** The ability of a stream to move particles of different size is called **carrying power**. The greater a stream's carrying power, the larger the particle size it can carry. The carrying power of a stream depends mainly on the *velocity* of the stream.

**Stream velocity.** The average **velocity** (speed) of a stream depends on stream discharge and the gradient. **Stream discharge** is the volume of water in the stream. **Gradient** is the steepness of the slope down which the stream is flowing. There is a direct relationship between discharge and/or gradient and the **velocity of the stream**. As either discharge or gradient increases, the velocity of the stream increases. A typical stream may vary greatly in slope between its source (head) and its mouth, where it empties into a lake or the ocean. Therefore, it may flow at different speeds in different places. At times, near the mouth of a river where the slope is small, the velocity may still be great if the discharge is great.

**Channel shape and velocity.** The position of maximum velocity in a stream cross section varies with changes in the direction of stream flow (see Figure 5-9). The velocity of a stream is generally greatest just beneath the surface near the center of the **channel**, where there is less friction with the banks of the river and the atmosphere. Water near the outside of a curve has greater velocity than water near the inside of the curve. Therefore, erosion takes place at the outside of a curve and deposition on the inside.

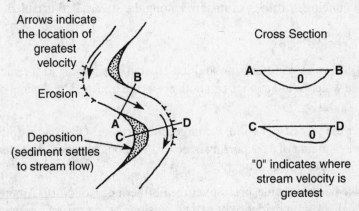

**Figure 5-9.** Variations in stream velocity. The cross sections (right) indicate that where the course of a stream is straight, velocity is greatest in the center, just below the surface. Where the course is curved, velocity is greatest at the outer part of the curve.

**Velocity and sediment size.** The size of particles that can be carried by a stream increases as the velocity of the stream increases (see Figure 5-10). The sediment moves at a slower speed than does the water in the stream.

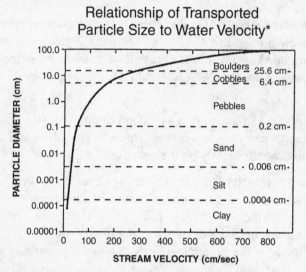

* This generalized graph shows the water velocity needed to maintain, but not start, movement. Variations occur due to differences in particle density and shape.

**Figure 5-10.** This graph shows that the size of the particles which can be moved by a stream is directly related to stream velocity.

**Stream load**. The **load** is the material a stream carries. The load of a stream is carried in three major ways: (1) dissolved particles in **solution**, (2) fine sediments of clay, silt and colloids in **suspension**, and (3) larger sand and pebbles that are bounced, pushed, or rolled along the stream bed. The bouncing or rolling of material along the stream bed is called **saltation**.

## Wind and Ice Erosion

The factors affecting wind erosion and ice erosion are similar to the factors affecting erosion by running water. Wind and ice can both act as the transporting agents of broken rock materials.

**Wind.** The greater the velocity of wind, the larger the particles it can carry. Although erosion by wind is generally thought of as occurring in deserts or along beaches, dust storms can occur inland following long periods of drought.

**Ice.** Erosion by ice has been widespread over the northern part of North America, with most of New York State displaying evidence of glacial erosion. As in erosion by running water, the greater the volume of ice and/or the steeper the slope, the greater its velocity and the more it erodes. Glaciers can transport the largest particles. In fact, entire forests can be found on some modern glaciers. The largest boulders moved by erosion are carried by glaciers.

## Effects of Erosional Agents

Much has already been discussed about the effects of erosional agents. Each agent of erosion produces distinctive changes in the material that it transports. Running water causes particles to be rounded and smooth; glaciers cause them to be angular and rough, with some scratches; wind causes them to be frosted and angular; particles moved downslope by gravity are angular. The longer it takes a material to erode, the rounder and smoother it tends to become. Valleys carved by streams or rivers tend to be **V-shaped**, while valleys carved by glaciers tend to be **U-shaped**.

## Effects of Humans on Erosion

Humans add to the erosion of the land through individual and societal activities. The natural processes of erosion can take a very long time; human activities can erode the land almost overnight. Large gaps are carved out of mountains, and valleys are filled with rock in order that superhighways may be built. Earthmovers, holding enough rock to fill a railroad car, leave the surface exposed to erosion by wind and running water. Today, human activities contribute more than ever before to the erosion of Earth's surface.

## QUESTIONS

1. Transported rock materials are more common than residual rock materials in the soils of New York State. Which statement best explains this observation?

   (1) Solid rock must be transported to break.
   (2) Weathering changes transported rock materials more easily than residual rock material.
   (3) Most rock materials are moved by some agent of erosion at some time in their history.
   (4) Residual rock material forms only from bedrock that is difficult to change into soil.

2. On Earth, the predominant agent of erosion is

   (1) wave action     (2) moving ice     (3) running water     (4) moving air

3. A pebble is being transported in a stream by rolling. How does the velocity of the pebble compare to the velocity of the stream?

   (1) The pebble is moving slower than the stream.
   (2) The pebble is moving faster than the stream.
   (3) The pebble is moving at the same velocity as the stream.

**4.** Which graph best represents the relationship between the velocity of a stream and the average slope of the streambed?

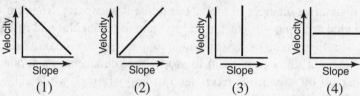

(1)          (2)          (3)          (4)

**5.** According to the *Earth Science Reference Tables*, a stream flowing at a velocity of 100 centimeters per second can transport

(1) silt, but not sand, pebbles, or cobbles
(2) silt and sand, but not pebbles or cobbles
(3) silt, sand, and pebbles, but not cobbles
(4) silt, sand, pebbles, and cobbles

**6.** The velocity of a stream is 100 centimeters per second. According to the *Earth Science Reference Tables*, what is the largest diameter particle that can be transported?

(1) 1.0 cm          (2) 0.1 cm.          (3) 0.01 cm          (4) 0.0001 cm

**7.** A river transports material by suspension, rolling, and

(1) solution          (2) sublimation          (3) evaporation          (4) transpiration

**8**. The diagram below represents an aerial view of a stream which is generally flowing from north to south. Which pair of numbers indicates areas where erosion normally occurs more rapidly than deposition?

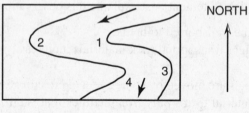

(1) 1 and 2          (2) 1 and 3          (3) 1 and 4          (4) 2 and 3

**9.** For a given location in a stream channel, which graph best shows the relationship between the changes in the volume of the stream and the resulting stream velocity?

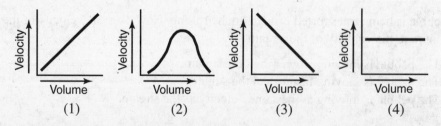

(1)          (2)          (3)          (4)

10. Which characteristic of a transported rock would be most helpful in determining its agent of erosion?

    (1) age        (2) density        (3) composition      (4) physical appearance

11. The diagram below shows the stump of a tree, a root of which grew into a small crack in bedrock and split the rock apart.

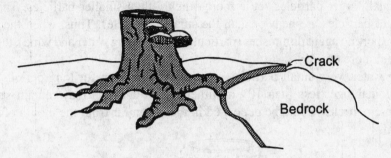

    The action of the root splitting the bedrock is an example of
    (1) chemical weathering        (2) deposition
    (3) erosion                     (4) physical weathering

# DEPOSITION

**Deposition** is the final step in an erosional-depositional system. Rock particles that are picked up and transported by one of the eroding agents will ultimately be deposited somewhere else, and agents of erosion become agents of deposition. When the carrying power of a transporting agent decreases, some of the particles being carried by that agent will be dropped and deposited in a process called **sedimentation**. Sediments are composed primarily of rock fragments of all sizes. Since running water is the principal eroding agent, most sedimentation occurs in deep lakes, seas, or oceans, where streams and rivers slow down and lose their carrying power. Dissolved ionic minerals are released by the process of **precipitation**. (This use of the term "precipitation" should *not* be confused with weather-related precipitation, such as rain, snow, etc.) As used here, the term refers to the process by which dissolved minerals precipitate, or "fall," out of solution when the liquid (water) portion of the solution evaporates. This usually occurs in relatively quiet water. Precipitation produces, deposits of salt, gypsum, and other soluble minerals.

When wind, waves, glaciers, and gravity lose carrying power, sediments are deposited on the surface of the land.

# Factors Affecting Deposition

The principal factors affecting the deposition of particles are: particle size, particle shape, particle density, and the velocity of the transporting agent.

**Particle size.** The settling rate of particles is determined mainly by the particle size. All other factors being equal, larger particles settle more quickly than smaller particles. This occurs because the larger particles are heavier than the smaller particles. Thus, when the carrying power of the transporting agent diminishes (particularly in running water and wind), the heavier particles settle out more quickly.

In running water, very small particles remain in suspension for long periods of time. Particles of colloidal size (less than $10^{-4}$ millimeters in diameter) may remain suspended indefinitely. These particles would be deposited in the ocean far from the mouth of the river that carried them.

**Figure 5-11**. Vertical sorting. In still water, sediments will sort into horizontal layers, with the largest particles on the bottom.

When a mixture of sediment sizes settles in a quiet medium such as still water or air, sorting into horizontal layers takes place (see Figure 5-11). The largest rocks are found on the bottom and the finest particles on the top. Most sediments deposited in water form horizontal layers called **beds**. When mixtures of different-size sediments settle out rapidly in quiet water, graded bedding results (see Figure 5-12). **Graded bedding** shows vertical sorting within the bed, with sediment sizes decreasing from bottom to top. Repeated depositions show a series of graded beds.

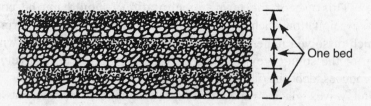

**Figure 5-12**. Graded bedding.

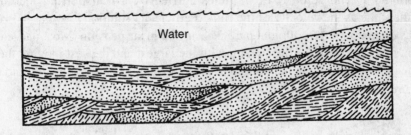

Water

**Figure 5-13**. Cross-bedding. Cross-bedding is the result of sudden changes in velocity of the transporting medium.

Winds and fast-moving rivers produce cross-bedding (see Figure 5-13). **Cross-bedding** is the result of sediments being deposited at an angle to the horizontal. This occurs because of sudden decreases in the velocity and carrying power of the medium.

**Particle shape.** If all other factors are equal, the *shape* of a particle may determine its settling rate. Smooth, spherical (round) particles usually settle faster than angular, flatter particles. This is true because there is less friction (resistance) between the water and rounder particles than between the water and flatter particles.

**Particle density.** The *density* of particles also influences the rates at which sediments settle out of running water and wind. If particles are about the same size and shape, higher-density particles will settle faster than the lower-density particles, because the high-density particles are heavier. The particles will form layers of rocks of different densities, with the densest on the bottom.

**Velocity of transporting medium.** The velocity of the transporting medium determines when the sediments will be released and sedimentation can occur. As the velocity of the **sediment-laden flow** (transporting medium with sediments) decreases, there is a loss of carrying power and the larger, heavier, denser particles settle out first.

**Horizontal Sorting.** As a stream or river enters a large body of water such as a lake or ocean, its velocity decreases as distance from its mouth increases, producing horizontal sorting. In horizontal sorting the larger, denser sediments settle out first, with the smaller, less dense particles carried farther (see Figure 5-14). In a river system, the larger particles will be deposited near the shore, with the particle size decreasing as distance from the shore increases. Most precipitation of dissolved sediments usually occurs far from the shore. When precipitation occurs nearer the shore, it provides the cement for the formation of sedimentary rocks.

**Particle Velocity.**   The velocity of particles carried by a transporting medium is not necessarily the same as the velocity of the fluid. Particles in solution move at the velocity of the stream, as do many of the colloidal particles carried in suspension. Most particles carried in suspension move slower than the stream, with the largest and densest moving the slowest. Rocks rolling or bouncing along the bottom usually move much slower than the stream itself.

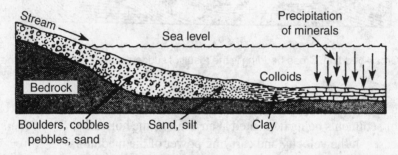

**Figure 5-14**. Horizontal sorting. Where a stream enters a large body of water, sediments are deposited in a horizontal pattern, with the largest particles deposited nearest the shore.

**Glacial Deposition.**   Sorting in a quiet, solid medium, such as ice, is more complex than in a fluid medium. Glacial deposits of gravel, boulders, and sand are *unsorted* (all mixed together), with no layering or bedding. There are mainly two types of glacial deposits - till and outwash. **Till** is unsorted rock material deposited directly by glaciers. Outwash is rock material deposited by the meltwater of a glacier. **Outwash** can show horizontal sorting. Long Island is composed of both types. The northern part of Long Island is essentially formed of till, while the southern part is primarily formed of outwash. Large boulders deposited by glaciers are called **erratics**.

## QUESTIONS

1. According to the *Earth Science Reference Tables*, which rock type is most likely deposited when a stream flowing at a rate of 300 centimeters per second changes to a rate of 100 centimeters per second?
   (1) shale          (2) siltstone          (3) sandstone          (4) conglomerate

2. The diagram below represents a top view of a river emptying into an ocean bay. A-B is a reference line along the bottom of the bay. Which characteristic would most likely decrease along the reference line from A to B?

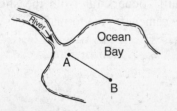

   (1) the amount of salt in solution
   (2) the size of the sediments
   (3) the density of the water
   (4) the depth of the water

**3.** When the velocity of a stream decreases, there will most likely be an increase in

(1) downcutting by the stream
(2) deposition by the stream
(3) the size of the particles carried in suspension by the stream
(4) the amount of material carried in solution by the stream

Base your answers to questions 4 through 6 on your knowledge of Earth Science, the *Earth Science Reference Tables*, and the cross-sectional diagram below. The diagram shows a sediment-laden stream entering the ocean. The ocean is divided into four zones, A, B, C, and D.

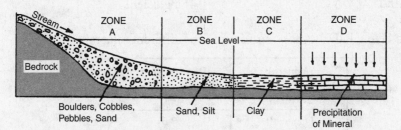

**4.** In which zone would the stream normally deposit particles of largest size?

(1) A       (2) B       (3) C       (4) D

**5.** Which material would most likely be held in suspension in zone D?

(1) cobbles       (2) sand       (3) silt       (4) colloids

**6.** Which zone would contain particles mostly in the range of 0.05 to 0.10 centimeter in diameter?

(1) A       (2) B       (3) C       (4) D

**7.** If all the particles below have the same mass and density, which particle will settle fastest in quiet water? [Assume settling takes place as shown by arrows.]

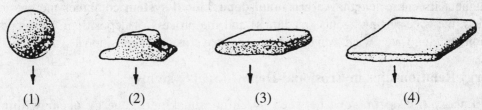

(1)       (2)       (3)       (4)

**8.** A mixture of sand, pebbles, clay, and silt of uniform shape and density, is dropped from a boat into a calm lake. Which material most likely would reach the bottom of the lake first?

(1) sand       (2) pebbles       (3) clay       (4) silt

**9.** The diagram below shows a cross-section of soil from New York State containing pebbles, sand, and clay.

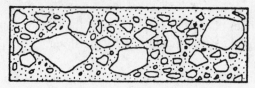

The soil was most likely deposited by

(1) an ocean current          (3) a river

(2) the wind                 (4) a glacier

**10.** The chart below indicates the densities of four different minerals.

| Mineral | Density (g/cm³) |
|---------|-----------------|
| Calcite | 2.8 |
| Diamond | 3.5 |
| Hematite | 5.3 |
| Quartz | 2.7 |

If spheres 5 millimeters in diameter of these four minerals are dropped at the same time into a large tube filled with water, which would settle to the bottom first?

(1) calcite       (2) diamond       (3) hematite       (4) quartz

# AN EROSIONAL-DEPOSITIONAL SYSTEM

A river is a combination of continuous erosion and deposition, both processes occurring throughout its entire length. An **erosional-depositional system** combines the erosional process, the transporting agents (mediums) and the process of deposition. All agents of erosion–running water, wind, waves and ice–produce erosional depositional systems.

## Energy Relationships in Erosional-Depositional Systems

Energy transformations between potential and kinetic energy occur within an erosional-depositional system. A river has its greatest potential energy at its **source**, where the river begins. As the river flows toward its **mouth**, where the river ends, the potential energy decreases, being continuously transformed into kinetic energy. Erosion occurs during this transformation, transporting rocks and sediments **downstream**, toward the mouth.

Whenever there is a loss of kinetic energy, the rocks and sediments carried by the river are deposited. Some kinetic energy is lost to friction between the flowing water and the channel walls. When the slope is steepest, the stream has its greatest velocity and therefore its greatest kinetic energy. As the slope becomes less steep, the velocity and kinetic energy of the stream decrease. When the river reaches base level, the lowest level the river can reach (usually the ocean), the potential energy of the river is zero. Whatever kinetic energy remains is used up as the river flows into the ocean.

Since the potential energy due to position decreases, and some energy is used as the river flows downstream, the amount of energy available at the river's mouth is less than the amount of energy available at its source. Therefore, in an erosional-depositional system, the total energy within the system is decreasing.

## Dominant Processes in an Erosional-Depositional System

Depending on conditions at a particular location, either erosion or deposition may be dominant in an erosional-deposition system. The gradient of the slope is one condition that may determine which is the dominant process. The erosional process is usually dominant when the slope is very steep and the velocity of the river is fast. As the slope becomes less steep and the velocity of the river slows, the erosional process decreases. When the slope becomes very gentle, the depositional process becomes dominant.

At the source of a river and throughout most of its length, the erosional process is dominant. The depositional process is more dominant at the mouth of a river and on the inside curve, or **meander** of a river. The velocity of a river is greater at the outside of a curve than at the inside of a curve. The erosional process is dominant at the outside of a meander, where the water is flowing the fastest. The depositional process is dominant at the inside of a meander, where the water is flowing the slowest.

## Life History of A Stream

A stream passes through a series of stages in its history, each having certain characteristics. They are youth, maturity and old age (see Figure 5-15). The **youthful** stage has poor drainage and is characterized by lakes, waterfalls and rapids. The stream flow is rapid and downcutting is greater than sidecutting. A V-shaped valley is produced, and the stream may fill the entire valley. **Maturity** occurs when sidecutting becomes greater than downcutting, and a flood plain forms. A **flood plain** is the land between the stream and the steep walls of the valley that is usually covered by the stream during floods. The rapids and falls are almost gone and the stream is now **graded** (has a smooth gradient). During the mature stage, the stream begins to meander sinuously over the valley floor.

Full maturity occurs when the flood plain becomes wide enough to accommodate the meanders. Meanders may be cutoff, producing **oxbow lakes** (the curved sections of the river channels that have been abandoned by the river). When the valley floor becomes wider than the river meanders can fill, the stream has reached **old age**. **Natural levees** are broad low ridges along both sides of the stream that form during times of flooding. As the water from the stream overflows its banks, the water slows down and the carrying power decreases. This causes the sediment in the water to be deposited on the banks.

If the gradient of a stream is steepened, the stream takes on some younger characteristics. The stream increases in velocity and cuts downward more than sideward. It is said to be **entrenched**. Stream features such as meanders become entrenched meanders. **Natural bridges** occur where the stream breaks through the wall of two entrenched meanders on opposite sides of a ridge.

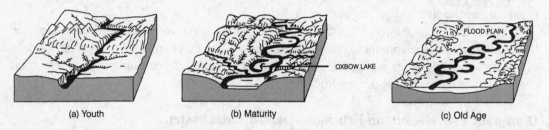

(a) Youth        (b) Maturity        (c) Old Age

**Figure 5-15**. Stages of a Stream. A stream has three stages of history, (a) Youth (b) Maturity (c) Old Age. Frequently, streams have all 3 stages at once. Near the source, the stream is youthful, while near its mouth it is in old age. The middle of the stream is mature.

## Erosional-Depositional Interfaces

Interfaces (or boundaries) between erosion and deposition can often be found throughout the length of a stream or river. They are common at the mouth and curves of a stream and where there is a change in slope.

## Dynamic Equilibrium of a Stream

Whenever there is a balance between erosion and deposition–when the rate of deposition equals the rate of erosion–a state of dynamic equilibrium exists. In a stream system, a state of dynamic equilibrium can be found near the mouth of the river and near the middle of a curve in the river channel. As a river flows into the ocean and loses kinetic energy, a state of dynamic equilibrium exists at the interface where the amount of sediment deposited equals the amount eroded. As water flows around the curve of a river channel, erosion will dominate on the faster-moving side and deposition will dominate on the slower-moving side. Somewhere between the two sides, at the interface, the rate of deposition will equal the rate of erosion and a state of dynamic equilibrium will exist.

## Erosional-Depositional Changes

The erosional and depositional processes produce characteristic observable changes in the surface of the land. Two major forms of deposition that owe their existence to stream flow are the delta and the alluvial fan. A <u>**delta**</u> is a deposit of sediment formed at the mouth of a river where the river loses its carrying as it enters a quiet body of water. An **alluvial fan** is a deposit of sediment formed where the velocity of a river slows as it flows out of the mountains onto the flatland.

# QUESTIONS

1. Which characteristic exists at an erosional-depositional interface in a stream where equilibrium occurs?

    (1) The downstream profile is the same as the across-stream profile.
    (2) The rate of deposition equals the rate of erosion.
    (3) The composition of the sediments deposited is the same as the composition of the sediments eroded.
    (4) The volume of streamflow equals the volume of deposition.

Base your answers to questions 2 through 5 on your knowledge of Earth Science and on the vertical cross section showing a stream profile with reference points A through F within the stream bed.

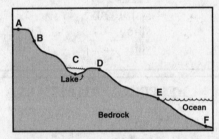

2. The primary force causing the movement of materials from point B to point F is

    (1) air pressure      (2) insolation      (3) water      (4) gravity

3. At which point would erosion most likely be greatest?

    (1) A      (2) B      (3) C      (4) F

4. Deposition in the lake at point C is most likely caused by

    (1) a loss of potential energy by the lake
    (2) a loss of kinetic energy by the sediments
    (3) a gain of kinetic energy by the sediments
    (4) a gain of potential energy by the sediments

5. Which would most likely happen if the stream discharge between points D and E were to increase?

    (1) The average velocity of water would increase.
    (2) The amount of soil erosion would decrease.
    (3) The size of the particles carried in suspension would decrease.
    (4) The length of the stream would decrease.

## CHAPTER 5 -Section 1
## CORE VOCABULARY

| | | |
|---|---|---|
| abrasion | infiltration | sorted |
| capillarity | mass movement | stream |
| channel | meander | transpiration |
| chemical weathering | outwash | transported sediment |
| delta | permeability | U-shaped valleys |
| deposition | permeable | unsorted |
| erosion | physical weathering | V-shaped valleys |
| evaporation | porosity | velocity |
| flood plain | precipitation | water cycle |
| gradient | runoff | water table |
| gravity | sediments | weathering |
| ground water | slope | |
| hydrologic ( water) cycle | soil | |

## HELPFUL VOCABULARY

| | | |
|---|---|---|
| alluvial fan | load | stalactite |
| aquifer | maturity | stalagmite |
| beds | mouth | stream discharge |
| carbonation | natural bridges | strip cropping |
| carrying power | natural levees | subsoil |
| contour plowing | old age | suspension |
| crop rotation | organic decay | talus |
| cross-bedding | oxbow lake | terraced |
| depletion | oxidation | till |
| desertification | regolith | topsoil |
| downstream | residual sediment | transported soil |
| entrenched | residual soil | transporting agents |
| erosional-depositional system | saltation | velocity of a stream |
| erratics | sediment laden flow | watershed |
| evapotranspiration | sedimentation | weathering agents |
| graded | sink holes | wind breaks |
| graded bedding | soil profile | youthful |
| hydration | soil solution | zone of aeration |
| impermeable | solution | zone of saturation |
| karst topography | source | |

## PRACTICE FOR CONSTRUCTED RESPONSE

Base your answers to questions 1 through 3 on the data table below and your knowledge of Earth Science. The table represents data collected about water in three separate columns, A, B, and C, each filled to the 500 milliliter level with dry rock particles. Each column had a different sized particle. The particles in each column were uniform in shape, loosely packed and well sorted.

**DATA TABLE**

| | Amount of Water Needed to Fill Pore Spaces (milliliters) | Infiltration Time [time required for water to flow through the particles] (seconds) | Amount of Water Retained by Particles After Draining (milliliters) |
| --- | --- | --- | --- |
| Column A | 220 | 15 | 20 |
| Column B | 220 | 10 | 4 |
| Column C | 220 | 8 | 3 |

1. The porosity of a material can be defined as the percentage of open space in a material compared to its total volume. According to this definition, describe how you can determine the porosity of the particles in column A.

_____

_____

2. According to the data table, which column has the largest particles? State two pieces of evidence from the data table that support your choice.

_____

_____

3. A fourth column, D, is filled with a mixture of particles from the 3 other columns. Compare the porosity, permeability, retention and capillarity of column D to that of column C.

_____

_____

Base your answers to questions 4 through 6 on the diagram below and your knowledge of Earth Science. The diagram represents the dominant types of weathering for various climatic conditions.

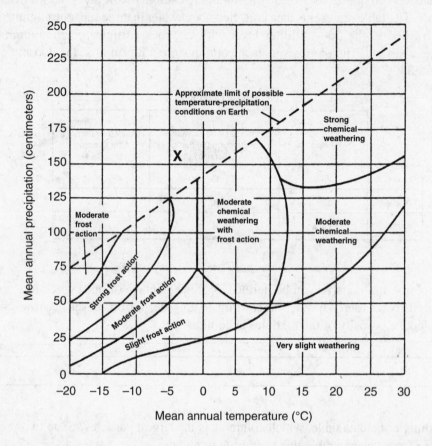

**4.** Describe the climatic conditions which would produce strong chemical weathering.

_____

_____

**5.** Weathering or frost action is not taking place at location X. Explain why weathering or frost action does not occur under these conditions.

_____

_____

**6.** Assume the rate of precipitation through the year is constant at 150 mm. At what time of year will the rate of weathering be the greatest and why?

_____

_____

Base your answers to questions 7 through 9 on the data Table below, your knowledge of Earth Science and the *Earth Science Reference Tables*. The table contains data taken at locations A through E in a stream. The volume for the stream is the same at all three locations.

| Location in the Stream | Average Velocity (cm/sec) | Elevation above Sea Level (m) | Distance from Source (km) |
|---|---|---|---|
| A | 10 | 640 | 0 |
| B | 130 | 570 | 20 |
| C | 210 | 200 | 80 |
| D | 100 | 100 | 130 |
| E | 70 | 40 | 200 |

**7.** On the grid below, graph the streamprofile from location A to location E.

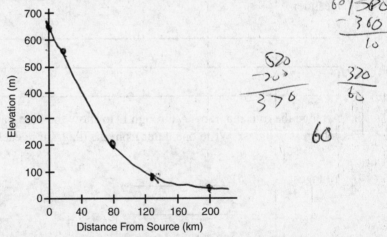

Distance From Source (km)

$6.10$

$60 \overline{)370}$
$\underline{-360}$
$10$

$\begin{array}{r} 570 \\ -200 \\ \hline 370 \end{array}$

$\dfrac{370}{60}$

$60$

**8.** Calculate the gradient of the stream flow between locations B and C using the directions below.

**a.** Write the equation for the gradient.

$G = \dfrac{\text{change}}{\text{distance}}$

**b.** Substitute data from the table into the equation.

$\dfrac{370}{60}$

**c.** Calculate the gradient.

$6.10$

**d.** Label your answers with the proper units.

$6.10 \ \text{Km/m}$

9. The average velocity of the stream is different at each of the locations A through E. In one or more complete sentences, describe the probable cause of the different average water velocities at each location.

_____

_____

Base your answers to question 10 on the diagram below and your knowledge of Earth Science. The diagram shows a river and its landscape during four stages of erosion.

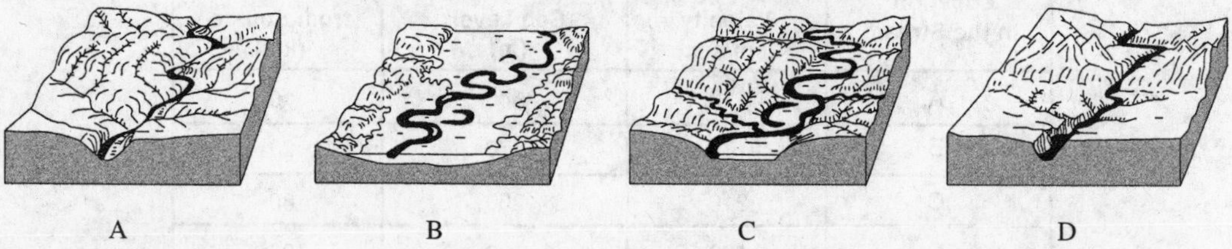

    A                    B                    C                    D

10. **a.** Describe the most likely sequence of river and landscape development in terms of downward versus sideward erosion and the development of flood plains and meanders.

_____

_____

_____

**b.** Arrange the four diagrams A through D to show the landscape development from youngest to oldest. Write one letter from the diagram in each of the spaces below.

Youngest        1._____

                2._____

                3._____

Oldest          4._____

Base your answer to question 11 on the diagram below and your knowledge of Earth Science.

**11.** A stream is entering the calm waters of a large lake.

**a.** Which diagram best illustrates the pattern of sediments being deposited in the lake from the stream flow?

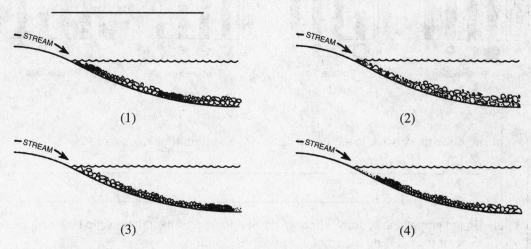

(1)          (2)

(3)          (4)

**b.** Describe the process that makes your choice correct.

_____

_____

**12.** The diagram below shows four identical columns containing the same amount of water. Four different-sized spherical particles, made of the same uniform material are dropped into the columns and settle to the bottom.

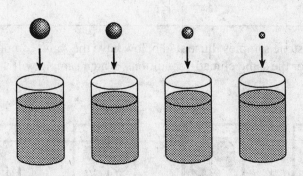

**a.** Which graph best shows the relative settling times of the four particles? _____

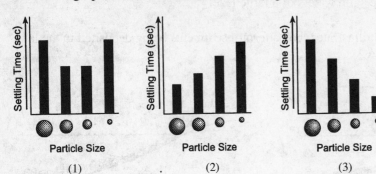
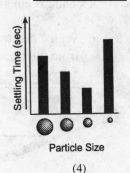

          (1)                       (2)                     (3)                    (4)

**b.** In this activity, what is the factor causing the settling time to change?

_____

_____

**13. a.** On the graph below, draw a line which best illustrates the relationship between the slope of the land and the amount of surface runoff.

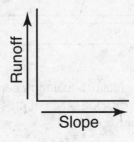

**b.** State why you drew the line as you did.

_____

**14. a.** The four limestone samples illustrated below have the same composition, mass, and volume. Under the same climatic conditions, which sample will weather fastest?

_____

          (1)                       (2)                     (3)                    (4)

**b.** State a reason for your choice in **14a.**

_____

_____

Base your answers to questions 15 through 18 on the *Earth Science Reference Tables*, the information provided in the diagrams below, and your knowledge of Earth Science.

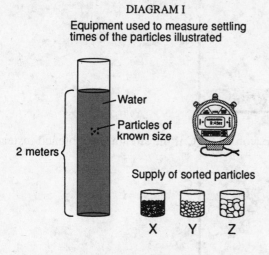

DIAGRAM I
Equipment used to measure settling times of the particles illustrated

DIAGRAM II
A map showing a stream flowing from north to south emptying into the ocean

**15.** If the three samples in diagram I, X Y and Z were mixed, dropped into a cylinder containing water and the particles were allowed to settle, what would have been the order in which they settle. In the cylinder below, identify the 3 sediments by letter in layers, 1, 2, and 3 of the cylinder.

**16. a.** If each of the three samples were dumped into separate cylinders open at the bottom and resting in a pan of water, which samples, X, Y, or Z, would have the greatest capillarity? _____

**b.** State one reason for your choice in **16 a**.

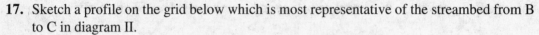

_____

_____

**17.** Sketch a profile on the grid below which is most representative of the streambed from B to C in diagram II.

**18.** Sketch how the streambed would change from B to C if the stream straightened instead of being on a curve.

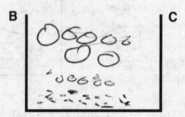

Base your answers to questions 19 through 24 on the *Earth Science Reference Tables*, on the map below, and your knowledge of Earth Science. The map represents a meandering stream with a constant gradient. The arrows show the direction of stream flow. Points A through F are locations in the stream.

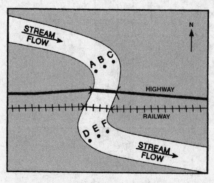

**19. a.** At which points in the stream, A, B, C, D, E, or F, would the most material be deposited? _____

**b.** State the reasons you believe most material would be deposited at these points.

_____

_____

_____

**20. a.** Of the following sediments, clay, sand, silt, pebbles, which would be deposited by the stream first? _____

**b.** State the reason(s) for your choice.

_____

_____

_____

**21. a.** With which landscape feature would this meandering stream most likely be associated? _____

**b.** State reasons that describe how you made the determination in **21a.** above.

_____

_____

**22. a.** At which points A, B, C, D, E, or F, would the stream most likely flow the fastest?

_____

**b.** State the reason(s) for your choice in **22a.** above.

_____

_____

**23. a.** Which diagram below best represents the cross section of the stream through points A, B, and C? _____

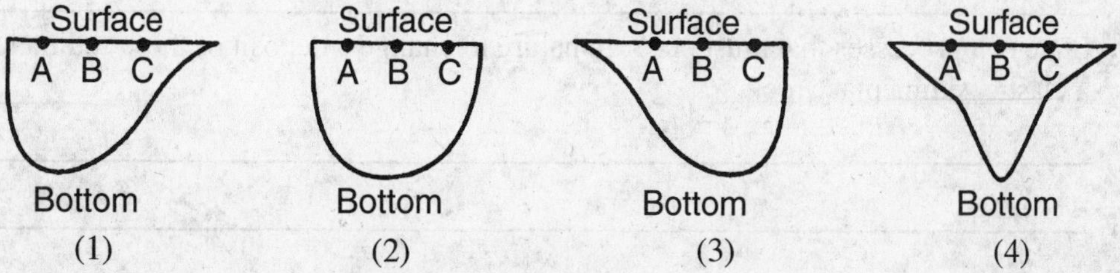

| Surface | Surface | Surface | Surface |
| A B C | A B C | A B C | A B C |
| Bottom | Bottom | Bottom | Bottom |
| (1) | (2) | (3) | (4) |

**b.** State the reason(s) for your choice in **23a.**

_____

_____

**24. a.** At which location along the bank of the stream would you be most likely to build a shopping mall? _____

**b.** State your reasons for building a mall at the point you have chosen.

_____

_____

Base your answers to questions 25 through 27 on the information, diagram, and data table below.

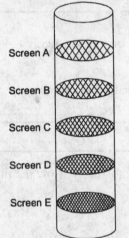

Screen A

Screen B

Screen C

Screen D

Screen E

(Screen mesh not drawn to scale)

**Student Data Table**

| Screen | Screen Mesh Opening Size (cm) | Percentage of Particles Trapped by the Screen (%) |
|---|---|---|
| A | 0.1 | 0 |
| B | 0.05 | 30 |
| C | 0.025 | 45 |
| D | 0.0125 | 15 |
| E | 0.00625 | 10 |

**25.** Explain why screens B through E must be arranged in the order shown in the diagram to separate the sediments as shown in the student data table.

_____

_____

**26.** State *two* processes that must occur in nature to change a deposit of these sediments into a clastic sedimentary rock.

_____

_____

162

**27.** Which clastic sedimentary rock may be formed from particles of the same size as this quartz sediment sample? _____

Base your answers to questions 28 through 30 on the map and cross section below. The map shows measured changes in the position of Niagara Falls since 1678. The cross sections show the two parts of Niagara Falls: Horseshoe Falls and American Falls. Letters A through D represent the same rock layers at both location.

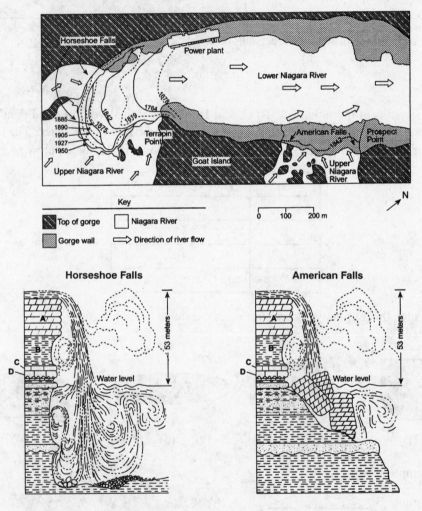

**28.** What best explains why Horseshoe Falls has eroded back more than American Falls since 1842?

_____

_____

**29. a.** Which lettered rock layer, A, B, C, or D, shows the most resistance to weathering and erosion at Horseshoe Falls? _____

**b.** What is the evidence that indicates the layer you chose in **29 a.** above to be the most resistant?

_____

_____

**30.** What is the name of the most resistant rock. _____

Four samples of aluminum, A, B, C, and D, have identical volumes and densities, but different shapes. Each piece is dropped into a long tube filled with water. The time each sample takes to settle to the bottom of the tube is shown in the table below.

| Sample | Time to Settle (sec) |
|--------|---------------------|
| A | 2.5 |
| B | 3.7 |
| C | 4.0 |
| D | 5.2 |

**31. a.** Which diagram most likely represents the shape of each sample?

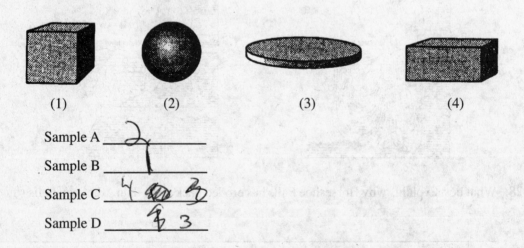

(1)            (2)            (3)            (4)

Sample A ___2___

Sample B ___1___

Sample C ___4 ⊗ 2___

Sample D ___3___

**b.** State the reason(s) for your choices.

_____

_____

Base your answers to questions 32 and 33 on your knowledge of Earth Science, the *Earth Science Reference Tables*, and the bar graphs below. The graphs show the percentages by volume of the sediment sizes that are found in four different sediment deposits, A, B, C, and D.

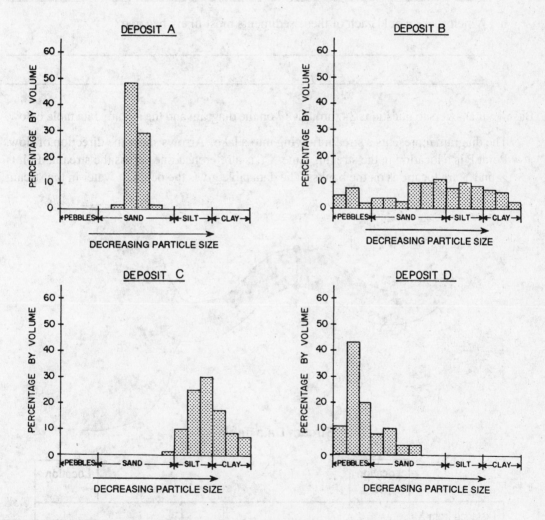

**32. a.** Which deposit contains the highest percentage of sediments that would stay in suspension for the shortest time before settling? _____

**b.** State a reason for your selection.

_____

_____

**33. a.** Describe the processes which could cause these sediment deposits to become sedimentary rocks.

_____

_____

**b.** Which rocks would each of these sediments most likely become?

_____

_____

Base your answers to questions 34 through 37 on the diagram and the stream data table below.

The diagram represents a stream flowing into a lake. Arrows show the direction of flow. Point P is a location in the stream. Line XY is a reference line across the stream. Points X and Y are locations on the banks. The data table gives the depth of water in the stream along line XY.

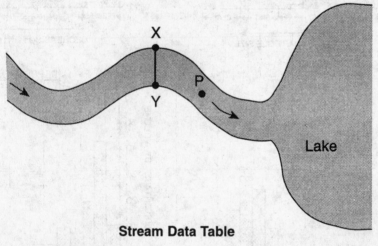

**Stream Data Table**

| | Location X | | | | | | | Location Y |
|---|---|---|---|---|---|---|---|---|
| Distance from X (meters) | 0 | 5 | 10 | 15 | 20 | 25 | 30 | 35 |
| Depth of Water (meters) | 0 | 5.0 | 5.5 | 4.5 | 3.5 | 2.0 | 0.5 | 0 |

Use the information in the data table above to construct a profile of the depth of water. Use the grid below.

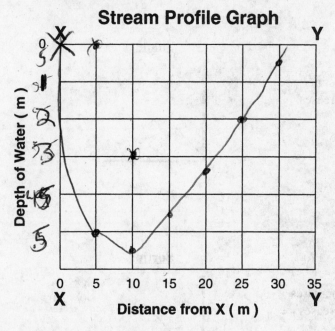

**Stream Profile Graph**

34. On the vertical axis, mark an appropriate scale for the depth of water. Note that the zero (0) at the top of the axis represents the water surface.

35. Plot the data for the depth of water in the stream along line XY and connect the points. (Distance is measured from point X.)    Example:

36. State why the depth of water near the bank at point X is different from the depth of water near the bank at point Y.

_____

_____

37. At point P, the water velocity is 100 centimeters per second. State the name of the largest sediment that can be transported by the stream at point P.

_____

_____

**167**

**38.** The three factors that affect porosity are shape, sorting and packing. On the appropriate graph construct the proper graphing relationships to show that:

### Shape

**a.** as roundness increases, porosity increases

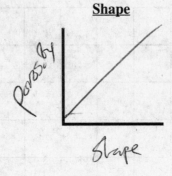

### Sorting

**b.** as sorting increases, porosity increases

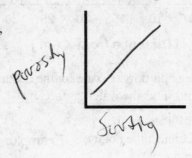

### Packing

**c.** as packing increases, porosity decreases

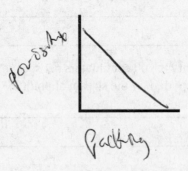

# CHAPTER 5: SECTION 2
# SURFACE PROCESSES AND LANDSCAPES

## OCEANS - GLACIERS AND ENVIRONMENTAL CHANGES

Section 1 of Chapter 5 dealt with the geologic agents of weathering, ground water, and the erosion, transportation, and deposition processes of streams. Water waves, glaciers, and winds are other agents of erosion, transportation and deposition of sediment.

As waves break against the shore, they can either tear it down or build it up. The energy of waves comes from the wind. Understanding how waves travel and move sediment is important to understanding how beachfront homes can be destroyed by waves or how harbors can be blocked with sand.

Wherever glaciers exist, they are more effective in the erosional-depositional system than are streams. Geologic features produced by glaciers are far different from those produced by running water or water waves. To understand how the present landscape of New York State was formed, it is essential to understand how glaciers erode, transport and deposit material.

Although their impact is small in New York, winds are important agents of erosion and deposition.

## OCEAN CURRENTS AND WAVE ACTION

Great rivers without solid banks, **ocean currents**, flow at and beneath the ocean surface. Ocean currents are important for their impact on local and global climate patterns.

Erosion and deposition by **wave action** cause changes in shoreline features, including beaches, sandbars, and barrier islands. Wave action rounds sediments as a result of abrasion. Waves approaching a shoreline move sand parallel to the shore within the zone of breaking waves.

## INTRODUCTION TO OCEANS

Oceans cover approximately 70% of Earth's surface. Life came from the oceans. Humans have feared and misunderstood the seas, which explains in part why the oceans have been so abused. Our very survival may depend on the next generation's knowledge of, and respect for "planet ocean."

**Sediments and bedrock materials**. The basaltic crust of the sea floor is covered in many places with layers of sediment. This sediment is either terrigenous or pelagic. **Terrigenous** sediment is land sediment that has settled on the ocean floor. Most of it comes from mountain streams and rivers, and is deposited by turbidity currents or similar processes near the continental margins - about 13 billion tons per year. Deposits made by turbidity currents are called **turbidites**. They are important because they produce graded beds.

**Pelagic** sediment is sediment made up of fine-grained clays and the skeletons of microscopic organisms that settle slowly through the ocean water. It covers 75% of the ocean bottom. Fine grained pelagic clay can be transported great distances and is found almost everywhere on the ocean floor. Some clay sized particles can take over 50 years to settle. About 100 million metric tons per year of these sediment particles are carried to the ocean by winds.

Volcanic eruptions contribute large quantities of ash to the ocean. Chemical and biological processes also produce sediments, as do particles from space. Microscopic shells and skeletons of plants and animals settle to the ocean floor when marine organisms die. **Oozes** are sediments of microscopic shells. *Calcareous oozes* are rich in calcium carbonate. The most common ooze comes from the shells of *Globigerina,* a very small one-celled animal. Because *Globigerina* is a genus of foraminifera, this type of ooze is sometimes called *Foraminifera Ooze. Siliceous oozes* are rich in silicon dioxide and are the remains of radiolaria and diatoms.

Because water is such an excellent solvent, ocean water contains a variety of dissolved minerals, mostly from land erosion. Nodules, produced when sediment collects slowly in ocean basins, are primarily composed of iron, manganese, copper, cobalt and nickel. They occur in regions far from major sediment sources. Materials such as sand, gravel and shells are mined from the shallow ocean bottom and used to pave roads and construct buildings. Heavy metals—gold, tin, chromium and titanium—are also recovered from the ocean bottom. Phosphorous nodules (used in fertilizer) occur on continental shelves where they are easily dredged.

**Topography of the Sea Floor.** If the ocean floor were drained of water, it would show a number of features similar to those on land. The ocean floor does not begin at the water's edge. The continental margin extends for some distance into the ocean as it slopes downward to the ocean floor (see Figure 5-16). The **continental shelf** is a gently sloping surface which extends under the ocean from the shoreline to a depth of about 100-200 meters. The continental shelf is composed primarily of sediments from rivers. Next to the continental shelf is the continental slope. The **continental slope** is relatively steep, extending downward as deep as 2 kilometers from the shelf. Along the base of the slope lies the continental rise. The **continental rise** is a wedge of sediment that extends from the lower part of the continental slope to the deep sea floor.

V-shaped valleys that run across continental shelves and down continental slopes are **submarine canyons**. A major cause of canyon erosion are dense mixtures of water and sediment called **turbidity currents** that are pulled downslope by gravity like huge avalanches. Some submarine canyons were cut during the ice ages by rivers of meltwater flowing into the ocean.

The ocean floor has many features similar to those on land. Flat regions of the deep ocean floor, found at the base of the continental rise, are the **abyssal plains** (see Figure 5-16). They are formed of horizontal layers of sediment deposited over thousands of years. They are among the flattest features on Earth. Abyssal plains form where turbidity currents can carry in enough sediment to bury and smooth the rugged surface. The deep ocean sediments are composed of microscopic organisms.

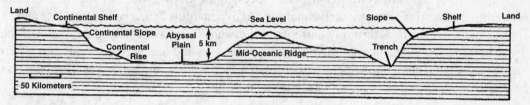

**Figure 5-16**. Ocean Topography. This profile includes features that do not necessarily occur in the same ocean floor.

Undersea mountain ranges in the ocean basins are called **mid-ocean ridges** (see Figure 5-16). Deep ocean chasms parallel to the edge of a continent or island arc are **trenches**. The deepest spots on Earth, almost 12 kilometers below sea level, are in ocean trenches. Volcanic mountains rising 1,000 m above the ocean floor are called seamounts (see Figure 5-17). **Seamounts** form at volcanic hot spots. When volcanic islands stop growing, wave action flattens them, forming **guyots**.

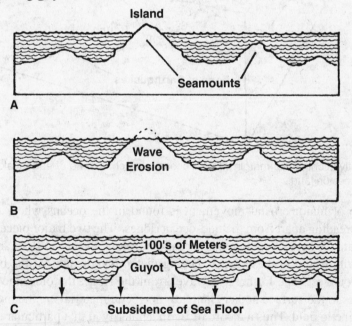

**Figure 5-17.** (A) Seamounts are volcanic mountains on the sea floor, rising above sea level to form islands. (B) The flat guyot was eroded by waves when the top of a seamount was above sea level. (C) The present depth of a guyot is due to subsidence.

## Ocean Floor Activity

Continental margins and ocean bottoms that are active have changed through time. Active areas are characterized by earthquakes, young mountain ranges, volcanoes and oceanic trenches. Most activity occurs at plate boundaries. The plates may spread apart, slide beside each other or one may sink under another. Ocean trenches form where oceanic plates subduct or sink beneath continental plates (see Figure 5-18). Most of the land masses bordering the Pacific Ocean are active margins. Active margins lack a continental rise and an abyssal plain. Deposition, turbidity currents, and earthquakes have changed the shape of the ocean bottoms. Hills, seamounts, guyots, atolls, volcanoes and the mid-ocean ridges with rift valleys have developed on the ocean basins. On a global scale, the processes of subduction have been balanced by the process of sea floor spreading.

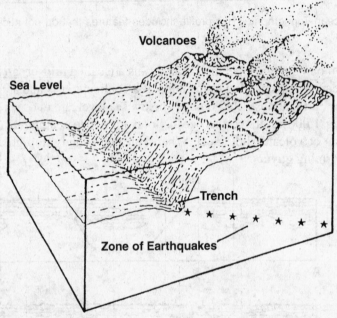

**Figure 5-18.** Active continental margin with an oceanic trench, a zone of earthquakes, and a chain of andesitic volcanoes on land.

Evidence of major crustal movement is found in the oceans where the ocean floors appear to be spreading apart from the mid-ocean ridges. The two major pieces of evidence for this inference are the ages of the igneous rocks found along the ocean floor and the reversal of magnetic polarity found in these rocks. Dating methods indicate that the basalt nearest the ridges is the youngest. The farther you travel from the ridge, the older the basalt becomes. As magma rises to the surface and crystallizes, magnetic materials in the magma are aligned by Earth's magnetic field. Thus a record of Earth's polarity at that particular time is preserved in the solidified rock. Parallel strips of basalt found on both sides of the mid-ocean ridges show periodic reversals of magnetic polarity (see Figure 4-16). This indicates that Earth's polarity reverses every several thousands of years.

Hot spots or mantle plumes are areas of active volcanism in the lithosphere. Their cause is not clear, but they seem to remain in the same location as the lithospheric plate moves above them. The result is a line of extinct volcanoes increasing in age away from the active area. The Hawaiian islands appear to be products of a hot spot (see Figure 4-12). Analysis of these volcanic islands allows us to calculate some plate motions.

## QUESTIONS

**1.** The profile below shows four regions of the ocean bottom.

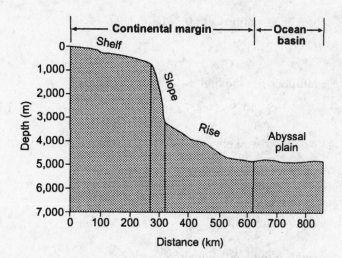

In which list are these regions arranged in order of gradient from least steep to most steep?

(1) rise → abyssal plain → shelf → slope
(2) slope → rise → shelf → abyssal plain
(3) abyssal plain → shelf → rise → slope
(4) shelf → abyssal plain → rise → slope

Base your answers to questions 2-6 on the graph below, your knowledge of Earth Science and on the *Earth Science Reference Tables*. The graph shows changes in the salt concentration of surface water in parts per thousand (‰).

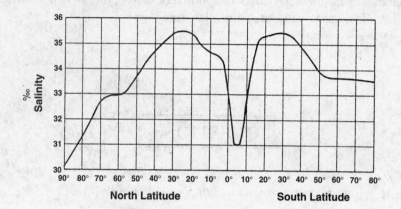

2. What is the approximate salinity at 60°N latitude?

   (1) 31‰           (2) 32‰           (3) 33‰

3. Which of these latitudes has the highest salinity?

   (1) 30°N           (2) 40°S           (3) 60°N           (4) 62°S

4. Which factors would most likely cause the salinity to increase?

   (1) melting of ice and runoff
   (2) precipitation and melting ice
   (3) evaporation and freezing of sea water
   (4) water flow and sedimentation

5. The correct amount of the land above sea level is

   (1) 0%           (2) 30%           (3) 50%           (4) 70%

6. The density current that flows through the Straits of Gibraltar is created by

   (1) rapid cooling of the water
   (2) evaporation of water in the Mediterranean Sea
   (3) sediments falling out of water
   (4) mixing of sediments with water

7. Material from the mantle rises up under the ocean to form

   (1) submarine canyons           (2) continental rises
   (3) ocean ridges                (4) sea-floor trenches

8. Ocean trenches form where

   (1) oceanic plates pass beside each other
   (2) oceanic plates sink below continental plates
   (3) continental plates collide
   (4) continental plates sink below oceanic plates

9. Most deep ocean trenches are located in the

   (1) Antarctic Ocean               (2) Indian Ocean
   (3) Pacific Ocean                (4) Atlantic Ocean

10. Active continental margins have

    (1) coastal plains and oceanic trenches      (2) oceanic trenches and coastal plains
    (3) earthquakes and oceanic trenches       (4) ocean ridges and rugged shorelines

# OCEAN CURRENTS

Ocean currents are generated by winds and density differences. **Surface currents** are very broad, slow movements of surface water. They are set in motion by the prevailing surface winds at that location. The air flowing over a water surface drags the water slowly forward, creating a current as broad as the current of air, but rarely more than 70 to 100 meters deep. The effect of winds on the ocean is evident when we compare a map of surface ocean currents (see Figure 5-19) with the positions of the belts of prevailing winds (see Planetary Wind and Moisture Belts in the Troposphere in the *Earth Science Reference Tables*). In low latitudes, surface water moves westward with the trade winds. In higher latitudes, it moves eastward with the westerlies.

Warm currents begin in the Equatorial regions and flow north. Cold currents begin in the northern latitudes and flow south. The surface currents of the ocean form a pattern, curving to the right in the Northern Hemisphere and to the left in the Southern Hemisphere (see Figure 5-19). In the Northern Hemisphere, the warm currents flow north along the western sides of the oceans while the cold currents flow south along the eastern sides. This pattern is produced partly by the rotation of Earth and partly by deflection, where a current "runs into" a continent. The Gulf Stream is part of such a pattern (see Figure 5-20). With other currents, it forms a complete circle around the Sargasso Sea. As water evaporates from the Sargasso Sea, it leaves the salts behind and the water there becomes more **saline**, or salty.

Surface Ocean Currents

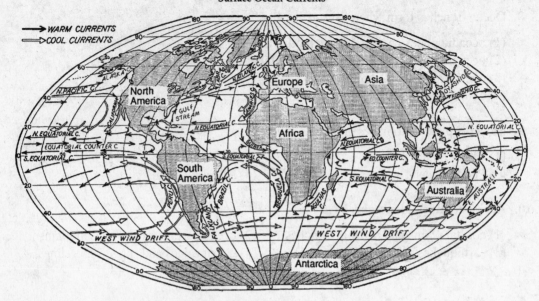

**Figure 5-19.** Surface Ocean Currents

**Figure 5-20.** Gulf Stream. The Gulf Stream is a warm water current that flows north along the east coast of the United States across the Atlantic to Europe, where it turns south and becomes the Canary Current and then completes its clockwise journey back across the Atlantic Ocean to the United States. Water piles up in the Sargasso Sea and evaporates leaving highly saline ocean water behind.

While currents set in motion by the winds are moving through the ocean surface, a deeper circulation of water occurs beneath the surface as a result of differences in density. The density of sea water increases as the water gets colder and also as it becomes more saline. Dense cold water from the Polar regions sinks and slides slowly along the ocean floor toward the Equatorial regions, displacing less dense water as it travels (see Figure 5-21). Three large water masses are formed as density currents at the polar regions: the Antarctic Bottom Current, the North Atlantic Deep Water Current and the Antarctic Intermediate Water Current. The most dense is the Antarctic Bottom Current with each current above listed being successively less dense.

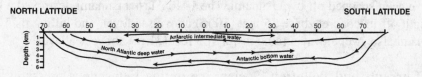

**Figure 5-21**. Density currents from polar regions. The arrows show the direction of flow of the three major density currents found in ocean waters.

In the Mediterranean Sea, the water sinks mainly because it is very saline. Water in the warm, nearly enclosed, Mediterranean Sea evaporates at such a rapid rate that it becomes saline at the surface and therefore more dense (see Figure 5-22). The denser saline water sinks and flows out the bottom of the Mediterranean Sea. It is replaced by less dense water from the Atlantic Ocean.

**Oceans Distribute Solar Energy.** Oceans help the atmosphere to distribute Earth's uneven solar energy. Most of Earth's **solar energy** is received at the lower latitudes. Water, with its high specific heat, has the ability to absorb and store large amounts of heat energy. Water currents carry the stored heat energy from the lower latitudes to the higher latitudes, and the colder currents from the higher latitudes is carried to the lower latitudes where it is heated.

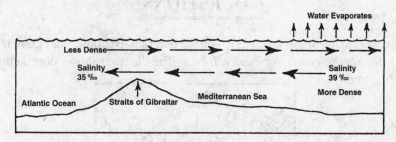

**Figure 5-22**. Density currents in the Mediterranean Sea. The denser sea water flows out the bottom of the Mediterranean and is replaced by less dense Atlantic water.

**Tsunamis**. The sudden movement of the sea floor upward or downward during an earthquake at or near the water can generate very large waves called "tidal waves" or **tsunamis**. Because the ocean tides have nothing to do with these large waves, they were given the name tsunami. In addition to earthquakes, tsunamis can also be caused by submarine landslides or volcanic explosions. Tsunamis can be over 400 times larger that wind-generated waves, having wavelengths of 100 miles (160 km) and heights of 50 to 100 feet (15-30 m) when they break. Because the wave is so long, the water continues to rise for 5 to 10 minutes, causing great flooding before it withdraws. Tsunamis can bring widespread destruction and loss of life to the shoreline on which it lands. Spruce trees 2 feet (0.7 m) thick and 100 feet (30 m) above sea level have been snapped off by a tsunami. The 1946 Alaska tsunami destroyed a lighthouse, sweeping it off its concrete base 35 feet (10 m) above sea level, and killing its 5 occupants. The tsunami also swept away a radio tower 103 feet (31 m) above sea level.

**Ocean Currents and Pollution**. Society is exerting tremendous pressures to prevent pollution from harming the oceans, particularly along the coastal areas. Ocean currents are important because they distribute man-generated pollutants. Large oil spills are among the most dramatic forms of ocean pollution. The spilled oil is spread widely by waves and currents. When the *Exxon Valdez* went aground near Valdez, Alaska in 1989, more than 10 million gallons of crude oil was spilled and moved by currents. Much of the oil went onto beaches. Sea birds and otters were affected. In most cases, bottom-dwelling organisms are seriously affected because they cannot move away.

The ocean is an important recreational resource, yet beaches have been closed by "garbage" (medical wastes from hospitals) dumped into the ocean and later washed up onto the shore. Some agricultural and industrial waste products are directly poisonous to marine life and can kill or cause severe poisoning to those who feed on them.

## QUESTIONS

Base your answers to questions 1 through 4 on the diagram to follow, your knowledge of Earth Science and the *Earth Science Reference Tables*. The diagram shows ocean currents off the coast of North America.

1.  Which letter indicates the Gulf Stream?

    (1) A              (2) B            (3) C            (4) D

2.  Which letter(s) indicate a warm ocean current?

    (1) A              (2) A and B        (3) B and C        (4) C and D

3.  Which letter(s) indicate a cold ocean current?

    (1) A              (2) A and B        (3) B and C        (4) C

4.  Of the places below, at which location is the water temperature probably the highest?

    (1) at the lowest latitude        (2) at the highest latitude
    (3) in a current flowing north    (4) in a current flowing south

5.  Warm water from tropical oceans is carried to northern Europe by the Gulf Stream and the

    (1) Alaska Current            (2) Canaries Current
    (3) North Atlantic Current    (4) Brazil current

Base your answer to question 6 on the diagram below, your knowledge of Earth Science and the *Earth science Reference Tables*.

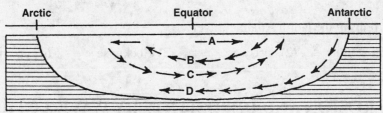

6.  The current containing the densest water is

    (1) A              (2) B            (3) C            (4) D

7.  Large bodies of water are never still because
    (1) tides are constantly churning up the water
    (2) radiant energy from the sun causes evapotranspiration
    (3) the water cycle transfers heat energy into the atmosphere
    (4) winds are the causes of wave motion

Base your answers to questions 8 through 10 on the diagram below, your knowledge of Earth Science and the *Earth Science Reference Tables*.

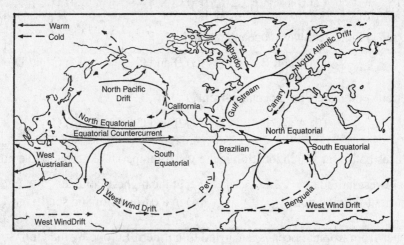

**8.** Warm ocean currents originate at the

    (1) Polar regions      (2) Equator          (3) ocean bottom      (4) coast of Antarctica

**9.** Cold ocean currents originate at the

    (1) Polar regions      (2) Equator          (3) ocean bottom      (4) coast of Africa

**10.** The currents in the North Atlantic travel

    (1) north-south      (2) east-west      (3) clockwise      (4) up and down

# EROSION AND DEPOSITION BY WAVE ACTION

## Waves

The dynamic nature of ocean waters is most apparent along the shore where **waves** continually roll in and break. Sometimes waves are low and gentle, while at other times they pound the shores with great destructive force. Waves acquire their energy and motion from the wind. The tops of the waves are the **crests**, which are separated by **troughs** (see Figure 5-23). The horizontal distance separating wave crests (or troughs) is the **wavelength**. The vertical distance between the trough and the crest is the **wave height**. The height of waves is the key factor in determining wave energy. The height, length and period (time between successive waves) that are achieved by a wave depend on three factors: (1) the wind speed; (2) the length of time the wind has blown; and (3) the **fetch**, or distance that the wind has travelled across the open water. As the amount of energy transferred from the wind to the water increases, the heights of the waves transmitting it increases. To find the speed of a wave, divide the wavelength by the period.

$$\text{Speed} = \frac{\text{wavelength}}{\text{period}}$$

---

### SAMPLE PROBLEM

**What is the speed of a wave 30 meters long with a period of 6 seconds?**

$$\text{Speed} = \frac{\text{wavelength}}{\text{period}}$$

$$\text{Speed} = \frac{30 \text{ meters}}{6 \text{ seconds}}$$

$$\text{Speed} = 5 \text{ meters/second}$$

---

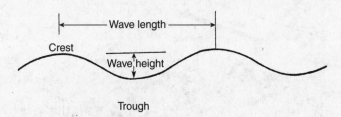

**Figure 5-23**. Wave height is the vertical distance between the wave crest and the wave trough. Wave length is the horizontal distance between two crests.

In the open sea, the motion of the wave is different from the motion of the water particles within it. It is only the wave that moves forward, not the water itself (see Figure 5-24). A particle of water moves in a nearly circular path as the wave passes. The particle returns to nearly its original position after the wave has passed. In deep water, when a wave moves across the water, energy moves with the wave, but the water does not move with the wave. When a wave approaches the shore, the wave begins to "feel" bottom and slows. When the depth to the bottom equals half the wavelength, the wave length begins to decrease. Because the height is increasing while the length is decreasing, the waves become steeper and steeper until they break. When the steep wave front is unable to support the wave, it collapses or *breaks*. The turbulent water caused by breaking waves is the **surf**. The motion of water up the beach is **swash** (see Figure 5-25). The water running back down the beach and under the next waves is the **backwash**. Strong narrow currents that flow straight out to sea through the surf zone are rip currents. Due to their high speed, **rip currents** are very dangerous to swimmers.

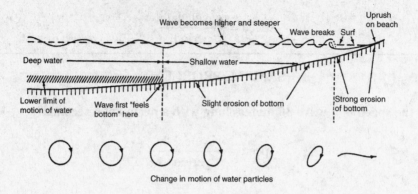

**Figure 5-24.** Waves change form as they travel from deep water through shallow water to shore.

Below the ocean surface, wave movement decreases until the motion is practically gone. This is why submarines can cruise in deep, calm water beneath surface ships that are being tossed about on the surface by large waves.

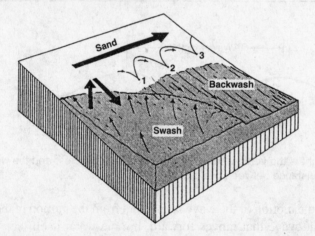

**Figure 5-25.** Beach drifting of sand, caused by angled approach of swash.

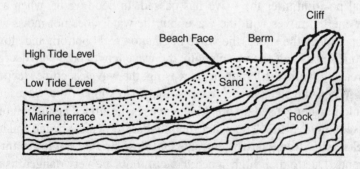

**Figure 5-26.** Parts of a beach

## Beaches

A **<u>beach</u>** is a strip of sediment (usually sand or gravel) that extends from the low-tide line to a cliff or zone of permanent vegetation (see Figure 5-26). The steepest part of the beach is the beach face. The **beach face** is the section the waves are constantly pounding. Offshore from the beach face, there is usually a **marine terrace**, a wide, gentle sloping platform that may be exposed at low tide if the shore has significant tidal activity. The wave-deposited upper part of the beach which is usually dry and covered by waves only during severe storms is the **berm**. The sediment of the beach face and berm is usually sand, with a high percentage of quartz grains.

The nature of the beach sediments depends upon the source material and the weathering processes. Some beach sand comes from the erosion of nearby rock. But, the greater part of the sand on most beaches comes from river sediment brought down to the ocean. Beaches may be made of almost any size and composition of Earth materials. In New York, some heavy minerals found on the beach are black magnetite and red garnet. They lag behind as lighter minerals are carried away by the waves. Beaches without a sand supply eventually disappear.

In seasonal areas, beaches are different in summer and winter (see Figure 5-27). In winter, the waves are higher and closer together than summer waves. In winter the short, high storm waves erode sand from the beach and berm. During summer, long, low waves wash sand from deeper water onto the beach and build up the berm. Offshore, in less turbulent water, the sediment settles to the bottom, building an underwater sandbar (usually parallel to the beach). Each season, the beach changes in shape until it comes into equilibrium with the wave type at that time.

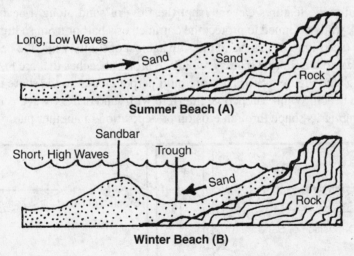

**Figure 5-27.** Seasonal cycle of a beach caused by differing wave types. (A) Summer beach. (B) Winter beach. Waves may break once on the winter sandbar, then re-form and break again on the beach face.

# Longshore Drift

The movement of sediment parallel to the shore as waves strike the shoreline at an angle is **longshore drift** (see Figure 5-28). Longshore currents can be referred to as "rivers of sand" because they tend to move sand parallel to the shoreline within the zone of breaking waves. As waves wash onto the beach, they carry sediment in suspension. When the waves wash in at an angle, they carry sand at the same angle. When the waves reach as far as they can go, they return to the ocean, but no longer at an angle. The water flows straight back away from the shoreline. The net effect of this motion is to move the sand in a series of arcs along the beach face.

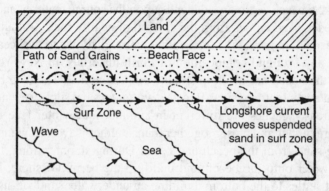

**Figure 5-28**. Longshore drift of sand on the beach by a longshore current within the surf zone.

Several man-made features can interrupt the flow of sand along a beach. **Jetties**, for example, are rock walls designed to protect the entrance of a harbor from sediment deposition and storm waves (see Figure 5-29). Sand piles up against one jetty while the beach beside the other erodes back into the shore. **Groins** are built to protect beaches that are losing sand from longshore drifting (see Figure 5-30). They are built perpendicular to the shore to trap moving sand and widen a beach. Whenever people interfere with sand drift or wave action, the beach responds by changing its shape through erosion or deposition in another part of the beach.

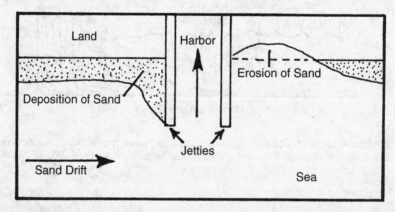

**Figure 5-29**. Jetties. Sand piles up against one jetty, while the other side, deprived of sand, erodes.

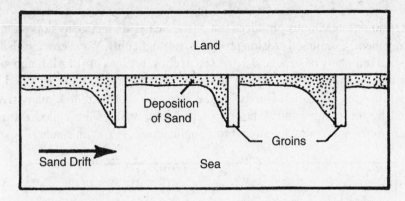

**Figure 5-30**. Groins. The walls trap the sand to prevent beach erosion.

## Coast and Coastal Features

A beach is a small part of the **coast**, which is all the land near the sea, including the beach and a strip of land inland from it. Many coasts have been drowned by glacial meltwater, while others have been raised by tectonic forces. Drowning of the land produces very irregular shorelines. The main valleys become short, deep, narrow bays. The points of land between the valleys became **headlands**. The hills near the water became islands. The east coast of the United States is considered to be an example of a drowned coastline. The west coast is an example of a coastline that has been raised by tectonic forces. These shorelines are, for the most part formed on the boundary between two plates, with long lines of mountains running parallel to the coast.

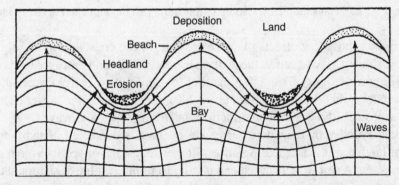

**Figure 5-31**. Wave refraction on an irregular coast. Shallow water slows waves off headlands while the same waves move faster through the deep bays. Arrows show energy concentrated on headlands, spread out in bays.

An irregular coast with bays separated by headlands can be gradually straightened by wave action (see Figure 5-31). Shallow water slows waves off the headlands, while those same waves move faster through the deep bays. This bending of the wave is called **wave refraction**. Eventually, the irregular coastline will be straightened through wave erosion of the headlands and wave deposition in the bays.

Wave erosion of headlands produces sea cliffs. **Sea cliffs** are steep slopes that erode as waves undercut them. Continued erosion produces a straight cliff. Wave erosion also produces **stacks**, erosional remnants of headlands, and **sea arches**, bridges of rock left above openings like caves, sometimes joining two stacks. Glaciers carved long, deep, steep sided bays that, when filled with water, are called **fjords**. As the great ice sheets melted, many river valleys were drowned by the rising water. These drowned river valleys are called **estuaries**. The Hudson River from New York City almost to Poughkeepsie, NY is an estuary.

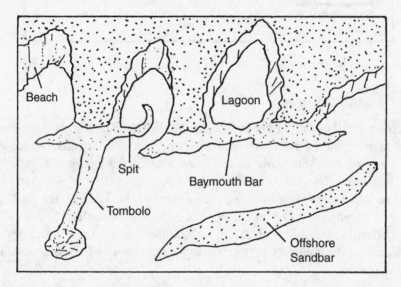

**Figure 5-32**. Coastal shapes. Longshore drift of sand can be deposited in several forms.

Some coasts show few effects of wave erosion. These coasts are primarily shaped by sediment deposition. Coasts such as these often have sandbars and barrier islands (see Figure 5-32). **Sandbars** are ridges of sand that parallel the shoreline, usually underwater. **Barrier islands** are sandbars that reach above sea level. A lagoon separates the barrier island from the mainland and protects the water behind them from strong winds and waves.

Sand that is eroded by longshore currents is eventually deposited. If sediment builds up off a point of land, a spit is formed. A **spit** is a finger-like ridge of sediment that extends out into the open water. A spit with a curved end is called a **hook**. A ridge of sediment that cuts off an earlier open bay from the ocean is a **baymouth bar**. A bar of sediment connecting a former island to the mainland is a **tombolo**.

# QUESTIONS

1. Which graph best shows the relationship between windspeed and the average height of ocean waves formed by the wind?

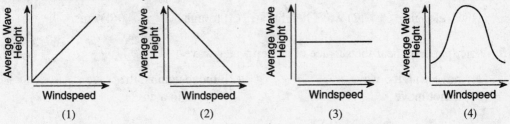

(1)　　　　　　　(2)　　　　　　　(3)　　　　　　　(4)

2. The map below shows Rockaway Peninsula, part of Long Island's south shore, and the location of several stone barriers, A, B, C, and D, that were built to trap sand being transported along the coast by wave action.

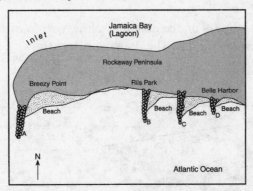

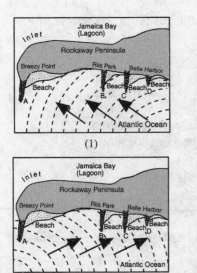

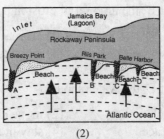

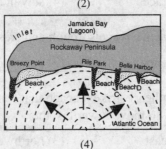

On which map do the arrows best show the direction of wave movement that created the beaches in this area?

3. The wavelength of a wave is the

    (1) highest point on the wave        (2) lowest point on the wave
    (3) distance from crest to trough    (4) distance from crest to crest

4. The lowest point of a wave is called the

    (1) wavelength       (2) wave height      (3) trough        (4) crest

5. Water particles near the surface of a deep water-wave

    (1)  move with the wave          (2)  move against the wave
    (3)  do not move               (4)  move in a circle

6. Currents very dangerous to swimmers because they produce a strong undertow are

    (1) swash currents             (2) rip currents
    (3) backwash currents         (4) longshore currents

Base your answers to questions 7-9 on the drawing below, your knowledge of Earth Science and the *Earth Science Reference Tables*. The drawing below shows a series of ocean waves moving onto a beach.

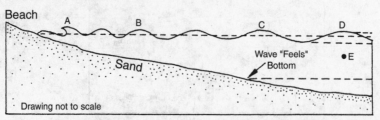

7. As each wave passes point B, the amount of erosion that takes place on the beach

    (1) increases               (2) decreases
    (3) increases, then decreases     (4) remains the same

8. As each wave passes point E, the water should

    (1) move closer to the beach      (2) move closer to the bottom
    (3) move closer to the surface    (4) stay in the same location

9. The vertical distance between a wave's trough and crest is the

    (1) wavelength      (2) energy      (3) period      (4) wave height

10. When waves from the southeast strike a beach that runs east and west, the direction the longshore current is likely to move toward is  the

    (1) west        (2) east       (3) northwest    (4) southeast

# GLACIAL EROSION AND DEPOSITION

An abundance of landscape features provide evidence of the great ice sheets that covered New York State during the Pleistocene Epoch (the period 10,000 to 1.6 million years ago). Most of the landscape in New York State is directly related to the glaciers that covered the state to depths of 1-2 kilometers. A **glacier** is a large, long lasting mass of ice which forms on the land and moves downslope because of gravity. It forms due to the compaction and recrystallization of snow where more snow accumulates than melts away over a period of time.

Our lives and environment today have been strongly influenced by glaciers. The Finger Lakes, Lake Ontario, the Hudson Valley, and Long Island all owe their existence to the scouring, gouging and deposition of glacial ice. Nationally, the fertile soils of the Great Plains and the spectacular scenic beauty of some of our national parks such as Yosemite Valley in California are all due to the activities of glaciers.

The processes of **glacial erosion** include the formation of U-shaped valleys, parallel scratches, and grooves in bedrock. Glacial features include *moraines*, *drumlins*, *kettle lakes*, *finger lakes*, and *outwash plains*.

# WHAT ARE GLACIERS?

Glaciers are found in the polar regions or in mountain areas at lower latitudes, where there is little melting of snow during the summer. At present, about 10% of Earth's surface is covered by glaciers (compared to about one/third during the peak of glacial activity). Today, 85% of all glaciers are in Antarctica and 10% in Greenland. If all the ice in Antarctica were to melt, sea level would rise about 60 meters (200 feet). This would flood the world's greatest cities.

**Types of Glaciers.** There are two types of glaciers that have covered Earth's surface. A **valley glacier** (or **Alpine glacier**) is a glacier that is confined to a valley and flows from higher to lower elevations. Most present day glaciers in the United States and Canada are of the valley type. A thick mass of ice that covers a large area of land (over 50,000 square kilometers) is an ice sheet. Only two ice sheets exist today–in Antarctica and Greenland. The glacier that covered Eastern North America during the Ice Ages was called the **Laurentide Ice Sheet** (see Figure 5-33).

Snow changes to glacier ice in a manner similar to the way sediments turn into sedimentary rocks and then metamorphic rocks.

**Figure 5-33**. Pleistocene ice sheets of North America at their maximum spread reached as far south as the present Ohio and Missouri rivers.

After enough snow falls, the snowflakes settle by compaction under their own weight. The sharp points of the snowflakes are destroyed as the flakes reform into granular snow (the "corn snow" of spring skiing) called **firn** or **neve** (see Figure 5-34). As more snow covers the firn and the pressure increases, the grains recrystallize, developing a texture similar to that of quartzite, a metamorphic rock. The force of gravity causes glaciers to flow slowly downhill and outward. If a glacier reaches a body of water, blocks of ice called **icebergs** may break off and float free.

The **Zone of Accumulation** is the upper part of a glacier where more snow falls than melts. In the lower part of the glacier, more snow melts than falls (see Figure 5-35). The boundary between these two zones is the **snow line**, the lower limit the permanent snows reach in summer. During summer, the ice melts below the snow line, producing large amounts of **meltwater**, water from the melting snow.

**Glacial Movement.** Glaciers *advance*, move downslope, under the influence of gravity and their own weight (see Figure 5-36). They move from less than a few millimeters a day to more than 15 meters a day. Glaciers move at different rates depending on the steepness of the underlying material. Glaciers move more rapidly at the surface than at the deeper levels, and faster in the center than at the sides where there is less friction with the valley walls. The surface part of a glacier is brittle and nearly rigid. When the ice breaks while moving, it forms fissures or cracks called **crevasses**, across the width of the glacier. The deeper part of a glacier is more plastic due to the bendable nature of the ice itself.

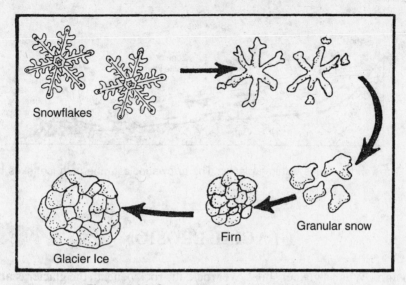

**Figure 5-34**. Conversion of snow to glacier ice.

When ice in a glacier melts back faster than the ice sheet moves downslope, the glacier *recedes*, or moves backward. Glaciers only appear to move backward, however. They are constantly moving downslope due to the pull of gravity, but the rapidly melting ice causes the leading edge of the glacier to appear to move backward, however. They are constantly moving downslope due to the pull of gravity, but the rapidly melting ice causes the leading edge of the glacier to appear to move backward.

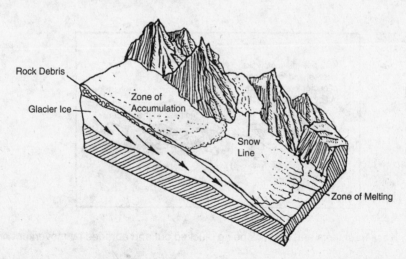

**Figure 5-35**. A valley glacier as it would appear at the end of a warm season. Below the snow line, glacier ice and snow have been lost due to melting. In the zone of accumulation above that line firn is added to the glacier from the winter snowfall.

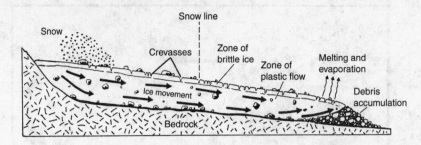

**Figure 5-36**. The various zones within a glacier. The arrows indicate the path ice takes through the glacier.

# GLACIAL EROSION

**Glacial Erosion.** When a glacier slides over rock, the rock beneath the glacier is **abraded**, or scratched. As meltwater fills in cracks in the bedrock and refreezes, pieces of rock are broken loose and frozen into the base of the moving glacier. These rocks, while being dragged along by the glacier, grind the rock beneath it (see Figure 5-37). The thicker the glacier, the greater the pressure on the rocks resulting in increased grinding and crushing of the rocks.

Sharp corners of rocks dragged along make long scratches (**striations**) and grooves on the bedrock. Pebbles and boulders dragged along by the glacier are **faceted**, given a flat surface by abrasion. The bedrock as well as the rocks being carried by the ice are polished by the grinding. The grinding of rock across rock produces powder called **rock flour.**

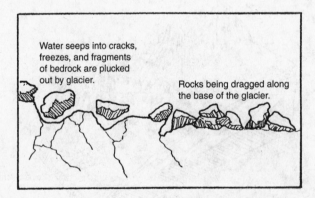

**Figure 5-37**. Rock fragments and bedrock being plucked out and abraded by movement of a glacier.

**Erosional Landscapes**. Mountain ranges that have been covered by valley glaciers are noted for their rugged landscape and spectacular scenery. Glacially carved valleys are *U-shaped* (see Figure 5-38). Valley glaciers tend to straighten the curves of valleys originally formed by streams. Erosional landscape features of glaciers are cirques, horns and aretes. A **cirque** is a bowl-shaped erosional scar on the side of a mountain formed by frost action and headword erosion of the glacier. The same processes that enlarge a cirque also create sharp peaks and ridges. A **horn** is the sharp peak that remains after cirques have cut back into a mountain on three or more sides. When two cirques "eat" into a ridge from both sides, a jagged, knife-edge ridge called an **aretes** is formed. Glaciers carve river valleys deeper than their smaller tributary valleys. After the glaciers melt, the tributaries remain as **hanging valleys** high above the main valley. Yosemite Valley in California has several hanging valleys which result in spectacular waterfalls. Glacial erosion of New York State's highest mountains show that the ice was close to two kilometers thick.

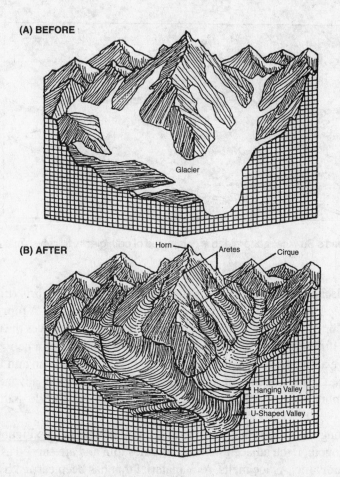

**Figure 5-38.** Erosional landscapes. (A) Glaciers cover the area. (B) When the glaciers melt, erosional landscapes are visible.

# GLACIAL DEPOSITION

**Glacial Sediment**. Most glaciers push, carry and drag great quantities of sediment called glacial sediment. Sediment carried by glaciers or the meltwater of glaciers is called **drift**. Most of the rock fragments carried by glaciers are angular, unsorted (all mixed together) and unlayered. Unsorted rock material deposited directly by glaciers is **till**. Glaciers carry rocks of mixed sizes, from clay to huge boulders. A large rock deposited by a glacier that is different from the type of rock beneath it is called an **erratic**. The great size of some erratics shows the tremendous power of a glacier. The rock type of some erratics is so distinct that their origins can easily be identified. The general direction of ice flow can be determined by tracing the bedrock exposure of the erratic to the north. Rock material deposited by the meltwater of a glacier is **outwash**. Long Island is composed of both till and outwash. The northern part of Long Island is essentially formed of till, while the southern part is primarily formed of outwash (see Figure 5-39).

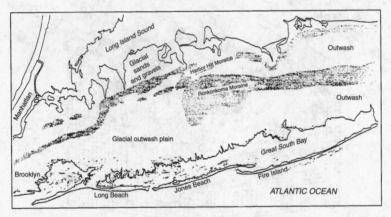

**Figure 5-39**. Long Island's Surface. Long Island is composed of both glacial till, which makes up moraines, and glacial outwash.

**Depositional Landscape Features.** When a glacier melts, the rock debris (till) it carried is deposited in the same location as it was in the glacier (see Figure 5-40). A **moraine** is a mass of glacial till left behind after a glacier has melted. A flowing glacier moves the till to the front edge of the glacier. If the front end of the glacier remains stationary for a period of years, the till piles up in a ridge along the front edge of the ice. This ridge of till is an **end moraine**. Two kinds of end moraines exist; a **terminal moraine** indicating the farthest advance of a glacier, and a **recessional moraine**, build up when the glacier recedes for awhile and then becomes stationary.

Piles of till along the sides of a glacier form **lateral moraines** (see Figure 5-41). When two glaciers come together, the adjacent lateral moraines join and are carried as a single ridge of till in a **medial moraine**. As ice melts, rock material that has been carried by the glacier is deposited on the ground to form a **ground moraine**, a fairly thin layer of till. In some areas, ground moraine has been reshaped into streamlined hills of till called drumlins. A **drumlin** is shaped like an inverted bowl of a spoon, with the long axis parallel to the direction of ice movement (see Figure 5-42). Drumlins were probably formed from a glacier passing over an older ground moraine.

Glacial outwash is carried by meltwater and dropped in **stratified** (layered), fairly well-sorted deposits. Bodies of stratified outwash are classified according to their shape (see Figure 5-40). A body of out wash that forms a broad plain beyond the moraine is an **outwash plain**. Short, steep sided hills of outwash that originated as meltwater stream or lake deposit are **kames**. When an ice block forms and then melts, it leaves a steep sided hole behind called a **kettle**. Many kettle holes are filled by small lakes. Kettles and kames are often found near each other. Meltwater rivers in glaciers often follow sinuous paths. When the glacier melts, the sinuous deposits from the rivers form an **esker**. In dry seasons, winds pick up the rock flour from these deposits and carry them long distances. These fine grained, wind-blown deposits of dust are called **loess**.

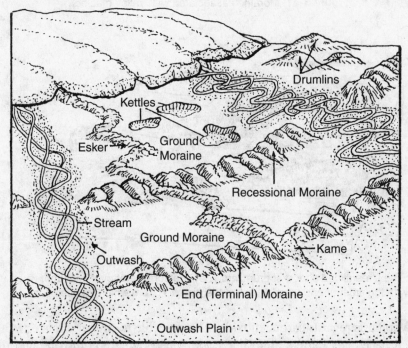

**Figure 5-40.** Depositional features in front of a receding ice sheet.

**Causes of the Glacial Ages**. The question "What caused the Ice Ages?" has been asked by scientists since the theory of glaciers originated. A number of hypotheses have been proposed to explain the Ice Ages, but none alone satisfactorily accounts for all of the data. The most accepted theory today says that the variations in our planetary orbit and the "wobble" of Earth's axis cause cycles of cooling and warming that are largely responsible for the global changes necessary to produce glaciers. This theory, known as the *Milankovitch Theory*, has wide acceptance today, but it fails to explain the absence of glaciation over most of geologic time.

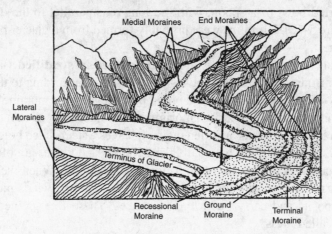

**Figure 5-41**. Moraines associated with valley glaciers.

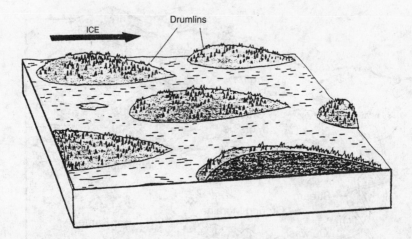

**Figure 5-42**. The streamlined shape of drumlins. They are somewhat oval in shape, when viewed from above, with the steeper end usually toward the direction from which the ice came.

One hypothesis regards carbon dioxide as responsible for major climate changes. Solar energy which penetrates Earth's atmosphere is trapped by carbon dioxide and the climate warms, accounting for the warm episodes between glaciers. Later, for some reason, the carbon dioxide content decreases, resulting in colder glacial periods. Another theory has to do with the positions of the continents during continental drift. Others believe that the circulation of sea water is a major contributor to glacial periods. Scientists do not completely understand what causes glacial periods and interim warm episodes, but the Milankovitch Theory is the most accepted for the moment because it seems to explain best what controls climate cycles.

**Present Glaciers and the Past.** Modern glaciers preserve samples of the atmosphere and dust from the time the ice formed. These samples include air, pollen, dust and meteorites. By studying these samples, it is hoped prehistoric conditions on our planet can be investigated.

# QUESTIONS

Base your answers to questions 1 through 5 on your knowledge of Earth Science, the *Earth Science Reference Tables*, and the diagram below. The diagram represent two branches of a valley glacier. Points A, B, G, and H are located on the surface of the glacier. Point X is located at the interface between the ice and the bedrock. The arrows indicate the general direction of ice movement.

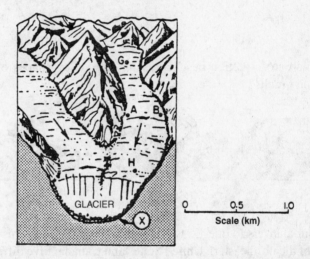

1. Which type of weathering most likely is dominant in the area represented by the diagram?

   (1) biologic activity    (2) frost action         (3) acid reactions       (4) chemical reactions

2. Which force is primarily responsible for the movement of the glacier?

   (1) ground water        (2) running water    (3) gravity              (4) wind

3. The sediment deposited by the valley glacier at position X is best described as

   (1) sorted according to particle size
   (2) sorted according to particle shape
   (3) sorted according to particle texture
   (4) unsorted

4. Metal stakes were placed on the surface of the glacier in a straight line from position A to position B. Which diagram best shows the position of the metal stakes several years later?

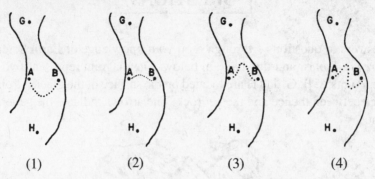

(1)  (2)  (3)  (4)

5. Which cross section best represents the valley shapes of this landscape area after the glacier melts?

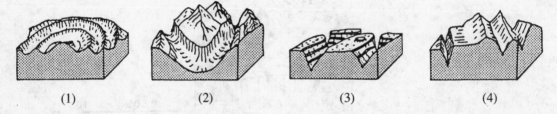

(1)  (2)  (3)  (4)

Base your answers to questions 6 through 10 on the diagrams below. Diagram I represents a section of the northeastern United States and Canada. Five different source regions, A through E, are shown along with the pattern of glacial deposits containing boulders which originated from each location. Diagram II represents the appearance of the surface of a typical boulder from any of the deposit locations.

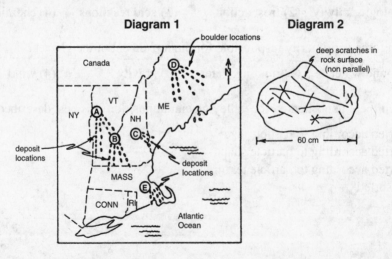

**6.** The force that caused the deposits to be distributed in the pattern shown in Diagram I most likely came from which general direction?

(1) northwest      (2) northeast      (3) southwest      (4) southeast

**7.** Which characteristic do all of the deposits most likely have in common?

(1) They have the same chemical composition.
(2) They were eroded from source region A.
(3) They are composed of unsorted sediments.
(4) They are found at the ends of large rivers.

**8.** According to the *Earth Science Reference Tables*, during which geological epoch were deposits most likely transported to the locations shown in Diagram I?

(1) Mesozoic      (2) Pleistocene      (3) Jurassic      (4) Paleocene

**9.** The scratches in the boulder shown in Diagram II were most likely caused by the

(1) internal arrangement of the minerals in the boulder
(2) splitting of a large boulder into two smaller boulders
(3) erosion of the boulder by running water
(4) movement of the boulder over bedrock

**10.** About how many times larger is the actual boulder than the model shown in Diagram II?

(1) 5 times      (2) 14 times      (3) 20 times      (4) 60 times

# THE GLACIAL HISTORY OF NEW YORK STATE

Since most of the till in New York State is fresh and little weathered, it was realized that the glacial invasion was recent in terms of the rate of weathering. But geologist began to find evidence of fresh till overlying till that was not so fresh, and whose upper part showed evidence of chemical weathering (see Figure 5-43). Superimposed layers of weathered till show that there have been several major periods of glaciation in the recent geological past. This indicates that New York State was repeatedly covered by thick ice in the Pleistocene Epoch, which began 1.6 million years ago. Of further significance is that Earth has undergone periods of climate changes during this epoch. The climatic changes necessary for a glacial age to occur are not as great as some might imagine. During the height of a glacial age, the worldwide annual average temperature was probably only 5°C cooler than at present. And during the interglacial periods the worldwide annual average temperatures were probably a bit warmer than present day temperatures.

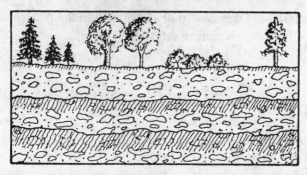

**Figure 5-43.** Evidence of repeated glaciation. A layer of "fresh" till, weathered only slightly at its surface, overlying an older till that had apparently been deeply weathered before the overlying till was deposited.

**Ice Over New York State.** The ice sheet that advanced over New York State was the *Laurentide Ice Sheet*. It started in the Laurentide Mountains of Quebec and covered almost all of New York State. The water that produced this ice came from the oceans, lowering sea level by at least 100 meters. The remnants of old stream channels which are a continuation of present rivers can be found on the submerged continental shelf. The rivers could not have eroded the continental shelf unless it was above sea level. The Hudson Canyon is an example of a submerged river canyon on the shelf. It is believed that the Hudson Canyon was formed during the Ice Ages, when the sea level was lower, and the meltwater from the great ice sheet poured down the Hudson channel. The Hudson River south of Troy is a fresh-water estuary (a drowned river valley); variously, it is a salt water estuary south of Poughkeepsie and a fjord through the Hudson Highlands. During the Pleistocene Epoch, the Laurentide Ice Sheet made four advances, although most traces of earlier glaciers were removed during the Wisconsin advance.

The last glacial advance, the *Wisconsin Stage*, reached its maximum in New York State about 22,000 years ago. This glacier produced spectacular erosional features, and deposited the rock debris carried southward by the glacier in a variety of landforms. The Wisconsin ice sheet retreated from New York about 10,000 years ago. As it melted, it released huge volumes of meltwater, producing large lakes, some of which later became the Great Lakes and the Finger Lakes. Glaciers change the landscape quickly compared to other geographic processes.

Nearly all of New York State displays evidence of glaciation. Soils covering most of New York State are composed of weathered till. Practically every landscape feature discussed earlier, both erosional and depositional, appear in New York State. The only areas of New York State that may not have been covered by glaciers are the Allegheny region and the southern part Long Island which is formed of glacial outwash. The remainder of New York State was covered by glaciers as evidenced in most cases by a veneer of till.

**Pleistocene Life**. The Ice Ages resulted in major ecological changes and very different plant and animal communities. During the Ice Ages, the natural environment of New York State might have looked more like the tundra of northern Canada, Alaska and Siberia. Fossil and geologic evidence indicates periodic changes in sea level that coincide with the advancing and retreating ice sheets. <u>Terrestrial</u> (land) fossils of the Pleistocene Epoch have been found on the continental shelf off the coast of Long Island.

South of the ice front, life was plentiful. A huge variety of plants and animals lived there, including evergreen trees that could withstand the cold. Many Pleistocene plants continue to exist, but many Pleistocene mammals are now extinct. Bones and teeth from now extinct elephant-like animals, wooly mammoths and mastodonts (formerly called mastodons) have been discovered on the continental shelf, indicating that these animals roamed over what must have been dry land. Mastodonts stood about 3 meters (9 feet) tall. Their bones and teeth have been found in peat bogs throughout New York State. Bones and remains of other extinct animals have also been found throughout New York State. Animals that roamed the state during Pleistocene were giant beaver and wild turkeys, ground sloths, musk oxen, and wolves, caribou and bison. The city of Buffalo was named after a fossil bison, probably the only city in the world named after a fossil mammal. Evidence indicates that human hunters hastened the extinction of several of these late Pleistocene animals.

**Impact of Global Warming Today. Global warming** or cooling is critical to our sea level. Increasing the global annual average temperature will cause the glaciers to melt and the sea level to rise, while decreasing the annual average temperature will cause the glaciers to grow in size and the sea level to subside. There is concern today that we are in a period of global warming due to increased amounts of carbon dioxide in the atmosphere. Increased amounts of carbon dioxide in the air increases the amount of infrared (heat) energy held in the atmosphere, raising global temperatures. Increased temperatures will melt some of the ice, causing the sea level to rise.

## QUESTIONS

1. What evidence exists to show that there were several periods of glaciation in New York State?

    (1) outwash plains on Long Island
    (2) superimposed layers of weathered till
    (3) Hudson River estuary at Poughkeepsie
    (4) kettles and kames along river banks

2. Which parts of New York State were most probably never covered by glaciers?

    (1) Catskill and Adirondack Mountains
    (2) Allegheny region and Southern Long Island
    (3) Hudson River Valley and New York City
    (4) Rochester to Syracuse region

**3.** What evidence of life during the Pleistocene Epoch is found in New York State?

(1) remains of dinosaurs
(2) human hunters
(3) bones and teeth of mastodonts
(4) early fish and reptiles

**4.** Which is the best evidence that more than one glacial advance occurred in a region?

(1) ancient forests covered by glacial deposits
(2) river valleys buried deeply in glacial deposits
(3) scratches in bedrock that is buried by glacial deposits
(4) glacial deposits that overlay soils formed from glacial deposits

**5.** Which process has most recently been the major influence on the total landscape of New York State?

(1) volcanism        (2) glaciation        (3) folding        (4) faulting

# GLACIERS, LANDSCAPE, AND THE ECONOMY
# OF NEW YORK STATE

Almost all of the glacial deposits in New York State were made during the advance of the Wisconsin Ice Sheet. The kind of bedrock and the shape of the landscape in a region strongly influenced the formation of glacial features. Many types of glacial features (erosional and depositional) occur in New York State.

**Glacial Erosion. Glacial erosion** has produced features throughout New York State such as north-south valleys and thin rocky soils. Glaciers over New York State eroded millions of cubic kilometers of bedrock, loose debris and soil. These chunks of debris were carried along, embedded in the ice, causing the glacier to slide along like a giant piece of coarse sandpaper. V-shaped river valleys were gouged out into deep, U-shaped troughs. New York's Finger Lakes lie in former river valleys carved into U-shaped troughs. Tributary streams formed in hanging valleys produced spectacular waterfalls. After a period of time, water slowly wore the rock away causing the waterfalls to move, up the tributary valleys, farther from the main valley. Waterfalls that have moved upstream are Taughannock Falls and several near Ithaca and Watkins Glen. As the continental glaciers retreated, the meltwater from smaller mountain glaciers carved river valleys into U-shaped valleys.

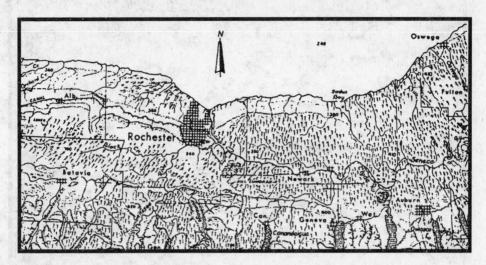

**Figure 5-44**. Drumlin Fields. The structures that look something like a question mark are drumlins. This map shows large drumlin fields that extend almost the entire width of the lake Ontario lowlands.

At the heads of the valleys, glaciers created large bowl-shaped cirques. Whiteface Mountain in the Adirondacks has several cirques around its peak. The existence of polish, striations and grooves near the summits of the Catskills and the Adirondacks help geologists to estimate the thickness of the glaciers.

**Glacial Deposition**. The dropping of rock debris carried by glaciers had a major effect on the landscape of New York State. With these deposits, the glacier dammed rivers and changed their courses. It left large amounts of sand and gravel on the top of the bedrock. Some buried preglacial stream valley are filled with over 300 meters of glacial debris. West of Glens Falls, the Hudson River meanders across a buried preglacial river that once drained the Lake George valley.

The lowland between Rochester and Syracuse has over 10,000 drumlins. It is one of the greatest drumlin fields in the world (see Figure 5-44). They formed when moving ice carved out of the till from a previous glacier.

The surface of New York State is marked by many kames, kettles, and eskers. There are many moraines in New York State (see Figure 5-45). Among the most well-known are the Harbor Hills and Ronkonkoma terminal moraines which make up the North and South Forks of Long Island (see Figure 5-39). South of each moraine are the outwash deposits carried by meltwater streams.

**The Retreat**. After Long Island was formed, the climate began to warm. The ice sheet retreated to the north and about 10,000 years ago it completely left New York. The melting ice sheets released huge volumes of water which flooded lowlands, making large lakes, called glacial lakes (see Figure 5-46) in front of the glacier. Lakes like Glacial Lake Albany, which filled the Hudson River valley, lasted up to 5,000 years. The clay deposits that formed in Glacial Lake Albany have been used to make bricks.

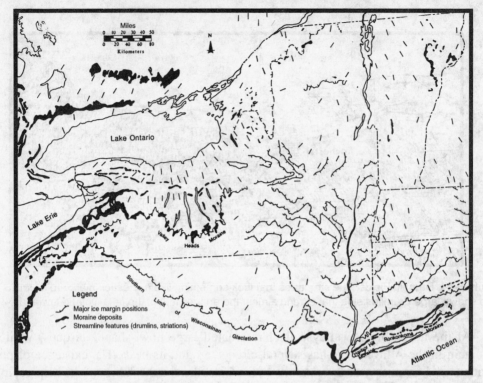

**Figrure 5-45**.  Moraines of New York State.  It also includes features like drumlins and striations that indicate the direction of glacial flow.  It was by looking at such evidence that scientist reconstructed the history of the Pleistocene Epoch in New York.  The map also indicates position of the edge of the ice sheet at various times.

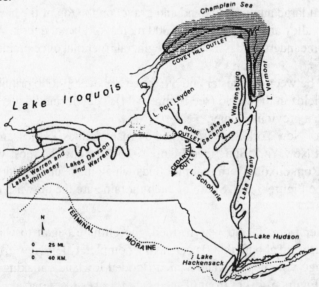

**Figure 5-46**. These glacial lakes of the Pleistocene formed from meltwater as the ice sheet retreated. The outlets show the directions in which these lakes eventually drained. The Champlain Sea in the north shows the area that was flooded by ocean water as the glaciers melted.

As the ancestral Mohawk River entered Glacial Lake Albany, it built a huge delta where the city of Schenectady now sits. As the lake drained, new deltas were built at lower levels. After the lake drained completely, the wind built a dune field on the former lake floor between Schenectady and Albany and north to Glens Falls called Pine Bush. The dunes were formed of the drifting sands from the deltas and the lake floor and have been held in place for thousands of years by a pine-barren vegetation.

The Valley Heads moraine across central New York State closed the southern ends of several formerly south-flowing river valleys producing the Finger Lakes. The moraine became a drainage barrier with streams and rivers on opposite sides of the moraine tending to flow in opposite directions.

The largest of the glacial lakes were the ancestors of the Great Lakes. Lake Ontario is what remains of Glacial Lake Iroquois. The tremendous outflow from Lake Iroquois scoured deep circular pits called potholes in the Mohawk Valley east of Syracuse. These potholes are big enough that one may climb into them.

Because water travel was critical to human life before highways and railroads were built, the drainage systems produced by the meltwater from the glacier played an important role in human history. These waterways were important during the Revolutionary War and later in the industrial development of the state. They were the source of power for mills and the most efficient way to move goods throughout the state.

When the thick glacial ice caused the crust to sag and melting ice raised the sea level, ocean water flooded into the northern Champlain and St. Lawrence valleys creating the ancient Champlain Sea. Evidence of this ocean incursion are the shells of marine clams and the bones of whales and seals found in the glacial sands and gravels of these valleys. The sea's visit was short lived. After the ice melted, the land began to rebound, raising the area above sea level and forcing the sea to withdraw. In northern New York, the crust rebounded as much as 150 meters.

**Sand and Gravel**. New York's commercial sand and gravel deposits come from glaciers. Sand and gravel washed out of the glaciers shows sorting and layering, making it immediately distinguishable from deposits left directly by the ice. Our most important resource in New York State, sand and gravel are used to make concrete for buildings and highway construction. The leading producers of sand and gravel are Suffolk, Dutchess and Rensselaer Counties.

# QUESTIONS

1. Which geologic evidence best supports the inference that a continental ice sheet once covered most of New York State?

   (1) scratched and polished bedrock
   (2) polished and smooth pebbles;  meandering rivers;  V-shaped valleys
   (3) sand and silt beaches;  giant swamps;  marine fossils found on  mountain tops
   (4) basaltic bedrock;  folded, faulted, and tilted rock structures;  lava flows

2. Which map best represents the inferred position of the ice sheet at the time of glacial deposition on Long Island? [The shaded portion represents the areas covered by glacial ice.]

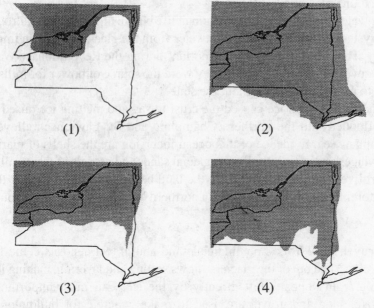

3. End moraines on Long Island tend to be

   (1) deposited in glacial lakes
   (3) outwash plains

   (2) composed of sediments
   (4) composed of unsorted ~~elements~~ *Sediments*

**4.** In the diagram below, the feature at A would most likely be found

    (1) on Long Island              (2) in the Adirondack Mountains
    (3) in the Catskill Mountains      (4) in New York City

**5.** In the region of the Catskills, which glacial feature is most likely to be found?
    (1) V-shaped valleys            (2) limestone caves
    (3) scratched bedrock surfaces     (4) drumlins

**6.** In the Rochester area, the glacial feature that occurs in groups of long, smooth, spoon-shaped hills are
    (1) kettles         (2) kames         (3) eskers         (4) drumlins

**7.** A hilly region of Long Island is composed of unconsolidated and unsorted sediments. Which erosional agent was probably most influential in forming this landscape?
    (1) wave action      (2) glaciers       (3) streams        (4) wind

**8.** What was one of the major effects of the continental glaciers on the landscapes of New York State?
    (1) They formed numerous sharp mountain peaks and knife-edged ridges.
    (2) They folded many of the rock layers.
    (3) They deposited a covering of transported rock material over most of the state.
    (4) They carved the wide U-shaped valleys into narrow V-shaped valleys.

**9.** In New York State, which of the following is least likely to be found in the same area as a terminal moraine?
    (1) tills         (2) erratics       (3) cirques       (4) outwash plains

**10.** Over the past 2 million years, which erosional agent has been most responsible for producing the present landscape surface features of New York State?
    (1) ground water     (2) wind       (3) glaciation      (4) human activities

# WIND ACTION

Wind action can be an important agent of erosion and deposition in any climate, as long as sediment particles are loose and dry. Erosion of sediments by wind is most common in arid climates and along shorelines. Wind-generated features include dunes and sand-blasted rocks. New York has many locations where features shaped by winds can be found. In general, the faster wind blows, the more sediment it can move. Because sand grains are heavier than silt and clay, sand moves close to the ground in a rolling or jumping fashion.

## EROSIONAL FEATURES

Sand grains rarely rise more than 3 feet above the ground surface, even in the strongest winds. Sand being carried at high speeds may sandblast smooth surfaces on hard rock and scour the windshields and paint of automobiles. Wind-blown sand may sculpture isolated pebbles, cobbles, or boulders into **ventifacts**: rocks with flat, wind-abraded surfaces (see Figure 5-47) which may have greasy or polished surfaces.

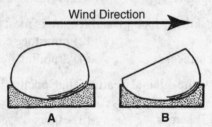

**Figure 5-47**. Ventifacts

The removal of clay, silt, and sand particles from the ground surface by wind is called **deflation**. Deflation is found where there are ample supplies of material capable of being picked up by the wind and where vegetation is scarce.

The erosion of small and fine sediments by the wind can substantially erode the land surface. A depression of the ground surface caused by wind erosion is called a **blowout** (see Figure 5-48). Blowouts occur over the central United States during dry periods.

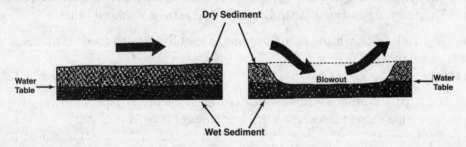

**Figure 5-48**. Deflation by wind erosion can form a blowout in loose dry sediment. Deflation cannot continue below the water table.

# SAND DUNES

A **dune** is a mound or ridge of sand deposited by the wind. As wind speed increases, its carrying power increases. Faster winds carry more sediment. As the wind rises up the long side of the dune, the wind's speed increases. However, when the wind moves over the top of the dune and spreads out, its wind speed, and therefore, its carrying power decreases. The decreased wind speed quickly deposits its sand load on the steep slope (or **slip face**) of the dune (see Figure 5-49).

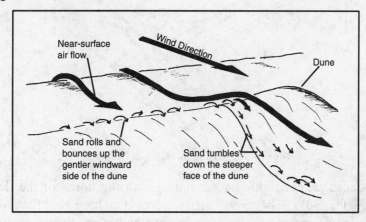

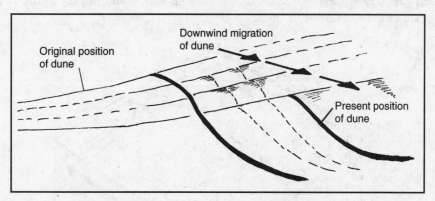

**Figure 5-49**. Slip Face of Dune

As sand is blown from the wind face side of a dune to the slip face side, it migrates downwind. The speed at which the dune migrates depends on the wind's speed and the smoothness of the surface over which it is migrating.

There are places in New York State where migrating sand dunes encroach on forests, completely covering them. This happens on Long Island, where U-shaped **coastal blowout dunes** (sometimes called simply **Parabolic Dunes**) occur (see Figure 5-50). The depth of erosion on coastal blowout dunes is controlled by the water table.

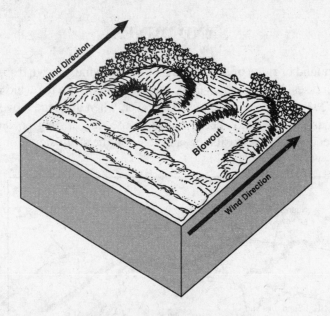

**Figure 5-50**.  Coastal Blowout Dunes

**Barchan** dunes are crescent-shaped dunes, with the horns of the dune pointing downwind (see Figure 5-51).  They form chiefly in areas that have hard flat ground surfaces and limited supplies of sand.  Barchan dunes become higher and thicker in the center with steep slip faces on the inside of the dune.

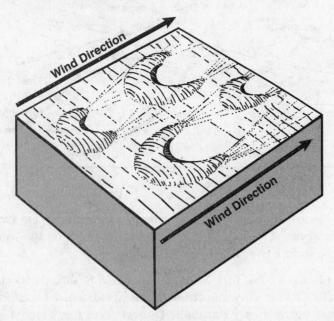

**Figure 5-51**.  Barchan Sand Dunes.  Note the steepness of the slipfaces.

The dropping of sand grains on the slip face of a dune produces layers much like those in a river delta (see Figure 5-52). Because of varying wind speeds and direction, there is no uniform arrangement of the layers. Zion National Park in Utah is noted for its ancient wind-deposited sand dune layers.

**Figure 5-52**. Cross section of a sand dune showing sets of cross-beds.

Wind-deposited silt, usually accompanied by some clay and fine sand, resembling fine-grained lake mud found in glacial and desert environments, is called **loess**. Loess is always deposited downwind of a plentiful supply of silt. Most loess grains are quartz, feldspar, mica, or calcite. The fine texture of loess promotes high moisture holding capacity and high agricultural potential.

In areas where wind-blown sand is a major concern, good practice includes the planting of windshields consisting of grasses, bushes, and hardy trees set in strips at right angles to the strongest winds. These windhields retard wind speed enough to prevent serious deflation to the land.

## QUESTIONS

**1.** Winds transport sand and other materials by

   (1) water and rolling            (2) suspension and bouncing
   (3) ice and snow                (4) ocean currents and waves

**2.** Where are winds most active as agents of erosion, transportation and deposition?

   (1) glaciers       (2) oceans       (3) deserts       (4) streams

**3.** Shallow depressions produced by deflation are called

   (1) barchans       (2) slip faces       (3) blowouts       (4) dunes

**4.** Of the material listed below, which is the most abrasive when blown across the ground surface?

   (1) quartz       (2) gypsum       (3) limestone       (4) shale

**5.** Which particle size is least likely to be found in a deposit of loess?

(1) pebbles    (2) sand    (3) silt    (4) clay

**6.** In what environments are you most likely to find wind erosion?

(1) humid areas    (2) beaches    (3) deserts    (4) forests

**7.** The diagrams below represent 4 steps in the development of a ventifact. What is the most likely sequence of ventifacts over a period of time?

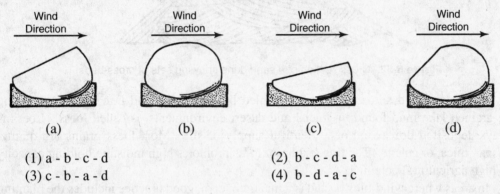

(a)            (b)            (c)            (d)

(1) a - b - c - d        (2) b - c - d - a
(3) c - b - a - d        (4) b - d - a - c

# MASS MOVEMENT

When Earth materials move downslope under the influence of gravity, the movement is called **mass movement** or **mass wasting**. It is common to apply the term "landslide" to most downslope movement of Earth material. It is possible to distinguish several types of movement based on the rate at which the movement takes place and the type of material involved.

An example of a slow type of movement is **creep**, sometimes called **soil creep**, which is the downhill movement of soil or weathered material which is so slow that it is difficult to measure over short periods such as a few days or even weeks (See Figure 5-53). Creep can be seen on the surface where fence posts have been tilted or slightly pushed over, or where trees show characteristic bends near their base. This bending is due to the soil creeping downhill, while the tree constantly adjusts to reach out for sunlight.

An example of slow to fast movement of Earth's surface is a mudflow. **Mudflows** are downhill movements of fine-grained surface material that has been saturated with water (See Figure 5-53). Most mudflows occur as runoff as heavy rains pick up the fine material and move it downslope.

Slumps are usually fast or sudden forms of mass movement. **Slumps** are downward slipping of rock material, usually with a backward rotation (See Figure 5-53). Slumps usually occur in fracture zones between rock layers or at the interface between soil and bedrock. Slumps can often be seen where highways have been constructed and the banks have been cut too steeply. They are particularly visible in New York State.

Rapid downhill movements, primarily of soil and weathered debris, are called **landslides** (See Figure 5-53). They move as a jumbled mass, destroying anything in their path, including houses, forests and roads. Earthquakes often produce landslides.

There are specific types of mass movement other than the four key types presented here, but the key idea to remember is that they all are moving due to the pull of gravity.

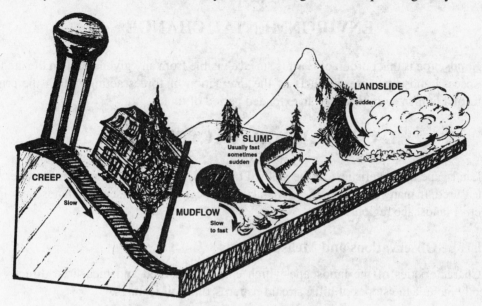

**Figure 5-53.** Examples of mass movement.

## QUESTIONS

**1.** Rock materials move downslope in response to the leveling tendency of

    (1) glaciation      (2) streams      (3) gravity      (4) waves

**2.** Fine material saturated with water which can move large blocks of rock is called a

    (1) landslide      (2) slump      (3) soil creep      (4) mudflow

**3.** What would be the impact of heavy periods of rain on loose rock material resting on the side of a hill?

    (1) increase the possibility of gravity pulls
    (2) decrease the possibility of waves
    (3) increase the possibility of slumping
    (4) decrease the possibility of landslides

**4.** The sudden movement of loose large rock material down the side of a hill is

    (1) a landslide      (2) soil creep      (3) slumping      (4) a mudflow

# LANDSCAPE DEVELOPMENT
# AND
# ENVIRONMENTAL CHANGE

**Landscape** is that portion of Earth's surface visible from any given point on the land or from space. Landscapes are products of the interaction of forces acting within the crust, climate, and human activities over an extended period of time.

# LANDSCAPE CHARACTERISTICS

Landscape characteristics can be studied quantitatively. That is, they can be observed and measured. In many situations, these characteristics can be used to separate landscapes into distinctive landscape regions.

## Landscape Observations and Measurements .

Characteristics of the landscape which can be observed and measured directly or indirectly include the slopes of hills, stream patterns, and soil features.

**Hillslopes.** The angle of slope (gradient) and the shapes of hillslopes can be observed, measured, and identified. The shapes and gradients of hills can be measured directly or on topographic maps. Hill shapes can also be identified through the use of aerial photos.

**Stream Patterns**. Streams can be identified and grouped by patterns. The area drained by a stream, or system of streams, is called a drainage basin. Patterns formed by the streams in a **drainage basin** are called **stream drainage patterns**. Stream patterns are determined by the type and structure of rock over which the streams flow and by how long they have been flowing. These patterns are easily identified on topographic maps.

**Soil Associations**. Just as rocks with similar characteristics can be grouped together, soils with similar characteristics are grouped together in soil associations. **Soil associations** are grouped on the basis of composition, particle size and shape, organic content, porosity and permeability, and the maturity of the soil (the development of soil horizons). Similar soil associations may be found in different locations, just as different associations may be found adjacent to one another.

## Relationship of Characteristics

When landscape characteristics are related, the landscape can be subdivided into regions.

**Landscape Regions.** Landscapes with similar characteristics can be grouped into distinctive **landscape regions**. The major landscape regions of New York State are classified by elevation, type of bedrock, and stream drainage patterns. The major landscape groups are *mountains*, *plateaus*, and *plains*.

A large mass of land which rises to a great height above its surroundings is a **mountain**. The rocks beneath the surface of a mountain may be faulted, folded, tilted, or deformed. Mountains may have gentle or steep slopes, depending on the type and amount of erosion that has affected them.

**Plateaus.** **Plateaus** are large regions having horizontal rock structures at high elevations above sea level. Plateaus are often heavily dissected by streams, so that they have steep valley slopes and thus, appear to be mountains. For example, the Catskill Mountains are actually a dissected plateau.

An extensive region of low elevation where the land is level or gently rolling is called a **plain**. The rock layers of the plains are generally horizontal.

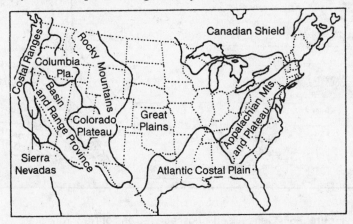

**Figure 5-54.** The physiographic provinces of the United States.

In smaller regions, there may be only one identifiable mountain or valley. Often the patterns showing a certain type of stream drainage are used to identify small landscape regions.

Overall, the boundaries between landscape regions are well defined by surface features. Those landscape regions with similar characteristics are called physiographic provinces. Any continental landmass has several distinctive **physiographic provinces**. Because of its large size, the continental United States has a number of well defined physiographic provinces (see Figure 5-54). Similar types of regions can be found on all the continents.

New York State has a wide variety of landscape regions (see Figure 5-55). The largest landscape region in New York State, the Adirondack Highlands, is separated from the Appalachian Upland (Plateau) by the Hudson-Valley Lowlands. The present landscape of northeastern New York State was formed mainly by mountain building and glacial erosion. Each region has a distinctive landscape and is directly related to the type and structure of bedrock on which it forms. Many of the landscape regions in New York State are hidden beneath a veneer of glacial deposits.

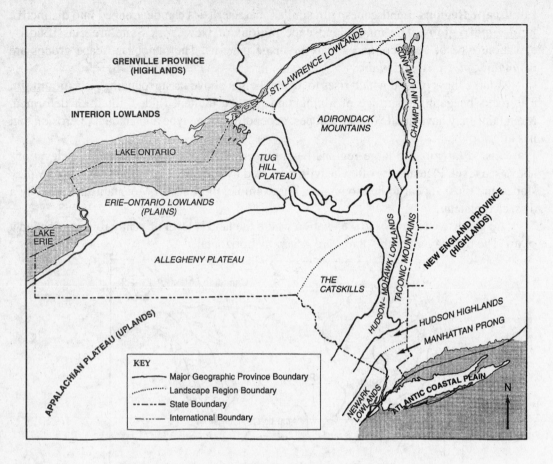

**Figure 5-55.** Generalized landscape regions of New York State.

## QUESTIONS

1. Landscape regions are generally determined by

   (1) underlying rock structure and elevation
   (2) amount of stream discharge and direction of flow
   (3) method of surface sediment deposition
   (4) amount of yearly precipitation

2. In which New York State landscape region is surface bedrock generally composed of metamorphic rock?

   (1) Tug Hill Plateau        (2) Adirondack Mountains
   (3) Newark Lowlands        (4) the Catskills

**3.** According, to the *Earth Science Reference Tables*, which New York landscape region is composed primarily of Cretaceous through Pleistocene unconsolidated sediments?

(1) Champlain Lowlands      (2) Erie-Ontario Lowlands
(3) Hudson-Mohawk Lowlands      (4) Atlantic Coastal Lowlands

**4.** In which New York State landscape region are the Taconic Mountains located?

(1) Adirondack Mountains      (2) New England Highlands
(3) Appalachian Plateau      (4) Tug Hill Plateau

**5.** According to the *Earth Science Reference Tables*, which New York State landscape region has the lowest elevation, the most nearly level land surface, and is composed primarily of Cretaceous through Pleistocene unconsolidated sediments?

(1) the Hudson-Mohawk Lowlands      (2) the Atlantic Coastal Lowlands
(3) the Champlain Lowlands      (4) the Erie Ontario Lowlands

**6.** Which landscape characteristic indicates a landscape has been formed primarily by streams?

(1) residual soil covering a large area      (2) coastal sand dunes
(3) V-shaped valleys      (4) parallel hills of unsorted sediments

**7.** What is the only difference between the Adirondacks and the Catskills that can be distinguished from the *Earth Science Reference Tables*?

(1) The Adirondacks have metamorphic bedrock, but the Catskills have sedimentary bedrock.
(2) The Adirondacks have mostly rounded hilltops and the Catskills have jagged hilltops.
(3) The Catskills have vegetation, but the Adirondacks do not.
(4) The Catskills are much higher in elevation than the Adirondacks.

**8.** Which characteristics are used to classify the different landscape regions of New York State?

(1) latitude, longitude, and county boundaries
(2) density of human population and type of industrial activities
(3) types of climate and plant life
(4) elevation, type of bedrock, and stream drainage systems

Base your answers to questions 9 and 10 on your knowledge of Earth Science, the information in the *Earth Science Reference Tables*, and the information shown in the map below. The map shows the major New York State Landscape Regions and rectangular reference sections A, B, and C.

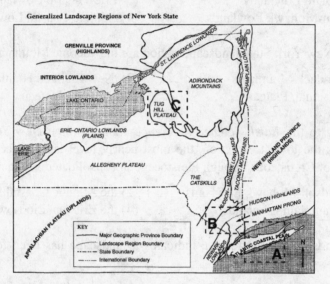

Generalized Landscape Regions of New York State

9. The surface of the Appalachian Uplands (Allegheny Plateau) in New York State was mostly formed by sedimentary bedrock deposited during which geologic time period?

    (1) Precambrian    (2) Ordovician    (3) Silurian    (4) Devonian

10. When were most of the nonsedimentary rocks of the Adirondack Mountains probably formed?

    (1) more than 570 million years ago    (2) approximately 540 million years ago
    (3) approximately 225 million years ago    (4) less than 65 million years ago

11. The Catskills landscape region is classified as a plateau because the region has

    (1) deep gorges
    (2) shallow valleys
    (3) rock type similar to the Adirondack Highlands
    (4) landscape characteristics most similar to the Appalachian Uplands

12. The major landscape regions of the United States are identified chiefly on the basis of

    (1) similar surface characteristics    (2) similar climatic conditions
    (3) nearness to major mountain regions    (4) nearness to continental boundaries

**13.** The primary reason that several landscape regions have formed in New York State is that the various regions of the State have different

(1) climates                 (2) latitudes

(3) soil characteristics         (4) bedrock characteristics

**14.** According to the *Earth Science Reference Tables*, which New York State landscape region contains the oldest bedrock?

(1) Erie-Ontario Lowlands       (2) Tug Hill Plateau

(3) Appalachian Uplands         (4) Adirondack Highlands

# LANDSCAPE DEVELOPMENT

The development of a landscape is a complex interaction of a number of environmental factors. However, only a few of the factors affect any one location at any one time. **Environmental factors** include the forces of uplift and erosion, the effects of climate changes, the type, strength, and structural features in the bedrock, the age of the landscape, and the effect of human activities on the landscape. Depending on the location and the dominant factors, the effects of these factors may differ from place to place.

## Uplifting and Leveling Forces

Two major factors influencing the formation and development of landscapes are the interaction of uplift and leveling. Uplift is a *constructional force*, while leveling is a *destructive* force.

Forces which build mountains, enlarge continents, and generally *raise* or roughen Earth's surface are called **uplifting forces**. Earthquakes, diastrophism (folding and faulting and tilting), volcanic activity, continental drift, and sea-floor spreading are examples of uplifting forces.

Forces which *lower* the elevation of Earth's surface through subsidence and erosion are called **leveling forces**. The major cause of leveling is the force of gravity. Gravity causes earth materials to be removed from places of high elevation and deposited at lower elevations. Moving water is the major leveling force.

When both uplifting and leveling forces are working simultaneously on the same landscape, one of the two forces will usually operate at a faster rate and be dominant. Wherever earthquakes and volcanic activity occur, uplifting is usually the dominant force. In these areas, slopes rise up and become steeper. Wherever rivers and streams are eroding and lowering the land, leveling is the dominant force. In these areas, the surface of the land becomes flatter.

During periods of mountain building, uplifting forces are more dominant than leveling forces. However, when erosion wears down the mountains faster than they can be uplifted, leveling forces are dominant. The rate of crustal uplift or subsidence may result in a modification (change) of the landscape during which hillslopes, drainage patterns or orographic wind patterns (due to the building of mountains in an area) are altered.

## Climate

Climatic changes may affect the landscape processes, either directly or indirectly. The indirect influences of climate are largely related to the amount, type, and distribution of vegetation covering the area. Some direct influences are the amount and type of precipitation, the relationship between precipitation and evaporation, temperature range, frost penetration, direction and velocity of the winds, differences between conditions on the windward and leeward sides of mountains, and the rapid changes in climatic conditions as the altitude changes.

The principal modifiers of landscape are changes in temperature and moisture conditions. The steepness of hillslopes in an area is affected by the balance between weathering and removal of materials. The intensity of weathering depends largely on temperature and on the amount of precipitation. Weathering will be minimal in hot, dry regions and in cold, dry regions. Abundant moisture is essential to the removal and movement of weathered material. The rate at which a landscape changes is greatly influenced by changes in temperature and moisture. For example, if average precipitation of a region increases by a small amount, the landscape changes slowly. But if the amount of precipitation increases greatly, the landscape changes quickly.

Landscapes that have developed under and conditions are characterized by steep slopes and angular features. Humid regions most typically are smooth, with gently rolling slopes (see Figure 5-56).

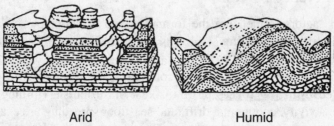

Arid                    Humid

**Figure 5-56.** The "same" landscape developed under varying moisture conditions. The drier the climate, the more angular the landscape features.

Landscapes that have developed under glacial conditions are characterized by spectacular jagged cliffs or U-shaped valleys and unique deposition forms left behind by the glaciers. Except in high latitudes and altitudes, glaciers are of minor importance in shaping present-day landscapes. However, glaciers played an important role in developing the landscape of New York State over the past million years, which is known as the Pleistocene Epoch. For example, Long Island is a product of glacial deposition that ended about 15 thousand years ago (see Figure 5-57). Along the coast, the shape of Long Island was further changed by ocean waves. Similar glacial features cover much of the northern United States.

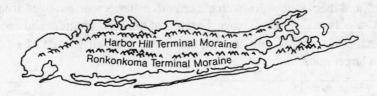

**Figure 5-57**. Long Island, New York, is a glacial deposit left by the Pleistocene Ice Sheet.

Stream characteristics are affected by the climate. Running water is the most powerful and important erosional agent in shaping landscapes. It is responsible for the development of valleys and the hills and ridges between valleys. Streams in and areas are usually temporary, and often drain into **landlocked lakes**, lakes that do not drain into the ocean. The Great Salt Lake is a landlocked lake. Streams in humid areas are permanent and generally drain into larger rivers or lakes, which ultimately drain into the oceans. Even though the Great Lakes are inland, they are not land-locked. They are connected to the Atlantic Ocean by the St. Lawrence River.

Soil associations differ, depending on climate. Arid regions and regions with large amounts of rainfall have shallow, poorly developed soils. Because of the lack of vegetation in arid regions and in regions of high elevation, the soils in these regions are very thin. Most of the soils in such regions will have eroded away, and the landscape has a barren look. Regions with moderate temperatures and moderate amounts of moisture have well developed soils and are generally covered with vegetation.

## Bedrock

The solid unbroken rock of Earth's crust is called **bedrock**. The characteristic shape of many landscapes is largely determined by the type of bedrock and its structure. The rate at which landscape development occurs can be influenced by the bedrock. The degree to which a rock can be changed depends on its hardness or resistance to, weathering and erosion. Generally speaking, the harder or more resistant the bedrock, the less weathering and erosion that can occur.

The shape and steepness of hills are affected by the local bedrock composition. When rocks of varying resistance are on top of each other, softer rocks, such as shale, will weather and erode more quickly than harder rocks, such as sandstone. Hard rocks tend to produce steep cliffs, while slopes produced by soft rocks tend to be less steep. Strong (competent) rocks are responsible for plateaus, mountains, and escarpments. Weak rocks usually underlie valleys and other low-level areas. Also, structural features in bedrock, such as faults, folds, and joints frequently affect the development of hillslopes (see Figure 5-58).

Plateaus with horizontal sedimentary rocks of varying resistances have steep cliffs, with the hard rock areas dominating the pace of erosion. If a rock layer produces a ridge that separates two gently sloping surfaces, the steep ridge is called an **escarpment**. Folded landscapes composed of rocks of varying resistances produce steep escarpments. Domed landscapes produce circular ridges and escarpments. The ridges along fault planes are very steep.

221

Streams and their valleys form characteristic patterns when viewed from above. These patterns vary widely from place to place, because of the rock structure and geologic history of the region. All drainage patterns are similar in that they all consist of smaller tributaries draining into larger ones.

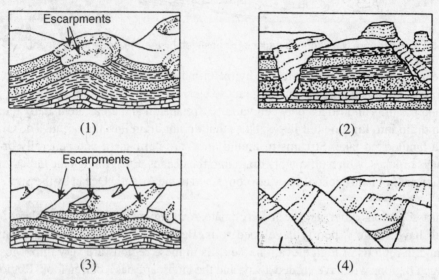

**Figure 5-58**. The bedrock of a region can have a strong influence on the landscape. The types of landscapes shown here are: (1) domed; (2) plateau; (3) folded bedrock of varying competence; and (4) fault block mountains.

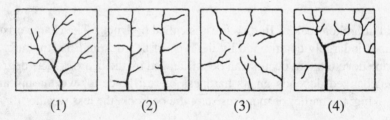

**Figure 5-59**. Stream drainage patterns. The patterns shown are (1) dendritic, or branching; (2) trellis; (3) radial; and (4) rectangular.

There are several common drainage patterns (see Figure 5-59). The **dendritic pattern** is characterized by branching similar to that of the limbs or roots of trees. Such patterns are found on plains and plateaus, where the rock layers are horizontal. The **trellis pattern** develops in valley-and-ridge terrain, where rocks of different hardness are folded. The **rectangular pattern** develops in a strongly jointed and faulted area, where the streams tend to follow the joint pattern. The **radial pattern** is found where streams radiate out from a central point on a large single peak, such as on a volcano or rounded hill.

Soil associations may be different in composition and are dependent upon the bedrock composition. The composition of the soil varies according to the composition of the bedrock. Areas of New York State, for example, underlain with limestone rocks, have soils that are rich in nutrients necessary for the growth of farm crops. If the climate is suitable, soils rich in limestone are quite fertile and landscapes are covered with vegetation. Soils formed from bedrock material are residual soils and have the basic characteristics of the bedrock.

## Time

Over a period of time, landscapes may pass through many stages or cycles. These stages can be classified as young, mature, and old. The duration of time during which the environmental factors have been active will determine the stage of development or condition of a landscape.

A **young landscape** is one in which a cycle of erosion is beginning. It is characterized by sharp craggy hills and mountains and a drainage system of steep, fast-moving streams in narrow V-shaped valleys.

A **mature landscape** has low, rounded hills and broad flat valleys. In a mature landscape, the streams of the drainage system are no longer eroding downward, but are sidecutting, building meanders and floodplains.

An **old landscape** occurs when the uplands have been eroded by erosion almost to sea level. The area has become a **peneplane**, a region that has been reduced by erosion to a nearly flat surface. It has a poor drainage system with almost no gradient, many meanders, and wide floodplains.

## Dynamic Equilibrium

A delicate balance of multiple environmental factors exists in all landscapes. A change in any one of the factors results in a modification of the landscape and the establishment of a new equilibrium. This is referred to as **dynamic equilibrium**.

## Human Activities

**Human activities** have greatly altered the landscapes in many areas. In earlier times, the land was stripped of trees and vegetation to accommodate agricultural needs. Later, landscapes were altered by the building of roads, railroads and cities. In many cases, little attention was paid to the long-range effects of these changes on the environment.

# QUESTIONS

1. Landscapes result from the interaction of what two opposing forces?

   (1) faulting and folding
   (2) weathering and abrasion
   (3) uplifting and erosion
   (4) potential evapotranspiration and precipitation

Base your answers to questions 2 and 3 on the diagram below.  The diagram shows the surface landscape features and the internal rock structure of a cross section of Earth's crust.

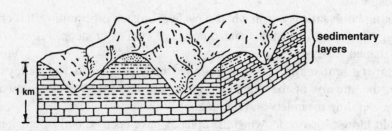

2. This landscape region would be best classified as
   (1) an eroded plateau          (2) a coastal plain
   (3) folded mountains           (4) volcanic mountains

3. How would this region most likely appear immediately after undergoing a period of glaciation?

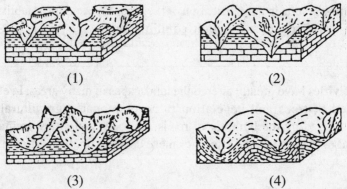

4. The composition of residual soil is most likely determined by the

   (1) amount of average annual insolation
   (2) type of bedrock material
   (3) range of yearly temperature extremes
   (4) amount of potential evapotranspiration

**5.** In addition to uplifting and leveling forces, bedrock, and time, what factor most strongly influences the stage of development of a landscape?

(1) vegetation          (2) climate

(3) ocean currents      (4) atmospheric pressure

**6.** The landscape shown below developed in a region with an arid climate.

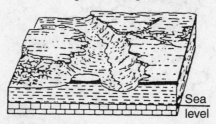

If the erosion of this plateau had taken place in a much more humid climate, which diagram below best represents how the landscape would appear?

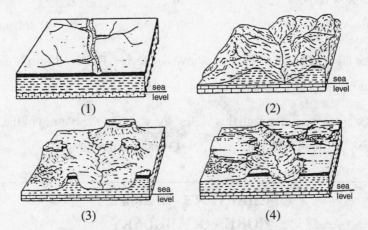

**7.** The diagrams below show the same region of Earth's crust at two different times.

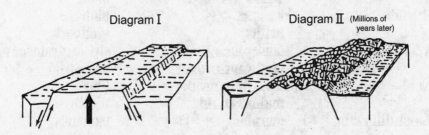

These diagrams seem to indicate that landscape features are the result of
(1) only uplifting forces within Earth's crust
(2) only leveling forces within Earth's crust
(3) both up-lifting and leveling forces acting on Earth's crust
(4) neither uplifting nor leveling forces acting on Earth's crust

Base your answers to questions 8 through 10 on your knowledge of Earth Science, the *Earth Science Reference Tables*, and the cross section of a canyon shown below.

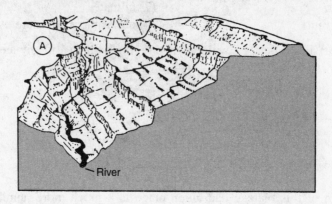

**8.** The landscape was most recently changed by

(1) running water      (2) faulting      (3) folding      (4) volcanism

**9.** The flat area labeled A is 2 kilometers above sea level. This landform is called a

(1) mountain      (2) highland      (3) plain      (4) plateau

**10.** If a glacier were to move through this valley, the width of the bottom of the valley would

(1) decrease      (2) increase      (3) remain the same

---

## CHAPTER 5 - Section 2
## CORE VOCABULARY

| | | |
|---|---|---|
| abraded | global warming | plain |
| barrier islands | ice ages | plateaus |
| beach | kettle | sandbars |
| bedrock | landscape | stream drainage patterns |
| climate | landscape regions | terrestrial |
| drumlins | mass movements | time |
| dune | mid-ocean ridges | trenches |
| dynamic equilibrium | moraine | tsunamis |
| escarpment | mountain | uplifting forces |
| glacial erosion | ocean currents | wave |
| glacial movement | outwash | wave action |
| glacier | outwash plain | wavelength |

# HELPFUL VOCABULARY

abyssal plains
Alpine glacier
aretes
backwash
barchan
baymouth bar
beach face
bedrock materials
berm
blowouts
breaks
cirque
coast
coastal blowout dunes
coastal features
continental rise
continental shelf
continental slope
creep (soil creep)
crest
crevaces
deflation
dentritic pattern
depositional landscape features
drainage basin
drift
end moraine
environmental change
environmental factors
erosional landscapes
erratic
esker
estuary
faceted
fetch
firn (neve)
fjords

glacial ages
glacial erosion
glacial sediment
groins
ground moraine
guyots
hanging valleys
headlands
hook
horn
human activities
icebergs
jetties
kames
land slides
landlocked lakes
landscape development
landscape observations
lateral moraine
Laurentide Ice Sheet
leveling forces
loess
longshore drift
marine terrace
mass wasting
mature landscape
medial moraine
meltwater
mudflows
neve (firn)
old landscape
oozes
parabolic dunes
pelagic
peneplane
physiographic provinces
radial pattern

recessional moraine
rectangular pattern
rip currents
rock flour
saline
sea arches
sea cliffs
seamounts
slip face (steep slope)
slumps
snow line
soil association
soil creep (creep)
solar energy
spit
stacks
stratified
striation
submarine canyons
surf
surface currents
swash
terminal moraine
terrigenous
till
tombolo
topography of sea floor
trellis pattern
troughs
turbidities
turbidity currents
valley glacier
ventifacts
wave height
wave refreaction
young landscape
zone of accumulation

## PRACTICE FOR CONSTRUCTED RESPONSE

Base your answers to question 1 through 4 on the map below, the *Earth Science Reference Tables*, and your knowledge of Earth Science. Figure 1 represents a topographic map of a landscape region. Contour lines show elevations in meters.

FIGURE 1 - TOPOGRAPHIC MAP

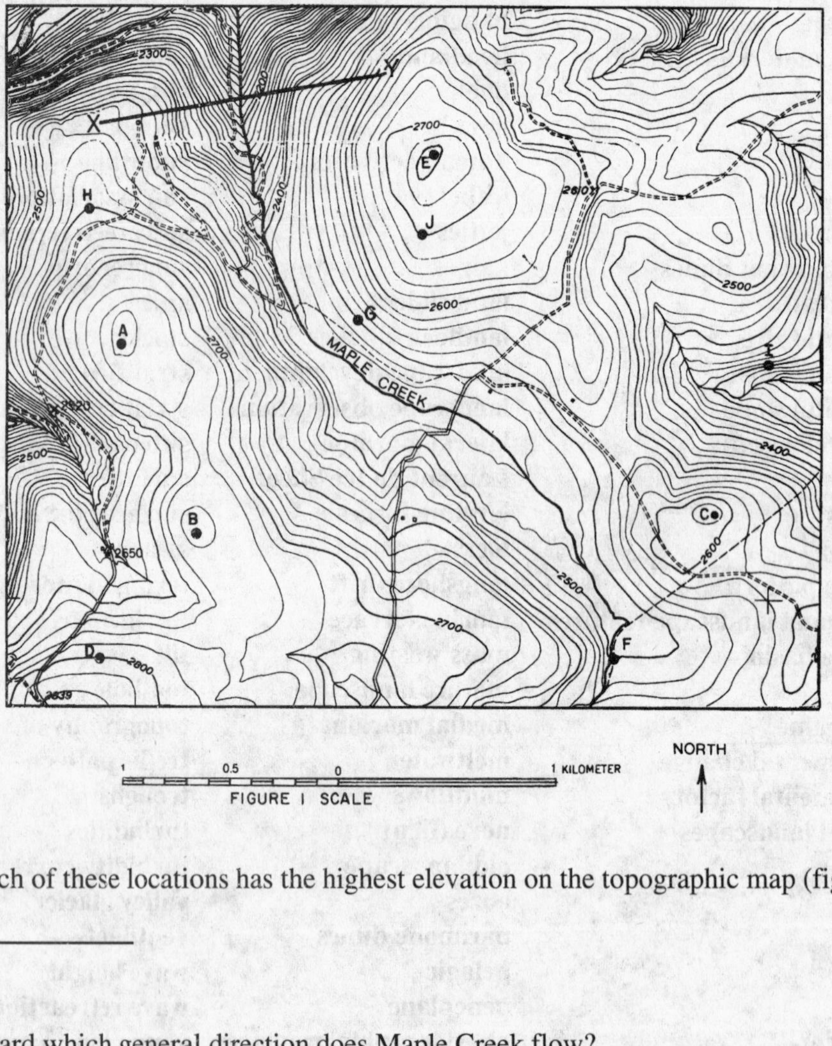

NORTH

FIGURE I SCALE

1. Which of these locations has the highest elevation on the topographic map (figure 1)?

_____

2. Toward which general direction does Maple Creek flow? _____

**3.** Which formula should be used to find the gradient of the hillslope from point J to Point G? _____

(1) gradient = $\dfrac{(2700\ m\ -\ 2500\ m)}{0.48\ km}$

(2) gradient = $\dfrac{(2700\ m\ +\ 2500\ m)}{0.48\ km}$

(3) gradient = $\dfrac{0.48\ km}{(2700\ m\ -\ 2500\ m)}$

(4) gradient = $\dfrac{0.48\ km}{(2700\ m\ +\ 2500\ m)}$

**4.** Which diagram best represents the elevation profile along the straight line between points X and Y? _____

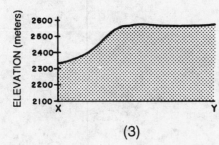

(1)

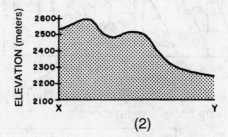

(2)

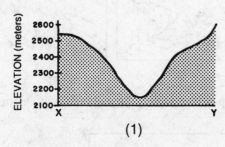

(3)

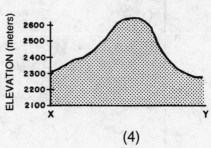

(4)

**5.** The diagram below represents a  landscape area.

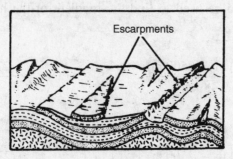

Which map represents the stream drainage pattern that has most likely developed within this area? _____

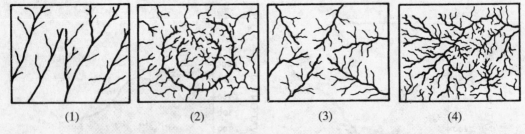

(1)          (2)          (3)          (4)

Base your answers to questions 6 and 7 on the map below, which shows Rockaway Peninsula, part of Long Island's south shore.

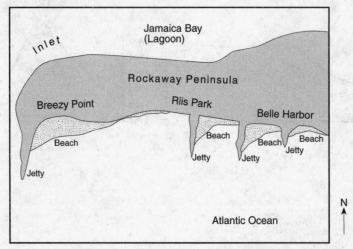

**6.** Students compared recent photographs of the beaches with photographs take three years ago and discovered that parts of the shoreline have changed.

   **a.** Which characteristic of the shoreline probably has changed most? _____

_____

   **b.** On what do you base your answer ? _____

_____

**7. a.** Toward which direction is sand being transported along the shoreline within the zone of breaking waves? _____

   **b.** State a reason for your answer.

_____

**8.** The cross section below shows the ocean floor between two continents. Points A through D represent locations on the ocean floor where samples of oceanic crust were collected.

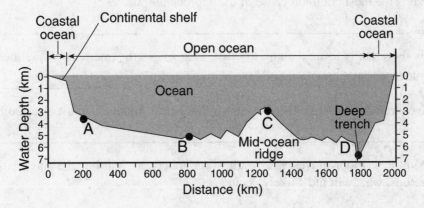

   **a.** The youngest rock sample most likely was collected from location _____

   **b.** On what do you base your answer? _____

**9.** Waste produced by people in New York State has been dumped into the Atlantic Ocean, where it is distributed by surface ocean currents.

   **a.** Which coastal areas is most likely to become polluted by this waste?

_____

   **b.** State a reason for your answer.

_____

_____

Base your answers to questions 10 and 11 on the diagram below, which shows ocean waves approaching a shoreline. A groin (a short wall of rocks perpendicular to the shoreline) and a breakwater (an offshore structure) have been constructed along the beach. Letters A, B, C, D, and E, represent locations in the area.

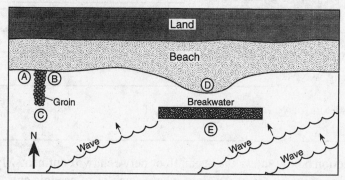

10. What is the most common cause of the approaching waves?

_____

11. This shoreline is located along the east coast of North America. Which ocean current would most likely modify the climate of this shoreline? _____

12. The curved pattern of surface currents in the North Atlantic is most affected by

_____

13. When the seafloor moves as a result of an underwater earthquake and a large tsunami develops, what will most likely occur?

_____

14. The shaded areas of the map below indicate concentrations of pollutants along the coastlines of North America.

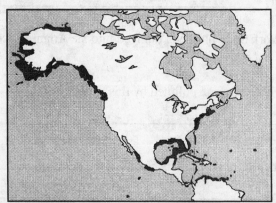

Polluting material may have been carried to the Alaska area by the

_____

_____

Base your answers to questions 15 and 16 on the diagram below. The diagram represents a shoreline with waves approaching at an angle. The exposed bedrock of the wavecut cliff is granite. Arrow A shows the direction of the longshore current and arrow B shows the general path of wave travel.

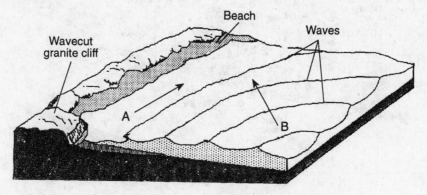

**15.** Which minerals are most likely to be found in the beach sand?

_____

**16.** A large storm with high winds that develops out at sea is most likely to result in

_____

Base your answers to questions 17 through 19 on the *Earth Science Reference Tables* and the graphs below. Graph I shows the yearly precipitation and evaporation at different latitudes, and graph II shows the salinity of the ocean at different latitudes. Salinity is a measure of the total amount of dissolved minerals in seawater, expressed as parts per thousand.

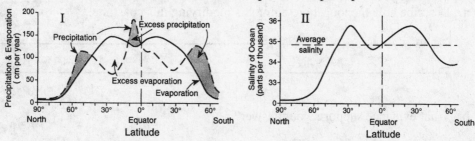

**17.** Compared to the amount of precipitation at the North Pole, the amount of precipitation at the Equator is _____

**18.** At which latitude is ocean salinity *least*? _____

**19.** The concentration of dissolved minerals in seawater would be increased by

_____

Base your answers to questions 20 through 22 on the diagram below. The diagram represents a shoreline in New York State along which several general features have been labeled. Letter B identifies a location on the shoreline.

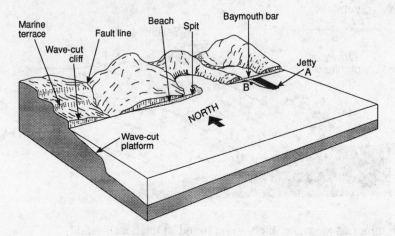

20. After the formation of the baymouth bar, the jetty (a structure made of rocks that extends into the water) labeled A was constructed perpendicular to the shoreline. Describe the result of the construction of this jetty in terms of water current velocity and sand deposition at location B?

_____

_____

21. a. Describe how the longshore current is modifying this coastline.

_____

_____

   b. What evidence supports your answer?

_____

_____

22. Which feature was formed because more erosion took place than deposition.

_____

Base your answers to questions 23 and 24 on the diagram below which shows the movement of water particles in ocean waves. The particles are represented by black dots. Letters A, B, C, and D are points of reference.

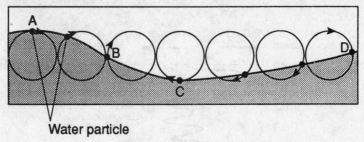

**Water particle**

**23.** The passage of a wave will cause a particle of water at the surface to

_____

**24.** The wave pattern shown in the diagram would occur most often in

_____

Base your answers to questions 25 and 26 on the tree maps below, which show the ice movement and changes at the ice front of an alpine glacier from the years 1874 to 1882. Points A, B, C, D, and E represent the positions of large markers placed on the glacial ice and left there for a period of eight years.

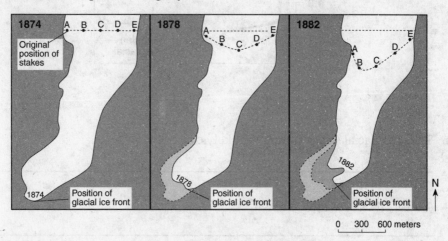

**25.** The changing positions of markers A, B, C, D, and E, show that the glacial ice is

_____

**26.** Which statement best describes the changes happening to this glacier between 1874 and 1882?

_____

235

Base your answer to question 27 on the chart below, which shows the changing climatic conditions that led to alternating glacial and interglacial periods.

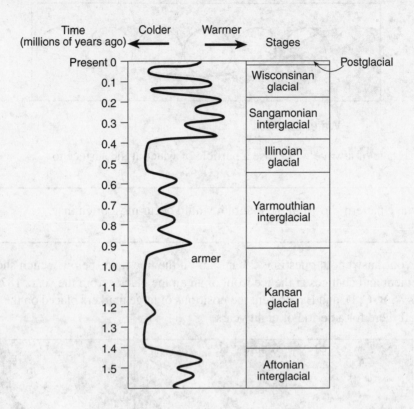

27. **a.** The interglacial stages were most likely caused by

_____

**b.** State a reason for your answer.

_____

_____

Base your answers to question 28 through 31 on the diagrams below. Diagram I shows an imaginary present-day continent covered by an advancing glacial ice sheet. Isolines called isopachs are drawn, representing the thickness of the ice sheet in meters. Diagram II show a cross section of the glacier with the land beneath it along reference line XY. Point A is a location on the glacier.

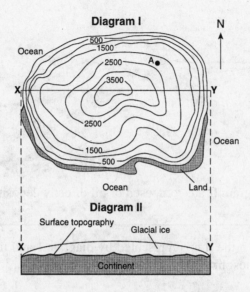

**28.** Chemical analysis of an ice sample taken from the central core of the glacier would most likely be used to study

_____

**29.** Describe the movement of this continental glacier?

_____

_____

**30.** What is the approximate thickness of the ice at location A? _____

**31.** Explain why the glacier originally formed.

_____

_____

Base your answers to questions 32 through 36 on the diagrams below. Diagram I shows melting ice lobes of a continental glacier during the Pleistocene Epoch. Diagram II represents the landscape feature of the same region at present, after the retreat of the continental ice sheet. Letters A through F indicate surface features in this region.

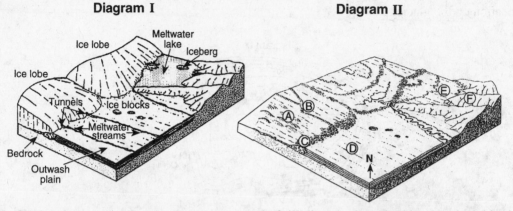

32. Which features in diagram II are composed of till directly deposited by the glacial ice?

_____

33. In the interval between the time represented by diagram I and the time represented by diagram II sea level most likely had

_____

34. Glacial movement is caused primarily by _____

35. The sediments deposited at location D are best described as

_____

36. The cross section below represents the transport of sediments by an advancing glacier. The arrow shows the direction of movement.

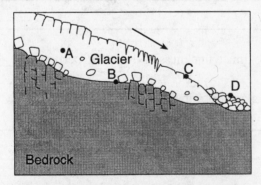

At which location are striations and glacial grooves most likely being carved?

_____

**37.** A deposit of rock particles that are scratched and unsorted have been found.

    **a.** How have these rocks been transported and deposited?

    _____

    **b.** What are the clues which support this decision.

    _____

**38.** Shaded areas on the diagram below show the part of New York State that was covered by glacial ice during the last ice age.

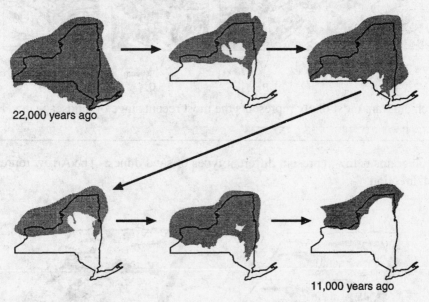

22,000 years ago

11,000 years ago

The best inference that can be made from these diagrams is that this glacial ice

_____

**39.** What condition causes glaciers to retreat?

_____

_____

**40.** What condition provides the best evidence that New York State's Finger Lakes formed as a result of continental glaciation?

_____

_____

**41**. What event would most likely cause a new ice age in North America?

_____

**42**. Another ice age would probably result in a change in _____

Base your answer to question 43 on the diagrams below. The diagrams represent glacial events in the geologic history of the Yosemite Valley region in California.

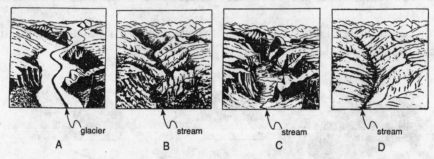

**43.** Which diagram most likely represents the most recent stage of landscape development?

_____

**44.** The diagrams below represent different types of sand dunes. The Arrow represents the wind direction.

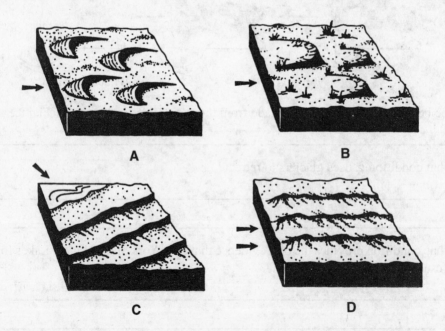

**a.** Which are coastal blowout dunes? _____

**b.** Which are barchan dunes? _____

**c.** Compare the conditions under which coastal blowout dunes and barchan dunes form.

_____

_____

**45. a.** Sketch a cross section of an idealized dune in the space provided. Indicate the wind direction side of the dune, and label the slip face.

**b.** What causes dunes to migrate?

_____

_____

Base your answers to questions 46 through 48 on the following map. The star symbol represents a volcano located on the mid-Atlantic Ridge in Iceland. The isolines represent the thickness, in centimeters, of volcanic ash deposited from an eruption of this volcano. Points A and B represent locations in the area.

46. On the grid provided, construct a profile of the ash thickness between point A and point B, following the directions below.

a. Plot the thickness of the volcanic ash along line AB by marking with a dot each point where an isoline is crossed by line AB.

b. Connect the dots to complete the profile of the thickness of the volcanic ash.

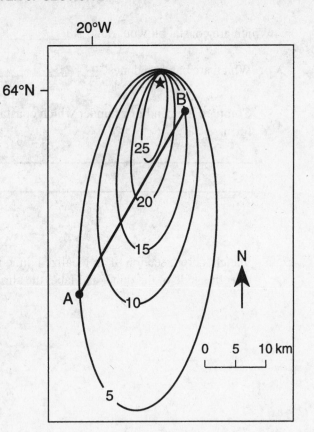

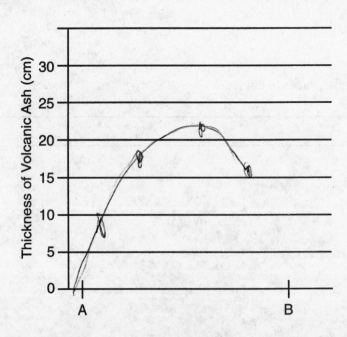

**47.** State one factor that could have produced this pattern of deposition of the ash.

_____

_____

**48.** State why volcanic eruptions are likely to occur in Iceland.

_____

_____

Base your answers to question 49 through 51 on the map below, which shows a portion of a drumlin field near Palmyra, New York. Elevations are in feet.

**49.** What is the contour interval of this map? _____

**50. a.** At this location, the glacial ice generally advance from what direction? _____

**b.** State a reason that explains your answer.

_____

_____

**51. a.** These drumlins are composed of sediments transported and deposited directly by glacial ice. These sediments are likely to be

_____

_____

**b.** Explain your conclusion

_____

_____

Base your answers to questions 52 through 55 on the *Earth Science Reference Tables*, the topographic map below, and your knowledge of Earth Science. The map represents Keuka Lake, one of the Finger Lakes in New York State, Branchport, Hammondsport, and Penn Yan are towns near the lake.

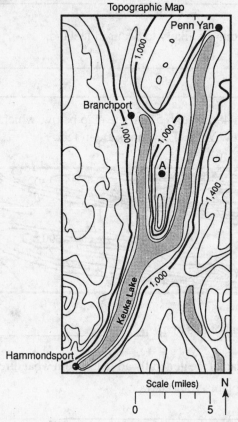

Topographic Map

**52.** Describe the best evidence that Keuka Lake formed as a result of continental glaciation.

_____

**53.** In which landscape region of New York State are the Finger Lakes located?

_____

**54.** According to the map, about how many miles long is Keuka Lake at its farthest points?

_____

**55.** If the lake level were to rise to 1,000 feet above sea level, the area at A would

_____

Base your answers to questions 56 through 58 on the diagram below and your knowledge of Earth Science. The diagram represents a geologic cross section in which no overturning has occurred.

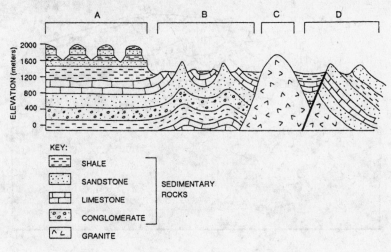

In one or more complete sentences:

**56.** Compare the differences in landscapes between Regions A and D.

_____

_____

**57.** Describe how Region B was formed.

_____

_____

**58.** Describe a typical stream drainage pattern which might be found around the hill in Region C.

_____

_____

Base your answers to questions 59 through 61 on the cross section below, your knowledge of Earth science and on the *Earth Science Reference Tables*.

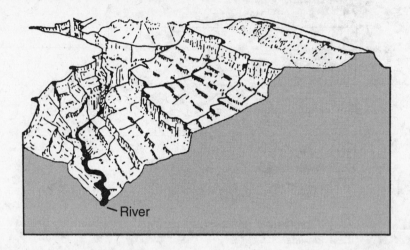

~River

In one or more complete sentences:

**59.** Describe the probable change on the landscape if there were an increase in precipitation.

_____

_____


**60.** Describe the river valley after a glacier were to pass through it.

_____

_____


**61.** Describe what causes the variation in the steepness of the eroded hillslope.

_____

_____

Base your answers to question 62 on the information and map below.

The eruption of Mt. St. Helens in 1980 resulted in the movement of volcanic ash across the northwestern United States. The movement of the ash at 1.5 kilometers above sea level is shown as a shaded path on the map. The times marked on the path indicate the length of time the leading edge of the ash cloud took to travel from Mt. St. Helens to each location.

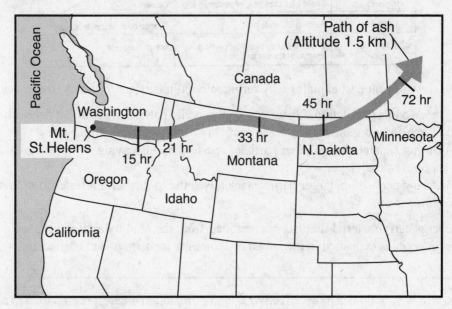

62. Calculate the average *rate* of movement of the volcanic ash for the first 15 hours, following the directions below.

    **a.** Write the equation used to determine the average rate of the volcanic ash movement.

    **b** Substitute values into the equation.

    **c.** Solve the equation and label the answer with the correct units.

Base your answers to questions 63 and 64 on the table below, which lists the four main classes of ocean-floor sediments and shows the origin and an example of each sediment.

**Ocean-Floor Sediments**

| Classification | Origin | Examples |
|---|---|---|
| Lithogenic | Land-derived | Muds and clays |
| Biogenic | Shells of microscopic organisms | Oozes |
| Turbigenic | Turbidity currents | Graded beds in the deep ocean |
| Authigenic | Ocean water by chemical precipitation directly on the ocean floor | Manganese nodules |

63. Which statement best explains why turbigenic sediments are found in graded beds?

    (1) the Moon's gravitational force causes the cyclic pattern of sediment deposition.

    (2) Ocean-floor organisms sort fresh sediments into layers of similar sizes.

    (3) During cementation, smaller particles rise to the top, leaving larger particles at the bottom of each layer.

    (4) During deposition, larger particles usually settle to the bottom faster than smaller particles do.

64. Icebergs carry material that has been eroded from the land by a moving glacier. When this material is deposited in the ocean by a melting iceberg, it is classified as

_____

65. Explain why wind is a more effective agent of erosion in a desert region than in a humid region.

_____

_____

66. Below is dune profile with the wind direction given.

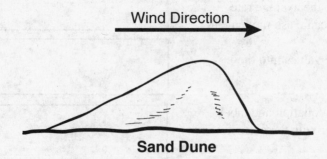

    **a.** Draw a solid line to indicate where the dune was a few months ago.

    **b.** Draw a dashed line to indicate where it will be a few months from now.

**67.** Identify a result of glaciation that has had a positive effect on the economy of New York State.

_____

_____

**68.** Historically, political boundaries have been associated with land areas. Most of the ocean basins however, have not been divided politically. Why are people becoming more concerned about the political status of the ocean basins?

_____

_____

**69. a.** At which location is ocean water most likely to be clean and unpolluted? _____
  (1) near the west coast of North America
  (2) near the east coast of South America
  (3) in the mid-Pacific
  (4) around Australia

**b.** State reasons for your answer.

_____

_____

**70.** The table below shows the percentage by mass of dissolved ions in seawater.

| Dissolved Ion | Percentage |
|---|---|
| Chloride ($Cl^-$) | 55.04 |
| Sulfate ($SO_4^{2-}$) | 7.68 |
| Bicarbonate ($HCO_3^-$) | 0.41 |
| Bromide ($Br^-$) | 0.19 |
| Sodium ($Na^+$) | 30.61 |
| Magnesium ($Mg^{2+}$) | 3.69 |
| Calcium ($Ca^{2+}$) | 1.16 |
| Potassium ($K^+$) | 1.10 |
| All others | 0.12 |
| | 100.00 |

**a.** Which mineral is most abundant in seawater? _____

**b.** Describe the evidence which supports your answer.

_____

# CHAPTER 6
# EARTH'S HISTORY

Earth is over 4 billion years old, and much of its history is recorded in the rocks. **Geologic history** is the study and interpretation of Earth's past. Evidence of faulting, uplift, rock types, fossils, igneous activity, and a multitude of other clues are waiting in the rock record to reveal happenings in Earth's structure since its origin. Interpreting what has happened to Earth over a period of time is like solving a puzzle. The clues are examined and, from them, Earth's geologic history is inferred.

## GEOLOGIC EVENTS

One of the basic principles of geologic history is that the geologic processes that are going on today, such as weathering, erosion, volcanism, and earthquakes, also went on in the past. This is known as the **principle of uniformitarianism** and is often stated "The present is the key to the past." For example, there are places today where layers of sediments are forming in a particular pattern. The same type of pattern can be found in rocks formed long ago. Since the patterns are the same, it can be inferred that the processes that are layering the sediments today are the same processes that layered the sediments in the rock many years ago.

### Sequence of Geologic Events

Although much can be learned from the rock record, it is often difficult to determine *exactly* when a particular event or occurrence took place. It is usually much easier to determine the sequence of a series of geologic events, without putting an absolute date on any of the events. When the age of a rock or event is compared to the ages of other rocks or events in a geologic sequence, the **relative age** of the rock or event is determined. The actual age of a rock or event is called its **absolute age**. The first goal of a historical geologist is to determine the relative ages of events and rocks; then, if possible, to determine the absolute ages.

**Chronology of layers**. In determining the order, or chronology, of rock layers, geologists use two major principles as starting points in making interpretations of geologic history. The first is the **principle of original horizontality**, which states that sediments are deposited in horizontal layers that are parallel to the surface on which they were deposited (see Figure 6-1). Therefore, tilted or folded layers indicate that the crust has been deformed.

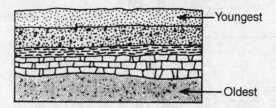

**Figure 6-1**. This rock formation illustrates both the principle of original horizontality and the principle of superposition.

The second principle is the **principle of superposition**, which states that, in a series of undisturbed layers, the oldest layer is on the bottom and each successive overlying layer is progressively younger. The principle of superposition does not apply, however, in cases where layers have been overturned or where older rocks have been forced over younger layers along a fault (see Figure 6-2).

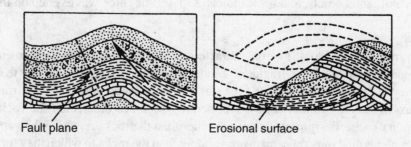

Fault plane          Erosional surface

**Figure 6-2** The displacement of rocks along a fault line can result in older rock overlying younger rock. After erosion, this apparent inconsistency becomes visible at Earth's surface.

## Evidence of Events

**Igneous intrusions and extrusions**. When molten magma forces its way into cracks or crevices in crustal rock and solidifies, it forms a mass of igneous rock called an *intrusion*. Since the rocks through which the magma moved existed prior to the intrusion, they must be older than the intrusion (see Figure 6-3).

When lava solidifies at Earth's surface, it forms a mass of igneous rock called an *extrusion*. Rock layers located below an extrusion are older than the extrusion. Any rock found above an extrusion must have formed after the extrusion and are thus younger than it.

Sometimes, the only way to determine if a horizontal mass of igneous rock is an intrusion or an extrusion is to examine the rocks on either side of the igneous mass. If *contact metamorphism* has altered the rocks above and below the igneous mass, the mass must be an intrusion. The magma forced its way between the two layers of rock (see Figure 6-3). On the other hand, if only the rock layer beneath the igneous mass shows evidence of contact metamorphism, this indicates that the igneous mass is most likely an extrusion. Any rock layers found overlying the igneous mass must have formed at a later date.

**251**

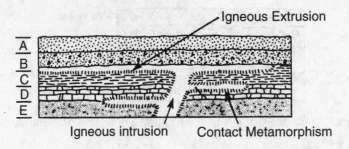

Igneous Extrusion

A B C D E

Igneous intrusion    Contact Metamorphism

**Figure 6-3**. All rock layers that show contact metamorphism must be older than the intrusion. In this illustration, layers C, D, and E are older than the intrusion. Layers A and B are younger.

**Faults, joints and folds.** Such features as faults, joints, and folds must be younger than the rocks in which they are found. A **joint** is a crack in a rock formation. A joint is similar to a fault except that the rock only separates along a joint (see Figure 6-4). There is no displacement. The presence of faults, joints, and folds indicates that some force was exerted on the rocks in the past.

**Internal characteristics.** Some internal characteristics of rocks include rock fragments, cracks, veins, and mineral cement. Rock fragments found in larger rock masses are older than the rock in which they appear. At some earlier time, the fragments were broken away from existing rock. For example, the sediments in a sedimentary rock are older than the rock itself. In nonsedimentary rocks, the mineral grains are older than the rocks in which they appear.

Cracks, veins, and mineral cement are younger than the rocks in which they form. Cracks are simply very small joints. A **vein** is a mineral deposit that has filled a crack or permeable zone in existing rock.

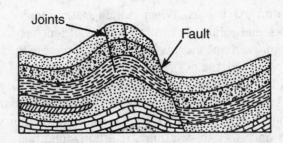

Joints    Fault

**Figure 6-4**. This rock formation shows both jointing and faulting. Both of these features are younger than the rock in which they occur.

# QUESTIONS

1. The cross sections of crust below represent two regions of sedimentary rock layers that have been altered.

   The sedimentary bedrock in both regions originally formed as

   (1) horizontal layers   (2) recrystallized layers   (3) faulted layers   (4) folded layers

2. The diagrams below represent two different geologic cross sections in which an igneous formation is found in sedimentary bedrock layers. The layers have not been overturned.

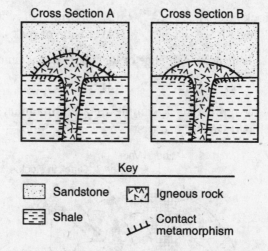

   Which statement best describes the relative age of each igneous formation compared to the overlying sandstone bedrock?

   (1) In A, the igneous rock is younger than the sandstone and in B, the igneous rock is older than the sandstone.
   (2) In A, the igneous rock is older than the sandstone and in B, the igneous rock is younger than the sandstone.
   (3) In both A and B, the igneous rock is younger than the sandstone.
   (4) In both A and B, the igneous rock is older than the sandstone.

Base your answers to questions 3 through 6 on your knowledge of Earth Science, the *Earth Science Reference Tables*, and the diagram below. The diagram represents a geologic cross section of a portion of Earth's crust.

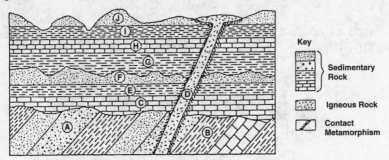

3. Which rock layer provides the best evidence for crustal movement?

   (1) E          (2) B          (3) C          (4) H

4. Which rock layer most likely was deposited directly on an erosional surface?

   (1) A          (2) E          (3) C          (4) H

5. Which event occurred most recently?

   (1) deposition of rock layer A      (2) deposition of rock layer G
   (3) erosion of rock layer F         (4) erosion of rock layer J

6. In which rock layer is there *no* evidence of local contact metamorphism?

   (1) A          (2) E          (3) H          (4) J

7. The diagram below represents a sample of a sedimentary rock viewed under a microscope. Which part was formed first?

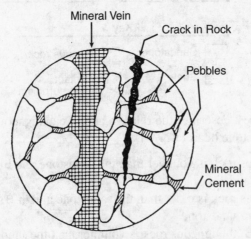

   (1) the crack             (2) the pebbles
   (3) the mineral vein      (4) the mineral cement

**8.** The diagram below represents folded and faulted rock layers cut by an igneous intrusion. What is the relative age of the intrusion?

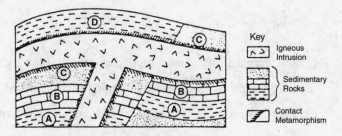

Key

⌐⌐⌐ Igneous Intrusion

Sedimentary Rocks

Contact Metamorphism

(1) older than rock unit A and older than the fault
(2) younger than rock unit B and older than the fault
(3) older than rock unit C and younger than the fault
(4) younger than rock unit D and younger than the fault

**9.** An unconformity between two sedimentary layers is most likely produced by

(1) the deposition of gravel followed by the deposition of sand and silt
(2) continuous sedimentation in a deep basin over a long period
(3) uplift followed by extensive erosion, submergence, and deposition
(4) a period of extrusive vulcanism followed by another period of extrusive vulcanism

**10.** Evidence suggests that the geologic processes of the past were

(1) similar to those of the present
(2) different from those of the present
(3) occurring at a faster rate than those of the present
(4) occurring at a slower rate than those of the present

**11.** Unless a series of sedimentary rock layers has been overturned, the bottom rock layer usually

(1) contains fossils
(2) is the oldest
(3) contains the greatest variety of minerals
(4) has the finest texture

12. The diagram below represents a core drilling in a region consisting of only four sedimentary rock layers, A, B, C, and D. Which geologic event could explain the order of the rock layers in the core drilling?

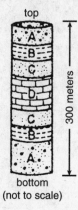

top

300 meters

bottom
(not to scale)

(1) Volcanic activity caused rapid deposition of the sedimentary layers.

(2) Large scale erosion caused a gap in the time record.

(3) Extensive folding caused the rock layers to overturn.

(4) Intrusion of igneous material occurred sometime between the deposition of layer A and layer D.

13. What process most directly caused the formation of the feature shown by line AB in the geologic cross section below?

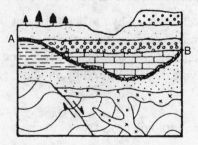

(1) erosion    (2) faulting    (3) igneous intrusion    (4) folding

14. An oil well is drilled through a series of sedimentary rock layers in which no unusual geologic deformation has occurred. Compared to the top layers of sedimentary rock, each successive layer encountered by the drill will be
(1) more weathered    (2) composed of smaller particles
(3) older    (4) of lower density

15. Which is the youngest rock shown in the diagram below?

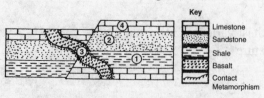

Key

Limestone
Sandstone
Shale
Basalt
Contact
Metamorphism

(1) 1    (2) 2    (3) 3    (4) 4

# CORRELATION TECHNIQUES

Although rocks in one location may appear to be different from rocks in another location, they all may have been products of the same geologic event. Matching rocks in one location to those in another location is part of the puzzle that must be solved in order to accurately determine the history of geologic events on Earth.

The process of matching rocks and geologic events in one location with rocks and geologic events in other locations is called **correlation**. Some of the methods used in correlating geologic events include continuity and similarity of rocks, fossil evidence in the rocks, and volcanic time markers in the rocks. Sometimes, what appears to be a correlation is really an *anomaly*, something that does not fit the normal pattern.

## Continuity of Rock and Correlation

The solid, unbroken rock of the crust is called **bedrock**. Bedrock exposed at Earth's surface is called an **outcrop**. Rock layers can often be traced from one location to another directly by "walking an outcrop." Walking an outcrop means observing and following a particular rock layer along Earth's surface for a great distance. For example, outcrops may be traced along the sides of mountains or in areas where streams, glaciers, or excavations have exposed the rocks (see Figure 6-5). Outcrops in one location may be compared with outcrops in other locations to correlate and reconstruct their geologic history.

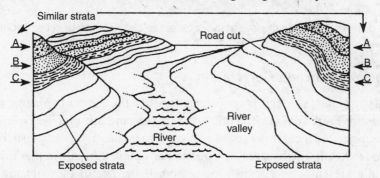

**Figure 6-5**. The bedrock exposed by the river's erosion and the road cut. This exposure makes it possible to correlate strata on both sides of the river.

## Similarity of Rock and Correlation

In the field, rocks in different locations can often be tentatively matched on the basis of similarities in appearance, color, and composition. These rock properties can be examined more closely in the lab to obtain a more accurate correlation between the rocks. It is important for the observer to carefully distinguish evidence from inference. For example, rocks near each other that appear to be the same may have actually formed at different times in the past. Without careful examination, the observer might infer that these rocks were the same age. The more layers that appear to correlate from one location to another, the more likely the correlation is to be accurate.

## Fossil Evidence and Correlation

Fossils are found almost exclusively in sedimentary rocks. Fossil evidence is one of the most reliable methods available for correlating rocks at different locations. Fossils also provide clues to the environments in which the rocks formed. For example, if rocks located at high elevations contain fossils of shallow-water organisms, the layers from which the rocks formed must have been deposited in a shallow sea and were later uplifted.

The most useful fossils for purposes of correlation are index fossils. **Index fossils** are fossils or organisms that lived over an extensive area–preferably over the entire Earth–for relatively short periods of time. These factors ensure that the fossils have a wide horizontal distribution and a small vertical distribution. The widespread and short-lived history of such organisms makes their fossils very useful in correlating sedimentary rocks in which they are found (see Figure 6-6).

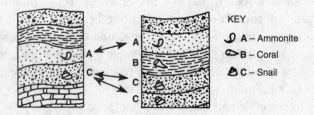

KEY
A – Ammonite
B – Coral
C – Snail

**Figure 6-6**. This diagram illustrates the use of index fossils to correlate strata in two separate rock formations.

## Volcanic Time Markers and Correlation

A particularly violent volcanic eruption can deposit a thin layer of **volcanic ash** over the surface of the entire Earth. Eventually, this layer of volcanic ash may be covered by other sediments. In a rock sequence, however, this layer remains easily distinguishable from the layers above and below it. Such ash layers are similar to index fossils in that they cover the entire Earth and represent a very short time period. If the age of the volcanic eruption is determined, the ash time marker will provide valuable clues about the exact ages of the rocks above and below it. These time markers can be used to accurately correlate rock layers thousands of kilometers apart.

## Anomalies to Correlation

Sometimes, the evidence of geologic history can be oversimplified, thus leading to misconceptions and erroneous interpretations. For example, two very similar rock formations may actually be of different ages. Or, a single formation maybe older in some places than others. Such deviations from what is expected are called anomalies. Careful observation and study combined with cautious interpretation can minimize errors due to the presence of **anomalies.**

# QUESTIONS

1. The best method for the correlation of sedimentary rock layers several hundred kilometers apart is by comparing the

   (1) index fossils in the layers      (2) layers by walking the outcrop
   (3) thickness of the rock layers      (4) color of the rock layers

2. What is indicated by the presence of trilobite fossils in many layers of the Devonian-age rocks in New York State?

   (1) Trilobites lived in terrestrial environments during the Devonian Period.
   (2) The trilobites became extinct during the Devonian Period.
   (3) The surface of New York State was greatly eroded during the Devonian Period.
   (4) Areas of New York State were under seas during the Devonian Period

3. Which is the best method of determining the relative ages of a layer of sandstone in western New York State and a layer of sandstone in eastern New York State?

   (1) Compare the thickness of the two layers.
   (2) Compare the colors of the two layers.
   (3) Compare the size of sand particles of the two layers.
   (4) Compare the index fossils in the two layers.

4. Why can layers of volcanic ash found between other rock layers often serve as good geologic time markers?

   (1) Volcanic ash usually occurs in narrow bands around volcanoes.
   (2) Volcanic ash usually contains index fossils.
   (3) Volcanic ash usually contains the radioactive isotope carbon-14.
   (4) Volcanic ash is usually rapidly deposited over a large area.

5. According to the *Earth Science Reference Tables*, near which community in New York State would you be *least* likely to find fossils?

   (1) Old Forge      (2) Albany      (3) Elmira      (4) Watertown

Base your answer to question 6 on the block diagram below of a portion of Earth where the rock layers have not been overturned.

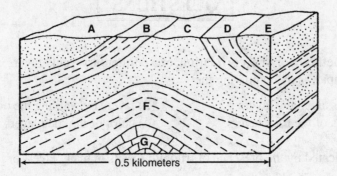

0.5 kilometers

6. The evidence present in the diagram supports the inference that

(1) rock B is the same age as rock F
(2) rock B is the same age as rock D
(3) rock C is older than rock G
(4) rock D is younger than rock A

7. Which characteristics of a fossil would make it useful as an index fossil in determining the relative age of widely separated rock layers?

(1) a wide time range and a narrow geographic range
(2) a wide time range and a wide geographic range
(3) a narrow time range and a wide geographic range
(4) a narrow time range and a narrow geographic range

8. According to the *Earth Science Reference Tables*, a comparison of the bedrock at Syracuse, New York, with the bedrock at Massena, New York, best supports the observation that

(1) no fossils are found in the bedrock of these areas
(2) both areas have sedimentary bedrock of the same age
(3) both areas have sedimentary bedrock, but the bedrock at Syracuse is younger
(4) the bedrock at Massena contains salt and gypsum, but the bedrock at Syracuse does not

Base your answers to questions 9 through 13 on your knowledge of Earth Science, the *Earth Science Reference Tables*, and the cross section of a portion of Earth's crust shown below. Letters A through H and Z represent rock formations. I and II indicate a zone of geologic events.

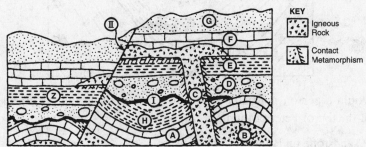

**9.** If overturning has *not* occurred, then rock layer E is younger than

(1) igneous intrusion C (2) rock layer F
(3) rock layer G (4) rock layer D

**10.** Rock layer Z represents the same rock layer as letter

(1) F (2) E (3) H (4) D

**11.** Which probably occurred most recently?

(1) the event that formed line I (2) the event that formed line II
(3) the intrusion of rock layer C (4) the folding of rock layer A

**12.** Where would well-preserved fossils most likely be found?

(1) within rock B
(2) within rock C
(3) where rock layers F and G contact each other
(4) where rock layers E and C contact each other

**13.** In which rock are fossils *least* likely to be found?

(1) A (2) E (3) F (4) C

Base your answer to question 14 on the cross-sectional diagram of a folded region shown below.

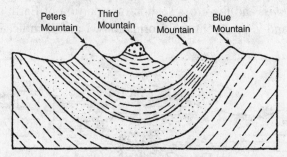

**14.** Where would a person normally expect to find the same type of fossil remains as are present at the top of Peters Mountain?

    (1) in the sandstone on Blue Mountain

    (2) in the sandstone on Second Mountain

    (3) in the conglomerate on Third Mountain

    (4) in the shale between Second Mountain and Blue Mountain

# DETERMINING GEOLOGIC AGES

The older a rock, the more difficult it is to determine its absolute age. The relative age of a rock is easier to determine. Although relative age does not give the exact time a rock was formed, it does allow the rock to be placed in a sequence of events. This placement might ultimately lead to the rock's absolute age.

Without the rock record, there would be no geologic history. Even now, there are many gaps in the record in which there are no rocks, no clues, from which historical inferences can be made. The geologic history of an area is determined primarily from fossil evidence, the age of the rocks, and the erosional record in the rocks.

## Fossil Evidence

Before fossils could be used as indicators of age, the relative ages of the major rock units had to be determined on the basis of super position. Then index fossils could be used to correlate rock layers. Events in geologic history can often be placed in relative order using evidence provided by certain fossils. For example, if the index fossil *graptolite* is found in a rock layer, historical geologists are sure that the rock is Ordovician in age, because this is the only time period in which the graptolite lived. Similarly, dinosaurs existed only during the Mesozoic time period of Earth's history. Thus, if evidence of dinosaurs is found in rocks, then the rocks must be Mesozoic in age. Being able to place a series of fossils in sequence by age allows you to place the rocks in which the fossils are found in the same sequence by age.

## Scale of Geologic Time

Geologists have subdivided geologic time into units based on fossil evidence. This division of time is called the **Geologic Time Scale** (see the Geologic Time Scale in the *Earth Science Reference Tables*). The Time Scale has been subdivided into four major divisions. The **Precambrian** represents the first 85% of Earth history. It is essentially devoid of a fossil record for two basic reasons. First, most of the plants and animals of that period were small and did not have the hard parts needed for preservation as fossils. Second, most of the rocks formed during that period are nonsedimentary. They have been distorted and transformed by heat and pressure, and any fossil evidence that may have existed has been destroyed.

The other three divisions, the Paleozoic, the Mesozoic, and the Cenozoic all exhibit some evidence of life forms as indicated by fossils. The **Paleozoic Era** represents about 8.5% of Earth's geologic history. Invertebrates, fishes, amphibians, vertebrates, and land plants and animals all appear for the first time in the Paleozoic Era. In rocks of the **Mesozoic Era**, which represents about 3.5% of Earth's geologic history, evidence of dinosaurs and the earliest birds and mammals is abundant. Rocks of the **Cenozoic Era** contain fossils of many modern plants and mammals. This era represents the most recent 3% of geologic history. Humanoids showed up late in the Cenozoic Era and have existed for about 0.04% of Earth's 4.5 billion years.

## Erosional Record

Buried erosional surfaces, called **unconformities**, indicate gaps or breaks in the geologic time record. These gaps represent periods of destruction of the geologic record. Four steps combine in sequence to produce an unconformity - uplift, erosion, subsidence (submergence), and deposition. The process begins when the land is uplifted above sea level. Uplift is followed by erosion of the uplifted rocks. At some time after erosion has occurred, the land once again subsides (submerges) below sea level so that additional deposition of sediments may take place over the eroded surface.

The three most common types of unconformities are angular unconformities, parallel unconformities and nonconformities (see figure 6-7). **Angular unconformities** consist of tilted, folded, or faulted rocks which have been eroded and then covered again. **Parallel unconformities**, also called **disconformities**, occur when parallel rock layers of different ages are separated by an erosional surface. **Nonconformities** are formed when sedimentary rocks are deposited on top of an eroded surface of igneous rocks. When deposition on submerged rock stops without any erosion taking place, a break or gap in the rock record, called a **hiatus**, is produced.

An unconformity indicates that some of the layers in a rock record are missing. Unconformities are useful because they indicate that a geologic event of some magnitude took place. Unconformities are also useful in determining the relative ages of rocks in that they can be used to explain why a rock can occur between two layers in one location, but not appear between the same two layers in another location.

## Geologic History of an Area

The geologic history of an area can be inferred from the rock record of that area. The geologic map of New York State and the geologic time scale, both of which appear in the *Earth Science Reference Tables*, illustrate the portions of the rock record that have been preserved in New York State. The principal rocks in New York State are Cambrian, Ordovician, Silurian, Devonian, some Carboniferous, Triassic, and Cretaceous, all of which are covered by a veneer of Pleistocene deposits.

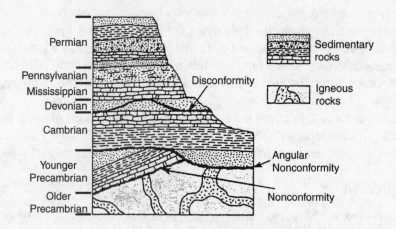

**Figure 6-7.** The Grand Canyon. This representative section of a wall of the Grand Canyon shows many different erosional features. Large exposures of bedrock such as this provide valuable rock records.

# QUESTIONS

1. According to the *Earth Science Reference Tables*, approximately when on the time line below did humans first appear on Earth?

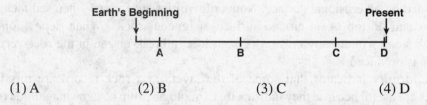

   (1) A                (2) B                (3) C                (4) D

2. Using the information in the *Earth Science Reference Tables*, students plan to construct a geologic time line of Earth's history from its origin to the present time. They will use a scale of 1 meter equals 1 billion years. What should be the total length of the students' time line?

   (1) 10.0 m           (2) 2.5 m            (3) 3.8 m            (4) 4.5 m

3. According to the *Earth Science Reference Tables*, during which geologic time period were the continents of North America, South America, and Africa closest together?

   (1) Tertiary      (2) Cretaceous      (3) Ordovician      (4) Carboniferous

4. According to the *Earth Science Reference Tables*, which era represents the shortest amount of geologic time?

   (1) Precambrian      (2) Paleozoic      (3) Mesozoic      (4) Cenozoic

Base your answers to questions 5 through 9 on the *Earth Science Reference Tables* and on your knowledge of Earth Science.

5. Where in New York State would you find rocks of the Triassic Age?

   (1) north central      (2) extreme southwest      (3) southeast      (4) northeast

6. In which section of New York State would you be most likely to find fossils of the earliest amphibians?

   (1) Southeast of Lake Erie      (2) in the Adirondacks
   (3) on Long Island      (4) along the shores of Lake Ontario

7. During which geologic period were rocks deposited in New York State that are now 400 million years old?

   (1) Triassic      (2) Devonian      (3) Cambrian      (4) Cretaceous

8. Which is the most probable reason why Precambrian fossil evidence is rarely found?

   (1) There were no living organisms at that time.
   (2) The organisms were not preserved.
   (3) There were no rocks formed at that time.
   (4) The rocks formed at that time have been destroyed.

9. What fossils would most likely be found within the bedrock of south central New York State?

   (1) mammals      (2) fishes      (3) dinosaurs      (4) birds

10. During which time was the majority of the exposed bedrock in New York State deposited?

   (1) Precambrian      (2) Mesozoic      (3) Cenozoic      (4) Paleozoic

**11.** According to the *Earth Science Reference Tables*, a rock formation containing fossils of many fishes and the earliest amphibians was probably formed during which period?

(1) Carboniferous    (2) Cambrian       (3) Devonian       (4) Ordovician

**12.** According to the *Earth Science Reference Tables*, during which geologic time interval did the mammoth live?

(1) Precambrian     (2) Paleozoic       (3) Mesozoic       (4) Cenozoic

**13.** Geologists have subdivided geologic time into units based on

(1) rock type    (2) fossil evidence    (3) erosion rates    (4) landscape development

**14.** According to the *Earth Science Reference Tables*, which of the following cities is located on the youngest bedrock?

(1) Watertown       (2) Syracuse       (3) Albany       (4) Binghamton

**15.** A rock formation in New York State contains fossils of many trilobites but of no fish. According to the *Earth Science Reference Tables*, in which general area is this rock formation probably located?

(1) Long Island               (2) south of Lake Ontario
(3) southwestern New York State     (4) northeastern New York State

# RADIOACTIVE DECAY

The process of correlating and dating rock layers is very difficult. One method used to determine the absolute age of some rocks is radioactive dating. A radioactive date indicates the time period when that rock actually formed. This method is particularly useful in dating igneous and metamorphic rocks.

## Decay Rates

**Radioactive decay** occurs when the nuclei of unstable atoms break down, or decay, giving off particles and energy. Radioactive decay changes the original atoms to atoms of another element. Atoms of the same element that have the same number of protons but different numbers of neutrons in their nuclei are called **isotopes**. For example, uranium 238 and uranium 235 are both isotopes of uranium. Many of the elements used in determining the absolute ages of rocks through radioactive decay have several isotopes.

Uranium 238 ($U^{238}$) is one of the most important isotopes used for the purpose of radioactive dating. Unstable atoms of $U^{238}$ will eventually become stable atoms of lead 206 ($Pb^{206}$). This stability is reached through a series of decay steps, all but the last involving unstable nuclei. $U^{238}$ decays to thorium 234, which in turn decays to protactinium 234. This process continues through several other unstable elements until the final, stable product, $Pb^{206}$ is produced. The entire process takes millions of years.

Depending on which atoms are involved, the process of radioactive decay can involve many steps or only a single step. The rate of decay is not affected by any external factor, and is thus very predictable.

## Half-life

The rate of radioactive decay is measured in terms of half-life. The **half-life** of a substance is the time it takes for one-half of the atoms of that substance to decay to another element. At the end of one half-life, one half the atoms of a radioactive sample will remain. After two half-lives, one-fourth of the original atoms will remain; after three half-lives, one-eighth of the original will remain, and so forth. Eventually, all the original radioactive material will have decayed (see Figure 6-8).

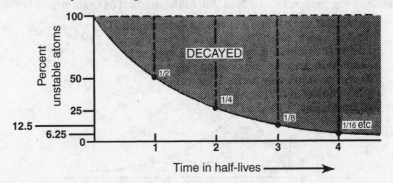

**Figure 6-8**. Half-life. For every half-life period, one-half of the unstable atoms in a radioactive sample decay to form atoms of some other element.

Different radioactive substances have different half-lives (see Table 6-1). Carbon 14, with a half-life of about 5700 years, is used to date the remains of plants and animals of the past 40,000 years or so. Radioactive elements with longer half-lives, such as uranium 238, rubidium 87, and potassium 40, are useful for dating older remains and rocks. Radioactive dating has helped determine thousands of dates for events in Earth history. Geologists have inferred the age of Earth to be over 4.5 billion years.

## Radioactive Decay Data

| RADIOACTIVE ISOTOPE | DISINTEGRATION | HALF-LIFE (years) |
|---|---|---|
| Carbon-14 | $C^{14} \rightarrow N^{14}$ | $5.7 \times 10^3$ |
| Potassium-40 | $K^{40} \nearrow Ar^{40} \searrow Ca^{40}$ | $1.3 \times 10^9$ |
| Uranium-238 | $U^{238} \rightarrow Pb^{206}$ | $4.5 \times 10^9$ |
| Rubidium-87 | $Rb^{87} \rightarrow Sr^{87}$ | $4.9 \times 10^{10}$ |

**TABLE 6-1.**

## Decay Product Ratios

The age of a rock can often be inferred from the relative amounts of the undecayed radioactive substance and the decayed product. For example, potassium has a radioactive isotope, $K^{40}$, which is useful in dating rocks. When potassium 40 decays, it produces calcium 40 and argon 40. Since argon 40 does not combine chemically with other elements (it is inert), the argon 40 found in a mineral is very likely to have originated from the decay of potassium 40. By comparing the amounts of potassium 40 and argon 40 present in a rock sample, the age of the rock can be determined. The more argon 40 found in a rock, the older the rock is (see Figure 6-9). An advantage of using the potassium-argon dating system is that potassium 40 is abundant in many of the common minerals. Large amounts of lead 206 are found in many rocks. Thus, comparing the amount of lead 206 to the amount of uranium 238 does not always yield accurate results in determining the age of rocks.

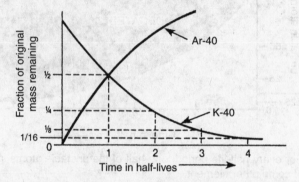

**Figure 6-9.** $K^{40}$ decays to form $Ar^{40}$. As the graph shows, the percentage increase of $Ar^{40}$ atoms is equal to the percentage decrease of $K^{40}$ atoms.

## QUESTIONS

1. One half of the radioactive potassium-40 ($K^{40}$) in an igneous rock has decayed to argon-40 ($Ar^{40}$). According to the *Earth Science Reference Tables*, about how many years ago was this rock formed?

   (1) $1.3 \times 10^9$       (2) $2.6 \times 10^9$       (3) $3.9 \times 10^9$       (4) $9.8 \times 10^9$

2. Uranium-238 is used to date the age of Earth rather than carbon-14 because uranium-238

   (1) was more abundant when Earth formed
   (2) has a longer half-life
   (3) decays at a constant rate
   (4) is easier to collect and test

**3.** When the quantity of a radioactive material decreases, the half-life of that substance will

(1) decrease          (2) increase          (3) remain the same

**4.** As the temperature of a radioactive substance increases, the rate at which that substance will disintegrate

(1) decreases          (2) increases          (3) remains the same

**5.** According to the *Earth Science Reference Tables*, which radioactive element would be best for determining the age of a 25,000-year-old rock sample containing organic remains?

(1) carbon-14          (2) potassium-40          (3) uranium-238          (4) rubidium-87

Base your answers to questions 6 through 10 on your knowledge of Earth Science and on the graph below which shows the relationship between mass and time for a radioactive element during radioactive decay.

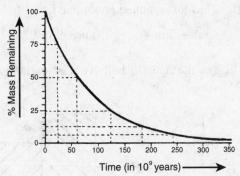

**6.** What is the half-life of the element?

(1) $20 \times 10^9$ years     (2) $60 \times 10^9$ years     (3) $125 \times 10^9$ years     (4) $180 \times 10^9$ years

**7.** When 35% of the original radioactive material is left, the sample will be approximately how many years old?

(1) $5 \times 10^9$ years     (2) $60 \times 10^9$ years     (3) $100 \times 10^9$ years     (4) $120 \times 10^9$ years

**8.** According to the graph, which statement best describes the decay of the radioactive element?

(1) The actual mass of radioactive material that decays in each half-life decreases with time.
(2) The rate of decay is greatest between $150 \times 10^9$ years and $250 \times 10^9$ years.
(3) There is the greatest loss in mass between $250 \times 10^9$ and $300 \times 10^9$ years.
(4) The same number of atoms of radioactive material decay during each half-life.

9. Based on the trend indicated in the graph, the radioactive element will be completely decayed

(1) in $60 \times 10^9$ years              (2) in $250 \times 10^9$ years
(3) in $350 \times 10^9$ years            (4) at a time greater than $350 \times 10^9$ years

10. If the rock containing this radioactive material is buried deeper in Earth's crust and subjected to an increase in temperature and pressure, the rate of radioactive decay will probably

(1) decrease         (2) increase         (3) remain the same

11. Which radioactive substance would probably be used in dating the recent remains of a plant found in sedimentary deposits?

(1) carbon-14      (2) potassium-40      (3) rubidium-87      (4) uranium-238

12. According to the *Earth Science Reference Tables*, which radioactive element formed at the time of Earth's origin has just reached about one half-life?

(1) carbon-14      (2) potassium-40      (3) uranium-238      (4) rubidium-87

13. The graph below indicates the age (in half-lives of carbon-14) of four specimens of fossils.

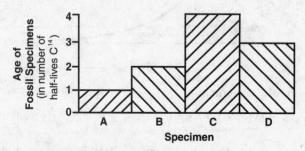

According to this graph and the *Earth Science Reference Tables*, the age of which fossil specimen is approximately 11,200 years?

(1) A           (2) B           (3) C           (4) D

14. What is the total amount of uranium-238 that will remain in a 1-gram sample of $U^{238}$ after $4.5 \times 10^9$ years of radioactive decay?

(1) 1 gram         (2) 2 grams         (3) 0.25 gram         (4) 0.5 gram

**15.** Which radioactive substance shown on the graph below has the longest half-life?

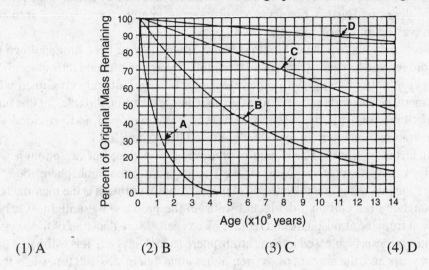

(1) A          (2) B          (3) C          (4) D

# THE HISTORY AND EVOLUTION OF
# EARTH'S ATMOSPHERE

Earth was "born" about 4.5 billion years ago as a cloud of dust and gases left over from the creation of the Sun. For about 500 million years, the interior of Earth was solid, composed primarily of iron and silicates with small amounts of other elements, some of them radioactive. As millions of years passed, Earth heated up and gradually melted the solid materials. The iron melted first, and, because of its greater density, sank toward the center forcing up the other material found there. Earth's surface was probably in turmoil with bubbling and heaving, exploding volcanoes and lava flows covering the surface. As Earth cooled, a stable crust developed and slowly Earth acquired its present appearance.

Earth's earliest atmosphere was entirely different from the primarily nitrogen-oxygen atmosphere that surrounds it today. The planetesimals, which collected together to form Earth, could not have had atmospheres because they were too cold and small for their gravity to hold any gases around them. The evidence for the origin of Earth's atmosphere is based on events happening today and surmising that events happening today also happened in the past.

The primary source of gases of Earth's earliest atmosphere is believed to be outgassing by volcanoes. **Outgassing** is the release of gasses from the interior of Earth due to internal heat and chemical reaction. Volcanic gases consist mainly of water vapor, carbon dioxide, nitrogen, and lesser amounts of other gases. The light hydrogen molecules would not have been held by Earth's gravity and much of it escaped into space as it continues to do today. Our present atmosphere is sometimes called a secondary atmosphere because it did not form from the original mass, but rather from later outgassing processes.

It is believed that most of the atmosphere and oceans formed rapidly during the first few hundred million years of Earth's history. More gaseous material was going into the atmosphere than was returning to Earth.

As the water vapor reached the outer atmosphere, it would have been broken down by sunlight into hydrogen and oxygen. Once again the lighter hydrogen escaped into space. The **free oxygen** (oxygen not combined with other elements) however, quickly combined with other gases like methane and carbon monoxide to form water and carbon dioxide. In this time period, the beneficial atmospheric greenhouse effect was developed and provided the appropriate temperatures and environment which allowed life to develop.

Almost all forms of life on Earth require free oxygen to live, but not enough was produced here for people to survive. Most of the free oxygen in the atmosphere today is produced through the process of photosynthesis in plants. **Photosynthesis** is the manufacture of sugars and starches from carbon dioxide and water in the presence of sunlight. Carbon dioxide is removed from the atmosphere and replace by oxygen. More than half of the oxygen produced in photosynthesis is released into the atmosphere as free oxygen. It is estimated that over 500 million years ago, the amount of oxygen in our atmosphere was 100 times less than is present today.

# THE FOSSIL RECORD

Geologists study fossils preserved in the rocks to determine the variety and evolution of life forms that have existed on Earth in the past. These fossils provide clues to how plants and animals lived and grew in the past and how they fit into the total web of life.

## Variety of Life Forms

Fossils provide evidence that a great many kinds of animals and plants have lived on Earth in the past under a great variety of environmental conditions. Most of them have become extinct, with only a tiny fraction of the organisms that have lived during the geologic past preserved as fossils. Two special conditions seem to be necessary for fossils to survive. The organisms must be buried soon after they die and the animals must have hard shells, bones, or teeth.

Following the principle of uniformitarianism, geologists study the conditions under which various organisms live and develop today and compare these conditions with similar fossils found in the rock record. From this comparison, they infer past environments and climates. The geographic distribution of both present-day and prehistoric plants and animals is closely controlled by various climatic conditions, such as temperature, the amount and kind of food available, and the amount of water available in a particular location.

## Evolutionary Development

The process of evolution assumes that a species of living plants or animals may change over a period of time. A **species** is a group of organisms that can mate and produce fertile offspring. If a plant or animal species changes, the following generations are different from their ancestors. These natural changes are called <u>variations</u> within a species. The members within a species may vary greatly from each other. These variations within a species can be observed, measured, and described.

Theories of evolutionary development infer that variations within a species may provide some members with a higher probability for survival. Some may not need as much food, or may be more resistant to disease. Others may simply blend into the background, so that predators do not find them. Some theories suggest that organisms most suited to survive pass these traits on to their offspring.

Similarity among some fossil forms found in various time periods suggest a transition that may be a result of evolutionary development.

In a few lifetimes, changes in a species may be small. However, over a series of generations, an organism may be produced that is recognizably different from its ancestors. In general, older life forms of a particular species are less complex than later life forms of the same species. Whether evolution has been gradual or punctuated by a series of stop-and-go changes has not been agreed upon.

## QUESTIONS

1. According to the *Earth Science Reference Tables*, near the end of which era did the dinosaurs become extinct?

   (1) Precambrian    (2) Paleozoic    (3) Mesozoic    (4) Cenozoic

2. Which pair of index fossils can be found in Ordovician bedrock?

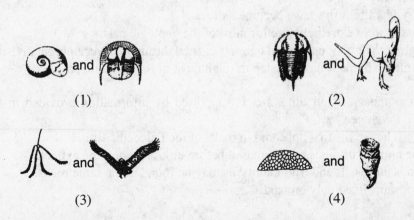

3. Surface bedrock of the Allegheny Plateau is most likely to contain fossils of the earliest
   (1) grasses                       (2) flowering plants
   (3) dinosaurs             (4) amphibians

4. The fossil record indicates that most of the plants and animals that lived on Earth in the past
   (1) have become extinct            (2) lived on the land
   (3) appeared before the Cambrian Period     (4) became index fossils

5. Which fact provides the best evidence for the scientific theory of the evolutionary development of life on Earth?
   (1) Fossils are found almost exclusively in sedimentary rocks.
   (2) Characteristics of simpler forms of life can be found in more complex forms of life.
   (3) Only a small percentage of living things have been preserved as fossils.
   (4) Most species of life on Earth have become extinct.

6. According to the *Earth Science Reference Tables*, what change occurred between the late Paleozoic and the early Mesozoic Eras?
   (1) The amphibians evolved into the earliest dinosaurs.
   (2) The trilobites became extinct and the earliest dinosaurs appeared.
   (3) The dinosaurs became extinct and the mammals became dominant.
   (4) The flowering plants evolved into large seed-bearing fern trees.

7. According to the *Earth Science Reference Tables*, which event occurred at the time of the Alleghenyan Orogeny?
   (1) the extinction of many kinds of marine animals
   (2) the extinction of many kinds of land animals
   (3) the development of primitive aquatic plants
   (4) the development of birds and mammals

8. According to the *Earth Science Reference Tables*, which inference can be made about the fossil record?
   (1) Very few life forms have become extinct.
   (2) Fossils were extremely rare for most of the geologic past.
   (3) A great variety of plants and animals existed during the Precambrian division.
   (4) Primitive humans have existed through most of the geologic past.

9. Which statement about dinosaurs is supported by information provided in the *Earth Science Reference Tables*?
   (1) Dinosaur fossils first appeared in rocks of the Paleozoic Era.
   (2) The number of dinosaurs increased before dinosaurs became extinct.
   (3) Dinosaur fossils and trilobite fossils may be found in the same rocks.
   (4) Dinosaurs lived only on land.

**10.** Fossils of two trilobite species from different geologic periods are illustrated below.

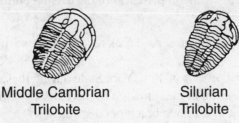

Middle Cambrian
Trilobite

Silurian
Trilobite

A comparison of these fossils provides evidence that these species may have

(1) undergone evolutionary development    (2) undergone metamorphism
(3) experienced identical lifespans    (4) experienced weathering and erosion

Base your answers to questions 11 through 14 on your knowledge of Earth Science, the *Earth Science Reference Tables*, and the graphs below. Graph I shows the population distribution of the fossils from four species of brachiopods (A, B, C, and D) found in the rocks of New York State. Graph II shows the range of the average shell thickness of adult individuals of each species.

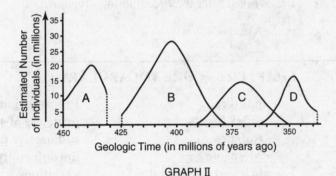

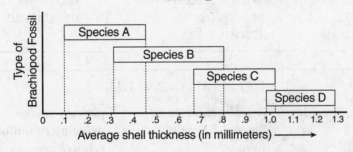

**11.** Which species of brachiopods had the *greatest* maximum population during its presence on Earth?

(1) A    (2) B    (3) C    (4) D

**12.** Which species of brachiopod had the *least* variation in shell thickness?

(1) A    (2) B    (3) C    (4) D

13. Which would best explain the incompleteness of the fossil records of species A, B, and D, as seen in Graph I,

    (1) the existence of a gap in the preserved rock record for these time periods in New York State
    (2) the flooding of large portions of New York State during these time periods
    (3) volcanic activity resulting in the intrusion of the Palisades Sill
    (4) the sudden extinction of all three brachiopod species

14. An undisturbed sequence of sedimentary rocks contains each of these four types of brachiopod fossils. Which species would be found farthest below the surface?

    (1) A              (2) B              (3) C              (4) D

15. What is one possible explanation why very few fossils are found in Precambrian rocks?

    (1) No life existed during the Precambrian division.
    (2) Most primitive fossils have been destroyed through time.
    (3) Most forms of life became extinct during the Precambrian division.
    (4) No new forms of life evolved after the Precambrian division.

---

### CHAPTER 6 - CORE VOCABULARY

| | | |
|---|---|---|
| absolute age | half-life | Precambrian |
| bedrock | index fossils | principle of superposition |
| Cenozoic Era | isotopes | radioactive decay |
| correlation | Mesozoic Era | unconformity |
| free oxygen | original horizontality | variations |
| geologic history | outgassing | volcanic ash |
| geologic time scale | Paleozoic Era | |

---

### HELPFUL VOCABULARY

| | | |
|---|---|---|
| angular unconformities | igneous extrusion | photosynthesis |
| anomaly | igneous intrusion | principle of uniformitarianism |
| disconformity | joint | relative age |
| fault | nonconformity | species |
| fold | outcrop | vein |
| hiatus | parallel unconfornities | |

## PRACTICE FOR CONSTRUCTED RESPONSE

1. A geologist comes upon an outcrop of rock where the types of rock are easily identified. She sketches the outcrop and when she returns to her office, she writes the geologic history of the area. The sketch is below.

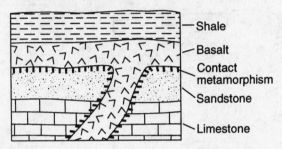

Write a geologic history of the rocks in the outcrop describing two possible sequences of rocks from oldest to youngest.

_____

_____

_____

_____

_____

_____

_____

_____

_____

_____

Base your answers to questions 2 through 4 on the geologic cross section below. The cross section shows an outcrop in which the layers have not been overturned. Rock units are labeled A through E.

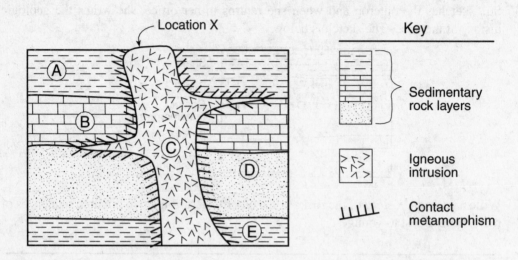

2. Using letters A through E, list the rock units in order from oldest to youngest.

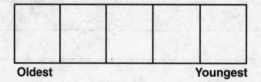

Oldest           Youngest

3. State the name of the sediment that was compacted to form rock unit A.

_____

4. State one observation about the crystals at location X that would provide evidence that igneous rock unit C was formed by very slow cooling magma.

_____

_____

**5.** The diagrams below show the sequence of events that formed sedimentary rock layers A, B, C, and D.

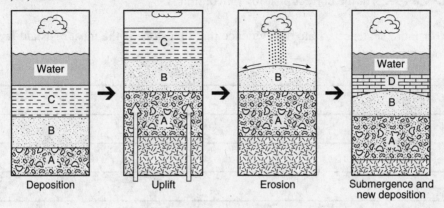

Deposition          Uplift          Erosion          Submergence and new deposition

    **a.** Describe the sequence of events best illustated in the diagrams above.

_____

    **b.** Between which 2 layers is there an uncomformity? _____

    **c.** How do you know?

_____

Base your answers to questions 6 through 9 on the diagrams below. Columns A and B represent two widely separated outcrops of rocks. The symbols show the rock types and the locations of fossils found in the rock layers. The rock layers have not been overturned.

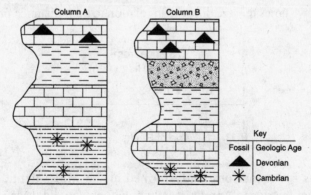

Column A          Column B

| Key | |
| --- | --- |
| Fossil | Geologic Age |
| ▲ | Devonian |
| ✳ | Cambrian |

    **6.** State one method used to correlate rock layers found in the outcrop represented by column A with rock layers found in the outcrop represented by column B.

_____

_____

**7.** An unconformity (buried erosional surface) exists between two layers in the outcrop represented by column A. Identify the location of the unconformity by drawing a thick wavy line ( $\sim\sim\sim$ ) at the correct position on column A.

**8.** In one or more sentences, state the evidence that limestone is the most resistant layer in these outcrops.

_____

_____

_____

_____

_____

**9.** State the oldest possible age, in millions of years, for the fossils in the siltstone layer.

_____ million years.

**10.** Present-day corals live in warm, tropical ocean water. What does the discovery of Ordovician-age corals in the surface bedrock of western New York State cause you to infer?

_____

_____

**11.** The scale below shows the age of rocks in relation to their distance from the Mid-Atlantic Ridge.

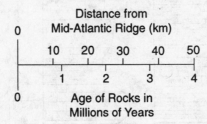

Some igneous rocks that originally formed at the Mid-Atlantic Ridge are now 37 kilometers from the ridge. Approximately how long ago did these rocks form?

_____

**12.** The diagram below represents a cross section of a series of rock layers of different geologic ages.

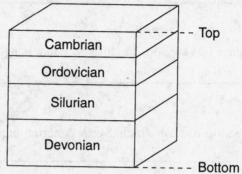

Develop a geologic history of the area a geologist might write to explain the sequence of these rock layers.

_____

_____

_____

_____

Base your answers to questions 13 through 15 on the diagram below. The diagram represents the supercontinent Pangea, which began to break up approximately 220 million years ago.

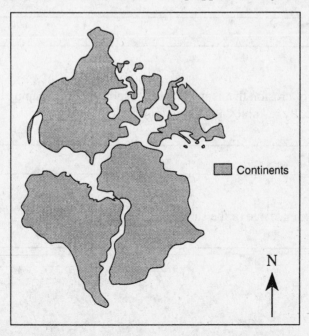

13. During which geologic period within the Mesozoic Era did the supercontinent Pangaea begin to break apart? _____

14. State one form of evidence that supports the inference that Pangaea existed.

_____

15. State the compass direction toward which North America has moved since Pangaea began to break apart. _____

Base your answers to questions 16 through 18 on the information below.

A mountain is a landform with steeply sloping sides whose peak is usually thousands of feet higher than its base. Mountains often contain a great deal of nonsedimentary rock and have distorted rock structures caused by faulting and folding of the crust.

A plateau is a broad, level area at a high elevation. It usually has an undistorted, horizontal rock stucture. A plateau may have steep slopes as a result of erosion.

16. State why marine fossils are *not* usually found in the bedrock of the Adirondack Mountains.

_____

_____

17. State the agent of erosion that is most likely responsible for shaping the Catskill Plateau so that it physically resmbles a mountainous region.

_____

_____

18. State the approximate age of the surface bedrock of the Catskills.

_____

Base your answers to questions 19 and 20 on the table below, which shows the results of a student's demonstration modeling radioactive decay. To begin, the student put 50 pennies heads up in a container. Each penny represented one radioactive atom. The student placed a top on the box and shook the box. Each penny that had flipped over to the tails up side was replaced with a bean that represented the stable decay product. The student continued the process until all of the pennies had been replaced by beans.

| Shake Number | Number of Radioactive Atoms (pennies) | Number of Stable Decay Atoms (beans) |
|---|---|---|
| 0 | 50 | 0 |
| 1 | 25 | 25 |
| 2 | 14 | 36 |
| 3 | 7 | 43 |
| 4 | 5 | 45 |
| 5 | 2 | 48 |
| 6 | 1 | 49 |
| 7 | 0 | 50 |

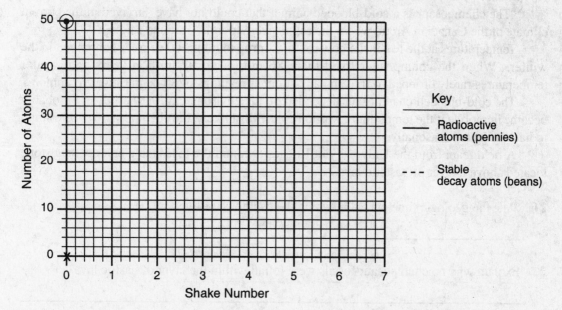

**19.** On the grid above, graph the data shown on the table by following the steps below.
  **a.** Mark with a dot each number of radioactive atoms (pennies) after each shake. Surround each dot with a small circle (⊙). The zero shake has been plotted for you.

  **b.** Connect all the dots with a solid line.

  **Example:**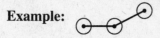

    **c.** Mark with an X the number of stable decay atoms (beans) after each shake. The zero shake has been plotted for you.

    **d.** Connect all the X's with a dashed line.

**20.** Assume that each shake number represents an additional 100 years. State the half-life of the radioactive material in this model. _____

Base your answers to questions 21 and 22 on the newspaper article below.

## New Fossils Indicate Arctic Climate Used To Be Floridian

    The frigid Arctic regions were as warm as present-day Florida some 90 million years ago, according to researchers who found fossils of a crocodile-like animal in northern Canada.

    Six hundred miles from the North Pole, researchers from the University of Rochester found the fossilized remains of the champosaur, a toothy, 8-foot-long extinct crocodile.

    "We found a whole collection of fossils, from both young and adults," said scientist John H. Tarduno.

    "The champosaur is a cold-blooded animal that could not have survived in the current climate of the Canadian Arctic where the fossils were found," Tarduno said.

    Temperatures at the fossil site now routinely drop to minus 60 degrees Fahrenheit in the winter. When the champosaur lived there 86 million to 92 million years ago, winter temperatures rarely dropped to freezing and summer readings of 80 degrees were common.

    The cold-blooded champosaur depended on the environment for warmth and probably became immobile if the temperature was too cold. Most likely, the champosaur was too small to have migrated seasonally.

    A field team from the University of Rochester found the fossils in a layer of sandstone located above a layer of basaltic lava.

**21.** State the geologic time period in which the champosaur lived.

_____

**22.** Explain why no champosaur fossils were found within the layer of basltic lava.

_____

_____

_____

_____

Base your answer to question 23 on the diagram below and your knowledge of Earth Science. The cross section represents a portion of Earth's crust.

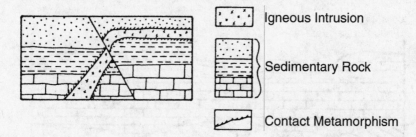

**23.** What is the evidence that indicates that the fault is the most recent geological event to have occurred in this area? Write your answer in one or more complete sentences.

_____

_____

Base your answer to question 24 on the diagram below and your knowledge of Earth Science. The diagram represents layers of rock.

**24.** What is the evidence that indicates that rock layer B is younger than rock layers A and C? Write your answer in one or more complete sentences.

_____

_____

Base your answers to questions 25 and 26 on the diagram below and your knowledge of Earth Science. The diagram shows a geologic cross section of a region where no faulting has occurred. Write your answers to questions 25 and 26 in complete sentences.

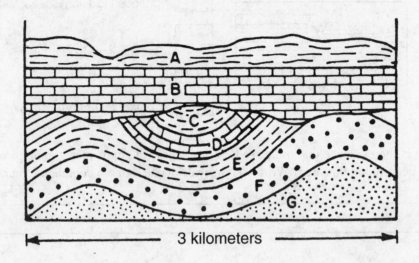

3 kilometers

25. What is the evidence that indicates that an unconformity (a buried erosional surface) is found at the bottom of rock layer B?

_____

_____

26. Describe the evidence that indicates that rock layers C through G were formed before the folding occurred.

_____

_____

# EARTH'S HISTORY

Base your answers to questions 27 through 30 on the diagram below, your knowledge of EarthScience and on the *Earth Science Reference Tables*. The diagram represents a cross section of Earth's crust showing several rock layers containing marine fossils. Overturning has not occurred. Write your answers to questions 27 and 28 in complete sentences.

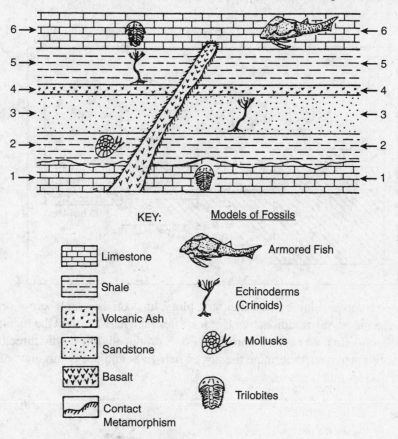

27. Describe why layer 4 is a good time marker.

_____

28. What is the explanation for the irregular surface between layers 1 and 2?

_____

29. List the names of the rocks in their order from oldest to youngest. Use number one (1) for the oldest rock.

_____

_____

30. What is the most recent geologic period that rock layer 6 could possibly be?

_____

Base your answers to questions 31 through 33 on the diagram below, your knowledge of Earth Science and the *Earth Science Reference Tables*. The diagram represents the radioactive decay of uranium-238 and shows the percentages of uranium-238 ($U^{238}$) and the stable element lead-206 ($Pb^{206}$) after three half-lives.

### Radioactive Decay of Uranium-238

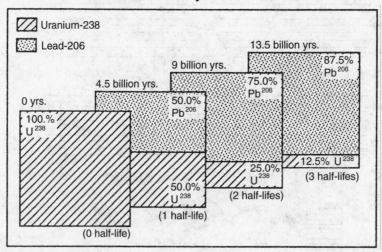

31. **a.** Using the data available in the diagram, plot 2 lines on the graph below, one showing the percentage (%) of radioactive $U^{238}$ left after each half-life, and the second showing the resulting amount of decay-product, $Pb^{206}$, produced. Since only three half-lives have been provided, determine the next 3 half-lives and decay products of $U^{238}$ and $Pb^{206}$, and plot that data as well.

**b.** Label the 2 lines properly.

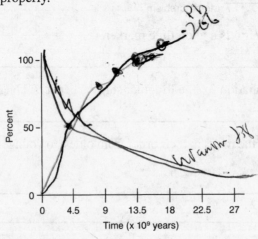

**32.** If an original sample of radioactive $U^{238}$ had a mass of 1600 grams, what is the total amount of the $U^{238}$ sample that would be left after 18 billion years?

_____ 100 grams

**33.** A rock contains 200 grams of radioactive $U^{238}$ and 600 grams of $Pb^{206}$. How old is the rock sample? $9 \times 6^9$

_____

Base your answers to questions 34 through 40 on the table below, your knowledge of Earth Science and the *Earth Science Reference Tables*. The table shows the geologic time ranges of 12 groups of plants and animals. The width of each shaded area represents the relative abundance of each group.

**34.** Of all the animals listed, which is more abundant today than at any time in the past?

_____

**35.** List the groups that have become extinct.

_____

_____

**36.** List the groups which were more abundant during the Carboniferous than during the Jurassic period.

_____

_____

**37.** During which period did the dinosaurs become extinct? _____

**38.** Of all of the animals listed, which animal originated most recently? _____

**39.** Of all the organisms listed, which originated and became extinct between the Cambrian and Tertiary periods? _____

**40.** What major environmental change might have occurred between the end of the Devonian and the beginning of the Triassic period? How did this environmental change affect the type of plants and animals which lived in this region? Please answer in complete sentences.

_____

_____

_____

_____

# CHAPTER 7

# STUDY OF THE ATMOSPHERE

The atmosphere was most likely created by the process of volcanic outgassing. These gases held in place above Earth by gravity formed the first atmosphere. The major gases of this atmosphere were water vapor, carbon dioxide, nitrogen and lesser amounts of other gases from its interior. Because carbon dioxide absorbs heat, the heat could not escape and the atmosphere became warmer. When Earth cooled, the water vapor condensed and fell to Earth's surface as precipitation.

Earth has continuously been recycling water since the outgassing from volcanoes early in its history. This constant re-circulation of water at and near Earth's surface is described in the hydrologic (water) cycle (see Chapter 5).

At one time or another, most people have studied the atmosphere, because few things affect a person's daily life more than the weather. **Weather** is the state or condition of the atmosphere at a particular location for a short period of time. The study of weather is called **meteorology**. Changes in the weather are caused by variations in insolation distributing heat energy unevenly throughout the troposphere. These **atmospheric (weather) variables** describing changes in weather are temperature, air pressure, moisture (relative humidity and dewpoint), precipitation (rain, snow, hail, sleet, etc.), wind speed and direction, and cloud cover.

## ATMOSPHERIC ENERGY

The Sun is the main source of energy on Earth for weather changes. **Energy** is described as the ability to do work. Earth processes, such as erosion, weathering convection, and volcanism all involve energy.

## ELECTROMAGNETIC ENERGY

All matter at temperatures above absolute zero radiates, or gives off, electromagnetic energy. **Absolute zero** is considered to be the lowest possible temperature, the temperature at which all molecular motion ceases. This is a theoretical temperature, since it has never been reached, even in the laboratory. Thus *everything* radiates electromagnetic energy.

## Properties of Electromagnetic Energy

**Electromagnetic energy** is energy that has the properties of transverse waves (see Figure 7-1). These waves are made up of several parts: the **crest** is the top of the wave; the **trough** is the bottom of the wave; and the **amplitude** is the height of the wave, from center to crest. The <u>**wavelength**</u> of a transverse wave is the distance between two successive crests or troughs, or between corresponding points on successive cycles. Wavelength identifies the type of electromagnetic energy that is radiated. The entire range of electromagnetic wavelengths is known as the <u>**electromagnetic spectrum**</u> (see Figure 7-2).

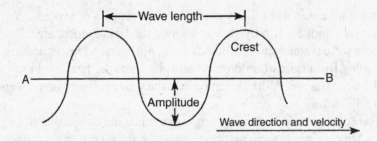

**Figure 7-1**. Parts of a wave.

Regardless of wavelength, all electromagnetic energy travels through space at a speed of $3.0 \times 10^8$ meters per second, which is the "speed of light." The number of wavelengths, or <u>**cycles**</u>, that pass a particular point in a given period of time is called **frequency**. Frequency is usually expressed in cycles per second. Frequency depends on wavelength. Since all electromagnetic energy travels at the same speed, the shorter the wavelength, the greater the frequency.

In the electromagnetic spectrum (Figure 7-2), electromagnetic waves are arranged in order of their wavelengths, or frequencies, with the shortest wavelengths at one end of the spectrum and the longest wavelengths at the other end.

## Solar Energy

All stars, our Sun included, constantly produce and emit electromagnetic energy. <u>**Solar energy**</u>–energy from the Sun–is the major source of energy for Earth. The Sun produces energy in all frequencies of the electromagnetic spectrum. The energy we are most familiar with, of course, is visible light. As Figure 7-2 shows, visible light makes up a very small part of the electromagnetic spectrum. Most of the energy from the Sun is in the form of invisible waves, especially ultraviolet and infrared waves.

Visible light can be separated into different wavelengths. These different wavelengths make up the colors of the **visible spectrum** (Figure 7-2). Although the visible portion of the electromagnetic spectrum is quite small, visible light has the greatest intensity of all the electromagnetic energy received from the Sun.

As an energy source moves towards or away from an observer, there is an apparent change in wave frequency. This apparent change is called the **Doppler effect**. For example, as a source of visible light moves away from an observer, the wave frequency decreases and wavelength increases, creating a shift toward the red end of the visible spectrum. This phenomenon is called the **red shift**. Most stars are moving away from Earth and, therefore, show a red shift. When a light source approaches, wave frequencies increase and wavelengths shift toward the blue end of the spectrum. This is called the **blue shift**. Light from the side of a star that is rotating towards Earth shows a blue shift.

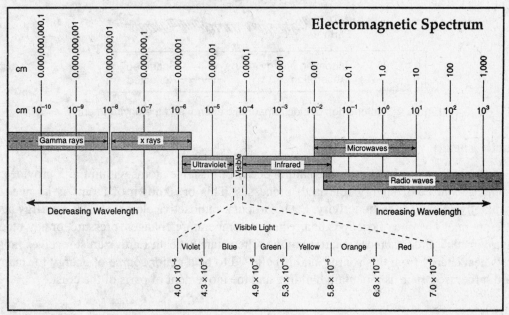

**Figure 7-2**. The electromagnetic spectrum. Most of the energy is in the form of invisible waves. The visible portion of the electromagnetic spectrum is made up of wavelengths of the colors shown.

## Matter and Electromagnetic Energy

When electromagnetic energy comes in contact with a material, it can interact in one of several ways. It can be bent, or **refracted**, as it passes through the material. It can be reflected to a new direction. It can be **scattered** (refracted and reflected) in several different directions. It can be taken in, or **absorbed**, by the material (Figure 7-3).

Any material that is a good absorber of electromagnetic energy is also a good radiator of electromagnetic energy. However, the energy radiated is of a longer wavelength than that which was absorbed. For example, dark soil will absorb light energy. It will radiate some of that energy back into space in the form of heat, which is in the infrared range of the spectrum. Materials with dark, rough surfaces are better absorbers of electromagnetic energy than are materials with smooth, light-colored surfaces.

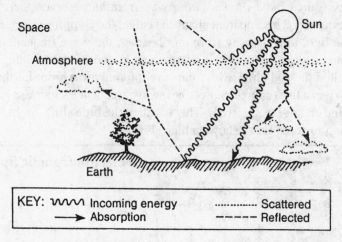

**Figure 7-3**. Interaction of electromagnetic energy and the environment.

## Earth Energy

In addition to solar energy, the natural decay of unstable atoms within Earth provides a secondary source of energy for Earth processes. This breakdown of atoms is known as **radioactive decay**, or **radioactivity**. Each particular radioactive element releases energy at a different rate. The rate of decay is unaffected by temperature changes, pressure, or any other environmental circumstances. Matter in the molten state beneath Earth's crust receives most of its heat energy from this source, and is believed to be a major source of energy for many Earth processes, such as mountain building and the movement of parts of the crust.

## QUESTIONS

1. Earth's surface temperatures are due chiefly to energy received from

   (1) insolation from the Sun          (2) radioactivity within Earth's crust
   (3) fusion in Earth's core           (4) friction between the crust and the mantle

2. Infrared, ultraviolet, and visible light are all part of the solar spectrum. The basic difference between them is their

   (1) wavelength     (2) speed     (3) source     (4) temperature

3. Which of the following is a source of electromagnetic waves?

   (1) matter     (2) temperature     (3) gravity     (4) magnetism

**4.** At which temperature will an object radiate the greatest amount of electromagnetic energy? [Refer to the *Earth Science Reference Tables*.]

(1) 0°Fahrenheit      (2) 5°Celsius      (3) 10°Fahrenheit      (4) 230°Kelvin

**5.** The amount of electromagnetic energy given off by an object depends on its

(1) wavelength      (2) wave frequency      (3) potential energy      (4) temperature

**6.** If we increase the wavelength of electromagnetic waves, what will happen to the frequency of the waves?

(1) It will increase.      (2) It will decrease.      (3) It will remain the same.

**7.** Which of the following will not give off electromagnetic energy?

(1) any object at a temperature above absolute zero
(2) all objects at temperatures of absolute zero
(3) all objects at temperatures below absolute zero
(4) any object at a temperature above or below absolute zero

**8.** As the ability of an object to absorb electromagnetic energy increases, the ability of that object to radiate electromagnetic energy

(1) decreases      (2) increases      (3) remains the same

**9.** How does the amount of heat energy reflected by a smooth, dark-colored concrete surface compare with the amount of heat energy reflected by a smooth, light-colored surface?

(1) The dark-colored surface will reflect less heat energy.
(2) The dark-colored surface will reflect more heat energy.
(3) The dark-colored surface will reflect the same amount of heat energy.

# ENERGY TRANSFER IN THE ATMOSPHERE

There are three methods of energy transfer: convection, conduction, and radiation. The movement of heat energy is particularly important in Earth Science. Radiation is the transfer of energy through space in the form of waves, while conduction and convection both require matter for transfer.

## Convection

**Convection** is the transfer of heat energy by movements of liquids and gases (fluids). These movements are caused by differences in density within the fluids. When most fluids are heated, they expand, and their density decreases. If a pot of tea is heated, the water at the bottom expands and becomes less dense (Figure 7-4). The colder, denser water at the top pushes down, displacing the warmer, less dense water at the bottom, forcing it to rise. The circulation of a gas or a liquid resulting from this heat transfer process is called a **convection cell** or **convection current**. Convection cells occur in all bodies of water, in the air, and even the molten rock of the mantle just below the lithosphere. Convection is the cause of ocean currents, winds, and very probably "continental drift", the driving force of plate tectonics.

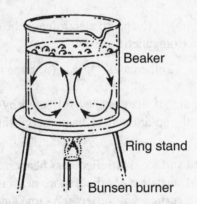

**Figure 7-4**. As the liquid is heated at the bottom of the beaker, the warm liquid rises and the cooler, denser liquid sinks, setting a convection cell in motion.

## Conduction

**Conduction** is the transfer of heat energy by the collision of atoms with adjoining atoms, or molecules with adjoining molecules. For example, if one end of an iron bar is held in a flame, eventually the other end will become hot as heat is transferred, atom by atom, along the length of the bar. Conduction is most effective in solids, although it can occur in liquids and gases.

## Radiation

**Radiation** is the transfer of electromagnetic energy through space in the form of invisible transverse waves. No medium is required for this tranfer of energy. The energy travels in a straight line at the speed of light. All objects are constantly radiating and absorbing electromagnetic energy. Radiation from the Sun is the major source of Earth's energy.

## QUESTIONS

Base your answers to questions 1 through 5 on your knowledge of Earth Science and the diagrams below. Figure I represents the physical setup of an energy absorption investigation. A black metal container and a shiny metal container are placed equal distances from a lamp heat source. A thermometer is inserted in each container. Inside air-temperature measurements are taken for 12 minutes while the lamp is on. Figure II is a graph of the temperatures recorded for the 12-minute period.

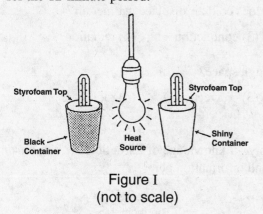

Figure I
(not to scale)

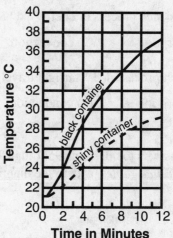

Figure II

1. The heat source in figure I is transferring its energy primarily by

   (1) refraction      (2) radiation      (3) convection      (4) conduction

2. During the 12 minutes of heating, the black container and the shiny container both

   (1) received the same amount of energy      (2) absorbed the same amount of energy
   (3) radiated the same amount of energy      (4) reflected the same amount of energy

3. As energy from the heat source interacts with its surroundings, it is being absorbed and

   (1) reflected, only                  (2) refracted, only
   (3) scattered, only                 (4) reflected, refracted, and scattered

4. According to figure II, the temperature difference between the black container and the shiny container after 5 minutes of heating was

   (1) 30°C          (2) 25°C          (3) 5°C          (4) 4°C

5. At what rate did the air temperature inside the black container rise in the first 10 minutes?

   (1) 1.5°C/min      (2) 2.6°C/min      (3) 3.6°C/min      (4) 4.5°C/min

6. Which process transfers heat from one part of a solid object to another part of the object by direct contact when molecules collide?

   (1) radiation         (2) advection         (3) conduction         (4) convection

7. During which process of energy exchange does cold air displace warmer air?

   (1) absorption        (2) convection        (3) conduction        (4) radiation

8. By which process does starlight travel through space?

   (1) absorption        (2) conduction        (3) convection        (4) radiation

Base your answers to questions 9 through 13 on your knowledge of Earth Science, the *Earth Science Reference Tables*, and on the diagram and information below.

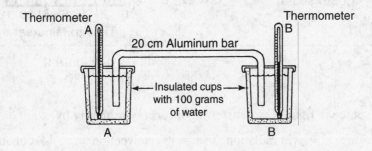

A student used the apparatus shown in the diagram above to perform an experiment. At the beginning of the experiment, the temperature of the water was 90°C in cup A and 10°C in cup B. The student took readings from the two thermometers for 14 minutes and recorded the following information:

| Time (min) | Cup A Temperature (°C) | Cup B Temperature (°C) |
|---|---|---|
| 0 | 90 | 10 |
| 2 | 87 | 10 |
| 4 | 84 | 10 |
| 6 | 81 | 11 |
| 8 | 78 | 13 |
| 10 | 75 | 15 |
| 12 | 72 | 17 |
| 14 | 69 | 19 |

9. Which graph best represents the relationship between time and the temperature of the water in cup A?

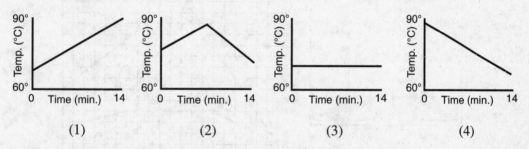

(1)     (2)     (3)     (4)

10. Which statement best explains why the amount of heat energy gained by cup B is less than the amount of heat energy lost by cup A?

(1) Water heats more slowly than it cools.
(2) The aluminum bar is losing some heat to the air.
(3) The thermometer in cup A generated heat energy.
(4) Heat energy flows from heat sinks to heat sources.

11. The difference between the amount of heat energy lost by cup A and the amount of heat energy gained by cup B could be decreased by

(1) replacing the 20-cm aluminum bar with a 10-cm aluminum bar
(2) using more water in cup A
(3) using metal cups instead of insulated cups
(4) lowering the room temperature to 10°C

**12.** If all of the heat lost by cup A were gained by cup B, what would be the highest possible temperature of the water in cup B?

(1) 19°C (2) 31°C (3) 50°C (4) 80°C

**13.** At the start of the investigation, which could be considered a heat source?

(1) the water in calorimeter A       (2) the water in calorimeter B
(3) the air surrounding the calorimeters       (4) the metal bar between the calorimeters

Base your answers to questions 14 and 15 on your knowledge of Earth Science, the *Earth Science Reference Tables*, and the diagram and graph below. In the diagram, equal masses of water and soil are located at identical distances from the lamp. Both were heated for ten minutes and then the lamp was removed. The water and soil were then allowed to cool for ten minutes. The graph shows the temperature data obtained during the investigation.

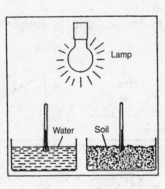
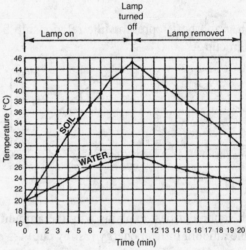

**14.** By which process was most of the energy transferred between the lamp and the water during the first 10 minutes of the investigation?

(1) conduction       (2) convection       (3) reflection       (4) radiation

**15.** What was the rate at which the soil temperature changed during the first ten minutes of the investigation?

(1) 0.8°C/min       (2) 2.5°C/min       (3) 8°C/min       (4) 25°C/min

# ENERGY TRANSFORMATION

## Conservation of Energy

The study of energy often involves a series of changes. A **closed energy system** is one in which no energy from outside the system can get in and no energy from the inside can get out. A good example of a closed energy system is a thermos bottle, where no heat energy can get in or out. In any closed energy system, the total amount of energy does not change. Thus, the amount of energy given off by an object (an **energy source**) must equal the amount of absorbed by some other object (an **energy sink**). The principle which states that energy can be neither created nor destroyed, but can be transformed from one type to another without any loss of energy within a closed system is the principle of **conservation of energy**.

## Kinetic and Potential Energy

All objects in motion have **kinetic energy**. Energy related to position or state, often thought of as "stored" energy, is called **potential energy**. Even the atoms and molecules of our bodies have kinetic energy, although we cannot feel the movement. And the fact that molecules of water vapor "floating" around in the air carry potential energy is also a difficult concept to accept. Kinetic and potential energy are interchangeable-each is capable of being transformed into the other.

The movement of matter toward or away from Earth's center results in an energy transformation from kinetic to potential or potential to kinetic. For example, a baseball thrown straight up into the air has kinetic energy (see Figure 7-5). As the ball rises, it slows down, losing kinetic energy (and gaining potential energy) until, for an instant, it stops and has zero kinetic energy. For the instant the ball stops and appears suspended in space, it has maximum potential energy because of its position with respect to Earth. The higher the position at which it stops, the greater is its potential energy.

As soon as the ball begins to fall, some of its potential energy is transformed into kinetic energy again. The ball falls faster and faster until it hits the ground. At its greatest speed, just before it hits the ground, the ball has the greatest amount of kinetic energy. Once it hits the ground, all the kinetic energy is transformed back into potential energy. Because it is closer to the center of Earth's mass, it has less potential energy on the ground than it did for the instant it seemed suspended in space. Water at the top of a waterfall, just before it falls, has a certain amount of potential energy. The farther it has to fall, the more potential energy it has. As it falls, some of its potential energy is transformed into kinetic energy. Just before the water reaches the bottom of the falls, it has its maximum kinetic energy.

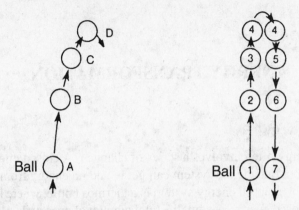

**Figure 7-5**. Energy transformations. In the ball at the left, kinetic energy (K.E.)/(PE.) is changing to potential energy as the ball rises. At point D, kinetic energy is 0; potential energy is at its maximum. On the right, from 1 to 4, K.E. is decreasing, PE. is increasing. From 4 to 7, PE. is decreasing, K.E. is increasing.

## Friction and Energy Transformation

Energy is also transformed at interfaces where friction occurs. For example, as a wind blows over the land, some of its kinetic energy is transformed into heat energy at the interface between the wind and the land. This loss of kinetic energy causes the wind to slow down. This energy transformation takes place because of the friction between the wind and the land.

## Wavelength Reradiation

The characteristics of the surface of a material determine the quantity and type of electromagnetic energy it absorbs. In general, a good absorber of electromagnetic energy is also a good radiator. When shortwave electromagnetic radiations, such as ultraviolet waves and visible light, are absorbed by Earth, they are subsequently re-radiated as longer-wavelength radiation, such as infrared (heat). This energy transformation is particularly important in supplying heat to the atmosphere.

# HEAT AND TEMPERATURE

## Temperature

Heat and temperature are often mistakenly thought of as being the same when, in fact, they are different. According to the modern theory of matter, all matter is made up of individual particles (atoms and molecules) that are in constant, random motion. Thus, all particles of matter have kinetic energy. The faster the motion, the greater the kinetic energy.

The temperature of a sample of matter is a measure of the kinetic energy of the particles of that sample. Since all particles do not move at the same speed, **temperature** is defined as a measure of the *average* kinetic energy of the particles in the sample being measured. The faster the particles are moving (greater kinetic energy), the higher the temperature. If the particles in two different samples of matter have the same average kinetic energy, the samples will be at the same temperature.

## Temperature Scales

In most cases, the terms "hot" and "cold" are not sufficient for indicating temperatures. **Thermometers** are instruments used to measure temperature. Thermometers have scales that are marked off in units called **degrees**. There are a variety of temperature scales, but in Earth Science, the Celsius scale is used for most temperature measurements, while the Fahrenheit scale is frequently used to measure air temperature. The relationships between three commonly used temperature scales–Celsius, Fahrenheit, and Kelvin–are given in the *Earth Science Reference Tables*.

## Heat

Temperature is a measure of the average kinetic energy of the particles in a sample of matter. Heat, on the other hand, is itself a form of energy, called **heat energy**. It can be thought of as the *total* kinetic energy of the particles in a sample of matter. To understand the difference between temperature and heat, consider two different volumes of water, both at a temperature of 75°C. (See Figure 7-6.) Since the temperatures are the same, the average kinetic energy of the molecules in each sample is the same. However, because the larger volume has more molecules in motion, it has a greater total kinetic energy, and thus contains more heat energy.

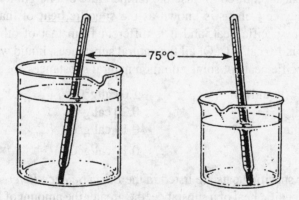

**Figure 7-6.** Although both samples of water are at the same temperature, the larger sample (left) contains more heat energy.

Heat always flows from a region of higher energy to a region of lower energy. Thus, when two objects at different temperatures are placed in contact with one another, some of the kinetic energy of the hotter object will be transferred to the colder object. The hotter object loses kinetic energy, and its temperature falls; the colder object gains kinetic energy, and its temperature rises. For example, if a rock at a temperature of 90°C is placed into water at a room temperature of 20°C, energy will be transferred from the rock to the water until both samples are at the same temperature, which will be between 90°C and 20°C. The energy that is transferred from the hotter to the colder body of matter is heat energy, or heat. Heat energy can also be transferred by electromagnetic radiation, as from the Sun to Earth.

## Calories

When an object is heated, the heat energy is transformed to kinetic energy and the particles of the object move faster. Thus, the average kinetic energy of the particles increases, and the temperature of the object goes up. The process of cooling (removing heat from) an object is just the opposite.

Different substances heat up at different rates. In order to establish a unit for measuring heat quantity, water was chosen as a standard substance, and the name *calorie* was selected for the unit. One **calorie** is defined as the quantity of heat needed to raise the temperature of one gram of liquid water by one degree Celsius. Thus, to raise the temperature of 2 grams of water by 1 degree C, 2 calories of heat are needed; to raise the temperature of 5 grams of water by 1 degree C, 5 calories are needed, etc. On the other hand, to raise the temperature of 1 gram of water by 2 degrees C, 2 calories are needed; to raise the temperature of the same mass of water by 10 degrees C, 10 calories are needed, and so forth.

## Specific Heat

The quantity of heat required to raise the temperature of one gram of a substance by a temperature of one degree Celsius is known as the **specific heat** of that substance. Every substance has its own specific heat, and it is different from that of other substances. The specific heat of water is 1.0 cal/g°C. Of all the natural substances, liquid water has the highest specific heat. The specific heats of some common natural substances are shown here:

| | |
|---|---|
| Water (liquid) | 1.0 cal/g°C |
| Basalt | 0.20 cal/g°C |
| Granite | 0.19 cal/g°C |
| Iron | 0.11 cal/g°C |

These and other specific heats are listed in the *Earth Science Reference Tables*.

The higher the specific heat of a substance, the greater the amount of heat needed to raise its temperature. For example, it takes five times as much heat to raise the temperature of a mass of water than it does to raise the temperature of an equal mass of basalt by the same amount. Put another way, basalt will heat up 5 times faster than an equal mass of water, assuming heat is added at the same rate in both cases.

## Heat Gain or Loss

During any heat transfer, the amount of heat energy lost by a heat source equals the amount of heat gained by a heat sink. In the problem above, the heat lost by the basalt will be gained by the environment, most likely the air around the basalt.

# HEAT ENERGY AND PHASE CHANGES

## Latent Heat

Normally, when heat is added to a substance, the temperature of the substance will rise. There are conditions, however, when the addition of heat will *not* cause the temperature of a substance to change. Such a phenomenon occurs during a change of state, or a **phase change**. For example, when a substance changes from a solid to a liquid, the temperature of the substance remains the same even though heat is being added continually. All the heat energy is used in the phase change. The added heat is not being used to increase the kinetic energy of the molecules. It is being converted to a type of potential energy called **latent heat**.

## Latent Heat Loss or Gain During Phase Changes

Certain phase changes require the addition of heat. These changes include **melting** (solid to liquid), **evaporation** (liquid to gas), and **sublimation** (solid to gas). During such phase changes, latent heat is *gained* by the substance. Other phase changes require the removal of heat. These include **condensation** (gas to liquid), **freezing** (liquid to solid), and **sublimation** (gas to solid). During these changes, latent heat is *lost* by the substance. The total amount of heat lost or gained by a substance during a phase change can be found by multiplying the mass of the substance by the latent heat value of that substance. The latent heat value, which is the change in potential energy per unit of mass, varies with the substance and the type of change.

## Water and Latent Heat

The amount of heat energy needed to change a given mass of water from a liquid to a gas is greater than the amount of heat needed to change the same mass of water from a solid (ice) to a liquid. The heating curve in Figure 7-7 shows the temperature changes that occur as one gram of ice at -100°C is changed to water vapor at 200°C. During the entire time, heat is added to the water at a constant rate. When heat is added to the ice at -100°C, the kinetic energy of the water molecules increases and the temperature of the ice rises to 0°C, which is the melting point temperature of ice. At this point, the temperature stops rising. During the time needed for all the ice to change to liquid water, the temperature remains the same, even though heat is constantly being added. The heat is being changed to potential energy in the form of latent heat. The latent heat involved when 1 gram of ice changes to liquid water is 80 calories. This value is known as the heat of fusion of ice.

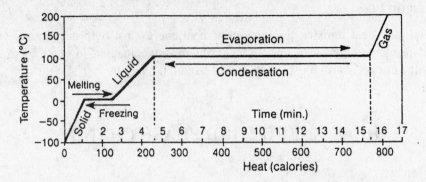

**Figure 7-7.** Heating/cooling curve for water. The graph is a heating curve when read from left to right, a cooling curve when read from right to left.

When all the ice has changed to a liquid at 0°C, the temperature of the water starts to rise as heat is added. The temperature continues to rise until it reaches 100°C, which is the boiling point of water. At this point, the temperature stops rising again. During the time needed for all the liquid water to change to a gas, the temperature remains the same. Again, the heat is changed to potential energy in the form of latent heat. The heat needed to change 1 gram of liquid water at 100°C to water vapor at the same temperature is called the latent heat of vaporization. The heat of vaporization of water is 540 calories per gram.

When all the liquid water has changed to a gas, the temperature begins to rise again, and continues to rise until it reaches 200°C, which is the limit of the curve on this particular graph.

By reading this graph from right to left, it becomes a cooling curve. You can trace the temperature changes that occur as one gram of water vapor at 200°C is changed to ice at -100°C. During the entire time, heat is being removed from the water at a constant rate. During each phase change, latent heat is released to the environment.

Solar energy stored in the process of evaporation is released when clouds form. Although we cannot see it, water vapor in the air carries with it tremendous amounts of potential energy in the form of latent heat. For every gram of water vapor that condenses to liquid water, 540 calories of heat is released to the environment. This heat becomes the "fuel" that feeds winds and major storms, such as hurricanes.

# QUESTIONS

1. The diagram below shows temperature values at various points in a solid piece of aluminum. Toward which point will heat flow from point P?

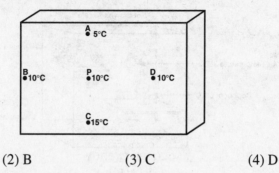

(1) A            (2) B            (3) C            (4) D

2. A boulder falls freely from point A to point B, as shown in the diagram below. Which statement best explains the relationship between the height of the boulder and its potential and kinetic energy as it falls?

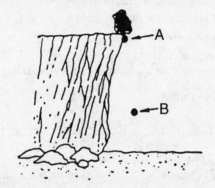

(1) Its potential energy decreases and its kinetic energy increases.
(2) Its potential energy increases and its kinetic energy decreases.
(3) Its potential energy and kinetic energy both decrease.
(4) Its potential energy and kinetic energy both increase.

Base your answers to questions 3 through 6 on your knowledge of Earth Science, the *Earth Science Reference Tables*, and the diagram below. The diagram represents a closed energy system consisting of air and equal masses of copper, granite, and water in a perfectly insulated container. The temperatures were taken at the time the materials were placed inside the closed system.

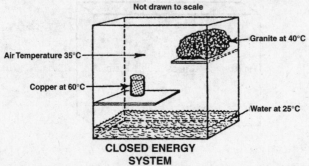

Not drawn to scale

Granite at 40°C

Air Temperature 35°C

Copper at 60°C

Water at 25°C

**CLOSED ENERGY
SYSTEM**

3. In this system, which material is a heat sink for another material?

   (1) The water is a heat sink for the air.
   (2) The copper is a heat sink for the granite.
   (3) The granite is a heat sink for the water.
   (4) The copper is a heat sink for the air.

4. Which material in the energy system has the highest specific heat?

   (1) copper        (2) granite        (3) dry air        (4) water

5. In the first day after the materials were placed in the system, the temperature of the water would probably

   (1) decrease        (2) increase        (3) remain the same

6. As time passes, the total energy in the system will

   (1) decrease        (2) increase        (3) remain the same

7. Compared with the temperatures of land surfaces, temperatures of water surfaces change

   (1) faster because water has a higher specific heat
   (2) faster because water has a lower speciflc heat
   (3) slower because water has a higher specific heat
   (4) slower because water has a lower specific heat

Base your answers to questions 8 through 11 on your knowledge of Earth Science, the *Earth Science Reference Tables*, and the graph below. The graph shows the temperatures recorded when a sample of water was heated at a constant rate from -50°C to 100°C during a 20-minute period.

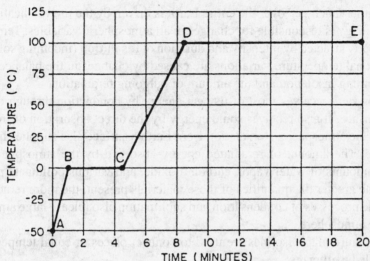

8. The water temperature reached 65°C after the sample had been heated for approximately how many minutes?

    (1) 5 min          (2) 7 min          (3) 3 min          (4) 9 min

9. Between points D and E the water most likely was

    (1) freezing       (2) melting        (3) evaporating    (4) condensing

10. Between which points was the temperature changing at the greatest rate?

    (1) A and B        (2) B and C        (3) C and D        (4) D and E

11. The greatest amount of energy is required to heat the sample from point

    (1) A to point B   (2) B to point C   (3) C to point D   (4) D to point E

12. A sample of water undergoes the phase changes from ice to vapor and back to ice as shown in the model below. During which phase change does the sample gain the greatest amount of energy?

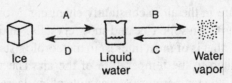

    (1) A              (2) B              (3) C              (4) D

# ATMOSPHERIC RELATIONSHIPS

## Temperature Variations

The "weather machine" over the entire Earth is driven by the uneven heating of Earth's surface. Heat energy is responsible for changes in all atmospheric variables. Temperature, for example, is greatly affected by intensity and duration of **insolation** (incoming solar radiation). Daily and seasonal temperature variations are caused by changes in the balance between the amount of incoming insolation and the amount of outgoing reradiation.

The atmosphere receives most of its heat energy by conduction through direct contact with Earth's surface. It also receives some energy by the direct absorption of insolation as it passes through the atmosphere. Reradiation from Earth's surface also supplies heat energy to the atmosphere. The amount of reradiated energy absorbed by the atmosphere is directly related to the amounts of water vapor, carbon dioxide, and various pollutants present in the atmosphere. The greater the quantities of these materials present, the more reradiated energy is absorbed. The processes of condensation and sublimation also release large amounts of heat energy into the atmosphere.

On temperature maps, isolines are used to connect places of equal temperature. These isolines are called **isotherms**.

**Factors affecting local temperatures**. Latitude, altitude, and closeness to large bodies of water can influence local daily and seasonal temperatures. The higher the latitude, the lower the intensity of insolation received and, thus, the lower the average daily and seasonal temperatures. For example, arctic regions are much colder, both daily and annually, than are tropical regions near the equator.

As you ascend into the troposphere, the average temperature decreases. Thus, locations at high altitudes generally have lower average temperatures than places at lower altitudes. Average daily and annual temperatures at the tops of mountains are lower than those at their bases.

Water heats up and cools down more slowly than land. Thus, the presence of large bodies of water has a modifying effect on temperatures of nearby land areas. For this reason, coastal regions have cooler summer temperatures and warmer winter temperatures than do inland locations at corresponding latitudes.

## Moisture Variations

The amount of moisture in the air is constantly changing. Moisture can be found in the air as a liquid (water droplets), as a solid (ice and snow crystals), and as a gas (water vapor). It is the invisible gaseous state that is of most interest to meteorologists. The ability of air to hold water vapor is directly related to the temperature of the air. The warmer the air, the more moisture it can hold. Thus, if the temperature of a sample of air decreases, the amount of water vapor it can hold–its **capacity**–also decreases.

When the air contains all the moisture it can hold at a particular temperature, it is said to be filled to capacity, or **saturated**. However, the air is not usually saturated. In order to attain saturation, more water vapor must be added, or the air must be cooled to the **dewpoint temperature**, the temperature at which condensation occurs. At the dewpoint, the air is holding all the moisture it can hold.

The amount of water vapor actually present in the air is known as **absolute humidity**. There is a direct relationship between absolute humidity and the dewpoint temperature. The greater the absolute humidity, the higher the dewpoint temperature. When air is cooled below the dewpoint temperature, condensation occurs, because there is more water vapor in the air than it can hold at the new temperature. When moist air rises, it cools. When the rising air is cooled below its dewpoint temperature, clouds begin to form. As the air temperature approaches the dewpoint, precipitation becomes more likely.

## Relative Humidity

**Relative humidity** is a comparison between the amount of moisture in the air with the amount the air can actually hold at that temperature. For example, if the air is holding half as much as it could be holding, the relative humidity is 50%. The air can be "half-full" of moisture, with a relative humidity of 50%, when the air temperature is warm or cool. But, when the temperature is high, the air will actually contain *more* water vapor than when the temperature is low. Think of a large glass and a small glass each half filled with water. Both glasses are 50% full, but the large glass contains more water.

As the dewpoint temperature and the air temperature come closer together, relative humidity increases and the probability of precipitation increases. The relative humidity is usually lowest in midafternoon, when the difference between air temperature and dewpoint temperature is the greatest (see Figure 7-8).

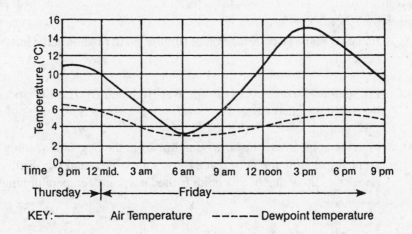

KEY: ———— Air Temperature    – – – – Dewpoint temperature

**Figure 7-8**. This graph illustrates the typical relationship between air temperature, dewpoint temperature, and time of day.

## Determining Dewpoint Temperature

An instrument called a **psychrometer** is used to find the dewpoint. It consists of two thermometers–a dry-bulb thermometer and a wet-bulb thermometer (Figure 7-9). The wet-bulb thermometer is so-called because it has a wet "sock" wrapped around its bulb. When the psychrometer is swung through the air, water evaporates from the wet sock, removing heat from the bulb of the thermometer, thus causing the temperature reading on that thermometer to be lowered. The smaller the difference between the wet-bulb and dry-bulb temperatures, the more humid the air.

The dewpoint temperature may be found by using the **Dewpoint Temperatures Chart** (see Figure 7-10).

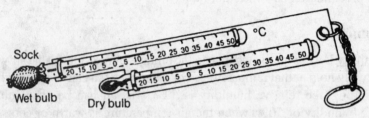

**Figure 7-9.** A sling psychrometer. As this instrument is "slung" through the air, rapid evaporation from the "sock" will result in a lower temperature reading on the wet-bulb thermometer.

## Determining Dewpoint Temperature With Chart

Assume a dry-bulb temperature of 10°C and a wet-bulb temperature of 6°C. The difference between these two readings is 4°C. Follow these steps to find the dewpoint temperature:

**Step A**:  Locate the Dry-Bulb Temperature (Figure 7-10) reading at the left of the chart (letter A).

**Step B**:  Locate the difference between the Wet-Bulb and DryBulb Temperatures at the top of the chart (letter B).

**Step C**:  Find the point where the horizontal line from the Dry Bulb reading meets the vertical line from the Difference Between the Wet- and Dry-Bulb readings (letter C). The value of this point is the Dewpoint Temperature in degrees Celsius.

The dewpoint in the problem above is 1°C

## Dewpoint Temperatures (°C)

| Dry-Bulb Temperature (°C) | Difference Between Wet-Bulb and Dry-Bulb Temperatures (C°) | | | | | | | | | | | | | | | |
|---|---|---|---|---|---|---|---|---|---|---|---|---|---|---|---|---|
| | 0 | 1 | 2 | 3 | 4 | 5 | 6 | 7 | 8 | 9 | 10 | 11 | 12 | 13 | 14 | 15 |
| −20 | −20 | −33 | | | | | | | | | | | | | | |
| −18 | −18 | −28 | | | | | | | | | | | | | | |
| −16 | −16 | −24 | | | | | | | | | | | | | | |
| −14 | −14 | −21 | −36 | | | | | | | | | | | | | |
| −12 | −12 | −18 | −28 | | | | | | | | | | | | | |
| −10 | −10 | −14 | −22 | | | | | | | | | | | | | |
| −8 | −8 | −12 | −18 | −29 | | | | | | | | | | | | |
| −6 | −6 | −10 | −14 | −22 | | | | | | | | | | | | |
| −4 | −4 | −7 | −12 | −17 | −29 | | | | | | | | | | | |
| −2 | −2 | −5 | −8 | −13 | −20 | | | | | | | | | | | |
| 0 | 0 | −3 | −6 | −9 | −15 | −24 | | | | | | | | | | |
| 2 | 2 | −1 | −3 | −6 | −11 | −17 | | | | | | | | | | |
| 4 | 4 | 1 | −1 | −4 | −7 | −11 | −19 | | | | | | | | | |
| 6 | 6 | 4 | 1 | −1 | −4 | −7 | −13 | −21 | | | | | | | | |
| 8 | 8 | 6 | 3 | 1 | −2 | −5 | −9 | −14 | | | | | | | | |
| 10 | 10 | 8 | 6 | 4 | 1 | −2 | −5 | −9 | −14 | −28 | | | | | | |
| 12 | 12 | 10 | 8 | 6 | 4 | 1 | −2 | −5 | −9 | −16 | | | | | | |
| 14 | 14 | 12 | 11 | 9 | 6 | 4 | 1 | −2 | −5 | −10 | −17 | | | | | |
| 16 | 16 | 14 | 13 | 11 | 9 | 7 | 4 | 1 | −1 | −6 | −10 | −17 | | | | |
| 18 | 18 | 16 | 15 | 13 | 11 | 9 | 7 | 4 | 2 | −2 | −5 | −10 | −19 | | | |
| 20 | 20 | 19 | 17 | 15 | 14 | 12 | 10 | 7 | 4 | 2 | −2 | −5 | −10 | −19 | | |
| 22 | 22 | 21 | 19 | 17 | 16 | 14 | 12 | 10 | 8 | 5 | 3 | −1 | −5 | −10 | −19 | |
| 24 | 24 | 23 | 21 | 20 | 18 | 16 | 14 | 12 | 10 | 8 | 6 | 2 | −1 | −5 | −10 | −18 |
| 26 | 26 | 25 | 23 | 22 | 20 | 18 | 17 | 15 | 13 | 11 | 9 | 6 | 3 | 0 | −4 | −9 |
| 28 | 28 | 27 | 25 | 24 | 22 | 21 | 19 | 17 | 16 | 14 | 11 | 9 | 7 | 4 | 1 | −3 |
| 30 | 30 | 29 | 27 | 26 | 24 | 23 | 21 | 19 | 18 | 16 | 14 | 12 | 10 | 8 | 5 | 1 |

**Figure 7-10**. Dewpoint Temperatures

## Determining Relative Humidity With Chart

To find the relative humidity of the problem above, use the **Relative Humidity Chart** (Figure 7-11) and complete the following steps.

**Step D**: Locate the Dry-Bulb Temperature 10°C (letter D).

**Step E**: Locate the Difference Between the Wet-Bulb and Dry-Bulb Temperatures 4°C (letter E).

**Step F**: Find the point where the horizontal line from the Dry-Bulb reading meets the vertical line from the Difference Between the Wet- and Dry-Bulb readings (letter F). The value of this point is the relative humidity.

The relative humidity of the problem above is 54%. The closer the air temperature and dewpoint temperature, the higher the relative humidity.

## Relative Humidity (%)

| Dry-Bulb Tempera-ture (°C) | Difference Between Wet-Bulb and Dry-Bulb Temperatures (C°) | | | | | | | | | | | | | | | |
|---|---|---|---|---|---|---|---|---|---|---|---|---|---|---|---|---|
| | 0 | 1 | 2 | 3 | 4 | 5 | 6 | 7 | 8 | 9 | 10 | 11 | 12 | 13 | 14 | 15 |
| −20 | 100 | 28 | | | | | | | | | | | | | | |
| −18 | 100 | 40 | | | | | | | | | | | | | | |
| −16 | 100 | 48 | | | | | | | | | | | | | | |
| −14 | 100 | 55 | 11 | | | | | | | | | | | | | |
| −12 | 100 | 61 | 23 | | | | | | | | | | | | | |
| −10 | 100 | 66 | 33 | | | | | | | | | | | | | |
| −8 | 100 | 71 | 41 | 13 | | | | | | | | | | | | |
| −6 | 100 | 73 | 48 | 20 | | | | | | | | | | | | |
| −4 | 100 | 77 | 54 | 32 | 11 | | | | | | | | | | | |
| −2 | 100 | 79 | 58 | 37 | 20 | 1 | | | | | | | | | | |
| 0 | 100 | 81 | 63 | 45 | 28 | 11 | | | | | | | | | | |
| 2 | 100 | 83 | 67 | 51 | 36 | 20 | 6 | | | | | | | | | |
| 4 | 100 | 85 | 70 | 56 | 42 | 27 | 14 | | | | | | | | | |
| 6 | 100 | 86 | 72 | 59 | 46 | 35 | 22 | 10 | | | | | | | | |
| 8 | 100 | 87 | 74 | 62 | 51 | 39 | 28 | 17 | 6 | | | | | | | |
| 10 | 100 | 88 | 76 | 65 | 54 | 43 | 33 | 24 | 13 | 4 | | | | | | |
| 12 | 100 | 88 | 78 | 67 | 57 | 48 | 38 | 28 | 19 | 10 | 2 | | | | | |
| 14 | 100 | 89 | 79 | 69 | 60 | 50 | 41 | 33 | 25 | 16 | 8 | 1 | | | | |
| 16 | 100 | 90 | 80 | 71 | 62 | 54 | 45 | 37 | 29 | 21 | 14 | 7 | 1 | | | |
| 18 | 100 | 91 | 81 | 72 | 64 | 56 | 48 | 40 | 33 | 26 | 19 | 12 | 6 | | | |
| 20 | 100 | 91 | 82 | 74 | 66 | 58 | 51 | 44 | 36 | 30 | 23 | 17 | 11 | 5 | | |
| 22 | 100 | 92 | 83 | 75 | 68 | 60 | 53 | 46 | 40 | 33 | 27 | 21 | 15 | 10 | 4 | |
| 24 | 100 | 92 | 84 | 76 | 69 | 62 | 55 | 49 | 42 | 36 | 30 | 25 | 20 | 14 | 9 | 4 |
| 26 | 100 | 92 | 85 | 77 | 70 | 64 | 57 | 51 | 45 | 39 | 34 | 28 | 23 | 18 | 13 | 9 |
| 28 | 100 | 93 | 66 | 78 | 71 | 65 | 59 | 53 | 47 | 42 | 36 | 31 | 26 | 21 | 17 | 12 |
| 30 | 100 | 93 | 86 | 79 | 72 | 66 | 61 | 55 | 49 | 44 | 39 | 34 | 29 | 25 | 20 | 16 |

**Figure 7-11**. Relative Humidity(%)

## Pressure Variations

Air has weight. The force, or weight, of the air pushing down on a unit area of surface is called **air pressure**, or **atmospheric pressure**. The more dense a sample, of air, the greater the weight of a unit volume and, therefore, the greater the air pressure exerted by that sample. Density and air pressure changes are closely related to temperature changes. Air pressure is inversely proportional to temperature changes and directly proportional to density changes. As the temperature of a sample of air decreases, the air contracts (its volume decreases). Thus, its density increases and the air pressure also increases (see Figure 7-12).

The instrument used to measure atmospheric pressure is the **barometer**. A mercury barometer is a very accurate instrument consisting of a glass tube containing a column of mercury. The mercury is supported in the tube by the pressure of the air outside the tube. *Standard airpressure* at sea level is 29.92 inches of mercury (the length of the mercury column supported by air pressure), or 1013.2 millibars. This pressure is often referred to *as one atmosphere of pressure*.

On weather maps, isolines called **isobars** join places of equal air pressure. The isobars are used to show pressure patterns over large areas of Earth's surface. The pressure interval between isobars on a weather map is 4 millibars (see Figure 7-13).

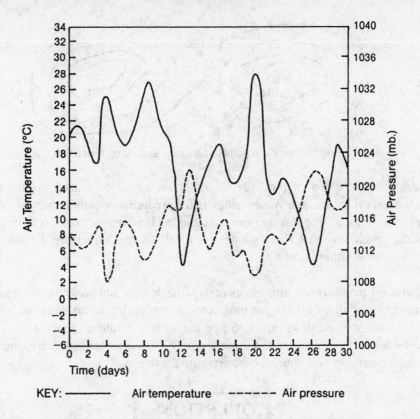

**Figure 7-12.** This graph illustrates the inverse relationship between air temperature and atmospheric pressure.

Air temperature is not the only variable that affects air pressure. Pressure is also affected by moisture and altitude.

Moisture and air pressure. Contrary to most popular beliefs, moist air is *not* heavier than dry air; it is lighter. Air pressure is *inversely* proportional to the amount of moisture in the air. The more moisture the air contains, the lower the air pressure. When water vapor enters the air, it does not "squeeze in" between air molecules. Water molecules *replace* other air molecules. A molecule of water vapor is actually lighter than a molecule of nitrogen or oxygen, the two major constituents of air. Thus, when these air molecules are replaced by water molecules, the air becomes lighter, or less dense, and air pressure goes down.

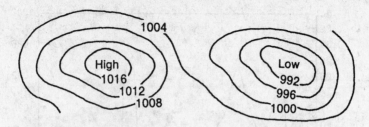

**Figure 7-13.** Isobars join points of equal pressure on a weather map.

Because of the effect of moisture on air pressure, the barometer is one of the most effective tools used by amateur meteorologists for predicting weather changes. When moist air moves into a region, air pressure decreases and the barometer "falls." A falling barometer indicates the probability that rainy weather is on the way. Conversely, a rising barometer indicates that fair weather is coming.

**Altitude and air pressure.** As altitude increases, the density and pressure of the air decrease. In fact, about one-half of all the air molecules in the entire atmosphere are within about 5.8 km (3.5 miles) of Earth's surface. Since the weight of these air molecules creates air pressure, the fewer the molecules, the lower the pressure. As altitude increases, the number of air molecules decreases and, thus, the air pressure decreases.

## QUESTIONS

Base your answers to questions 1 through 5 on your knowledge of Earth Science and the graph below, which shows the hourly surface air temperature, dewpoint, and relative humidity for a 24-hour period.

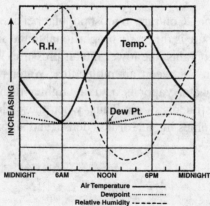

**1.** The greatest change in air temperature occurred during the period from

    (1) midnight to 6 a.m.        (2) 6 a.m. to noon
    (3) noon to 6 p.m.          (4) 6 p.m. to midnight

2. Which conclusion concerning the relationship between the dewpoint and the air temperature is best justified by the data shown?

   (1) Changes in air temperature are caused by dewpoint changes, but not in proportion to these changes.
   (2) The dewpoint increases in proportion to an increase in air temperature.
   (3) The dewpoint increases in proportion to a decrease in air temperature.
   (4) Changes in dewpoint do not necessarily occur when air temperature changes.

3. The graph indicates that as the air temperature increases, the relative humidity

   (1) decreases, only
   (2) increases, only
   (3) sometimes increases and sometimes decreases
   (4) remains the same

4. Condensation most likely occurred at approximately

   (1) 6 a.m.          (2) 9 a.m.          (3) 7 p.m.          (4) 10 p.m.

5. The greatest difference between the wet-and dry-bulb temperature on a sling psychrometer would occur at approximately

   (1) 6 a.m.          (2) 12 noon          (3) 3 p.m.          (4) 9 p.m.

6. Which combination of air temperature and dewpoint temperature would most likely occur in humid air?

   (1) air temperature 10°C, dewpoint temperature -4°C
   (2) air temperature 15°C, dewpoint temperature  3°C
   (3) air temperature 24°C, dewpoint temperature 23°C
   (4) air temperature 26°C, dewpoint temperature 10°C

7. The dry-bulb temperature is 20°C. The wet-bulb temperature is 17°C. What is the dewpoint?

   (1) 12°          (2) 13°          (3) 14°          (4) 15°

Base your answers to questions 8 through 11 on your knowledge of Earth Science, the *Earth Science Reference Tables*, and the graph below which shows the air temperature and dewpoint over a 24-hour period for a location in New York State.

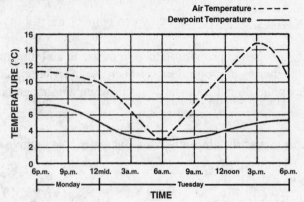

8. When was the air at ground level saturated with water vapor?

   (1) 6 p.m. Monday           (2) 6 a.m. Tuesday
   (3) 3 p.m. Tuesday           (4) 12 noon Tuesday

9. The air's capacity to hold water vapor was greatest at

   (1) 6 p.m. Monday    (2) 6 a.m.-Tuesday    (3) 3 p.m. Tuesday    (4) 12 noon Tuesday

10. If the trends shown continued, the air temperature at 7 p.m. Tuesday was probably about

    (1) 8°C            (2) 2°C            (3) 11°C           (4) 14°C

11. The relative humidity was lowest at

    (1) 12 midnight      (2) 6 a.m.          (3) 12 noon        (4) 3 p.m.

12. The air outside a classroom has a dry-bulb temperature of 10°C and a wet-bulb temperature of 4°C. What is the relative humidity of this air?

    (1) 1%           (2) 14%         (3) 33%         (4) 54%

13. According to the *Earth Science Reference Tables*, an air temperature of 15°C is equal to

    (1) -10°F         (2) 41°F         (3) 59°F         (4) 78°F

14. If the air temperature were 20°C, which dewpoint temperature would indicate the highest water vapor content?

    (1) 18°C         (2) 15°C         (3) 10°C         (4) 0°C

15. As the difference between dewpoint temperature and air temperature increases, the likelihood of precipitation

    (1) decreases        (2) increases        (3) remains the same

16. What is the approximate relative humidity if the dry-bulb temperature is 14°C and the wet bulb temperature is 9°C?

    (1) 20%        (2) 35%        (3) 50%        (4) 65%

17. What is the approximate dewpoint temperature if the dry-bulb temperature is 22°C and the wet-bulb temperature is 12°C?

    (1) -5°C        (2) 3°C        (3) 10°C        (4) 12°C

18. If the amount of water vapor in the air increases, then the dewpoint temperature of the air will

    (1) decrease        (2) increase        (3) remain the same

19. The air temperature is 10°C. Which dewpoint temperature would result in the highest probability of precipitation?

    (1) 8°C        (2) 6°C        (3) 0°C        (4) -4°C

20. According to the *Earth Science Reference Tables*, as altitude within the troposphere increases, the amount of water vapor generally

    (1) decreases, only        (2) increases, only
    (3) reamains the same      (4) decreases, then increases

## Moisture and Energy Input

The amount of moisture (water vapor) entering the atmosphere depends on evaporation and transpiration. **Evaporation** is the process of changing liquid water from the oceans, lakes, streams, and soils on Earth's surface into water vapor in the atmosphere. **Transpiration** is the process by which plants release water vapor through their leaves into the atmosphere. The term **evapotranspiration** refers to all the water vapor released into the atmosphere by both evaporation and transpiration. The oceans are the main source of moisture for the atmosphere.

The processes of both evaporation and transpiration require large amounts of energy to change liquid water into water vapor. This evapotranspiration constitutes an energy input of about 540 calories/gram of water evaporated (latent heat of vaporization) to the atmosphere in the form of more energetic molecules.

## Vapor Pressure

Air is composed of many gases, including water vapor, pressing down on Earth's surface. When the pressure exerted by only the water vapor in the air is measured, it is called **vapor pressure**. For example, assume the dew point temperature of the air is 16°C and the air pressure is 1000 mb, which is a measure of *all* the air–including water vapor–pressing down on Earth. If the air is saturated, the vapor pressure, due only to the water vapor in the air, is 18 mb. This means that 18 of the 1000 mb pressing down on Earth are due directly to the water vapor in the air. The remaining 982 mb are due to other gases - primarily nitrogen and oxygen–in the air. Lowering the amount of moisture in the air lowers both the vapor pressure and the dewpoint. The vapor pressure and the dew point are directly related.

As water vapor evaporates into the air, the vapor pressure of the air increases. The vapor pressure is greatest at the air-water interface, decreasing as the distance from the interface increases. The rate of evaporation decreases as the vapor pressure of the air at the interface increases.

## Factors Affecting the Rate of Evaporation

The rate and amount of evaporation of water that takes place from a particular surface depend on the following factors:

**Amount of energy available**. The more heat energy available, the faster and greater the amount of evaporation.

**Surface area.** The more surface area of water available, the greater the rate of evaporation.

**Amount of moisture in the air.** When the air is saturated, no evaporation takes place. Decreasing the amount of water vapor (the vapor pressure) in the air increases the rate of evaporation.

## Saturation Vapor Pressure

When the air is saturated, the amount of water vapor evaporating and the amount condensing are the same, and a state of dynamic equilibrium exists. **<u>Dynamic equilibrium</u>** occurs when the number of molecules changing from liquid to vapor equals the number of molecules changing from vapor to liquid. When the air is saturated, the vapor pressure is called **saturation vapor pressure**. There is a direct relationship between air temperature and saturation vapor pressure. Warm air has a greater capacity to hold water vapor than cold air. When the air temperature remains constant, and the amount of water vapor in the air increases, the vapor pressure, absolute humidity, dew point, and relative humidity all increase. When the air temperature cools below the dew point, the saturation vapor pressure decreases, and water vapor is squeezed out of the air, much as water is squeezed out of a sponge. The water vapor leaves the air by the process of condensation.

## Other Energy Inputs

The atmosphere acquires most of its energy by conduction and radiation from Earth's surface, and from solar radiation (insolation). The rate of energy input is related to such variables as the amount of water vapor and carbon dioxide in the atmosphere. These materials tend to allow the Sun's rays through but retain radiation from Earth's surface. **Frictional drag**, caused by Earth's rotation, is the energy of friction produced at the interface of Earth's surface and the atmosphere. This energy is added to the atmosphere in the form of heat.

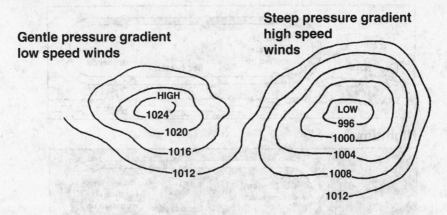

**Figure 7-14.** The spacing of isobars indicates pressure gradient.

## Air Movement

Large horizontal movements of air near Earth's surface are called <u>winds</u>, while smaller, local horizontal movements are called **breezes**. Vertical air movements are called <u>currents</u>. Winds are named for the direction *from* which they come. For example, if the wind is from the southwest, it is called a southwesterly wind, just as a breeze blowing onshore from the sea is called a sea breeze.

The primary causes of winds are differences in air temperature, which cause differences in air pressure. Air always moves from areas of high pressure to areas of low pressure. The rate of change in pressure between two locations is called the <u>**pressure gradient**</u> and is shown on a map by the spacing between isobars (see Figure 7-12). The closer the isobars, the steeper the pressure gradient. The steeper the pressure gradient, the greater the wind speed between locations.

# Local Breezes

Winds are caused by differences in pressure. Such differences can occur in limited, or local, situations. Along the shore of a large body of water, during the daytime the land heats up faster than the water. Thus, the air over the water, being cooler, is denser and has a higher pressure than the air over the land. The air, therefore, blows from the sea onto the land, forming a **sea breeze** or **onshore breeze** (see Figure 7-15). At night, the land cools below the water temperature, and the air over the land becomes denser and its pressure higher. Now, the air flows from the land to the sea, forming a **land breeze,** or **offshore breeze** (Figure 7-15).

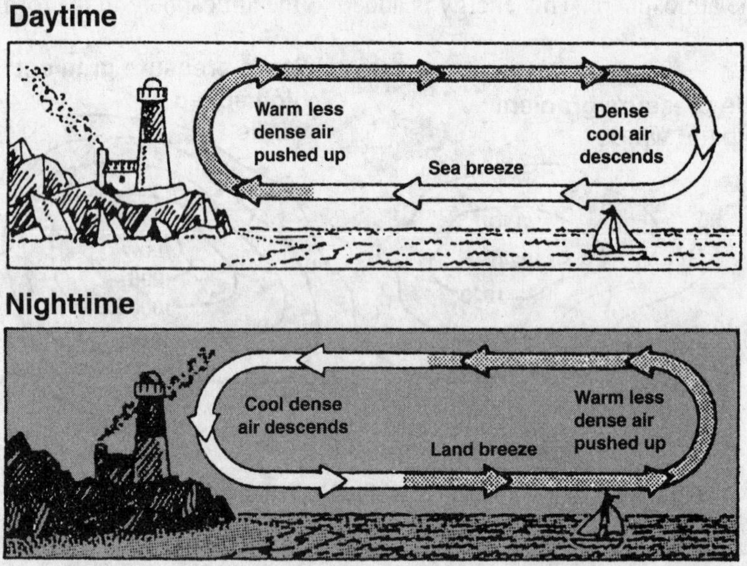

**Daytime**

Warm less dense air pushed up

Dense cool air descends

Sea breeze

**Nighttime**

Cool dense air descends

Warm less dense air pushed up

Land breeze

**Figure 7-15.** Local breezes are generated by unequal heating of Earth's surface due to local conditions.

# Planetary Convection Cells

A **convection cell** is the cyclical movement of a fluid due to differences in density and the effect of the gravity field (see Figure 7-16). Convection currents in the atmosphere occur because gravity pulls cool, dense air toward Earth's surface, forcing warmer, less dense air to rise, producing convection cells. Density differences in water and in molten rock cause convection cells to operate in the oceans and in Earth's mantle.

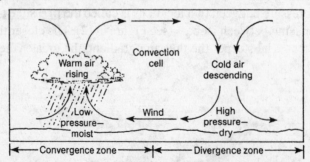

Warm air rising

Convection cell

Cold air descending

Low pressure— moist

Wind

High pressure— dry

Convergence zone

Divergence zone

**Figure 7-16.** A convection cell. Such cells are generated by the unequal heating of Earth's surface.

Variations in insolation result in unequal heating of Earth's surface and the atmosphere above it. In turn, this unequal heating results in density differences in the atmosphere, which produce convection cells. In the portions of these cells where air movement is vertical, pressure belts are produced at Earth's surface (see Figure 7-17). In regions where the air is rising (ascending), low-pressure belts are produced. In regions where the air is sinking (descending), high-pressure belts are produced.

In high-pressure regions, air is descending. When this descending air reaches Earth's surface, it spreads out, or moves away from the region. Thus, these high-pressure belts are known as **zones of divergence**. Divergent zones are dry. Air from these regions comes together, or converges, in the regions of low pressure, where it rises. The low-pressure belts are called **zones of convergence**. Convergent zones are moist (wet).

### Planetary Wind and Moisture Belts in the Troposphere

The following drawing shows the locations of the belts near the time of an equinox. The locations shift somewhat with the changing latitude of the Sun's vertical ray. In the Northern Hemisphere, the belts shift northward in summer and southward in winter.

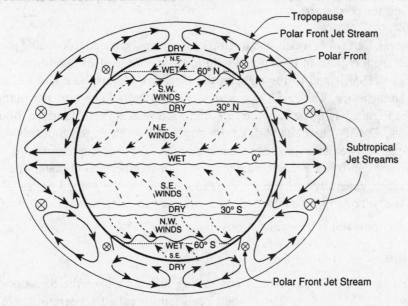

**Figure 7-17.** Note how the winds are deflected toward the right in the Northern Hemisphere and toward the left in the Southern Hemisphere.

## Planetary Winds

Air moves from regions of high pressure to regions of low pressure. If Earth did not rotate (and if its surface were evenly heated) winds along the surface would be part of one large cell (see Figure 7-18). Air would flow directly from the poles to the equator, where the air would rise and return at some altitude to the poles.

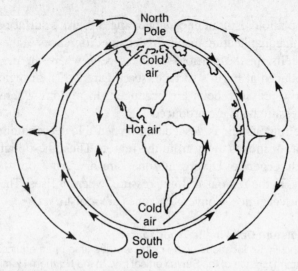

North
Pole

Cold
air

Hot air

Cold
air

South
Pole

**Figure 7-18**. If Earth did not rotate, planetary winds would blow directly from the poles (high pressure) toward the equator (low) pressure.

However, Earth *does* rotate, and its surface *is* unevenly heated (producing pressure belts). Winds flow from regions of high pressure to low pressure, and are modified by the Coriolis effect. They are deflected to the right in the Northern Hemisphere and to the left in the Southern Hemisphere. The result is a series of wind belts known as the **planetary wind system** (see Figure 7-17). The pressure belts and wind belts at Earth's surface follow the Sun's vertical rays. That is, the belts shift to the north and south as the Sun follows its annual migratory path between the Tropic of Cancer and the Tropic of Capricorn.

Planetary winds are a major influence on both weather and climate. The main reason why air-masses generally move from west to east across the United States is that we are located in the belt of winds known as the prevailing southwesterlies, which blow from west to east.

## Jet Streams

Winds at high altitudes exert a controlling influence over the direction traveled by air-masses at Earth's surface. These high-speed winds, called **jet streams,** are part of the planetary convection cells.

Jet streams travel 7 to 8 miles above the surface of Earth. Instead of moving along a straight line, the jet stream flows in a wavelike fashion in an eastward direction. Wind speeds average 35 mph in summer and 75 mph in winter. In the Northern Hemisphere, airplanes in the jet stream are speeded up as they travel eastward and slowed down as they travel westward.

The midlatitude jet stream is called the **polar jet stream**. The polar jet stream plays a major role in the weather of the midlatitudes. In winter the polar jet stream reaches as far south as 31 degrees North latitude, while in summer, it moves up to about 50 degrees North latitude (see Fig. 7-19).

The yearly migration north and south of the polar jet stream is followed by severe thunderstorms and tornadoes. Other jet streams exist, but none have been studied as extensively as the polar jet streams.

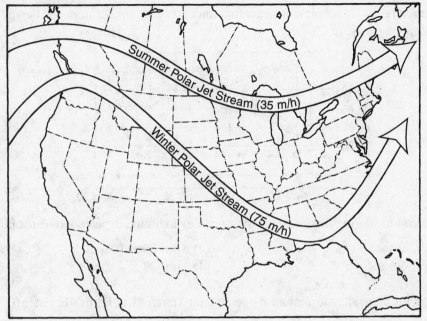

**Figure 7-19**. The position and speed of the polar jet stream changes with the seasons. Severe thunderstorms and tornadoes occur along the path of the jet stream.

## Atmospheric Transparency

On clear days, the atmosphere is transparent, scattering or reflecting little of the Sun's radiation. However, there are usually some **aerosols** (dust and water vapor) present in the air that do scatter and reflect some of the insolation. The transparency of the air affects the amount of insolation reaching Earth's surface, thereby greatly affecting our weather.

Atmospheric transparency varies inversely with the amount of material in the air produced by natural processes and human activities. The more aerosols in the air, the less transparent the atmosphere. For example, when a volcano erupts, tons of volcanic dust are added to the air, and the transparency of the atmosphere decreases. Humans, through pollution from automobiles, factories and homes, also add aerosols to the air, decreasing the atmospheric transparency.

## Other Variables

Other variables seem to be associated with weather changes in a more complex manner, than simply a direct or inverse relationship. For example, visibility depends upon temperature, humidity, and pollution. The type of clouds overhead at a particular time, although of seemingly small immediate significance, may fit a pattern that will help to predict the weather several hours or days in advance.

# QUESTIONS

1. The graph below is a computer-generated forecast of air temperature and dewpoint for a city during a period of 2¼ days.

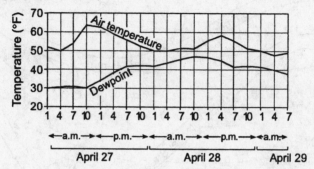

   At which time during this period is the rate of evaporation expected to be the highest?

   (1) April 27 at 10 a.m.          (2) April 28 at 10 a.m.
   (3) April 28 at 4 p.m.           (4) April 29 at 4 a.m.

2. What is the general pattern of air movement on March 21 at Earth's Equator (0°)?

   (1) upward, due to low temperature and high pressure
   (2) upward, due to high temperature and low pressure
   (3) downward, due to low temperature and high pressure
   (4) downward, due to high temperature and low pressure

3. As the amount of moisture in the air increases, the atmospheric pressure will probably

   (1) decrease          (2) increase          (3) remain the same

4. According to the *Earth Science Reference Tables*, an air pressure of 29.65 inches from mercury is equal to

   (1) 984.0 mb          (2) 999.0 mb          (3) 1001.0 mb          (4) 1004.0 mb

5. Which factor is most directly related to wind velocity?

   (1) dewpoint                      (2) relative humidity
   (3) cloud type                    (4) pressure gradient

6. Two weather stations are located near each other. The air pressure at each station is changing so that the difference between the pressures is increasing. The wind speed between these two locations will probably

   (1) decrease          (2) increase          (3) remain the same

7. The diagram below shows the isolines of air pressure around a low-pressure center. On which side of the low-pressure center will the wind speed be greatest?

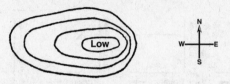

(1) north        (2) south        (3) east        (4) west

8. Which statement best explains why the air pressure is usually greater over the ocean than over the land during the daytime hours in the summer?

(1) Air temperature is lower over the ocean.
(2) Air is more humid over the ocean.
(3) Prevailing winds are usually blowing from the land.
(4) Water absorbs heat from the land.

9. Planetary winds do not blow directly north or south because of

(1) the Coriolis effect        (2) gravitational force
(3) magnetic force        (4) centripetal force

10. A barometer indicates a pressure of 30 inches of mercury at sea level; at $3^{1}/_{2}$ miles above sea level, it indicates a pressure of 15 inches. What is the best conclusion to be drawn from this data?

(1) humidity affects the pressure
(2) temperature affects the pressure
(3) of the total mass of air, about 99 percent is within $3^{1}/_{2}$ miles of sea level
(4) of the total mass of air, about 50 percent is more than $3^{1}/_{2}$ miles above sea level

11. Which graph best shows the relationship between atmospheric pressure and water vapor content at Earth's surface?

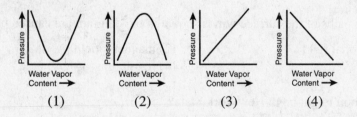

**12.** According to the *Earth Science Reference Tables*, which graph best represents the relationship between altitude and pressure in the atmosphere?

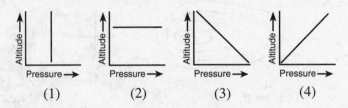

(1)        (2)        (3)        (4)

**13.** Wind moves from regions of

(1) high temperature toward regions of low temperature
(2) high pressure toward regions of low pressure
(3) high precipitation toward regions of low precipitation
(4) high humidity toward regions of low humidity

Base your answers to questions 14 through 17 on your knowledge of Earth Science and the diagram below. The diagram represents the general circulation of Earth's atmosphere and Earth's planetary wind and pressure belts. Points A through F represent locations on Earth's surface.

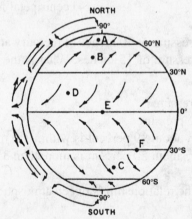

**14.** The curving paths of the surface winds shown in the diagram are caused by Earth's

(1) gravitational field          (2) magnetic field
(3) rotation                     (4) revolution

**15.** Which location might be in New York State?

(1) A            (2) B            (3) C            (4) D

**16.** Which location is experiencing a southwest planetary wind?

(1) A (2) B (3) C (4) F

**17.** Which location is near the center of a low-pressure belt where daily rains, are common?

(1) E (2) B (3) F (4) D

**18.** Which natural process tends to aid in the cleaning of the atmosphere?

(1) evaporation (2) precipitation (3) expansion (4) transpiration

**19.** The ability of sunlight to pass through Earth's atmosphere would normally increase

(1) after periods of volcanic activity
(2) after periods of precipitation
(3) during cloud formation
(4) during periods of atmospheric pollution

**20.** Which graph best represents the relationship between the number of dust particles in the atmosphere and atmospheric transparency?

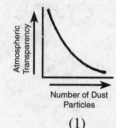

(1)          (2)          (3)          (4)

# CLOUDS AND PRECIPITATION

**Condensation and Sublimation.** <u>Condensation</u> is the process by which gaseous water vapor changes to liquid water. In order for condensation to occur, some surface, however small, must be present. In the atmosphere, condensation can occur when the air is saturated and **condensation nuclei**, such as particles of dust or salt from the ocean are available. At temperatures below 0°C, water vapor changes directly into solid water–ice or snow–through the process known as **sublimation**.

Condensation is a heating process. For every gram of water that condenses, 540 calories of heat energy are released into the atmosphere. This heat serves as the "fuel" for many storms. Hurricanes, for example, are fueled and intensified by the heat energy released by condensation.

**Dew and Frost**. When water vapor condenses directly onto a cold surface, **dew** is formed. Dew can be seen on the sides of a glass filled with a cold liquid, or on cold surfaces in the early morning hours, when air temperatures are lowest. If water vapor comes in contact with a freezing surface, the vapor will sublimate, and **frost** will be formed. Frost is *not* frozen dew.

**Clouds.** <u>Clouds</u> are collections of tiny water droplets or ice crystals suspended in the atmosphere. Clouds form when moist air expands and cools as it rises vertically in the atmosphere. When the air cools to the dewpoint temperature, it becomes saturated and condensation occurs.

When moist air rises and cools to the dewpoint, condensation takes place and clouds form. Rising air results from heating, convection currents, air moving over a mountain or a frontal boundary. When the air near Earth comes in contact with surfaces that have been heated, the air is heated by <u>**conduction**</u> (a transfer of heat energy from molecule to molecule). When the air is heated, it expands and is forced up by the cooler, denser air below. <u>**Convection**</u> is the transfer of heat energy by movements of liquids and gases (fluids). These movements are caused by differences in density within the fluids. Two mechanisms which initiate vertical movement of air are orographic lifting and frontal wedging. **Orographic lifting** occurs when mountains act as barriers to the flow of air, forcing it to rise to get to the other side (see Figure 7-20). **Frontal wedging** occurs when cool air acts as a barrier over which warmer, lighter air rises. When warm, moist air rises and cools to the dewpoint, condensation takes place and clouds form.

**Figure 7-20**. Orographic lifting. Air rises over the mountain. When the air and dewpoint temperature are the same, condensation occurs and a cloud forms.

Clouds are divided into four basic groups-high, middle, low, and vertical. Extended periods of rain or snow usually occur with low clouds, while thunderstorms occur in clouds having great vertical development. The word nimbus means "rain," so clouds that produce rain usually have the term nimbus as part of their names. For example, low rain clouds are called **nimbostratus**, while thunderclouds are called **cumulonimbus**. Fair weather is associated with **cumulus** (heap) clouds and **cirrus** (high) clouds. A cloud resting on Earth's surface is called a <u>**fog**</u>.

The atmosphere tends to clean itself periodically through natural processes, such as the formation of clouds and precipitation. Water vapor often condenses around the dust aerosols, and later falls as rain, cleansing the atmosphere of pollution. As the droplets of rain fall through the air, they collect other aerosols, further cleansing the atmosphere. Air sometimes becomes stagnant (does not move). When this occurs in areas where concentrations of pollution are great, smog forms. **Smog** is a combination of aerosols and water vapor in stagnant air. When sufficiently concentrated, smog can cause breathing difficulties and even death. Smog usually occurs during a **temperature inversion**, when warmer, less dense air is above a layer of colder, denser air.

## Precipitation

When the water droplets or ice crystals in a cloud grow large enough to fall, **precipitation** results. Precipitation may be in the form of rain, drizzle, sleet, snow, or hail. Large drops of water which fall to Earth's surface are called **rain**. Fine drops of water which float gently to the surface are called **drizzle**. When rain freezes as it falls, **sleet** forms. Ice crystals that form as a result of sublimation and grow large enough to fall are called **snow**. In thunderstorms, where strong vertical currents exist, a water droplet can be forced up into colder air where it freezes into ice. When this ice pellet falls through a warmer layer, water collects on the outside of that ice. If this ice and water are again forced up into colder air, the water freezes, forming a second layer of ice. This process can be repeated many times, forming an onionlike structure, called **hail** or **hailstones**.

Many scientists would like to develop a method of making it rain. Most efforts in this direction have been in the area of cloud **seeding**, placing condensation nuclei into the atmosphere where there is some available water vapor.

## QUESTIONS

1. Condensation of water vapor in the atmosphere is most likely to occur when a condensation surface is available and

   (1) a strong wind is blowing      (2) the temperature of the air is below 0°C
   (3) the air is saturated with water vapor      (4) the air-pressure is rising

2. As a sample of very moist air rises from sea level to a higher altitude, the probability of condensation occurring in that air sample will

   (1) decrease      (2) increase      (3) remain the same

**3.** People sometimes release substances into the atmosphere to increase the probability of rain by

(1) raising the air temperature within the clouds
(2) providing condensation nuclei
(3) lowering the relative humidity within the clouds
(4) increasing the energy absorbed during condensation and sublimation

**4.** Which process must directly result in cloud formation?

(1) condensation      (2) transpiration      (3) precipitation      (4) radiation

**5.** Which graph best represents the relationship between water droplet size and the chance of precipitation?

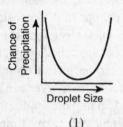 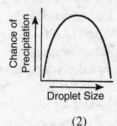 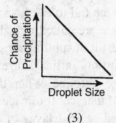 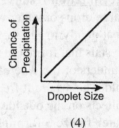

(1)           (2)           (3)           (4)

**6.** Which statement best explains why a cloud is forming as shown in the diagram below?

(1) Water vapor is condensing.      (2) Moisture is evaporating.
(3) Cold air rises and compresses.      (4) Warm air sinks and expands.

**7.** Why do clouds usually form at the leading edge of a cold air-mass?

(1) Cold air flows over warm air, causing the warm air to descend and cool.
(2) Cold air flows under warm air, causing the warm air to rise and cool.
(3) Cold air contains more dust than warm air does.
(4) Cold air contains more water vapor than warm air does.

8. The base of a cumulus cloud was determined to be 500 meters above Earth's surface. This is the altitude at which

   (1) cumulus clouds always form
   (2) no dust is present in the air
   (3) the air temperature drops below 0°C
   (4) the air temperature equals the dewpoint temperature

9. Which event will most likely occur in rising air?

   (1) clearing skies                    (2) cloud formation
   (3) decreasing relative humidity       (4) increasing temperature

10. The diagram below shows a sealed container holding liquid water and clean air saturated with water vapor. (Relative humidity is 100%.) The container has been placed on a block of ice to cool.

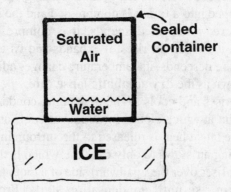

   Which statement best explains why a cloud has *not* formed in the sealed container?

   (1) The air in the container is above the freezing point.
   (2) The ice is cooling the water in the container.
   (3) The air in the container lacks condensation nuclei.
   (4) The water in the container is still evaporating.

11. Which natural process best removes pollutants from the atmosphere?

   (1) evaporation     (2) precipitation     (3) transpiration     (4) convection

12. Clouds usually form when moist air rises because

   (1) the air pressure increases
   (2) the dewpoint decreases
   (3) the air is cooled to its dewpoint
   (4) additional water vapor is added to the air

# MOISTURE AND ENERGY TRANSFER

Moisture and energy are transferred in the atmosphere by three basic methods: convection, winds, and the adiabatic process. The process of convection is driven by differences in density. The temperature and the amount of moisture in the air affect its density. If the temperature and/or the amount of moisture in the air increases, the density decreases. If the density decreases, the pressure decreases. The reverse is also true.

## Adiabatic Changes in Temperature

An **adiabatic** temperature change is any change in the temperature of a system without any heat being added to or removed from that system. For example, when a gas expands, its temperature decreases. When a gas is compressed, its temperature increases. To illustrate these adiabatic changes, think of an automobile tire. Air coming out of a tire is expanding and feels cool. When air is pumped into a tire, it is compressed and the sides of the tire become warm.

In the atmosphere, when air descends, it is compressed by the air around it and its temperature increases. When air rises, it expands and its temperature decreases. When a sample of dry air rises or descends, its temperature changes adiabatically at a rate of 10°C per kilometer. This is known as the **dry adiabatic lapse rate**.

When moist air rises and cools to the dew point, condensation takes place and clouds form. Up until the point at which clouds form, the air cools at the dry adiabatic rate of 10°C per kilometer. Because latent heat is released to the surrounding air during condensation, the cooling rate of the rising air slows to only 6°C/km, which is the **moist adiabatic lapse rate**. When warm, moist air rises over the windward side of a mountain, it cools at the dry adiabatic lapse rate of 10°C/km rise until condensation starts. From that point on, it cools at 6°C/km rise. When that air descends on the leeward side of the mountain, the processes of condensation and evaporation are not involved. Thus, it heats up at the dry adiabatic lapse rate of 10°C/km (see Figure 7-21). Therefore, the temperature of the air on the leeward side of the mountain is higher than the temperature of the air on the windward side and the air is drier.

**Lapse Rate**. As a parcel of air rises and cools, its capacity to hold water vapor decreases and its relative humidity increases. As moist air rises, the process of condensation releases latent heat energy (540 calories per gram of water) and slows the rate of cooling. This process keeps the rising air relatively low in density, and warmer than its surrounding air, sustaining the rising motion. If the heat energy given off during condensation makes the rising air warmer than the surrounding air (and thus less dense and more buoyant), it will continue to rise and expand until it becomes equal in density to the air around it. The tops of some thunderstorms penetrate even into the stratosphere for many kilometers.

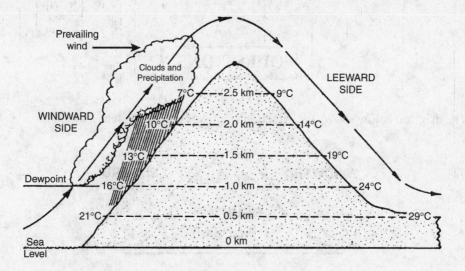

**Figure 7-21**. On the windward side of the mountain, moist air is cooled as it is forced over the mountain. Once the air has cooled to the dew point, it cools at the moist adiabatic lapse rate (6°C per km). On the leeward side, the dry air heats up at the dry adiabatic lapse rate (10°C per km) as it descends.

You have probably noticed that when a sky is filled with clouds, even "fair weather" puffy cumulus clouds, their bases are flat and they all seem to be the same distance from the ground. As air rises, the air temperature and the dewpoint temperature both decrease, but at different rates. The air temperature cools much more rapidly than the dewpoint temperature. When the air temperature and the dew point temperature reach an altitude where they are the same temperature, condensation occurs and clouds form.

The formation of a cloud by adiabatic cooling can be illustrated by taking a plastic soda bottle that contains warm water and smoke. Squeeze the bottle for a moment and then release it - a cloud forms. Squeezing the bottle compresses the air and heats it adiabatically. When the pressure on the bottle is released, the air expands and cools adiabatically. The cooling air causes the warm water vapor to condense on the smoke particles (condensation nuclei) and a cloud is formed. Dry air is cooled by the radiation of heat energy. Radiational cooling happens in the polar regions and deserts, causing the air to sink.

There is a surplus of incoming energy at tropical latitudes, and a deficit in the polar regions. The atmosphere distributes the solar energy over the whole Earth. If the global wind convection systems did not exist to redistribute the energy, the poles would steadily become colder and the tropics, warmer. Zones of prevailing winds result from uneven heating by the Sun and Earth's rotation. The convection pattern is made more complicated by the Coriolis Effect. See the section on planetary winds and the planetary winds map in the *Earth Science Reference Tables*.

## QUESTIONS

1. The diagram below shows the direction of movement of air over a mountain.

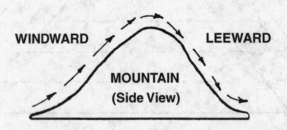

As the air moves down the leeward side of the mountain, the air will

(1) warm due to compression      (2) warm due to expansion
(3) cool due to compression      (4) cool due to expansion

2. The rate at which water will evaporate from a sponge could be increased by

(1) increasing the humidity
(2) decreasing the temperature
(3) increasing the surface area of the sponge
(4) decreasing the movement of air over the sponge

3. As a parcel of air moves up a mountainside and expands, the temperature of the air will

(1) decrease      (2) increase      (3) remain the same

4. During the formation of a cloud, which process would result in the release of heat energy?

(1) evaporation      (2) evapotranspiration
(3) transpiration      (4) condensation

5. Moisture is evaporating from a lake into stationary air at a constant temperature. As more moisture is added to this air, the rate at which water will evaporate will probably

(1) decrease      (2) increase      (3) remain the same

Base your answers to questions 6 through 10 your knowledge of Earth Science and on the drawing below which represents a part of the water cycle.

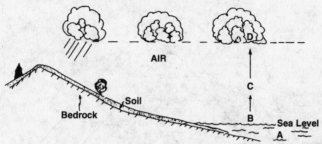

**6.** Which statement best describes the air at C?

(1) Its relative humidity is 0%.
(2) It contains water vapor.
(3) It is at a temperature below that of the dewpoint.
(4) It is saturated.

**7.** As the temperature of the air increases, the amount of water which enters the atmosphere in the area around B will

(1) decrease          (2) increase          (3) remain the same

**8.** As moisture is absorbed by air, the density of the air will

(1) decrease          (2) increase          (3) remain the same

**9.** The base of the clouds is located at D because at that altitude

(1) air temperature equals dewpoint temperature
(2) prevailing winds are strongest
(3) surface topography reaches its greatest elevation
(4) air pressure is the same as at B

**10.** At which location is heat energy being released into the atmosphere due to a change in state of water?

(1) A          (2) B          (3) C          (4) D

Base your answers to questions 11 through 15 on your knowledge of Earth Science and the diagram below which shows a mountain. The prevailing wind direction and air temperatures at different elevations on both sides of the mountain are indicated.

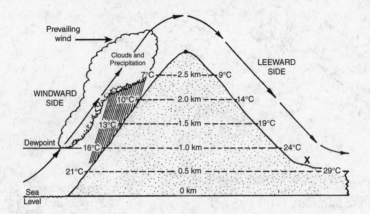

**11.** What would be the approximate air temperature at the top of the mountain?

(1) 12°C          (2) 10°C          (3) 0°C          (4) 4°C

**12.** On which side of the mountain and at what elevation is the relative humidity probably 100%?

(1) on the windward side at 0.5 km      (2) on the windward side at 1.5 km
(3) on the leeward side at 1.0 km      (4) on the leeward side at 2.5 km

**13.** How does the temperature of the air change as the air rises on the windward side of the mountain between sea level and 0.5 kilometer?

(1) The air is warming due to compression of the air.
(2) The air is warming due to expansion of the air.
(3) The air is cooling due to compression of the air.
(4) The air is cooling due to expansion of the air.

**14.** Which feature is probably located at the base of the mountain on the leeward side (location X)?

(1) an arid region      (2) a jungle      (3) a glacier      (4) a large lake

**15.** The air temperature on the leeward side of the mountain at the 1.5-kilometer level is higher than the temperature at the same elevation on the windward side. What is the probable cause for this?

(1) Heat stored in the ocean keeps the windward side of the mountain warmer.
(2) The insolation received at sea level is greater on the leeward side of the mountain.
(3) The air on the windward side of the mountain has a lower adiabatic lapse rate than the air on the leeward side of the mountain.
(4) Potential energy is lost as rain runs off the windward side of the mountain.

Base your answers to questions 16 and 17 on the diagram of a mountain shown below. The arrows represent the direction of airflow over the mountain.

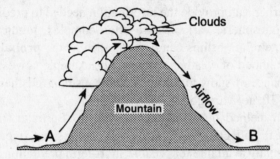

**16.** As the air moves up the windward side of the mountain, the air

(1) compresses and warms      (2) compresses and cools
(3) expands and warms      (4) expands and cools

**17.** Compared to the temperature and humidity conditions at location A, the conditions at location B are

(1) warmer and less humid      (2) warmer and more humid
(3) cooler and less humid      (4) cooler and more humid

# FORECASTING THE WEATHER

Modern society is constantly demanding more accurate weather forecasting. Weather forecasts have become so important that television channels exist to keep the public up-to-date. The need to know ranges from the general public's desire to make plans for various activities to NASA's desire for clear skies to launch a spacecraft. Airlines and farmers depend heavily on accurate forecasts. People want long-range predictions to help their planning. Knowing current weather patterns, methods used to determine the future state of the atmosphere are referred to as **weather forecasting**.

Anyone can easily determine what the weather is by simply looking outside. However, the goal of most weather watchers is to **predict** the weather; that is, to determine what the weather will be. Measurements of atmospheric variables, when compared with similar measurements taken earlier, can provide the information needed to predict the weather. Since relationships among atmospheric variables are often complex, predictions are not always accurate. However, these relationships can be expressed as the **probability of occurrence,** which indicates the likelihood of weather changes. For example, a weather prediction might be: "There is a 40% chance of snow today," which means that the chances that it will snow today are only 4 out of 10, not very good odds.

Meteorologists are helped by a worldwide system of ground stations, satellites and radar from which data is collected. Technology has had a great impact on the science of meteorology. Data is usually available for reliable short-term predictions of one to three days, but the variables change so rapidly that it is difficult at best to make consistently accurate predictions of the weather on a long-range basis. Computers aid in the analysis of the data. Computer models of the weather can be generated. Meteorologists use computer models to study squall lines, thunderstorms, tornadoes and climate.

Most of the improvement in weather forecasting has come in the last half century with satellites and improved technology. Weather predictions today, although people tend not to believe it, are much more accurate than they were a half century ago. Synoptic weather map forecasting was the primary method used in making weather predictions until the late 1950s. When a forecaster knows the type of weather being generated along a front and is able to predict its motion, a rather accurate short-term forecast can be made for that area.

Modern weather forecasting relies heavily on the fact that the gases of the atmosphere obey a number of known physical principles. Most modern approaches to weather forecasting try to predict the air flow pattern aloft (high in the sky). For long-range purposes, statistical methods are used to predict the weather. Yet complex development of atmospheric variables make accurate predictions of 1-2 weeks or more unlikely. Even extremely small disturbances can grow in importance to influence worldwide weather changes. A volcanic eruption can fill the air with dust that, over a period of years, can cause global cooling.

Although we tend to focus on the incorrect forecasts, meteorologists are quite, accurate on a day-to-day basis. In general, we are safe in saying that modern weather forecasts are relatively accurate from 6 to 12 hours and are generally good for a day or two.

# QUESTIONS

1. Radar and satellites are important in forecasting the weather because they provide information about

   (1) past weather
   (2) future weather
   (3) present weather missed by local observations
   (4) the impact of gravity on the weather

2. The process of predicting the weather based on information is

   (1) meteorology               (2) weather forecasting
   (3) statistics                (4) computer modeling

3. Most of the improvements in weather forecasting have occurred in the last

   (1) year          (2) 10 years          (3) half century      (4) century

4. The likelihood that the weather will change over a period of time is referred to as the

   (1) probability of occurrence          (2) probability of accurate forecasting
   (3) weather forecast                   (4) synoptic weather map

5. Modern weather forecasting relies heavily on the fact that

   (1) computer maps are easy to generate
   (2) weather changes very slowly
   (3) most improvements in forecasting have come in the last 99 years
   (4) gases of the atmosphere obey a certain number of known physical principles

# WEATHER MAPS AND FORECASTING

Weather maps, which show the development and movement of weather systems, are among the most important tools used in weather forecasting. We are most, familiar with the weather maps which show conditions at Earth's surface. A vast amount of data is packed onto the surface map: temperature, pressure, humidity, wind, clouds, precipitation, visibility, air-masses and fronts. The location of a reporting station is printed on the map as a small circle with the data arranged in a definite pattern around the circle.

## Station Model

The relationships among atmospheric variables can be observed locally. On a weather map, weather observations for a particular location are recorded on a **station model** (see Figure 7-22). These observations usually include data concerning at least the following weather variables:

**1**. amount of cloud cover (percent of circle darkened in)

**2**. barometric pressure (in millibars) and the pressure trend over the last 3 hours

**3**. temperature (in degrees Fahrenheit)

**4**. dewpoint (in degrees Fahrenheit)

**5**. wind direction

**6**. wind speed (in knots; 1 knot = 1.85 km/hr)

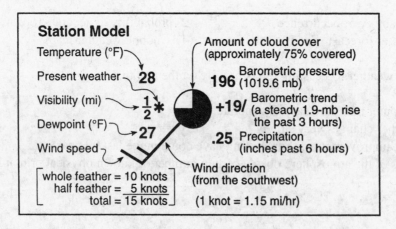

**Figure 7-22**. A station model.

Station models often include the present weather, the amount of precipitation, if any, over the past 6 hours, and the visibility (in miles). Present weather symbols primarily indicate types of precipitation (see Figure 7-23).

Barometric pressure, in millibars, is usually a number between 950 and 1050. For example, two pressure readings might be 997.4 mb and 1017.6 mb. On a station model, these numbers are abbreviated to save space. The initial 9 or 10 and the decimal point are omitted. Thus, the above readings would appear on a station model as 974 and 176. To reconstruct a pressure reading from the abbreviation: if the abbreviation is above 500, place a 9 before it; if the abbreviation is below 500, place a 10 before it. Place a decimal point between the last two numbers on the right. Thus, the abbreviation 890 stands for a reading of 989.0 mb. In the barometric trend, a pressure change of +19/ means that the pressure has increased steadily 1.9 mb over the last 3 hours.

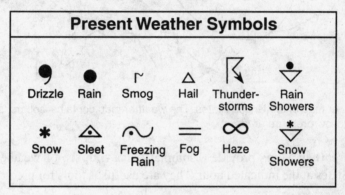

**Figure 7-23**. Present weather symbols.

On a weather map, isolines are used to connect stations with equal field values. Isolines connecting points of equal pressure are **isobars**. Isobars are labeled in millibars. Temperature and other measurable field values could be plotted by isolines. For example, temperature maps are often shown in television. Isolines connecting points of equal temperature are **isotherms.**

A surface weather map of the United States provides us with large pieces of information (see Figure 7-24). Station models are furnished for several locations. The solid lines are isobars. The spacing and orientation of these lines on weather maps are indications of the speed and direction of winds. In general, wind direction is almost perpendicular to these lines (isobars) with low pressure to the left of an observer with his back to the wind. Speed is directly proportional to the closeness of the isobars and is referred to as the **pressure gradient**. Isobars drawn closely together indicate places having steep pressure gradients and strong winds, while isobars that are far apart, indicate a slower gradient and slower wind speed.

The boundary between two different air-masses is called a **front**. Fronts occur where winds bring air of very different temperatures, humidity and winds. Important changes in weather often occurs with the passage of a front. The side on which the half-circles or triangles are placed indicates the direction of frontal movement.

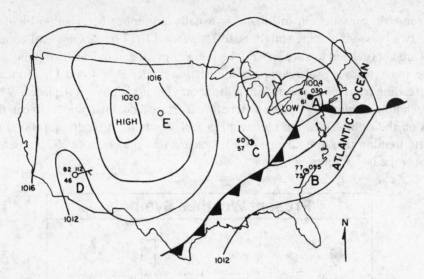

**Figure 7-24**. Weather map of the United States. The weather map contains isobars, station models, fronts, and high and low pressure areas.

Synoptic Weather Maps provide a summary, or **synopsis**, of weather conditions all over the United States at the indicated hour. They are useful as tools for predicting weather on a short-term basis.

## Air-mass Characteristics

An **air-mass** is a huge body of air in the troposphere, up to 2000 kilometers in diameter, having similar pressure, moisture, wind, and temperature characteristics throughout. At any given altitude within an air-mass, the air temperature field and the humidity field are nearly uniform. The longer an air-mass remains over a particular source region, the larger and more characteristic of the region it becomes.

## Source Regions

Air-masses have definite characteristics that depend upon their geographic region of origin, called their **source region**. Air-masses that develop over water (**maritime**) are relatively moist, while those which develop over land (**continental**) are dry. Air-masses that develop in higher (**polar**) latitudes tend to be cool, while those which develop in the lower (**tropical**) latitudes tend to be warm. Figure 7-26 shows the source regions of air- masses that affect weather in the continental United States.

On a weather map, air-masses are usually labeled with two letters indicating the moisture and temperature characteristics of their source region. The letter "c" is used for a dry continental air-mass; the letter "m" for a moist maritime air-mass; the letter "P" for a cold polar air-mass; and the letter "T" for a warm tropical air-mass. The letter "A" is used for very cold Arctic air-masses. An air-mass that originates over the state of Texas would be labeled "cT" and would be dry and warm. See Figure 7-25 which shows each type of air mass which can pass over the United States.

## Air Masses

cA   continental arctic

cP   continental polar

cT   continental tropical

mT   maritime tropical

mP   maritime polar

**Figure 7-25.** List shows the types of air masses which can pass over the United States.

## Air-mass Tracks

The normal **tracks**, or paths of air-masses that travel through the United States are shown in Figure 7-26. Based on past observations, air-mass tracks and rates of movement can be determined and predicted. Air-masses from the south tend to move east and north, while those from the north tend to move east and south. There seems to be a "corridor" in the northeast through which almost all air-masses pass, making it very difficult for meteorologists in that area to accurately predict the weather.

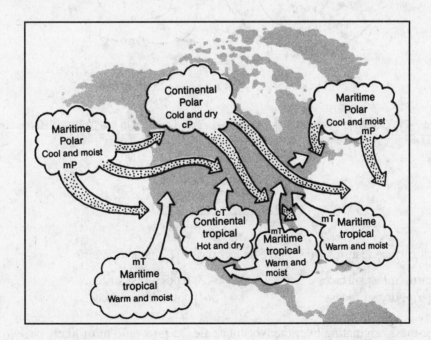

**Figure 7-26.** Source regions and "tracks" of air-masses in North America.

## Cyclones and Anticyclones

Cyclones and anticyclones are air-masses, in the Northern Hemisphere, which differ in the air pressure at their center and in the direction in which their winds spiral.

**Cyclones:** A **cyclone**, or **low**, is a low-pressure air-mass with the winds moving in a counterclockwise direction in toward its center (see Figure 7-27). A cyclonic system can be several hundred kilometers in diameter. When the moving air converges at the center of a low, it rises vertically, often producing rain. Cyclones or lows often bring clouds and precipitation.

**Anticyclones**: An **anticyclone**, or **high**, is a high-pressure air-mass with the winds moving in a clockwise direction away from its center (see Figure 7-27). Because anticyclones often originate in the north, and the air descending in their center is dry, they are usually identified with cool, clear weather.

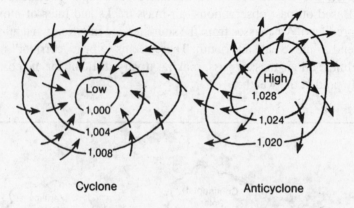

**Figure 7-27**. Circulation around high- and low-pressure centers in the Northern Hemisphere.

## QUESTIONS

1. Which surface features would give an air-mass mT characteristics?

   (1) warm, moist surfaces      (2) cold, moist surfaces
   (3) warm, dry surfaces      (4) cold, dry surfaces

2. An air-mass originating over the North Pacific Ocean would most likely be

   (1) continental polar      (2) continental tropical
   (3) maritime polar      (4) maritime tropical

3. The characteristics of air-masses depend chiefly upon the

    (1) rotation of Earth
    (2) surface over which the air-mass was formed
    (3) barometric pressure of the air-mass
    (4) wind velocity within the air-mass

4. On a weather map, an air-mass that is very warm and dry would be labeled

    (1) mP          (2) mT          (3) cP          (4) cT

5. An air mass classified as mT usually forms over which type of Earth surface?

    (1) cool land      (2) cool water      (3) warm land      (4) warm water

6. According to the *Earth Science Reference Tables*, an air-mass that originates over the Gulf of Mexico would be labeled on a weather map as

    (1) cA          (2) cT          (3) mT          (4) mP

7. The diagram below represents a cross-sectional view of air-masses associated with a low-pressure system. The cold frontal interface is moving faster than the warm frontal interface. What usually happens to the warm air that is between the two frontal surfaces?

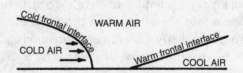

    (1) The warm air is forced over both frontal interfaces.
    (2) The warm air is forced under both frontal interfaces.
    (3) The warm air is forced over the cold frontal interface but under the warm frontal interface.
    (4) The warm air is forced under the cold frontal interface but over the warm frontal interface.

## Fronts

The boundary between two air-masses is called a **front**. Atmospheric conditions in the area of frontal interfaces, where warm and cold air meet, are usually unstable, often producing clouds, strong winds, precipitation, and other weather changes. One air-mass usually moves faster than the other, with the leading edge of the faster moving air-mass naming the front. On a weather map, fronts are identified by the symbols shown in Figure 7-28. The filled in half circles and triangles point in the direction the air-masses and front are moving.

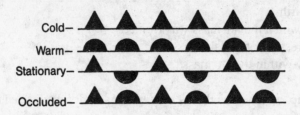

**Figure 7-28**. These symbols for fronts are used on weather maps.

**Warm fronts** occur when warm air meets and rises over cold air on the ground. These fronts have long gentle slopes (see Figure 7-29). The slope can be over 1000 kilometers long and bring with it a predictable sequence of clouds and weather. Far ahead of where the front meets the ground, extended periods of precipitation may break out and continue until the front passes. Until another front comes along, warm air-mass weather will dominate.

**Cold fronts** occur when cold air meets and pushes out warmer air. These fronts have short, steep slopes (see Figure 7-30). Cold fronts move faster than warm fronts, with no sequence of clouds warning of their approach. **Cumulonimbus** clouds, associated with violent thunderstorms, arrive quickly, along with a relatively short period of precipitation. After the front passes, precipitation falls for a very short time, and the weather changes abruptly. The winds shift sharply from a southerly to a northerly direction and the air becomes clear and cooler. Cold fronts are often identified on weather maps by a sharp shift in wind direction between two locations.

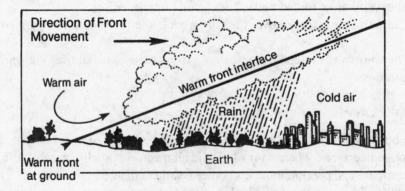

**Figure 7-29**. A warm front.

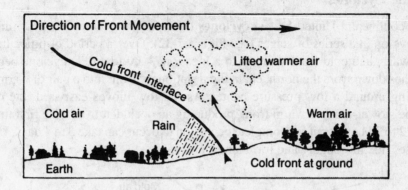

**Figure 7-30.** A cold front.

An **<u>occluded front</u>** occurs when a faster moving cold front overtakes a slower moving warm front and lifts the warmer air between the two fronts off the ground (see Figure 7-31). Above the ground, the original fronts are separate and distinct, while on the ground, the weather characteristic of both fronts occurs without any gap in the sequence.

A **<u>stationary front</u>** occurs when a warm air-mass and a cold air-mass are side-by-side, with neither air-mass moving. The slope tends to be gentle and the weather similar to that of a warm front.

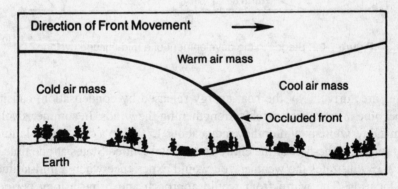

**Figure 7-31.** An occluded front.

# Mid-latitude Cyclones

In the continental United States, **cyclones** (low-pressure centers) called **mid-latitude cyclones** develop in a series of stages (see Figure 7-32). Over a period of time, these stages bring both warm and cold front weather to a location. A mid-latitude cyclone begins when cold air pushes down from the north, changing a stationary front into a pair of warm and cold fronts moving around a low pressure center. As the low moves eastward, the cold front overtakes the slower-moving warm front, producing an occluded front. The first three stages take about 12 to 24 hours, but for complete occlusion to occur can take 3 to 4 days. Ultimately, the air-masses mix thoroughly and form a new air-mass.

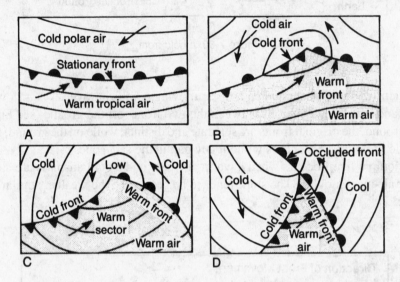

**Figure 7-32.** Stages in the development of a mid-latitude cyclone.

Cyclones are "driven" by the heat energy released by condensation, causing the low pressure to become even lower, thereby strengthening the winds. In summer, cyclones move about 800 km a day, while in winter they move about 1,100 km a day. A mid-latitude cyclone may cover as much as one-half of the entire continental United States at one time.

Figure 7-33 illustrates the weather you would experience when a mid-latitude cyclone passes your location. The warm front would approach and bring a long period of heavy precipitation. This would be followed by a period of clearing and warm humid weather. The cold front would arrive with brief heavy showers, followed by clearing and cooling. Understanding mid-latitude cyclones makes it much easier for amateur meteorologists (such as students) to predict weather on a short-term basis.

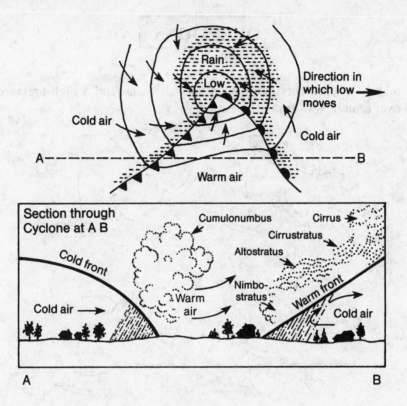

**Figure 7-33**. This drawing illustrates a "top view" of a mid-latitude cyclone and the weather associated with it.

**Making Predictions**. Decreasing air pressure often brings warm unsettled air and rainy weather, while increasing air pressure brings cool, clear weather. Because air pressure is such a strong indicator of approaching weather, the barometer is the very common weather instrument, other than a thermometer, that can be found in many homes. Weather systems in the United States usually move from west to east. Generally speaking, then, weather that is to our west will come east. Past weather records generally are important in allowing meteorologists to predict future weather as a probability of occurrence. Short term (1 to 3 days) weather forecasts are usually far more accurate than long term forecasts.

# QUESTIONS

1. Which map best represents the normal circulation around a high-pressure air-mass located over central New York State?

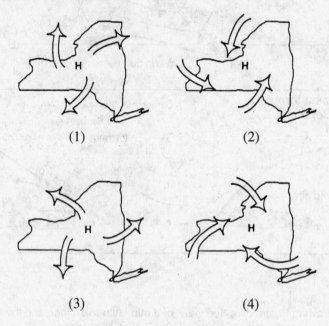

(1)          (2)

(3)          (4)

2. How does air circulate within a cyclone (low-pressure area) in the Northern Hemisphere?

   (1) counterclockwise and toward the center of the cyclone
   (2) counterclockwise and away from the center of the cyclone
   (3) clockwise and toward the center of the cyclone
   (4) clockwise and away from the center of the cyclone

3. New York State weather usually comes from which direction?

   (1) east          (2) northeast          (3) west          (4) north

Base your answers to questions 4 through 7 on your knowledge of Earth Science, the *Earth Science Reference Tables*, and the diagram below, which represents a surface weather map of a portion of the United States. The map shows a low-pressure system with frontal lines and five weather stations A through E. Note that part of the weather data is missing from each station. [All temperatures are in °F.]

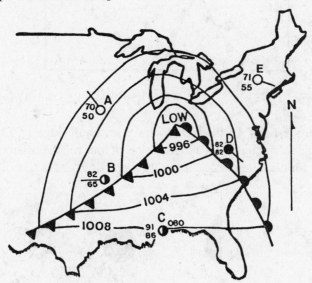

4. The weather at station C would most likely be

   (1) partly cloudy, windy, and very cold    (2) partly cloudy and warm
   (3) overcast, humid, and cool    (4) very dry and extremely hot

5. The atmospheric pressure at the center of the low would most likely be

   (1) 988 millibars    (2) 990 millibars    (3) 994 millibars    (4) 997 millibars

6. The wind direction at station A is

   (1) northwest    (2) northeast    (3) southwest    (4) southeast

7. Assuming that the low-pressure system follows a normal storm track, which weather station is probably located in the path of the approaching center of the low?

   (1) A    (2) B    (3) C    (4) E

8. At which location will a low-pressure storm center most likely form?

   (1) along a frontal surface between different air-masses
   (2) near the middle of a cold air-mass
   (3) on the leeward side of mountains
   (4) over a very dry, large flat land area

9. The diagram below shows four points on a map with their relative positions to a low-pressure weather system. Which point is most likely having heavy precipitation?

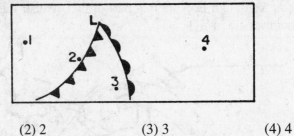

(1) 1    (2) 2    (3) 3    (4) 4

Base your answer to questions 10 through 14 on your knowledge of Earth Science, the *Earth Science Reference Tables*, and the diagrams below of four weather station models. Weather data were recorded at four different locations at the same time.

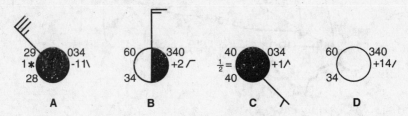

10. Which station has an air temperature of 29°F?

 (1) A    (2) B    (3) C    (4) D

11. The wind direction at station C is from the

 (1) northeast  (2) northwest  (3) southeast  (4) southwest

12. What is the air pressure at station D?

 (1) 340.0 mb  (2) 934.0 mb  (3) 1003.4 mb  (4) 1034.0 mb

13. Which station shows that the present air-pressure reading is lower than it was 3 hours ago?

 (1) A    (2) B    (3) C    (4) D

14. At which station are there winds of 35 knots?

 (1) A    (2) B    (3) C    (4) D

Base your answers to questions 15 through 19 on your knowledge of Earth Science, the *Earth Science Reference Tables*, and the surface weather map shown below. The map shows weather systems over the United States and weather station data for cities A, B, C, and D. Note that part of the weather data for city C and all of the weather data for city E are missing. The pressure field (isobars) on the map has been labeled in millibars.

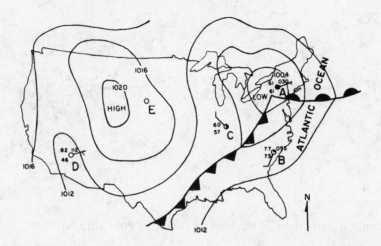

**15.** Which city is experiencing the *highest* air temperature?

(1) A           (2) B           (3) C           (4) D

**16.** What type of front extends eastward away from the low-pressure center?

(1) cold           (2) warm           (3) stationary           (4) occluded

**17.** Which city is probably experiencing a slow, steady rain?

(1) A           (2) B           (3) C           (4) D

**18.** Which weather station model best represents the weather conditions probably existing at city E?

(1)       (2)       (3)       (4)

**19.** If this low-pressure center has followed a normal storm track, which map shows its most likely path over the last two days?

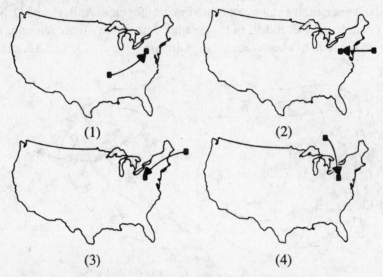

        (1)                        (2)

        (3)                        (4)

**20.** Why do clouds usually form at the leading edge of a cold airmass?

(1) Cold air flows over warm air, causing the warm air to descend and cool.
(2) Cold air flows under warm air, causing the warm air to rise and cool.
(3) Cold air contains more dust than warm air does.
(4) Cold air contains more water vapor than warm air does.

# HURRICANES AND TORNADOES

The occurrences of severe weather have a fascination that ordinary weather phenomena cannot provide. A single tornado outbreak or hurricane can cause billions of dollars in property damages as well as many deaths. Although hurricanes and tornadoes are cyclones, the great majority of cyclones are not hurricanes or tornadoes. Tornadoes and hurricanes are both smaller and more violent than mid-latitude cyclones. Mid-latitude cyclones may have a diameter of 1600 kilometers or more while hurricanes average 600 kilometers across and tornadoes average 1/4 mile across.

**Hurricanes.** Hurricanes form over tropical oceans. A **hurricane** is a doughnut shaped ring of strong counterclockwise winds exceeding 115 kilometers per hour (75 miles per hour) surrounding an area of extremely low pressure at the center (see Figure 7-34). It is impossible to stand in such a wind. It is even difficult to breath. Extremely low pressures in the center of the hurricane develop a steep pressure gradient which generates these rapid, inward spiraling winds (see Figure 7-35). As the air moves closer to the center of the storm, its velocity increases. The hole or **eye** of the hurricane is a relative calm area of clear skies in the middle of the hurricane. A hurricane may live for three weeks or more as it drifts along over tropical waters. The weather map symbol for a hurricane is ⟨ .

A hurricane is a heat engine that is fueled by the heat stored in the water vapor. The amount of energy produced by a hurricane in just one day is almost equal to the entire electrical energy production in the United States for one year. The released heat energy warms the air and provides lift for its upward flight. This reduces the pressure near the surface and encourages a more rapid inflow of air.

Hurricanes develop most often in the late summer when ocean waters have reached temperatures of 27°C or higher. The high temperature provides the necessary heat and moisture to the air. The exact mechanism of their formation is not completely understood. It is known that hurricanes begin as mild tropical disturbances, but only a few tropical disturbances ever reach hurricane status. Hurricanes lose strength (1) as they move onto land where the storm's source of warm, moist air is cut off, and (2) when they move over cooler ocean waters that cannot supply warm moist air. For the most part, hurricanes occur along the east coast of the United States.

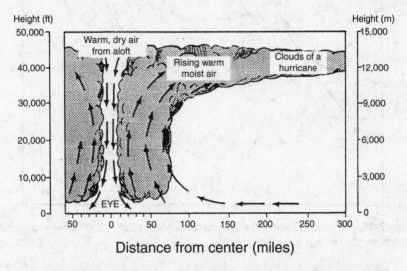

**Figure 7-34.** Vertical section of a hurricane and the patterns of wind, pressure, and rain.

The amount of damage caused by a hurricane depends on several factors, including the size and population density of the area, the shape of the near shore ocean bottom and the strength of the storm itself. Damage caused by hurricanes can be divided into three categories: wind damage, storm surge, and inland freshwater flooding. Although the winds cause damage, the most devastating damage is caused by the storm surge. A **storm surge** is a dome of water 65 to 80 kilometers wide near the point where the eye lands. A storm surge can raise the water level to higher than high tide level. Add the wave activity to that and the storm could inundate an area, kill thousands and destroy everything in its path. The third type of hurricane damage is flooding caused by the torrential rains that accompany most hurricanes.

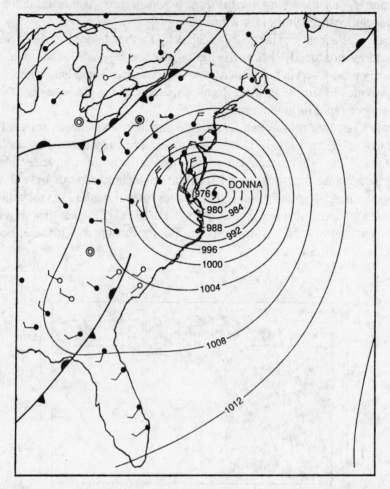

**Figure 7-35**. Hurricane Donna on the surface weather map, 1200 Greenwich mean time, September 12, 1960, just east of Virginia.

## Hurricane Safety

Each year, an average of ten tropical storms develop over the Atlantic Ocean, Caribbean Sea, and Gulf of Mexico. Many of these remain over the ocean. Six of these storms become hurricanes each year. In an average 3-year period, roughly five hurricanes strike the United States coastline, killing approximately 50 to 100 people anywhere from Texas to Maine. Of these, two are typically major hurricanes (winds greater than 110 mph.)

# Key Hurricane Alerts

Four key alert are issued that relate specifically to hurricanes.

**Tropical Storm Watch:**     Tropical storm conditions with sustained winds from 39 to 73 miles per hour (mph) are possible in your area within the next 36 hours.

**Tropical Storm Warning:**     Tropical storm conditions are expected in your area within the next 24 hours.

**Hurricane Watch:**     hurricane conditions are possible in your area within the next 36 hours.

**Hurricane Warning:**     hurricane conditions are expected in your area in 24 hours or less.

Hurricanes cause much damage, both in terms of life and property. The hurricane that demolished Galveston, Texas in 1900 took at least 8,000 lives and caused damage that would reach almost $1 billion in today's dollars. The great hurricane that pounded New England in 1938 took 600 lives and caused damage that would total $4.1 billion when adjusted for inflation. In 1992, Hurricane Andrew took 26 lives and caused $26.5 billion.

The main hazards associated with hurricanes are storm surges, high winds, heavy rain, flooding and even tornadoes. The Saffir-Simpson Hurricane Scale rates winds speeds, surface pressure, storm surges and damage potential (see Figure 7-36). The intensity of the hurricane is an indicator of damage potential. Along the coast, storm surges are the greatest threat to life and property.

## Saffir-Simpson Hurricane Rating Scale

| Saffir-Simpson Category | Maximum sustained wind speed | Minimum surface pressure | Storm surge | Damage |
|---|---|---|---|---|
| | mph | mb | ft | |
| 1 | 74 - 95 | greater than 980 | 3 - 5 | Minimal |
| 2 | 96 - 110 | 979 - 965 | 6 - 8 | Moderate |
| 3 | 111 - 130 | 964 - 945 | 9 - 12 | Extensive |
| 4 | 131 - 155 | 944 - 920 | 13 - 18 | Extreme |
| 5 | 156+ | less than 920 | 19+ | Catastrophic |

**Figure 7-36**. The Saffir-Simpson Hurricane Rating Scale indicating the effects of hurricane intensity.

Note that category 3, 4 and 5 hurricanes are collectively referred to as major (or intense) hurricanes. These major hurricanes cause over 83% of the damage in the USA even though they account for only 21% of the tropical cyclone landfalls.

Hurricane winds not only damage structures, but the wind debris they carry is quite damaging. Damaging winds begin before the hurricane eye hits land. A typical hurricane brings at least 6 to 12 inches of rainfall to the area it crosses, causing considerable damage, flash floods, mudslides and loss of life. Tornadoes often develop on the fringes of hurricanes.

Hurricane hazards are not all directly related to the storm. Fires develop due to people using candles to see when the electricity fails. Heart attacks and accidents often occur during the cleanup phase of a hurricane.

## Hurricane Safety Procedures

### To survive a hurricane, there are a few common sense procedures that can be applied:

1. **Listen to the radio/TV for updated storm announcements.**

2. **Stock up on necessary food supplies drinking water, flashlights, batteries and other items needed for several days without electricity - be sure all items are in working order.**

3. **Clean bathtubs and fill with water to use for cleaning and toilets.**

4. **During a hurricane, stay inside and away from windows, skylights and glass doors.**

5. **Find a safe area in your home - an interior, reinforced room like a closet or bath room on the lower floor or in the cellar.**

6. **After the hurricane is over, be careful of downed power lines and damaged trees.**

**Tornadoes**. Without a doubt, the most terrifying weather phenomena is the tornado. <u>Tornadoes</u> are local storms of short duration that are among nature's most destructive forces. Tornadoes, sometimes called twisters or cyclones, are violent windstorms that take the form of a rotating funnel of air that extends downward from a cumulonimbus cloud. Winds can exceed 500 kilometers per hour (300 miles per hour). The pressure drop between the outside and inside of a tornado is usually around 25 mb, but drops of up to 200 mb have been observed.

Tornadoes are extremely variable with a small diameter (usually less than a mile in diameter) and short lifetime (a few minutes) that are impossible to forecast precisely. They generally form in the vicinity of intense cold fronts and squall lines associated with mid-latitude cyclones. **Squall lines** are moving lines of thunderstorms. Throughout the spring, continental polar air from the north is still very cold and dry, and maritime tropical air from the

Gulf of Mexico is warm, humid and unstable. When these two air-masses meet, tornadoes are spawned. The greater the difference, the stronger the storm. Because these two air-masses are likely to meet in the central United States, this region produces more tornadoes than any other area of the world. Between 700 and 800 tornadoes are reported in the United States each year. **Waterspouts** are tornadoes over water.

Tornadoes have accomplished seemingly impossible tasks, such as driving a piece of straw through a thick wooden plank. It can uproot trees, pick up buses and train cars and create huge amounts of flying debris. Although the greatest damage is caused by violent winds, most tornado injuries and deaths are caused by flying debris.

## Tornado Safety

### The following are instructions on what to do when a tornado threatens:

**IN HOMES OR BUILDINGS**: Go to the basement (if available) or to an interior room on the lowest floor, such as a closet, bathroom or other interior room (pariculary in a large building. Protect yourself from flying debris. Stay away from exterior walls or glassy areas.

**IN CARS OR MOBILE HOMES**:

### *ABANDON THEM IMMEDIATELY!!*

If you are in either of these locations, leave them and go to a substantial structure or designated tornado shelter.

**IF NO SUITABLE STRUCTURE IS NEARBY**: Lie flat in the nearest ditch or depression and use your hands to cover your head.

## QUESTIONS

1. When do most tornadoes occur in the United States?

   (1) late summer and fall         (2) fall and early winter
   (3) late winter and early spring  (4) spring and early summer

2. When do most hurricanes occur in the United States?

   (1) late summer and early fall   (2) late fall and winter
   (3) winter and spring            (4) spring and early summer

Base your answers to question 3 through 7 on your knowledge of Earth Science, the *Earth Science Reference Tables*, the map below, and the graph on the next page. The map represents a portion of the United States with isolines showing the number of times destruction was caused by tropical storms during the years 1901 to 1986. The graph represents weather data, in inches of mercury, taken during a tropical storm that passed by Orlando, Florida.

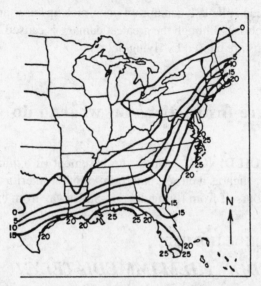

Number of times destruction was caused by tropical storms, 1901-1986

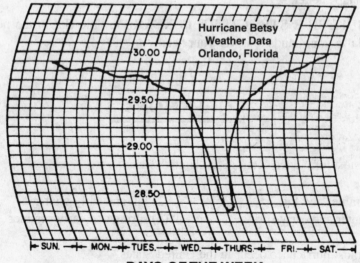

**DAYS OF THE WEEK**

**3.** Approximately how many times was destruction caused by tropical storms in Buffalo, New York, from 1901 to 1986?

(1) 1              (2) 5              (3) 12              (4) 20

**4.** Which inference is best supported by the data given?

(1) New York State is safe from destruction from tropical storms.
(2) The amount of damage from tropical storms increased from 1901 to 1986.
(3) Areas that are farther inland from the Atlantic and Gulf Coasts are safer from the damage of tropical storms.
(4) Tropical storms originate in the southeastern portion of the United States.

**5.** What type of weather data most likely is shown on the graph?

(1) air pressure              (2) air temperature
(3) relative humidity         (4) visibility

**6.** Approximately when did the storm center of Hurricane Betsy reach Orlando, Florida?

(1) 1 a.m. Monday             (2) 6 p.m. Wednesday
(3) noon Thursday             (4) 6 p.m. Saturday

**7.** According to the *Earth Science Reference Tables*, which air-mass would most likely be a source for a tropical storm?

(1) mP              (2) mT              (3) cT              (4) cP

Base your answers to question 8 through 11 on the *Earth Science Reference Tables*, the diagram below, and your knowledge of Earth Science. The diagram represents a satellite image of Hurricane Gilbert in the Gulf of Mexico. Each **x** represents the position of the eye of the storm on the date indicated.

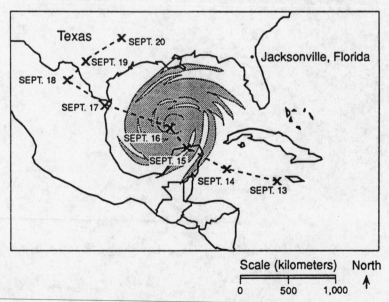

363

**8.** The general direction of Hurricane Gilbert's track from September 13 through September 18 was toward the

(1) southwest        (2) southeast        (3) northwest        (4) northeast

**9.** The surface wind pattern associated with Hurricane Gilbert was

(1) counterclockwise and toward the center
(2) counterclockwise and away from the center
(3) clockwise and toward the center
(4) clockwise and away from the center

**10.** What was the probable source of moisture for this hurricane?

(1) carbon dioxide from the atmosphere
(2) winds from the coastal deserts
(3) transpiration from tropical jungles
(4) evaporation from the ocean

**11.** On September 18, Hurricane Gilbert changed direction. Which statement provides the most probable reason for this change?

(1) The air-mass was cooled by the land surface.
(2) The storm entered the prevailing westerlies wind belt.
(3) The amount of precipitation released by the storm changed suddenly.
(4) The amount of isolation received by the air-mass decreased.

## CHAPTER 7 - CORE VOCABULARY

| | | |
|---|---|---|
| air(atmospheric)pressure | freezing | rain |
| air-mass | front | red shift |
| barometer | hail | relative humidity |
| calorie | heat energy | saturated |
| clouds | hurricanes | sleet |
| cold front | insolation | smog |
| condensation | isobar | snow |
| conduction | jet stream | solar energy |
| continental air mass | maratime air mass | specific heat |
| convection | melting | station model |
| currents | meteorology | stationary front |
| cycles | occluded front | tempreature |
| cyclones | planetary wind system | thermometer |
| dewpoint temperature | polar | tornadoes |
| Doppler effect | polar jet stream | transpiration |
| drizzle | precipitation | tropical |
| dynamic equilibrium | predict | warm front |
| electromagnetic spectrum | pressure gradient | wavelength |
| energy source | psychrometer | weather |
| evaporation | radiation | weather (atmospheric) variables |
| fog | radioactive decay | winds |

## HELPFUL VOCABULARY

| | | |
|---|---|---|
| absolute humidity | dry adiabatic lapse rate | probability of occurrence |
| absolute zero | electromagnetic energy | radioactivity |
| absorbed | energy sink | refracted |
| adiabatic | evapotranspiration | saturation vapor pressure |
| aerosol | eye of hurricane | scattered |
| amplitude | frequency | sea breeze(onshore breeze) |
| anticyclone | frictional drag | seeding |
| blue shift | frontal wedging | source region |
| breezes | frost | squall line |
| capacity | hailstone | storm surge |
| cirrus clouds | high (pressure area) | sublimation |
| closed energy system | isotherm | synopsis |
| condensation nuclei | kinetic energy | synoptic weather map |
| conservation of energy | land breeze (offshore breeze) | temperature inversion |
| convection cell | latent heat | tracks |
| convection current | low (pressure area) | trough |
| crest | mid-latitude cyclone | vapor pressure |
| cumulonimbus clouds | moist adiabatic lapse rate | visible spectrum |
| cumulus clouds | nimbostratus clouds | waterspout |
| cyclone | orographic lifting | weather forecasting |
| degrees | phase change | zones of convergence |
| dew | potential energy | zones of divergence |

## PRACTICE FOR CONSTRUCTED RESPONSE

Base your answers to questions 1 and 2 on the graphs below and your knowledge of Earth Science. The graphs show the noontime air temperatures, dewpoint temperatures, and air pressures recorded at a location in the United States.

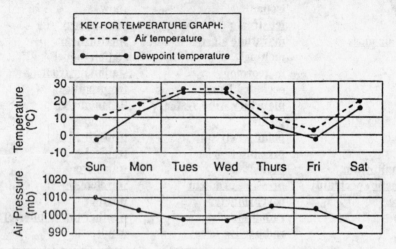

KEY FOR TEMPERATURE GRAPH:
- - - - Air temperature
———— Dewpoint temperature

1. Describe the evidence which indicates that the weather on Wednesday was cloudy, possibly raining and warm.

_____

_____

_____

_____

2. Describe the relationship between the dewpoint temperature and air pressure.

_____

_____

_____

_____

Base your answers to questions 3 through 6 on the surface map below, your knowledge of Earth Science and the *Earth Science Reference Tables*. The map represents a high pressure center located over the central United States. The air pressure field lines are in millibars and the letters represent the locations of weather stations.

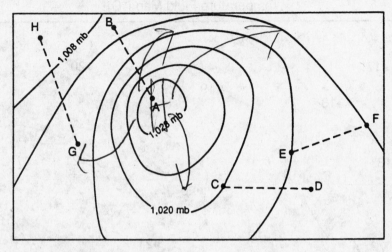

**3.** Explain why the pressure gradient from A to B is the highest, and the pressure gradient from E to F is the lowest.

_____

_____

**4.** Identify the type of pressure system shown on the map and at the center of the 1028 mb isobar. Label the pressure system.

_____

**5.** On the map, draw at least four (4) large arrows indicating the general direction of the wind circulation around the center of the pressure system.

**6.** Describe the evidence that indicates stations G and D have the same air pressure.

_____

_____

_____

_____

Base your answers to questions 7 through 9 on the temperature field map below. The map shows temperature reading (°C) recorded by students in a science classroom. The readings were taken at the same time at floor level Temperature reading points A and B are labeled on the map.

## Temperature Field Map (°C)

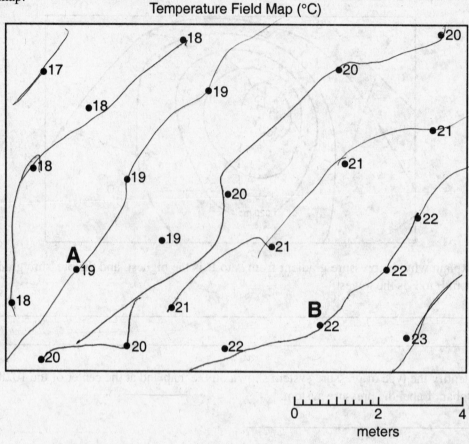

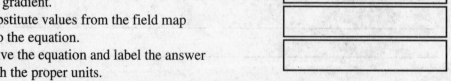

meters

7. On the temperature field map above, use solid lines to draw the 18°C, 20°C, and 22°C isotherm. Isotherms must extend to the boundary of the map. Label each isotherm to indicate its temperature.

8. Determine the temperature gradient from point A to point B by following the directions below.

   **a.** Write the equation used to determine the gradient.

   **b.** Substitute values from the field map into the equation.

   **c.** Solve the equation and label the answer with the proper units.

9. State the temperature of point A in degrees Fahrenheit (°F). _____

## THE ATMOSPHERE

Base your answers to questions 10 through 12 on the data table below, your knowledge of Earth Science and the *Earth Science Reference Tables*. The data table below shows the air pressures and air temperatures collected by nine observers at different elevations on the same side of a high mountain. The data were collected at 12:00 noon on a clear, calm day.

| Station | Elevation (m) | Air Pressure (mb) | Air Temperature (°C) |
|---------|---------------|-------------------|----------------------|
| 1 | sea level | 1,000 | 22 |
| 2 | 200 | 980 | 20 |
| 3 | 400 | 960 | 18 |
| 4 | 600 | 940 | 16 |
| 5 | 800 | 920 | 14 |
| 6 | 1,000 | 900 | 12 |
| 7 | 1,200 | 880 | 10 |
| 8 | 1,400 | 860 | 9 |
| 9 | 1,600 | 840 | 8 |

10. Determine the rate of change in air pressure between sea level and an elevation of 1200 meters using these directions:

    a. Write the equation for rate of change.

    b. Substitute data from the table into the equation.

    c. Calculate the rate of change.

    d. Label your answer with the proper units.

11. Describe the general relationship between air temperature and air pressure.

    _____

    _____

    _____

    _____

**12.** On the grid below:

   **a.** Draw a line which shows the general relationship between elevation and air pressure.

   **b.** Label the axis with the proper units.

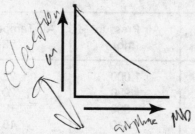

Base your answers to questions 13 and 14 on the data table and profile below. The data table gives the average annual precipitation for locations A and B. The profile represents a mountain in the western United States. Points A and B are locations on different sides of the mountain.

**Data Table**

| Location | Average Annual Precipitation (cm) |
|----------|-----------------------------------|
| A | 120 |
| B | 35 |

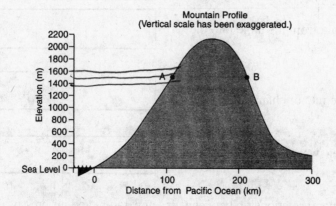

**13.** State the elevation of location A. _____ **meters**

**14.** State one probable reason for the difference in average annual precipitation between location A and location B.

_____

_____

Base your answers to questions 15 and 16 on the map below and your knowledge of Earth Science. The map shows the number of condensation nuclei measured during two ship voyages across the Atlantic Ocean, one in June and the other in August.

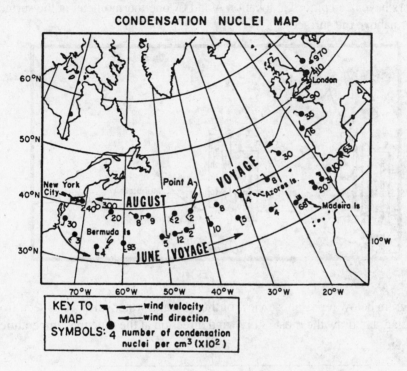

**CONDENSATION NUCLEI MAP**

15. At which latitude and longitude are the greatest particle counts found? _____

16. After studying the data for June and August, what conclusion can you draw regarding condensation nuclei and latitude?

_____

_____

_____

_____

Base your answer to question 17 on the diagram below and your knowledge of Earth Science. The diagram represents a profile of an air-ocean-land interface with locations A through E. Thermometers have been placed at location A and C, one thermometer at the surface and the other 2 meters above the surface.

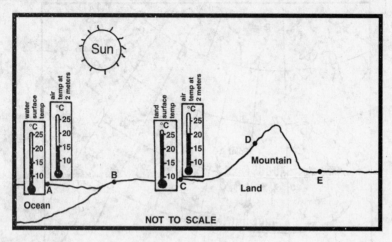

17. The diagram below represents a view of the land and water surfaces as seen from above. On the diagram, draw the most likely wind direction at the time the temperature readings were taken.

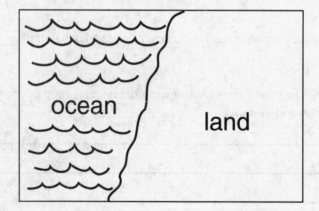

Base your answers to question 18 on the map and data table below, your knowledge of Earth Science, and the *Earth Science Reference Tables*. The map represents a weather system located over the central United States. Letters A, B, C, D, and E locate weather stations on the map. Also shown on the map are isobars, a low pressure center (letter L) and 2 lines coming out from point L.

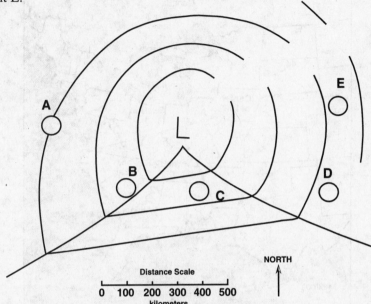

The data table provides the air temperature, dewpoint temperature, pressure, recent precipitation, cloud cover, and wind direction and speed.

| Station | Air Temp. (°F) | Dewpt Temp. (°F) | Pressure (mb) | Precip last 6 hours (in) | Cloud Cover | Wind Speed (Knots) | Wind Direction |
|---------|------|-------|----------|-------|-----------|------|-----------|
| A | 59 | 50 | 1004.0 | | clear | 15 | NW |
| B | 66 | 65 | 997.6 | .31 | overcast | 20 | NW |
| C | 82 | 76 | 998.1 | | prt cloud | 15 | SSW |
| D | 70 | 65 | 1005.0 | | overcast | 15 | SE |
| E | 65 | 60 | 1006.2 | | prt cloud | 5 | SE |

18. Use the weather data from the table above to complete the following on the map above:

  a. Plot the information from the data table on the map at each of the stations, A through E. Use the appropriate symbols given in the *Earth Science Reference Tables*.
  b. Label the following isobars on the map - 996, 1000, 1004, and 1008.
  c. On the map, draw the symbols for a warm front and a cold front on the 2 lines coming out from Point L. Be sure the symbols are on the correct side of the lines.
  d. Label the following air-masses with the appropriate symbols, continental polar and maritime tropical.

Base your answers to questions 19 through 22 on the weather map below, which shows partial weather data for several weather stations. Point A is the center of a low-pressure system. Lines AB and AC represent the frontal boundaries between different air masses.

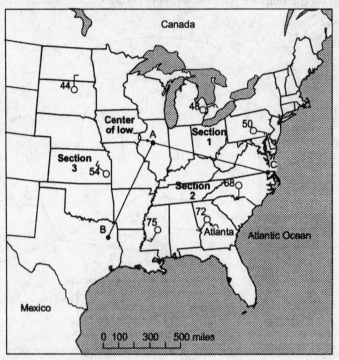

19. Draw the correct weather map symbols for the two different fronts located on lines AB and AC. The symbols must show the direction the fronts are moving.

20. In each of the *three* map sections (Section 1, Section 2, and Section 3), draw curved arrows to represent the general direction that surface winds will move in association with the center of the low-pressure system at location A.

21. Atlanta, Georgia, has the following additional weather variable measurement.

| Visibility | 6 miles |
|---|---|
| Amount of cloud cover | 1/2 or 50% |
| Air pressure | 1001.1 millibars |

On the station model to the right place these three weather measurements in their correct location using the proper format.

22. Name the weather instrument used to measure the air pressure at the center of the low.

**23.** State one way in which a hurricane differs from a tornado.

_____

_____

_____

_____

Base your answers to questions 24 and 25 on the map below, which represents a satellite image of Hurricane Gilbert in the Gulf of Mexico. Each **X** represents the position of the center of the storm on the date indicated.

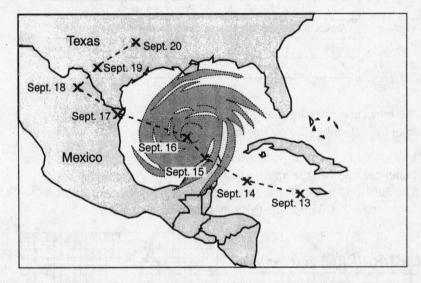

**24.** Describe _one_ threat to human life and property that could have been cause by the arrival of Hurricane Gilbert along the coastline at the Texas-Mexico border.

_____

_____

**25.** State _one_ reason Hurricane Gilbert weakened between September 16 and September 18.

_____

_____

Base your answers to questions 26 through 28 on the information and data table below.

In August 1992, Hurricane Andrew, the most costly natural disaster in United States history, hit southern Florida. The data table below shows the location and classification of Hurricane Andrew on 7 days in August 1992.

**Data Table**

| Day | Latitude | Longitude | Storm Classification |
|---|---|---|---|
| August 18 | 13° N | 46° W | Tropical storm |
| August 20 | 19° N | 59° W | Tropical storm |
| August 22 | 25° N | 66° W | Hurricane |
| August 24 | 25° N | 78° W | Hurricane |
| August 26 | 28° N | 90° W | Hurricane |
| August 27 | 32° N | 91° W | Tropical storm |
| August 28 | 34° N | 86° W | Tropical storm |

**26.** On the hurricane tracking map provided below, plot the location of Hurricane Andrew given in the data table, following the directions below.

**a.** Use an X to mark each location on the grid.
**b.** Label each X with the appropriate date.
    The data for August 18 has been plotted on the grid as an example.
**c.** Connect the X's with a line to show the hurricane's path.

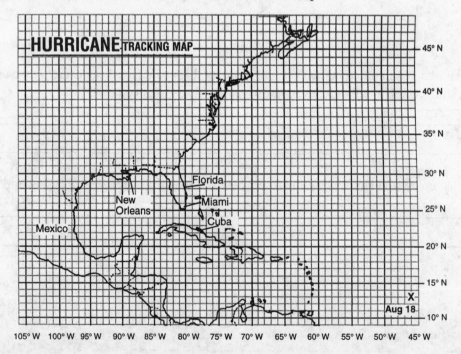

**27.** As Hurricane Andrew approached Miami, Florida, cloudiness and precipitation increased dramatically, State how the air pressure at Miami was changing at this time.

_____

_____

**28.** By August 27, Hurricane Andrew was downgraded from a hurricane to a tropical storm because its windspeed decreased. State one reason why Hurricane Andrew's windspeed decreased at this time.

_____

_____

Base your answers to questions 29 through 31 on the weather maps below. The weather maps show the positions of a topical storm at 10 a.m. on July 2 and on July 3.

**July 2**

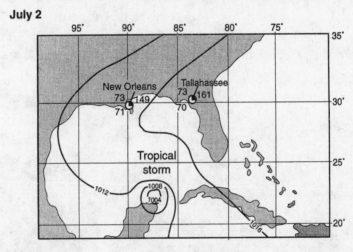

**July 3**

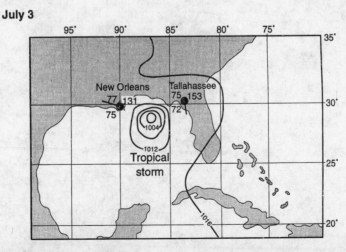

**29.** State the dewpoint temperature in Tallahassee on July 2. _____°F

**30.** Windspeed has been omitted from the station models. In one or more sentences, state how an increase in the storm's windspeed from July 2 to July 3 could be inferred from the maps.

_____

_____

**31.** The storm formed over warm tropical water. State what will most likely happen to the windspeed when the storm moves over land.

_____

_____

# CHAPTER 8

# CLIMATES

Global climate is determined by the interaction of solar energy with Earth's surface and atmosphere. This energy transfer is influenced by dynamic processes such as cloud cover and Earth's rotation, and the positions of mountain ranges and oceans. A location's climate is influenced by latitude, proximity to large bodies of water, ocean currents, prevailing winds, vegetative cover, elevation and mountain ranges. Temperature and precipitation patterns are altered by: (1) natural events such as El Niño and volcanic eruptions and (2) human influences including deforestation, urbanization, and the production of greenhouse gases such as carbon dioxide and methane.

Weather is defined as a short-term condition of the atmosphere over a region and **climate** as an *average* of weather conditions in a region over a long-term period of time. Climate is determined primarily by conditions of temperature and humidity. It is not the amount of moisture that determines a climate, rather it is the ratio of the amount of moisture to the potential for evapotranspiration.

Climate is important in determining the habitability of a given location and the most reasonable land uses within that region. One of the most important effects of climate is the availability of water at the surface and within the ground. Were does the water come from and what paths does it take through our environment?

## WATER CYCLE AND CLIMATE

A never-ending round of evaporation from sea and land creates the air's reservoir of water vapor, which then condenses to form clouds and subsequently returns to land and sea as precipitation. Figure 5-1 on page 124 provides an illustration of the water cycle. Precipitation varies from place to place and from year to year. The amount and distribution of precipitation help determine the habitability of an area. This cycle involving evaporation, condensation and precipitation involves a transfer of moisture between different latitude belts, and between the land and the sea.

**Latitude Moisture Exchange**. Some latitude zones have a surplus of precipitation over evaporation, while in others, the reverse is true. There are three main belts of precipitation excess - the equatorial zone and the middle latitude zones (40° to 70°) in each hemisphere. In contrast, there are two zones of precipitation deficit, located about 10° to 40° in each hemisphere. A belt of convection currents moves the moisture from places of high humidity to places of low humidity.

**Land-Sea Moisture Exchange**.  A moisture exchange between land and sea is required because continents have more precipitation than evaporation, and oceans more evaporation than precipitation.  Some of the water vapor added to the atmosphere by evaporation over the sea is transported by winds to the continents where, together with land-evaporated moisture, it condenses and falls as precipitation.

**Closed System**. Water that evaporates in one place usually precipitates hundreds to thousands of miles away. In the general circulation of the atmosphere, humid tropical maritime air masses travelling poleward, cool, precipitate most of their moisture, and are ultimately converted into polar air masses. In contrast, polar continental air masses moving over land toward the equator become warmer, absorb land evaporated moisture and are converted into warm, moist tropical air masses over the oceans. Air masses resemble great invisible rivers transporting vast amounts of water vapor. Water that falls to the ground as precipitation may evaporate, infiltrate or runoff into streams. Earth is a closed system. Our water is limited and must be recycled.

## QUESTIONS

1. Climate can be defined as

    (1) a short term condition of the atmosphere over a region
    (2) an average of weather conditions in a region over a long term period
    (3) a never ending round of evaporation from sea and land
    (4) a great invisible river transporting large amounts of water vapor

2. A transfer of moisture between different latitude belts and between the land and the sea through the processes of evaporation, condensation and precipitation describes

    (1) climate          (2) weather          (3) the water cycle    (4) an air mass

3. Which of the following zones has more precipitation than evaporation on a year-round basis?

    (1) Trade Wind belt                    (2) 40°N to 70°N
    (3) North Pole                         (4) 10°S to 30°S

4.  A polar air mass that moves over the land to water becomes a

    (1) maritime air mass                  (2) tropical air mass
    (3) dry air mass                       (4) continental air mass

**5.** The primary source of most of the moisture for Earth's atmosphere is

(1) soil-moisture storage        (2) rivers and lakes

(3) melting glaciers              (4) oceans

**6.** A diagram of the water cycle is shown below. Letters A through D represent the processes taking place.

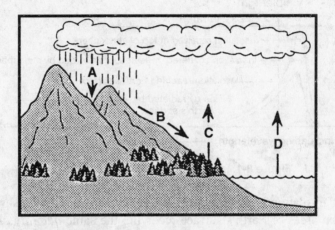

Which arrow represents the process of transpiration?

(1) A            (2) B           (3) C          (4) D

# INSOLATION AND EARTH'S SURFACE

## Insolation

As described earlier, solar radiation is, by far, the major source of energy for Earth. **Insolation** (INcoming SOLar radiATION) is the term used to refer to the radiation from the Sun that is received by Earth. Very hot objects, like the Sun, give off radiation in the form of short waves. Cooler objects, like Earth, radiate energy in the form of longer waves.

## Intensity of Insolation

The term **intensity** is frequently used in association with energy radiation. It always refers to a *rate*. **Intensity of radiation** is the rate at which energy is radiated from a body. Its value depends on temperature. The higher the temperature of the body, the greater its intensity of radiation. **Intensity of insolation** is the rate at which solar energy is received by a given area of Earth's surface per unit of time.

Earth receives only a very small fraction (about one two billionth) of all the radiation given off by the Sun. Of the amount it does receive, Earth makes use of less than half. Maximum intensity of insolation occurs within the range of visible wavelengths. Figure 8-1 compares intensity of radiation with varying wavelengths. About half of all the insolation received by Earth is short-wave radiation, which we *see* as light. The remainder is long-wave radiation, which we *feel* as heat. Most of the short-wave radiation absorbed by Earth is re-radiated from Earth's surface as long-wave infrared energy.

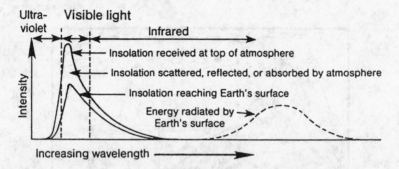

**Figure 8-1.** Intensity of radiation vs. wavelength.

Intensity of insolation is *inversely* related to the area of Earth's surface receiving it. Thus, two unequal areas of Earth's surface receiving the same *quantity* of insolation show different *intensities* of insolation. For example, in Figure 8-2, Area A is one square meter, while Area B is two square meters. Assume that each area receives insolation at a rate of 10,000 calories per second. The intensity of insolation at Area B would be only one-half that of Area A, because the insolation at Area B is spread out over twice the area. The intensity at A would be 10,000 calories per square meter per second. Intensity at B would be 5,000 calories per square meter per second.

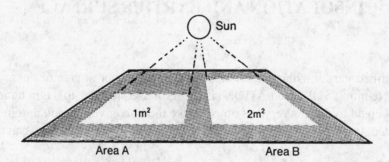

**Figure 8-2.** Intensity of insolation vs. area receiving it. The area of A is one-half the area of B, yet A receives the same quantity (10,000 calories/second) of insolation as B. Thus, each square meter of area A receives 10,000 cal/sec of insolation, while each square meter of area B receives 5,000 cal/sec of insolation.

# FACTORS AFFECTING INSOLATION

There are many factors that affect the intensity of insolation reaching Earth's surface. Some of these factors include the angle at which the insolation strikes the surface, the type of surface it strikes, the length of time the insolation is received, and atmospheric conditions.

## Angle of Insolation

The angle at which the Sun's rays strike Earth's surface is referred to as the **angle of insolation**. Because Earth's surface is curved, the Sun's rays strike it at angles ranging from 0° to 90°. At locations where the Sun is directly overhead (at zenith), the Sun's rays are perpendicular, and they strike the surface at an angle of 90°. Rays that strike Earth's surface at a 90° angle are called **direct**, or **vertical**, **rays**. Vertical rays provide the greatest intensity of insolation, because the insolation is concentrated over the smallest possible area (see Figure 8-3).

As the angle of insolation decreases from 90°, the Sun's rays become less direct and the amount of insolation is spread over larger and larger areas. Thus, as angle of insolation decreases, the intensity also decreases.

## Angle of Insolation and Temperature

The angle of insolation affects the temperature at Earth's surface. Locations receiving vertical rays receive more energy per unit area than do locations receiving slanted (less-than-vertical) rays (see Figure 8-3). Thus, locations receiving vertical rays will have higher temperatures than those receiving slanted rays.

## Time of Day and Intensity of Insolation

At any location on Earth's surface, the angle of insolation varies with the time of day (see Figure 8-4). At sunrise and sunset, the angle and intensity of insolation are the least. Between sunrise and noon, the angle and intensity of insolation increase. At solar noon, when the Sun is at its highest point in the sky, the angle and intensity of insolation are greatest. Between solar noon and sunset, the angle and intensity of insolation decrease. In Figure 8-4, the area of the shadow cast by the tree is smallest at solar noon, indicating that intensity of insolation is greatest. The area of the shadow is greatest at sunrise and sunset, indicating that these are the times when intensity of insolation is lowest.

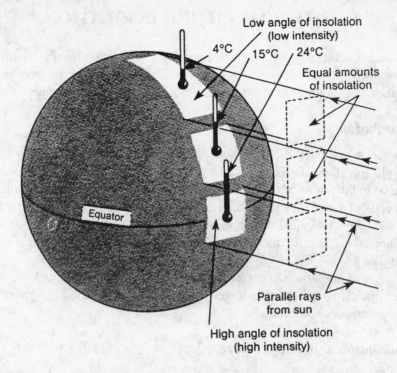

**Figure 8-3**. The greater the angle of insolation, the greater the intensity of insolation and the higher the temperature.

Keep in mind that, at solar noon, the Sun's rays are not necessarily vertical. Only locations between the Tropic of Cancer ($23^1/_2°$N) and the Tropic of Capricorn ($23^1/_2°$S) can experience the Sun's vertical rays. From any location in the United States, an observer must face toward the south in order to see the Sun at solar noon.

## Earth's Shape and Intensity of Insolation

The Sun is so far away, that when the Sun's rays reach Earth's surface, they are in effect parallel. If Earth were flat, all the rays would strike the surface at the same angle, and the intensity of insolation would be the same all over Earth's surface. However, Earth is not flat. Because Earth is a sphere, the Sun's rays strike the curved surface of Earth at angles ranging from 0° to 90°. At any given time, vertical rays can strike Earth at only one location (see Figure 8-5). As you move away from that location, the angle and intensity of insolation decrease.

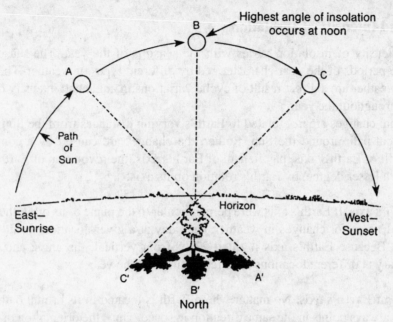

**Figure 8-4**. Intensity of insolation is greatest at noon, least at the times of sunrise and sunset.

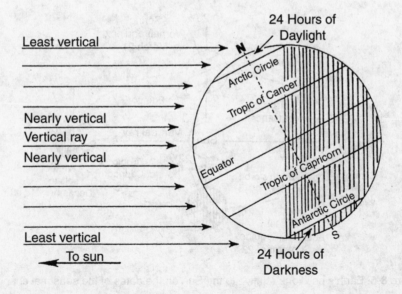

**Figure 8-5**. In this illustration, vertical rays of the Sun strike at 23$\frac{1}{2}$° North latitude. This occurs on June 22, the first day of summer in the Northern Hemisphere. On this date, locations south of the Antarctic Circle do not see the Sun at all.

## Seasons and Intensity of Insolation

The intensity of insolation varies with the **seasons** of the year. The seasons are four distinct time periods of the year characterized by different types of weather. These seasonal changes in weather are a direct result of cyclic variations in angle and intensity of insolation that occur throughout the year.

Seasonal changes are *not* related to Earth's varying distances from the Sun as it moves in its elliptical path around the Sun. Rather, the changes are caused by a combination of factors-the tilt of Earth's axis, parallelism of Earth's axis, the revolution of Earth around the Sun, and, to a lesser degree, by Earth's rotation on its axis.

**Tilt of Earth's axis.** If Earth's axis were perpendicular to the plane of its orbit, there would be no seasons. Except for changes in weather, each day at a given location would be just like every other. Because Earth's axis is tilted $23\frac{1}{2}°$ from vertical, the angle and intensity of insolation vary at different locations at different times of the year.

**Parallelism of Earth's axis.** No matter where Earth is located in its orbital path around the Sun, its axis always points in the same direction in space. Thus, the orientation of Earth's axis at any position in its orbit is always parallel to that at any other position (see Figure 8-6).

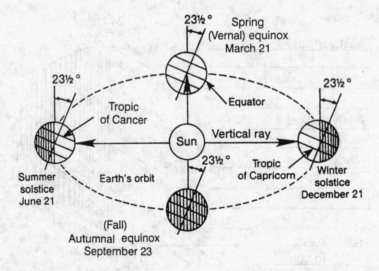

**Figure 8-6**. Earth's positions relative to the Sun on the dates of the seasonal changes.

**Revolution of Earth around the Sun.** If Earth did not revolve around the Sun, there would be no seasons. The tilt and parallelism of Earth's axis cause the angle and intensity of insolation to vary at different locations as Earth revolves around the Sun. These variations produce the seasons.

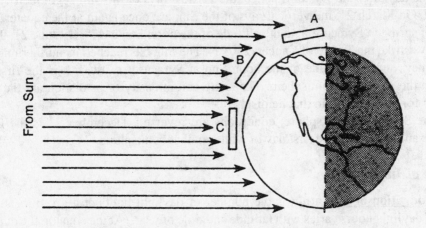

**Figure 8-7**. Intensity of insolation varies with latitude.

## Latitude and Intensity of Insolation

Because Earth is spherical, every degree of latitude has a different angle and intensity of insolation. When the Sun's vertical rays strike the equator (at the equinoxes), intensity of insolation decreases with an increase in latitude (see Figure 8-7). As Earth moves in its orbit around the Sun, the tilt of its axis causes the Sun to "migrate" between $23\frac{1}{2}°$N (Summer Solstice) and $23\frac{1}{2}°$S (Winter Solstice). Thus, only locations between these two latitudes can ever receive vertical rays of the Sun.

At any given latitude, the altitude (angle) of the Sun at solar noon varies throughout the year. Intensity of insolation at that location shows a corresponding variation. For example, consider the city of Syracuse, New York, which is at a latitude of 43°N. On September 23, the Sun is directly overhead at the equator (0° latitude). On that date, the altitude of the noon Sun at Syracuse is 47° (see Figure 8-8). Three months later, on December 22, the Sun is directly over the Tropic of Capricorn, at $23\frac{1}{2}°$S. At Syracuse on that date, the altitude of the noon Sun is only $23\frac{1}{2}°$. This is the smallest noon-Sun altitude experienced at Syracuse. It is the first day of winter in the Northern Hemisphere, and the angle and intensity of insolation are the smallest of the year for all locations in that hemisphere.

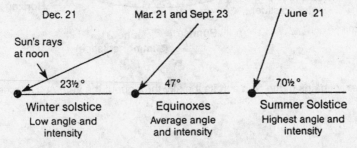

**Figure 8-8**. Changing altitude of the noon sun at Syracuse, New York, throughout the year.

On the day after the Winter Solstice, the vertical rays of the Sun begin their "journey" northward. On March 21, the vertical rays of the Sun are once again at the equator. It is the first day of spring in Syracuse, and the altitude of the noon Sun is 47°. On June 21, the Sun's vertical rays strike the Tropic of Cancer, $23^{1}/_{2}°$N. The Sun has reached its northernmost point in its journey, and the altitude of the noon Sun at Syracuse is $70^{1}/_{2}°$. It is the first day of summer in the Northern Hemisphere. The angle and intensity of insolation are the greatest of the year for all locations in that hemisphere.

In the Southern Hemisphere, conditions are reversed. December 21 is the first day of summer and June 21 is the first day of winter in that hemisphere.

## Duration of Insolation

The **duration of insolation** is the number of daylight hours at a given location. The number of daylight hours varies with latitude and time of year. (At the equator, the duration of insolation is approximately 12 hours every day throughout the year.) There is a direct correlation between angle and intensity of insolation and duration of insolation. For locations in the Northern Hemisphere, on December 21, when angle and intensity are smallest, duration is shortest. December 21 is "the shortest day of the year" in the Northern Hemisphere (fewest hours of daylight). Conversely, on June 21, angle, intensity, and duration of insolation are all at their greatest in the Northern Hemisphere.

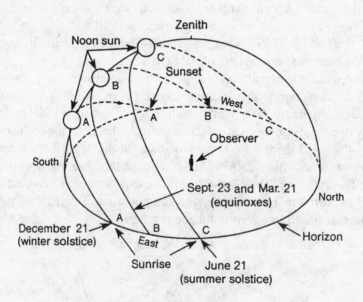

**Figure 8-9.** Apparent paths of the Sun across the sky throughout the year at Syracuse, New York.

## TABLE 8-1. ALTITUDE OF NOON SUN AND DURATION OF INSOLATION

| Latitude | December 21 Altitude of Noon Sun | December 21 Duration of Insolation | March 21 September 23 Altitude of Noon Sun | March 21 September 23 Duration of Insolation | June 21 Altitude of Noon Sun | June 21 Duration of Insolation |
|---|---|---|---|---|---|---|
| 90°N | – | 0 Hours | 0° | 12 Hours | 23½° | 24 Hours |
| 80°N | – | 0 | 10° | 12 | 33½° | 24 |
| 70°N | – | 0 | 20° | 12 | 43½° | 24 |
| 60°N | 6½° | 5½ | 30° | 12 | 53½° | 18½ |
| 50°N | 16½° | 7¾ | 40° | 12 | 63½° | 16¼ |
| 40°N | 26½° | 9 | 50° | 12 | 73½° | 15 |
| 30°N | 36½° | 10 | 60° | 12 | 83½° | 14 |
| 20°N | 46½° | 10¾ | 70° | 12 | 86½° | 13¼ |
| 10°N | 56½° | 11½ | 80° | 12 | 76½° | 12½ |
| 0° | 66½° | 12 | 90° | 12 | 66½° | 12 |
| 10°S | 76½° | 12½ | 80° | 12 | 56½° | 11½ |
| 20°S | 86½° | 13¼ | 70° | 12 | 46½° | 10¾ |
| 30°S | 83½° | 14 | 60° | 12 | 36½° | 10 |
| 40°S | 73½° | 15 | 50° | 12 | 26½° | 9 |
| 50°S | 63½° | 16¼ | 40° | 12 | 16½° | 7¾ |
| 60°S | 53½° | 18½ | 30° | 12 | 6½° | 5½ |
| 70°S | 43½° | 24 | 20° | 12 | – | 0 |
| 80°S | 33½° | 24 | 10° | 12 | – | 0 |
| 90°S | 23½° | 24 | 0° | 12 | – | 0 |

Figure 8-9 shows the apparent path of the Sun across the sky on the first day of each season as seen by an observer at Syracuse. Every 15 degrees of arc represents one hour of daylight. Thus, the longer the arc, the longer the duration of insolation. Table 8-1 shows the altitude of the noon Sun and duration of insolation on the first day of each season at ten-degree increments of latitude.

## Duration of Insolation and Temperature

Temperatures at Earth's surface are directly related to the duration of insolation. The longer the period of daylight (duration), the higher the temperature. This relationship is true because the total amount of insolation at a location increases as the duration increases. In the mid-latitudes, the maximum duration of insolation occurs at the Summer Solstice; minimum duration occurs at the Winter Solstice.

## Temperature Changes and Radiative Balance

If a body gains the same amount of radiant energy as it gives off, it is in **radiative balance**. The surface of Earth continuously receives insolation from the Sun. It also continuously radiates infrared energy from its surface. As the amount of insolation received by Earth increases, the amount of infrared energy radiated from Earth also usually increases. Conversely, as the amount of insolation decreases, the amount of infrared radiation usually decreases. Temperatures on Earth depend on the amount of energy absorbed and re-radiated. When the amount of incoming energy equals the amount of outgoing energy, temperature remains fairly constant over a long period of time, and Earth is in radiative balance. For the temperature to rise, the amount of incoming radiation must exceed the amount of outgoing radiation. For the temperature to fall, the opposite condition must exist.

## Maximum and Minimum Temperatures

Maximum radiative energy reaches Earth when the angle and intensity of insolation are the greatest. On a daily basis, this occurs at solar noon, On an annular basis, this condition occurs at the time of the Summer Solstice, June 21 in the Northern Hemisphere. You might expect the hottest time of day and hottest time of year to coincide with these times of maximum radiative energy. Yet, these highest temperatures actually occur sometime after the period of maximum radiative energy.

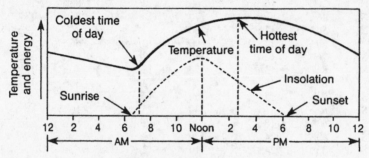

**Figure 8-10.** Hottest and coldest times of day.

**Hottest and coldest times of day**. The hottest time of day occurs some hours *after* solar noon. When the Sun rises in the morning, Earth begins to receive more energy than it reradiates. Thus, the temperature begins to rise. Although the greatest angle of insolation occurs at solar noon, the temperature continues to rise, because the amount of incoming radiant energy continues to exceed the amount of outgoing radiant energy (see Figure 8-10). The temperature continues to rise until around mid-afternoon, when the amounts of incoming and outgoing energy reach radiative balance. This is the hottest time of the day. From this point on, as the angle of insolation continues to decrease, the amount of incoming energy falls below the amount of outgoing energy, and the temperature starts to fall. It continues to drop until sunrise the next day, which is the coldest time of the average day. Then, insolation begins again and incoming and outgoing energy reach radiative balance. The daily temperature cycle then starts again.

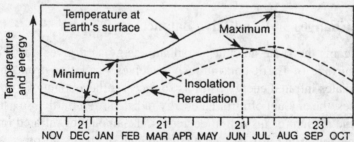

**Figure 8-11.** Hottest and coldest times of the year.

**Hottest and coldest times of year**. In a similar fashion, in the Northern Hemisphere, the hottest time of the year occurs after June 21 (see Figure 8-11). Even though the angle and duration of insolation are greatest on June 21, the amount of incoming energy continues to exceed the amount of outgoing energy for many days after that date. Therefore, the temperature continues to rise. In the Northern Hemisphere, the hottest day of the year occurs sometime in August, when the amounts of incoming and outgoing energy are in radiative balance. After that, as the amount of outgoing energy exceeds the amount of incoming energy, the daily temperature drops. Although the angle and duration of insolation are smallest on December 21, it is not the coldest day of the year. Even though the angle and duration of insolation begin to increase after December 21, the amount of outgoing energy continues to exceed the amount of incoming energy for a period of time after that, and the temperature continues to drop. Sometime in February, the amounts of incoming and outgoing energy reach radiative balance. The coldest day of the year occurs at this time. As the angle and duration of insolation continue to increase, the days become warmer, and the yearly cycle continues.

# QUESTIONS

1. In New York State, summer is warmer than winter because in summer, New York State has

   (1) more hours of daylight and is closer to the Sun
   (2) more hours of daylight and receives more direct insolation
   (3) fewer hours of daylight but is closer to the Sun
   (4) fewer hours of daylight but receives more direct insolation

2. Which graph best illustrates the relationship between the altitude of the noontime Sun and the level of insolation?

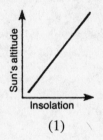 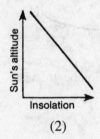 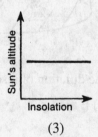 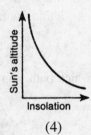

   (1)          (2)          (3)          (4)

3. For which date and location will the longest duration of insolation normally occur?

   (1) June 21, at 60° N.            (2) June 21, at 23$\frac{1}{2}$°N.
   (3) December 21, at 60° N.        (4) December 21, at 23$\frac{1}{2}$°N.

**4.** On which date does New York State receive maximum insolation from the Sun?

(1) March 21          (2) June 21          (3) July 21          (4) August 21

**5.** The diagram below represents the path of the Sun across the sky during a particular day.

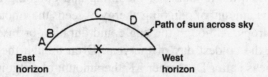

At location X, for which Sun position would the intensity of insolation be the greatest?

(1) A               (2) B               (3) C               (4) D

**6.** In New York State, July is warmer than February because in July

(1) the air is a better conductor of heat
(2) more heat is received than is lost
(3) Earth is closer to the Sun
(4) the Sun gives off more radiation

**7.** The diagram below represents a model of the Sun's apparent path across the sky in New York State for selected dates.

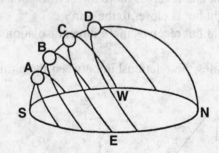

For which path would the duration of insolation be greatest?

(1) A               (2) B               (3) C               (4) D

**8.** In the diagram below, a vertical post casts shadows A, B, C, and D at four different times during the day. Which shadow was cast when this location was receiving the greatest intensity of insolation?

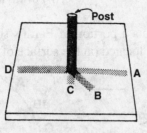

(1) shadow A      (2) shadow B      (3) shadow C      (4) shadow D

**9.** What happens to the angle of insolation on June 21 between solar noon and 6 p.m. in New York State?

(1) It decreases steadily.      (2) It increases steadily.
(3) It remains the same.      (4) It first increases and then decreases.

**10.** Which two factors determine the number of hours of daylight at a particular location?

(1) longitude and season      (2) longitude and Earth's average diameter
(3) latitude and season      (4) latitude and Earth's average diameter

**11.** The map below shows isolines of average daily insolation received in calories per square centimeter per minute at Earth's surface. If identical solar collectors are placed at the lettered locations, which collector would receive the least insolation?

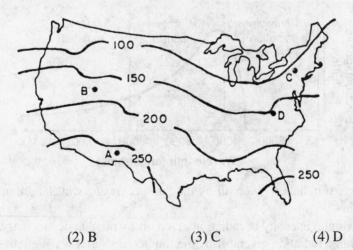

(1) A      (2) B      (3) C      (4) D

12. Short waves of electromagnetic energy are absorbed by Earth's surface during the day. They are later reradiated into space as

    (1) visible light rays          (2) X-rays
    (3) infrared rays               (4) ultraviolet rays

13. The diagram below represents a portion of Earth's surface that is receiving insolation. Positions A, B, C, and D are located on the surface of Earth.

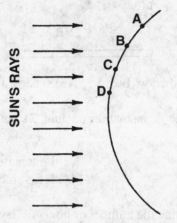

    At which position would the intensity of insolation be greatest?

    (1) A               (2) B               (3) C               (4) D

14. The graph below represents the relationship between the intensity and wavelength of the Sun's electromagnetic radiation.
    Which statement is best supported by the graph?

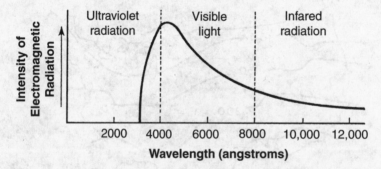

    (1) The infrared radiation given off by the Sun occurs at a wavelength of 2,000 angstroms.
    (2) The maximum intensity of radiation given off by the Sun occurs in the visible region.
    (3) The infrared radiation given off by the Sun has a shorter wavelength than ultraviolet radiation.
    (4) The electromagnetic energy given off by the Sun consists of a single wavelength.

Base your answers to questions 15 through 18 on your knowledge of Earth Science and on the graph below which shows the Sun's altitude and the air temperature during a 24-hour period in June at Binghamton, New York.

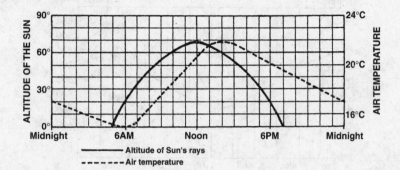

15. Approximately how long after the Sun reaches its maximum altitude did the air temperature reach its maximum reading?

    (1) 1 hr              (2) 2 hr              (3) 3 hr              (4) 4 hr

16. At which time was the intensity of insolation on a horizontal surface area in Binghamton the greatest?

    (1) 6:00 a.m.         (2) 2:00 p.m.         (3) noon             (4) 7:00 p.m..

17. At which times did a condition of radiative balance exist at Binghamton, New York?

    (1) 12 noon and 12 midnight          (2) 12 noon and 2 p.m.
    (3) 5 a.m. and 1 p.m.                (4) 6 a.m. and 2 p.m.

18. Which graph best represents the relationship between the average monthly temperature and the time of year for this city?

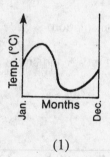
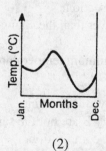
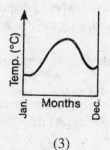
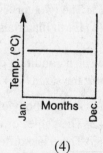

(1)              (2)              (3)              (4)

Base your answers to questions 19 through 23 on your knowledge of Earth Science and on the graph below which indicates the amount of insolation received by two cities (located at the same altitude and latitude) and their average surface temperatures.

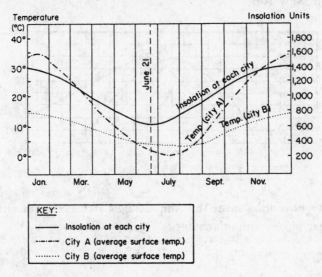

**19.** The minimum amount of insolation received by both cities was about

(1) 30 units          (2) 200 units          (3) 600 units          (4) 1,400 units

**20.** The latitude of the two cities is

(1) 10° N.          (2) 35° S.          (3) 40° N.          (4) 90° S.

**21.** Which statement best explains why the minimum temperature of city A occurs after the minimum insolation?

(1) The amount of insolation does not affect surface temperature.
(2) The radiative balance is still equal.
(3) The two curves have two points of intersection.
(4) Earth materials are losing their heat slower than the change in insolation.

**22.** Which condition could explain why the minimum temperatures of city A and city B are *not* the same?

(1) A large body of water is located near city B but not city A.
(2) The angles of insolation at city A and city B are not the same.
(3) There is a difference in bedrock and soil composition.
(4) There is a higher concentration of pollution in the air of city A than city B.

**23.** The minimum value of the insolation curve for a location that is 500 km due west of city A would probably be

(1) less than that of city A
(2) greater than that of city A
(3) the same as that of city A

**24.** The greatest amount of solar radiation will be reflected by

(1) soil          (2) snow          (3) plants          (4) water

# RADIATION AND THE ATMOSPHERE

## Layers of the Atmosphere

The atmosphere has four distinct layers, each with a particular set of properties. The layers vary in thickness and are separated by diffuse interfaces (see Figure 8-12). The layers are divided by temperature patterns, and the names of the interfaces between the layers end with the suffix "-pause."

**Troposphere.** As you move up through the **troposphere** (the layer closest to the surface), the average temperature drops about 6.4°C for every kilometer of altitude. The composition of the troposphere is approximately 78% nitrogen, and 20% oxygen, with the remaining 2% made up primarily of argon, carbon dioxide, neon, helium, and other gases. Dust and most of the water vapor are also found in the troposphere. Most of Earth's weather occurs in the troposphere. At the top of the troposphere is the **tropopause**.

### SELECTED PROPERTIES OF EARTH'S ATMOSPHERE

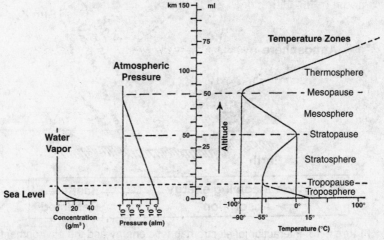

**Figure 8-12**. Layers and temperature zones of the atmosphere.

**Stratosphere.** The layer above the troposphere is the **stratosphere**. In the stratosphere, the temperature increases (see Figure 8-13) rather than decreases with altitude. Very little weather occurs in this layer. The top of the stratosphere is called the **stratopause**.

**Mesosphere.** Above the stratosphere is the **mesosphere**. With increasing altitude, the temperatures fall until, at the top of this layer, a low of about –90° C is reached. The **mesopause** is located where the temperature stops falling.

**Thermosphere.** The outer upper layer of the atmosphere is called the **thermosphere**. Temperatures can reach to 1,000 degrees Celsius at higher altitudes in this layer. Although there is very little matter in this layer, its high temperatures are caused by X-rays and ultraviolet radiation striking molecules of air.

## The Atmosphere and Insolation

More insolation reaches the upper atmosphere than reaches Earth's surface. The atmosphere is largely transparent to visible radiation, but it absorbs, reflects, or scatters much of the other radiation (see Figure 8-13).

**Absorption**. Most of the ultraviolet radiation is absorbed by ozone in the stratosphere, while much of the infrared radiation is absorbed by carbon dioxide and water vapor in the troposphere.

**Reflection.** On a typical day, clouds reflect approximately 25% of the incoming (incident) insolation. The amount of radiation reflected depends upon the angle of insolation. The lower the angle, the more insolation reflected and the less absorbed. Areas of ice and snow reflect almost all of the incoming insolation, causing these areas to be cooler than they would normally be. Although the polar regions have six months of continuous insolation, they have lower temperatures because, in addition to the low angle of insolation, the ice and snow reflect much of the insolation.

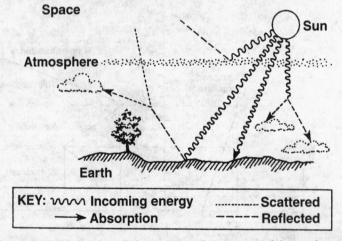

**Figure 8-13.** Interaction of electromagnetic energy and the environment.

**Scattering. Aerosols**, such as water droplets, ice crystals, air pollutants, and dust in the atmosphere cause a random reflection of insolation. The amount of scattering of insolation increases as the concentration of aerosols in the atmosphere increases. As the amount of random reflection increases, the amount of insolation reaching Earth's surface decreases. For example, following a volcano, when the sky is filled with volcanic dust, the aerosols can be so concentrated that they may cut off almost all the insolation from Earth's surface.

**Energy conversion.** Some insolation is converted into potential energy (latent heat) by the evaporation of water and the melting of ice and snow. When this occurs, the amount of energy available to heat an area of Earth's surface is reduced. This reduction increases the amount of water vapor in the air, which also reduces the amount of insolation available to heat an area. Therefore, the temperature of that area will be lower than it would otherwise be.

Any material that is a good absorber is also a good radiator of energy. However, the energy radiated is of a longer wavelength than that which was absorbed. For example, dark soil will absorb light energy. It will radiate some of that energy back into space in the form of heat, which is in the infrared range of the spectrum. Materials with dark, rough surfaces are better absorbers of electromagnetic energy than are materials with smooth, light-colored surfaces.

## Land and Water Surfaces

With equal amounts of insolation reaching equal areas of land and water at the same latitude, the average temperature of the land will increase and decrease more quickly than that of the water. Water has a much higher specific heat than land. The specific heat of water is 1cal/g°C, while the specific heat of land is only around 0.2 cal/g°C. To raise the temperature of water and land the same number of degrees, the water requires five times more insolation than the land. Because water is semi-transparent, much of the insolation that strikes water penetrates and is absorbed at greater depths. In addition, the insolation absorbed by the water can be distributed throughout the fluid by convection, thus heating a larger volume. Land, being a better absorber of insolation (and having a lower specific heat), heats up and cools down faster than water. Further, since a good absorber is a good radiator, the land radiates heat to the air more quickly than the water. Therefore, the air over the land heats up and cools down more quickly than the air over the water.

# TERRESTRIAL RADIATION

Insolation that reaches Earth's surface is either absorbed or reflected. Much of that which is absorbed is converted to heat energy, thereby raising the temperature of Earth's surface. However, because the temperature of Earth is much less than that of the Sun, the maximum intensity of outgoing radiation from Earth's surface is in the infrared region of the electromagnetic spectrum. Electromagnetic energy given off by the surface of Earth is called **terrestrial radiation.**

# The Greenhouse Effect

The atmosphere is transparent to most short-wave insolation from the Sun. However, it is not transparent to long-wave infrared energy radiated from Earth's surface. Water vapor and carbon dioxide in the air are good absorbers of infrared radiation. These gases permit short-wave visible radiation to pass through to Earth's surface, where the waves are absorbed and reradiated as long-wave infrared (heat) radiation. Water vapor and carbon dioxide absorb the longer heat waves, thus raising the temperature of the lower atmosphere. The process that allows short-wave energy to be transmitted through the atmosphere, but which reflects and captures the reradiated longwave infrared energy, is known as the **greenhouse effect** (see Figure 8-14). When you enter a car that has been sitting out in the summer Sun, you experience this effect. Short-wave insolation passes through the glass, is absorbed by the interior of the car and reradiated as long waves. The glass acts like the carbon dioxide and water vapor in the air and prevents the long-wave radiation from escaping from the car. Therefore, when you open the car door, you are hit by a blast of hot air. Many scientists believe that the amount of carbon dioxide in the atmosphere has a major effect on world climates. For example, an increase in carbon dioxide in the atmosphere could cause the air temperature to rise enough to cause the polar ice caps to melt which would flood coastal cities worldwide.

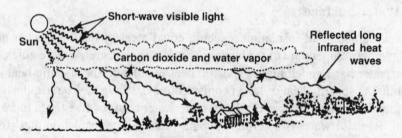

**Figure 8-14.** The greenhouse effect.

During the last 200 years, mankind has been releasing extra quantities of greenhouse gases trapping more heat and warming the atmosphere. Earth, for example, has warmed up by about 0.6°C in the last 100 years. During this period, manmade emissions of greenhouse gases have increased, largely as a result of the burning of fossil fuels and deforestation.

Earth's natural greenhouse effect keeps Earth 33° warmer than it would be without an atmosphere. The present average temperature of the entire Earth is about 15°C. The moon, which has no atmosphere, has a average surface temperature of 18°C.

## Radiative Balance Versus Time

In the course of a year, the incoming energy can equal the outgoing energy, and Earth can be in radiative balance. However, measurements of worldwide surface temperatures over thousands of years indicate that Earth is not in radiative balance. The theory that temperatures on Earth's surface have risen and cooled over extended periods is indicated by the fact that, at certain times, glaciers have covered much of Earth's surface. Measurements of worldwide surface temperatures taken decades apart seem to indicate that Earth is in radiative balance over long periods of time. However, temperature measurements made on a yearly basis indicate that Earth is not in radiative balance over short periods of time. The average temperatures vary from year to year.

## QUESTIONS

1. In which zone of the atmosphere would a temperature of 95°C most likely occur?

   (1) troposphere    (2) stratosphere    (3) mesosphere    (4) thermosphere

2. In Earth's atmosphere, the best absorbers of infrared radiation are water vapor and

   (1) nitrogen    (2) oxygen    (3) hydrogen    (4) carbon dioxide

3. Some scientists predict that the increase in atmospheric carbon dioxide will cause a worldwide increase in temperature. Which could result from this increase in temperature?

   (1) Continental drift will increase.
   (2) Isotherms will shift toward the Equator.
   (3) Additional landmasses will form.
   (4) Ice caps at Earth's poles will melt.

4. When is an object in radiative balance?

   (1) when the radiation emitted by the object is equal to that absorbed by the object
   (2) when the radiation emitted by the surroundings is equal to that absorbed by the object
   (3) when the radiation emitted by the object is equal to that absorbed by the surroundings
   (4) when the wavelength of the radiation emitted by the object is equal to that absorbed by the object

5. Which could occur if the amount of carbon dioxide in the atmosphere increased?

   (1) More ultraviolet rays would strike Earth.
   (2) More ultraviolet rays would be given off by Earth.
   (3) More radiation from Earth would be absorbed by the atmosphere.
   (4) More solar radiation would be absorbed by the oceans.

**6.** In which region of the electromagnetic spectrum is most of the outgoing radiation from Earth?

(1) infrared          (2) visible          (3) ultraviolet          (4) X-ray

**7.** The addition of dust to the atmosphere by volcanic eruptions will most likely increase the amount of

(1) radiant energy reflected by the atmosphere
(2) insolation absorbed at Earth's surface
(3) solar radiation absorbed by the oceans
(4) ultraviolet rays striking Earth's surface

**8.** What is the usual cause of the drop in temperature that occurs between sunset and sunrise at most New York State locations?

(1) strong winds                    (2) ground radiation
(3) cloud formation                 (4) heavy precipitation

Base your answers to questions 9 through 13 on your knowledge of Earth Science, the *Earth Science Reference Tables*, and the diagram and data on the below. The diagram represents a closed glass greenhouse. The data table shows the air temperatures inside and outside the greenhouse from 6 a.m. to 6 p.m. on a particular day.

**AIR TEMPERATURE**

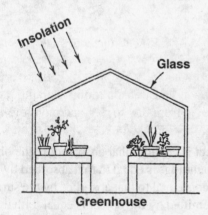

| Time | Average Outside Temperature | Average Inside Temperature |
|------|------|------|
| 6 a.m. | 10°C | 13°C |
| 8 a.m. | 11°C | 14°C |
| 10 a.m. | 12°C | 16°C |
| 12 noon | 15°C | 20°C |
| 2 p.m. | 19°C | 25°C |
| 4 p.m. | 17°C | 24°C |
| 6 p.m. | 15°C | 23°C |

**9.** The highest temperature was recorded at

(1) 12 noon outside the greenhouse          (2) 2 p.m. outside the greenhouse
(3) 12 noon inside the greenhouse            (4) 2 p.m. inside the greenhouse

**10.** By which process does air circulate inside the greenhouse due to differences in air temperature and air density?

(1) absorption      (2) radiation      (3) convection      (4) conduction

**11.** Several objects made of the same material, but with different surface characteristics, are tested in the greenhouse to determine which object will absorb the most sunlight. The object that absorbs the most sunlight most likely has a surface that is

(1) dark-colored and smooth          (2) dark-colored and rough
(3) light-colored and smooth         (4) light-colored and rough

**12.** Which statement best explains what happens to the insolation reaching the greenhouse?

(1) Most of the insolation is absorbed by the glass.
(2) All of the insolation is reflected by the glass.
(3) Insolation absorbed inside the greenhouse is reradiated at longer wavelengths.
(4) Insolation absorbed inside the greenhouse is reradiated at shorter wavelengths.

**13.** At approximately what rate did the temperature rise inside the greenhouse between 8 a.m. and 10 a.m.?

(1) 1.0°C/hr      (2) 2.0°C/hr      (3) 0.5°C/hr      (4) 12.0°C/hr

# THE WATER BUDGET

We know that climate is primarily determined by conditions of temperature and humidity. The amount of moisture (water vapor) entering the atmosphere depends on evaporation and transpiration. The term **evapotranspiration** refers to all the water vapor released into the atmosphere by both evaporation and transpiration. The amount of water gained, stored or lost in a specific location varies from day to day and month to month. A monthly account of what happens to the water in a particular location over the course of a year is called the **water budget**. A water budget is very much like a household budget except that it involves water instead of money.

**Income and Expenses**. The "income" in a water budget is the amount of precipitation. The monthly expenses or "bill" is potential evapotranspiration. **Potential evapotranspiration** in a water budget is the amount of water that would evaporate or transpire *if* the water were available. The potential evapotranspiration of an area is directly proportional to the amount of energy available and to the surface area from which the water can evaporate. The primary source of of evapotranspiration is the sun. Therefore, the potential evapotranspiration is highest in the summer, when temperatures are hottest and lowest in the winter, when temperatures are coldest. Places like forests, with their large surface areas give off more evapotranspiration than do the desert or grassland areas.

## Climate and the Water Budget

Each place has its own unique water budget. The graph of the New York City water budget is illustrated below (see Figure 8-15). New York City is located in the humid northeast, so rainfall is abundant all year long. Because the potential evapotranspiration is primarily dependent on the Sun, the need for rainfall in New York City is high in the summer and very low in the winter. As a result, New York has a moisture surplus about half the year.

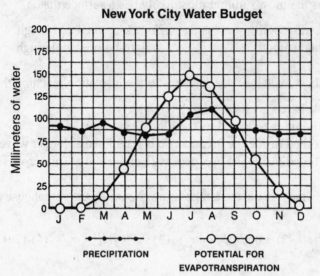

**Figure 8-15**. This graph makes it possible to "see" the relationship between precipitation and potential evapotranspiration.

Climatic regions can also be distinguished. If the total annual precipitation is less than the potential evapotranspiration the climate is said to be **arid**. If the total precipitation is greater than the potential evapotranspiration, the climate is said to be **humid**.

## Stream Discharge and the Water Budget

In areas where there is a great surplus of moisture, there is usually a large runoff into streams. The amount of water passing a given point in a stream in a certain period of time is known as **stream discharge**. The greater the amount of runoff, the greater the stream discharge. During dry or deficit periods, when the amount of runoff diminishes, streams take water from the ground water supply to maintain their flow, thus lowering the water table. Stream discharge being fed from the ground water beneath the water table is called **base flow**. Stream discharge is important in determining the energy of a stream.

Climate and the Water Budget. Climatic regions can be distinguished mathematically by determining the ratio of the amount of precipitation (P) to the amount of potential evapotranspiration (Ep) or P/Ep. Another factor used is P - Ep. For example, if the total annual precipitation is less than the potential evapotranspiration (P < Ep), the climate is said to be arid. If the total precipitation is greater than the potential evapotranspiration (P > Ep), the climate is said to be humid.

# QUESTIONS

1. Under which condition would the climate of a region of Earth be classified as humid?

   (1) when the soil moisture is undergoing usage all year long
   (2) when there is a soil moisture deficit all year long
   (3) when the annual precipitation is much greater than the annual potential evapotranspiration
   (4) when the annual precipitation is much less than the annual potential evapotranspiration

2. During which month will the potential evapotranspiration usually be the greatest in New York State?

   (1) January       (2) April       (3) July       (4) October

3. Which condition will usually occur after a drought in a region if the precipitation is greater than the potential for evapotranspiration?

   (1) The soil porosity will increase.
   (2) Available moisture will be removed from the soil.
   (3) The surface runoff will decrease.
   (4) Soil moisture will be recharged.

4. As the ground water supply during a drought (dry) period decreases, the amount of stream discharge will normally

   (1) decrease       (2) increase       (3) remain the same

5. The potential for evapotranspiration of an area will be increased if there is an increase in

   (1) soil porosity       (2) temperature       (3) storage capacity    (4) surface runoff

6. In order for soil moisture to decrease, the amount of precipitation must be

   (1) greater than the actual evapotranspiration
   (2) less than the amount of soil-moisture storage
   (3) less than the potential for evapotranspiration

7. Which graph best represents the relationship between air temperature and potential for evapotranspiration ($E_p$) for a given locality?

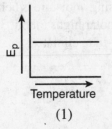
(1)
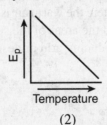
(2)
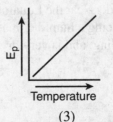
(3)
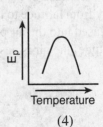
(4)

# FACTORS AFFECTING CLIMATE PATTERNS

The temperature and moisture conditions that affect a particular location depend on a number of factors, which include latitude, elevation, nearness to large bodies of water and ocean currents, mountain barriers, wind belts, and storm tracks. Figure 8-16 represents a hypothetical continent. Refer to this figure as you read about the different factors that affect climate.

## Latitude and Climate

Latitude is the most important factor affecting climate patterns because of its influence on temperature patterns. The angle and duration of insolation vary with latitude and season of the year. The greater the angle and duration of insolation, the hotter the area will be. At the lower latitudes, the angle of insolation is generally very high, resulting in high temperatures. Since the duration of insolation remains close to 12 hours a day at the lower latitudes, the temperatures remain fairly constant throughout the year and there are no seasonal changes. At the higher latitudes, temperatures are hottest in summer, when the angle and duration of insolation are the greatest. In the winter, when the angle and duration of insolation are smallest, temperatures are the coldest. The middle latitudes fall somewhere in between the two extremes. The summers can vary from warm to hot while the winters can vary from cool to cold. As latitude increases, the average yearly temperature decreases, although the seasonal range of temperatures increases.

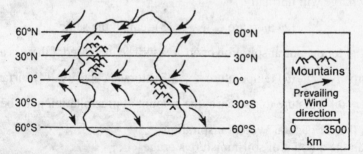

**Figure 8-16.** A hypothetical continent. This model can be used to visualize the effects of various factors on climate.

Because of the locations of the planetary winds and pressure belts, moisture conditions vary from latitude to latitude. Near the Equator, where the warm air is rising, moisture is being released into the air producing a humid climate. In the areas of the subpolar highs (about 30° latitude) the air is descending, and is very dry, producing arid or desert-like, climates.

# Elevation and Climate

The elevation (height above sea level) of an area influences temperature and moisture patterns, thereby modifying latitudinal climate patterns. Generally, as elevation increases, the temperature and saturation vapor pressure decrease, increasing the relative humidity. At a given latitude, places at higher elevations have more precipitation and a wider range of weather conditions than do places at lower elevations. Changes in elevation have similar effects on temperature patterns of climatic regions as do changes in latitude.

# Large Bodies of Water and Climate

Large bodies of water, such as lakes and oceans, modify the latitudinal climate patterns of their shoreline areas, because water takes large amounts of heat and a long period of time to heat up. In summer, these large bodies of water are cooler than the surrounding land, which helps to keep the atmosphere over their shoreline areas cooler than that over inland regions. In winter, the water takes much longer than the land to give up its heat, so the atmosphere over the surrounding shoreline areas is warmer than that over inland regions. Temperatures at locations along the shore have a much smaller annual range than those at inland locations at the same latitude. For example, because Long Island is surrounded by water, it has a smaller temperature range than most parts of inland New York State. Lakes may also modify the climate of neighboring areas.

More of the Southern Hemisphere is covered by water than is the Northern Hemisphere. Therefore, summers are cooler and winters warmer in the Southern Hemisphere than in the Northern Hemisphere. Locations where temperatures are modified by the presence of large bodies of water are said to have a **marine climate**. Inland areas, away from large bodies of water, which have cold winters, hot summers, and a large temperature range, are said to have a **continental climate**. Although inland, Buffalo, New York, has a marine type climate, because Lake Erie modifies the climate there.

# Ocean Currents and Climate

Ocean currents also modify the coastal climate patterns. Warm ocean currents, such as the Gulf Stream, bring warm water from the Gulf of Mexico to higher, colder latitudes, warming the air above them. The temperatures of locations as far away as Great Britain are modified by this warm stream of water. Cold ocean currents streaming out of the polar regions help cool the air-over southern locations.

# Mountain Barriers and Climate

Mountains, acting as barriers to circulation, modify latitudinal climate patterns. Air moving up over the windward side of a mountain range cools adiabatically at a rate of 10°C/kilometer rise in altitude. When condensation occurs, tremendous amounts of latent heat are released, and the cooling rate slows to 6°C/kilometer rise. Precipitation occurs on the windward side of the mountains.

As the air descends on the leeward side of the mountains, the temperature of the air rises adiabatically at the rate of 10°C/kilometer of descent. Because most of the moisture falls on the windward side of a mountain, air on the leeward side is warmer and dryer than on the windward side. Because little rain falls on the leeward side, a **rain shadow** is formed. This is an area where very little rainfall occurs. In fact, the location of many deserts, such as Death Valley, are on the leeward (rain shadow) side of mountains.

The overall effect of mountains on climate patterns is known as the **orographic effect**. A good example of the orographic effect occurs in the Hawaiian Islands. On the windward side of one of the mountains, the annual rainfall is about 500 cm/year, while on the leeward side, it is less than 50 cm/year. If mountains are high enough, they can act as barriers between two totally different climates, preventing the air on one side from reaching the other side.

## Wind Belts and Climate

Moisture and temperature patterns are affected by planetary wind and pressure belts. Air that originates over water may be carried over land by planetary winds, causing the winds to be very moist. If this is a continuous situation, the area influenced by these winds will be continuously humid. On the other hand, prevailing winds might pick up air that originates over dry continental areas, resulting in dry winds.

Pressure belts influence climate patterns. Low pressure belts, such as those over the Equator and 60° latitude, consist of rising air which results in high humidity at the surface. High pressure belts at about 30° latitude and in the polar regions produce dry conditions at the surface due to the descending air. Low-latitude deserts occur along these high pressure belts. These pressure and wind belts migrate with the seasons.

## Storm Tracks

Low pressure systems (mid-latitude cyclones), which affect temperature and moisture patterns, seem to follow statistically predictable paths. In the continental United States, the storm tracks are controlled by the prevailing westerlies, which track in a generally west-to-east direction. The consistent direction followed by these storms has a great effect on climate as well as daily weather.

# SEASONAL WIND PATTERNS

Many believe that the Equator always has the highest temperatures on Earth. However, since Earth is tilted 23.5° to the plane of its orbit around the Sun, the point on Earth directly beneath the Sun (where the incoming solar radiation is greatest) changes seasonally. On the Summer Solstice (June 21), the Sun is directly overhead at 23.5°N. At that time, the Intertropical Convergence Zone shifts north and the Northern Hemisphere receives much more solar energy (per unit area) than does the Southern Hemisphere. The highest temperatures can occur as far north as 30°N. During the Winter Solstice (December 21), the Intertropical Convergence Zone shifts south and the situation is reversed (See Fig. 8-17).

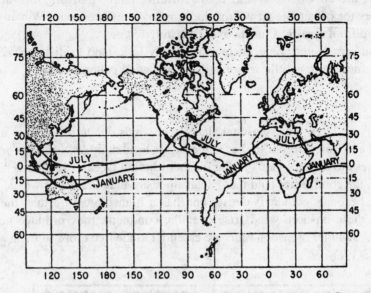

**Figure 8-17.** The thick solid line is the seasonal range for the Intertropical Convergence Zone.

Seasonal changes in wind patterns are especially pronounced in the Northern Hemisphere because of its large amounts of land. During summer months, land warms faster than the ocean. As the air over the land warms, a low-pressure area forms. Air over the ocean is cooler and forms high-pressure areas in the mid-latitudes. In summer, there is a much greater surge of warm moist air form the Gulf of Mexico over the central and eastern United States when the high-pressure centers over the middle North Atlantic are most intense (See Fig. 8-18).

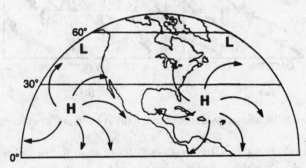

**Figure 8-18.** Summer surge of warm, moist air from the Gulf of Mexico to the central and eastern United States.

In winter, the air over the land cools forming large high pressure areas over the continents. Over the ocean, the air warms, forming low pressure areas. Winter winds tend to move southward from areas in Canada over the United States.

In the Southern Hemisphere, there is relatively little land to disturb large scale wind patterns. Therefore, there is little seasonal change in wind patterns there.

## Monsoons

**Monsoons** are large-scale seasonal changes in winds due to differences in heating and cooling of land and water similar to the smaller-scale local daily *land* and sea *breezes*. These seasonal changes are most obvious in the northern Indian Ocean. In summer, in Southeast Asia and India, the continental land mass heats up faster than the ocean water. Thus, the air over the water becomes cooler, is denser and has a higher pressure than the air over the continent. As these onshore winds rise over the continent, they produce heavy summer monsoon rains. Summer monsoon rains are essential to the rice crops in India and Southeast Asia (See Fig. 8-19a).

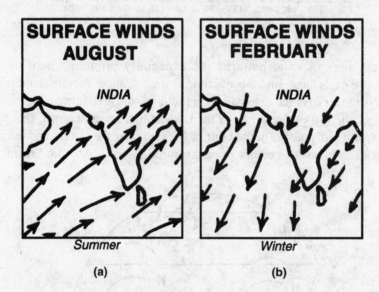

**Figure 8-19.** Monsoon winds of India: (a) in summer (b) in winter

In winter, the winds reverse. The land cools more than the ocean and the air over the continent becomes cooler than the water, the density of the air increases and the pressure over the continent is higher than the pressure over the water. Now, the air flows from the land to the sea producing the cooler, dryer winter monsoons (See Fig. 8-19b).

For centuries, ships of the northern Indian Ocean depended on these seasonal wind reversals to carry them back and forth between India and Africa. Winds drive surface ocean currents, therefore these wind reversals also cause major shifts in currents in the northern Indian Ocean.

## El Niño and La Niña

Ocean currents, winds, and weather patterns are closely linked, especially along the equator in the Pacific Ocean. For example, the warmest temperatures on Earth normally occur along the western Pacific of the equator. The colder waters occur along the eastern Pacific and the surface winds flow from east to west. But, every 3-5 years, this pattern of ocean and atmospheric conditions changes dramatically. Warmer waters occur along the equator and the west coast of South America causing the surface wind patters to shift from west to east. These ocean conditions affect weather over most of Earth, especially in North America. Today, the **El Niño** is applied to those periods of ocean warming along the Pacific Coast of South America. El Niños are caused by shifts in winds and movements of warm equatorial waters. During El Niño years in the Atlantic, there are fewer hurricanes than normal. El Niño events last 1-2 years.

Following an El Niño period, instead of unusually warm waters along the South American coast, the ocean conditions become unusually cold. The term **La Niña** refers to these conditions of unusually cold ocean temperatures in the Equatorial Pacific following an El Niño. La Niñas also lead to large-scale weather patterns impacting large areas of North America.

Knowing the sequence of El Niños and La Niñas helps to predict long-term weather and climate patterns. For example, in years when El Niños occur, Florida has cold wet winters. As a result, there are fewer forest fires there in summer. However, in La Niña years, Florida has warm, dry winters and many more forest fires the following summer.

When the warm water in the western Pacific cools and normal ocean current patterns return to the equatorial ocean, the atmosphere resumes its normal wind patterns and it is another 3-5 years before the cycle repeats itself.

## QUESTIONS

1. Which single factor generally has the greatest effect on the climate of an area on Earth's surface?

   (1) the distance from the Equator  (2) the extent of vegetative cover
   (3) the degrees of longitude  (4) the month of the year

2. Which graph best represents the general relationship between the latitude of locations north or south of the Equator and the average annual surface temperatures for those locations?

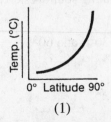
(1)

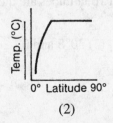
(2)

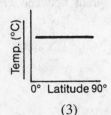
(3)

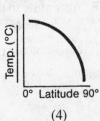
(4)

**3.** How does the average annual surface temperature compare from latitude to latitude?

(1) As latitude increases, the average annual surface temperature decreases.
(2) As latitude increases, the average annual surface temperature increases.
(3) As latitude increases, the average annual surface temperature remains the same.

Base your answers to questions 4 through 7 on your knowledge of Earth Science and on the diagram below. The diagram represents a map of an imaginary continent on Earth. The continent is surrounded by oceans. Two mountain ranges and five locations, A through E, are shown.

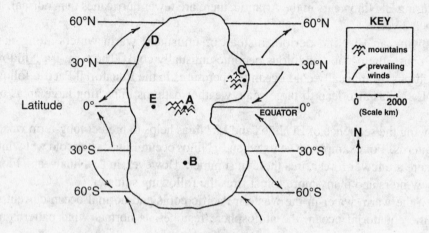

**4.** Which location probably has the highest average yearly temperature?

(1) A (2) B (3) C (4) E

**5.** Which location most likely would have an arid climate?

(1) A (2) B (3) C (4) D

**6.** As air rises on the windward side of the mountain near location C, the air will

(1) cool due to expansion (2) cool due to compression
(3) warm due to expansion (4) warm due to compression

**7.** According to this diagram, between which two latitudes are the prevailing southwesterly winds located?

(1) 30°N and 60°N (2) 30°N and 0° (3) 30°S and 0° (4) 30°S and 60°S

**8.** Which graph best represents the yearly temperature variation for location B?

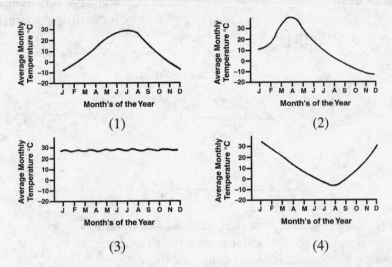

(1)                                    (2)

(3)                                    (4)

**9.** The diagram below shows the postions of the cities of Seattle and Spokane, Washington. Both cities are located at approximately 48° North latitude, and they are separated by the Cascade Mountains.

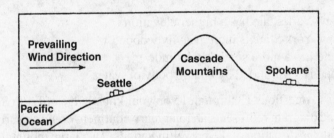

How does the climate of Seattle compare with the climate of Spokane?

(1) Seattle - hot and dry, Spokane - cool and humid
(2) Seattle - hot and humid, Spokane - cool and dry
(3) Seattle - cool and humid, Spokane - warm and dry
(4) Seattle - cool and dry, Spokane - warm and humid

**10.** Which statement best explains why climates at continental shorelines generally have a smaller yearly temperature range than inland climates at the same latitude?

(1) Land is a poor absorber and a poor conductor of heat energy.
(2) Land changes temperature rapidly, due to the high specific heat and lack of transparency of land.
(3) Ocean water is a good absorber and a good conductor of heat energy.
(4) Ocean water changes temperature slowly, due to the high specific heat and transparency of water.

**11.** The diagram below represents a map of Western and Central New York State on a day in August. The location of an 18°C isotherm is shown. Why is the 18°C isotherm line farther north over the land than it is over Lake Ontario?

(1) There is a high plateau at the eastern end of Lake Ontario.
(2) The air is warmer over the land than over Lake Ontario.
(3) Isotherms are the same shape as the latitude lines.
(4) The prevailing winds alter the path of the isotherms

**12.** Why are temperature variations usually not as great on Long Island as they are in central New York State?

(1) central New York State has a higher elevation
(2) central New York State is more heavily wooded
(3) Long Island has a more southerly latitude
(4) Long Island is surrounded by a large body of water

Base your answers to questions 13 through 15 on your knowledge of Earth Science and on the diagram below. The diagram represents an imaginary continent on Earth surrounded by water. The arrows indicate the direction of the prevailing winds. Two large mountain regions are also indicated. Points A, B, E, and H are located at sea level; C, D, and F are in the foothills of the mountains; G is high in the mountains.

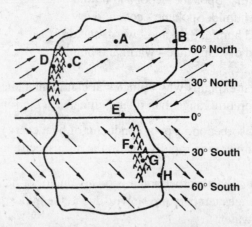

13. Which physical characteristic would cause location G to have a colder yearly climate than any other location?

    (1) the nearness of location G to a large ocean
    (2) the location of G with respect to the prevailing winds
    (3) the elevation of location G above sea level
    (4) the distance of location G from the Equator

14. Which location probably has the greatest annual rainfall?

    (1) A          (2) F          (3) C          (4) D

15. Which location probably has the greatest range in temperature during the year?

    (1) A          (2) B          (3) H          (4) D

---

## CHAPTER 8 - CORE VOCABULARY

| | | |
|---|---|---|
| angle of insolation | intensity | stratopause |
| arid | intensity of insolation | stratosphere |
| climate | La Niña | thremosphere |
| duration of insolation | mesopause | tropopause |
| El Niño | mesosphere | troposphere |
| greenhouse effect | monsoon | |
| insolation | seasons | |

---

## HELPFUL VOCABULARY

| | | |
|---|---|---|
| aerosol | humid | radiative balance |
| base flow | intensity of radiation | rain shadow |
| continental climate | marine climate | stream discharge |
| direct rays | orographic effect | terrestrial radiation |
| evapotranspiration | potenial evaportranspiration | water budget |

## PRACTICE FOR CONSTRUCTED RESPONSE

1. Which diagram most correctly shows the portion of Earth that is illuminated by sunlight and the portion that is in shadow on the first day of summer in the Northern Hemisphere?

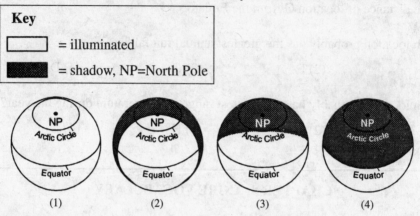

**Key**

☐ = illuminated

■ = shadow, NP=North Pole

(1)  (2)  (3)  (4)

Base your answers to questions 2 through 4 on the diagrams below and your knowledge of Earth Science. The diagrams represent plastic hemisphere models. Lines have been drawn to show the apparent path of the Sun across the sky on June 21 for observers at three different Earth locations. The zenith (Z) is the point in the sky directly over the observer.

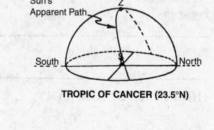

**TROPIC OF CANCER (23.5°N)**

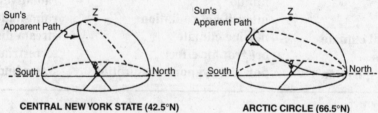

**CENTRAL NEW YORK STATE (42.5°N)**     **ARCTIC CIRCLE (66.5°N)**

2. Explain why the shortest duration of insolation for the three locations is the Tropic of Cancer.

_____

_____

**3.** Describe what the Sun's apparent path will look like in 3 months in Central New York State.

_____

_____

_____

**4.** Explain why, of the 3 locations, the longest noontime shadow will be observed at the Arctic Circle.

_____

_____

_____

Base your answers to questions 5 through 7 on the graph below and on your knowledge of Earth Science. The Graph shows the average monthly temperatures at cities A, B, C and D.

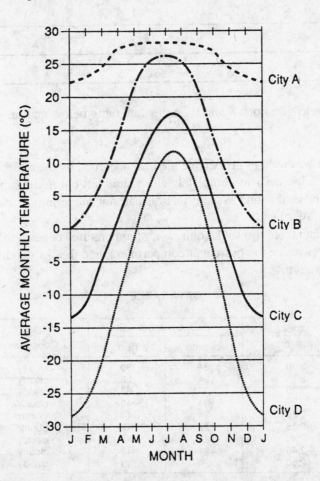

**5.** What evidence shows that city A is closest to the Equator?

_____

_____

**6.** What evidence shows that the cities are in the Northern Hemisphere?

_____ The cdd h _____

_____

_____

_____

**7.** What evidence is provided by the shape of the temperature curves for the cities to indicate that cities B, C and D are located inland and city A is located near the coast?

_____

_____

_____

_____

Base your answers to questions 8 and 9 on the data table below and on your knowledge of Earth Science.

A car was used to investigate the heat absorbed by the air inside a closed automobile. The car was completely closed and left out in the sunlight during the entire investigation. Assume that air can not move into or out of the car during the investigation.

The data table shows the outside air temperatures beneath the car, the air temperatures inside the passenger compartment, and the sky conditions during the investigation.

**DATA TABLE**

| Clock Time (pm) | Air Temperature (°C) | | Sky Conditions |
|---|---|---|---|
| | outside | inside | |
| 2:10 | 24 | 30 | cloudy |
| 2:15 | 24 | 33 | cloudy |
| 2:20 | 24 | 38 | cloudy |
| 2:25 | 24 | 40 | cloudy |
| 2:30 | 24 | 41 | cloudy |
| 2:35 | 24 | 42 | sunny |
| 2:40 | 24 | 43 | cloudy |
| 2:45 | 24 | 43 | cloudy |
| 2:50 | 24 | 43 | cloudy |

8. Calculate the rate at which the inside air temperature changed during the first five minutes of the investigation using these directions:

   a. Write the equation for rate of change

   b. substitute data from the table into the equation.

   c. Calculate the rate.  _____ $6°C/min.$ _____

   d. Label your answer with the proper units. _____

9. Explain why the temperature inside the car did not increase above 43°C during the last ten minutes.  _____ less water vapor in _____
   _____ the air _____
   _____
   _____
   _____
   _____

Base your answers to questions 10 through 12 on the graph below and your knowledge of Earth Science. The graph shows the insolation received and the energy used by a house in New York State. There is a solar energy collector on the roof that absorbs solar radiation and converts the energy to a form useful for heating and cooling the home.

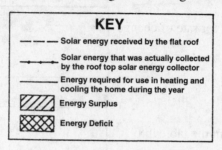

KEY

---  Solar energy received by the flat roof

-·-·-  Solar energy that was actually collected by the roof top solar energy collector

———  Energy required for use in heating and cooling the home during the year

▨  Energy Surplus

▩  Energy Deficit

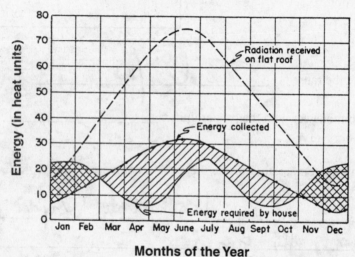

**Months of the Year**

**10.** Describe why the amount of energy required for cooling the house is greatest in July rather than in June.

_____

_____

_____

**11.** If observations were made for an identical house in similar surroundings at a location of 500 kilometers due north, how would the energy collected at the two locations compare over a year?

_____

_____

_____

**12.** Describe why there is more energy needed in the house during the month of July than during the month of January.

_____

_____

_____

Base your answers to questions 13 and 14 on the climate graphs below. Each graph represents data for a different city in North America. The line graphs connect the average monthly temperatures in degrees Celsius. The bar graphs indicate the average monthly precipitation in millimeters.

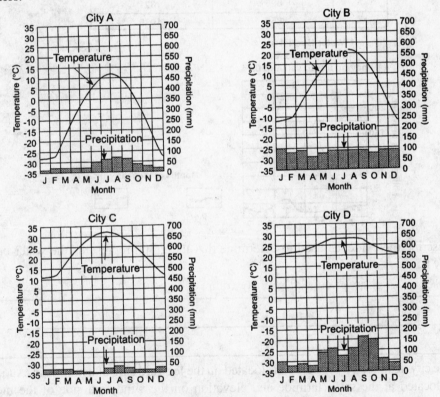

**13.** For which cities is the winter precipitation most likely to be snow?

_____

**14.** In which sequence are the cities listed in order of decreasing average yearly precipitation?

_____

Base your answers to questions 15 and 16 on the sources of data below and on your knowledge of Earth Science. The table gives information about five United States cities and the graph shows the water budget for one of the five cities.

**Climate Data for Certain U.S. Cities**

| City | Total Annual Precipitation (in millimeters) P | Total Annual Potential Evapotranspiration (in millimeters) $E_p$ |
|---|---|---|
| R | 194 | 1340 |
| S | 291 | 434 |
| T | 708 | 877 |
| X | 825 | 621 |
| Z | 859 | 1035 |

Water Budget for a Certain U.S. City having a P/$E_p$ value of 0.14

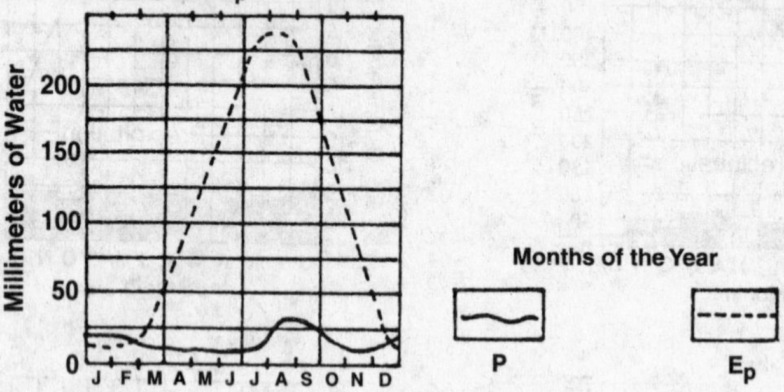

**15.** Describe the evidence used to determine that the graph represents the water budget of city R.

_____

_____

**16.** The city described by the graph is located on the leeward side of a mountain. Another city is located at the same latitude and elevation on the windward side of the mountain. Describe how the climate of the city represented by the graph probably compares to the other city.

_____

_____

_____

_____

Base your answer to question 17 on the graph below and your knowledge of Earth Science. The graph represents the discharge of a stream at a location that has little temperature change throughout the year.

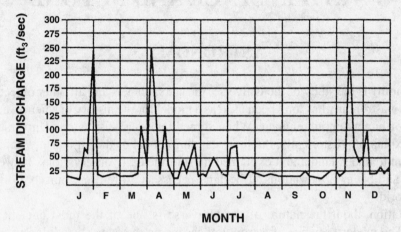

**17.** Describe the probable cause for the peaks in the graph.

_____

_____

# CHAPTER 9
# EARTH IN SPACE AND BEYOND

## ASTRONOMY

**Astronomy** is the study of the Universe, the stars, planets and all other objects in space. The history of astronomy has long been used as a model for the history of science, and perhaps the history of human enlightenment. When something is as vast as our Universe, we need models to explain it. Historically, the long standing model of the Universe was easy for the common man to understand and it explained most of the early observations. However, as we made more and better observations, it became necessary to re-think our comfortable ideas about the world.

Speculation about the nature of the Universe is one of the most ancient of human endeavors. The modern science of astronomy carries on the ancient tradition of observation and inferring, using the latest in technology and mathematics. Astronomers use the laws of physics to explore and understand the Universe. By exploring the planets, astronomers uncover clues about the formation of Earth and the solar system. By studying stars, astronomers discover how stars are born, grow old, and eventually die. By observing galaxies, astronomers learn about the creation and fate of the Universe. This is an age of discovery more profound than any since Columbus.

## EARTH IN THE UNIVERSE

Where does Earth fit into the Universe? When observing a star, we see the star where it was when the light left it. In fact, when we look at distant stars, we are actually looking back in time at astronomical history. The light from some stars has been travelling thousands of years. Because the Universe is so large, the speed of light (300,000 kilometers per second or 186,000 miles per second) is used to measure distances in space. Light is so fast that it can travel around the equator 7 times in just one second.

**Light Year.** To measure long distances in space, astronomers use the **light year**, the distance light travels in one year - about 9.5 trillion kilometers or 6 trillion miles. Light years are measured in **Astronomical Units (AU).** Although a light year seems like an enormous distance, consider that, other than the Sun, our closest star, Proxima Centauri, is about 4.3 light years (4.3 AU) away. Light from the Sun takes only 8 minutes to travel the 149,600,000 kilometers (93,000,000 miles) to Earth. Light from Proxima Centauri takes 4.3 years to reach us. Polaris is about 300 light years away. The distance to the farthest known star system is about 12 billion light-years away. Light from those stars began their journey toward Earth long before Earth had even formed. Compared with the vast distance between most stars, the stars and planets are very small.

**Galaxies.** A **galaxy** is a system of billions of stars. The Universe includes a very large number of galaxies, each containing billions of stars. There are, several types of galaxies, but most fit into three types. Many galaxies are **spiral galaxies**, shaped like pinwheels with huge spiral arms. In addition to the Milky Way Galaxy another spiral galaxy, the *Andromeda Galaxy*, is visible to the naked eye, even though it is about 200 million light years away. Perhaps the most common type of galaxies are **elliptical galaxies**; they look like blobs with no spirals and can be circular or flattened. The third type of galaxies have no definite shape and are called **irregular galaxies**. The *Large and Small Magelanic Clouds* are irregular galaxies.

All the stars, and other objects in space fit into a Universe that is about 15 billion light years in radius and therefore the Universe is about 15 billion years old. Earth is just one small planet orbiting a typical star among billions in the Universe.

**Milky Way Galaxy.** Over a period of years, astronomers became convinced that our Sun was not the center of the Universe, but just one of billions of stars in a large disk-shaped system of stars called the **Milky Way Galaxy**. The Milky Way can be visible as a band of light across the dark night sky. The American astronomer, Harlow Shapely believed that the real center of the Universe was the center of the Milky Way Galaxy. The primary difficulty with visual observations of the structure of the galaxy is the gas and dust between the stars in the Milky Way. In the early 1950's, radio telescopes had been perfected to such a degree that they could detect radio waves from the stars which could penetrate the gas and dust between the stars. The final picture to emerge is that we live in a huge spiral system of billions of stars approximately 100,000 light years in diameter and 15,000 light years thick (see Figure 9-1). As seen from space, the Milky Way, appears to be a huge pinwheel-shaped disk of spiraling arms with a bulge in the center which is rotating in a counterclockwise direction. The Sun is located on a spiral arm about 30,000 light years from the nucleus (center). Astronomers estimate that it takes 230 million years for the Milky Way to complete one revolution around its center.

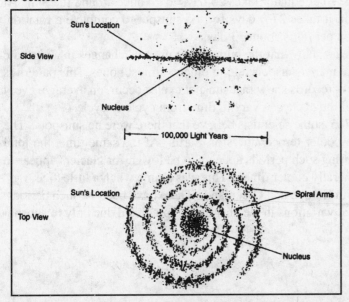

**Figure 9-1.** The Milky Way Galaxy. The Sun is one of billions of stars in the Galaxy. Seen top view, the Galaxy has the spiral appearance. Seen side view, it would resemble two dishes back to back.

**Sun**.  As far as our lives are concerned, the gaseous sun is the most important object in the sky.  The **Sun** provides the heat and light that make our life on our planet possible.  Energy from the Sun is responsible for the currents in the oceans and the weather in the atmosphere.  Without the Sun, our planet would be a barren and frozen wasteland.  The mass of the Sun is about 330,000 times the mass of Earth with a diameter about 109 times the diameter of Earth.  Our Sun is an average star when its diameter, density and mass are compared to other stars.  Temperatures of the Sun range from over 6,000 K at its surface to over 12 million degrees Kelvin at the Sun's center.  The Sun, as are all the stars, is composed primarily of hydrogen and helium.  It rotates faster at its equator than at its poles.  The Sun is about 5 billion years old and it is expected to last another 5 billion years.

## Sunspots

For over three centuries, men have studied the dark patches on the surface of the Sun called **sunspots**.  Sunspots are regions on the surface of the Sun that consist of cooler gases than those surrounding it.  They appear dark by contrast with their surroundings, although they are brighter than most artificial sources of light.  The dark central portion of a sunspot is called the umbra and has a temperature of about 4300K.  The gray *penumbral* region surrounding the umbra has a temperature of about 5000K, compared to the general surface temperature of about 6000K.  Although they vary greatly in size, sunspots generally measure a few tens of thousands of kilometers across.

On rare occasions, a sunspot group will be so large that it can be seen if you project the Sun's image on a white surface (**Never look directly at the Sun**).  Galileo used sunspots to measure the speed of rotation for the Sun to be about 4 weeks.  A typical sunspot group lasts about two months, so it can be followed for two solar rotations.  Careful observations show that the Sun does not rotate as a rigid body.  The equatorial regions rotate more rapidly than the polar regions.  A sunspot near the solar equator takes 25 days to go once around the Sun.  At 30° north or south of the equator, it takes 27½ days for the sunspot to complete a rotation.  At 75° north or south, the rotation period is about 33 days.

Observations over many years show that the number of sunspots changes in a periodic fashion.  In some years, there are many sunspots and in others, almost none.  This pattern is called the **sunspot cycle**.  Sunspot records show that sunspot cycles occur, on average, every 11 years.  However, the period of the cycle can vary in time from cycle to cycle.

Between the years 1645-1715, some scientists believe that there were no sunspots.  The impact of that would have been cooler temperatures on Earth.  At the same time, the total energy received from the Sun during such periods appears to be lower, for glaciers appear to have developed during these generally cooler times.  This was a time when a little "Ice Age" may have occurred, particularly in Europe and Greenland.  There have been 12 such periods.  That does not mean, however that variations in weather can be predicted due only to sunspot cycle changes.

# QUESTIONS

1. If a star is 5 light years away, how many years will it take light from that star to reach Earth?

   (1) 1 year        (2) 5 years        (3) 30 years        (4) 32.5 years

2. Compared to the other stars, the diameter, density and mass of the Sun is

   (1) greater        (2) less        (3) about the same

3. The composition of the Sun is primarily

   (1) iron and nickel        (2) hydrogen and helium
   (3) nitrogen and oxygen        (4) carbon dioxide and ozone

4. The Milky Way is an example of

   (1) an irregular galaxy        (2) a spiral galaxy
   (3) an elliptical galaxy        (4) a constellation

5. From the surface of the Sun to its center, temperatures

   (1) increase        (2) decrease        (3) remain the same

6. The Sun rotates

   (1) faster at the poles than at the equator
   (2) slowest between the poles and the equator
   (3) faster at the equator than at the poles
   (4) slower at the equator than at the poles

7. Galaxies are classified into groups based on their

   (1) shapes        (2) sizes
   (3) number of stars        (4) all of the above

8. Sunspots appear darker than the surrounding surface of the Sun because

   (1) the sunspot cycle varies from year to year
   (2) sunspots absorb energy rather than emit energy
   (3) sunspots consist of cooler gases than the gases surrounding them
   (4) the Sun rotates on an axis

# THE SOLAR SYSTEM

The **solar system** includes our Sun, the nine planets, the many moons and all the other objects that revolve around our Sun (see Table 9-1). Six of the nine plates (Mercury, Venus, Earth, Mars, Jupiter, Saturn) are visible to the naked eye, while the remaining three (Uranus, Neptune, Pluto) were observed with telescopes. There are numerous very tiny objects orbiting the Sun such as comets, asteroids and meteoroids.

## Formation of Solar System

Our solar system formed about five billion years ago from a giant cloud of gas and debris. The planets were formed by the accumulation of material in the solar nebula during the birth of the Sun. The type of planet that forms at a particular distance from a star depends on conditions such as the temperature and the substances (rock fragments, ice crystals, gases) which exist at such distance. Gravity caused Earth and the other planets to become layered according to density differences in their materials.

## Terrestrial and Jovian Planets

The characteristics of the planets in the solar system are affected by each planet's location in relationship to the Sun. In our solar system, planets composed primarily of rock formed near the Sun where its heat drove off ices and gasses. Far from the Sun, where temperatures are low, planets retained volatile substances, resulting in worlds composed primarily of gas.

The planets fit naturally into two categories: (1) **terrestrial planets** which are most similar to Earth, and (2) **Jovian planets** which are similar to Jupiter. The four terrestrial planets are Mercury, Mars, Earth and Venus. The four Jovian planets are Jupiter, Saturn, Uranus and Neptune. Pluto is treated separately because it does not fit either of the designations above.

What does it mean to be a terrestrial or Jovian planet? Table 9-1 shows that the terrestrials are small (no larger than Earth size). They have low mass and high densities when compared to the Jovians. The higher densities of the terrestrials indicate a large amount of heavy elements and less significant atmosphere. Except for Venus, when computing the diameters and masses of the terrestrial planets their atmospheres are not even considered. This suggests that the terrestrial planets are primarily solid. In sharp contrast, the Jovian planets have very low densities. Saturn is even less dense than water. This suggests that the giant outer planets are composed primarily of gases.

## Solar System Data

| Object | Mean Distance from Sun (millions of km) | Period of Revolution | Period of Rotation | Eccentricity of Orbit | Equatorial Diameter (km) | Mass (Earth = 1) | Density (g/cm³) | Number of Moons |
|---|---|---|---|---|---|---|---|---|
| SUN | — | — | 27 days | — | 1,392,000 | 333,000.00 | 1.4 | – |
| MERCURY | 57.9 | 88 days | 59 days | 0.206 | 4,880 | 0.553 | 5.4 | 0 |
| VENUS | 108.2 | 224.7 days | 243 days | 0.007 | 12,104 | 0.815 | 5.2 | 0 |
| EARTH | 149.6 | 365.26 days | 23 hr 56 min 4 sec | 0.017 | 12,756 | 1.00 | 5.5 | 1 |
| MARS | 227.9 | 687 days | 24 hr 37 min 23 sec | 0.093 | 6,787 | 0.1074 | 3.9 | 2 |
| JUPITER | 778.3 | 11.86 years | 9 hr 50 min 30 sec | 0.048 | 142,800 | 317.896 | 1.3 | 16 |
| SATURN | 1,427 | 29.46 years | 10 hr 14 min | 0.056 | 120,000 | 95.185 | 0.7 | 18 |
| URANUS | 2,869 | 84.0 years | 17 hr 14 min | 0.047 | 51,800 | 14.537 | 1.2 | 21 |
| NEPTUNE | 4,496 | 164.8 years | 16 hr | 0.009 | 49,500 | 17.151 | 1.7 | 8 |
| PLUTO | 5,900 | 247.7 years | 6 days 9 hr | 0.250 | 2,300 | 0.0025 | 2.0 | 1 |
| EARTH'S MOON | 149.6 (0.386 from Earth) | 27.3 days | 27 days 8 hr | 0.055 | 3,476 | 0.0123 | 3.3 | — |

**Table 9-1**

The terrestrial planets are small and dense, with craters, canyons, and volcanoes common on their hard rocky surfaces. They have large average densities. For example, the average density of Earth is 5.5g/cm³, which may not seem large until you compare it to the density of rock, about 3g/cm³, and water, 1g/cm³. Earth must therefore contain a large amount of material that is more dense than rock–perhaps an iron core.

The appearance of the Jovian planets is dominated by vast swirling cloud formations. Scientists believe that the solid cores of these planets (similar to the size of Earth) are buried beneath atmospheres that are tens of thousands of kilometers thick.

Pluto is an exception. Although it is even smaller than the dense inner planets, its average density seems to be much like those of the outer planets. Although called a planet, Pluto is an oddity. Its physical properties are not typical of either terrestrial or Jovian planets. Some astronomers "guess" that Pluto may be a satellite (moon) that escaped from Neptune. Many of the satellites of the outer planets are composed of ice, the density of which is about 1g/cm³. This is the density of Pluto; so, Pluto may be large ball of ice.

# EARTH AND THE NEARBY PLANETS

People have wondered about the planets for hundreds of years. Only recently have spacecraft begun to examine the planets in detail. Some planets are so distant that it takes several years for the spacecraft to reach them. One view about the planets has become clear however: they have a wide variety of surface and atmospheric features.

## Temperature

As you might expect, the range of surface temperatures that each planet experiences is related to its distance from the Sun. The four inner planets are quite warm. Noontime temperatures on Mercury climb to 327°C (621°F or 600 K). Mars sometimes reaches 27°C (81°F or 300 K). The outer planets are much cooler. Neptune has temperatures of -210°C (-346°F or 63 K). Temperature plays a major role in determining whether substances exist as solids, liquids or gases. Earth's oceans and atmosphere help keep temperatures relatively constant. Only Earth has a temperature range that can support life.

## Water

Life, which first appeared in the oceans depends heavily on water. Earth is the only planet which has large amounts of water at its surface (71% covered by water) with temperature and pressure balanced enough to allow water to exist in its three forms: ice, liquid and vapor. It is the presence of water that facilitates the variety and density of life that exists on Earth. In contrast, Venus and Mars are extremely arid.

Most scientists believe that about 3.5 billion years ago, bacteria and tiny plant-like organisms began to grow in the seas of Earth, Over millions of years, some evolved into complex plants which used chlorophyll and sunlight in the process of photosynthesis to make their own food. They took in carbon dioxide and sugar and gave off oxygen and water. The oxygen they gave off first reacted with the iron dissolved in sea water, causing it to oxidize, or rust, and settle to the ocean floor. When most of the iron was used up, the surplus oxygen started escaping into the atmosphere, forming part of the air we breathe today.

## Atmosphere

Earth is the only planet in the solar system today with the type of atmosphere to support life as we know it. Surrounding the Sun, there is a region called the ecosphere in which the temperatures of a planet would be suitable to support life. This theoretical **ecosphere** extends from within the orbit of Venus, about 108 million kilometers (61 million miles) from the Sun, to just beyond the orbit of Mars, about 228 million kilometers (140 million miles). Venus has an atmosphere composed of almost pure carbon dioxide, that tends to trap most of the heat reflected from its surface (the Greenhouse Effect), thereby maintaining a surface temperature too high to sustain life as we know it. Mars also has an atmosphere composed of almost pure carbon dioxide, but it is so thin it allows temperatures on the Martian surface to vary widely.

The atmospheric pressure on Mars is about one-hundredth that of Earth's atmosphere and has seasonal variations. Liquid water would quickly boil away in Mars' thin atmosphere, but the polar ice caps do contain considerable amount of frozen water.

Venus is similar to Earth in size, mass, average density and surface gravity, but is covered by nearly featureless unbroken clouds. The clouds are confined to a thick layer well above the ground and consist of droplets of concentrated sulfuric acid.

Neither Mercury nor the Moon have significant atmospheres. Overall, the inner planets have thin atmospheres overlying rocky cores while Jupiter, Uranus and Saturn are known as the gas giants because of their thick, dense atmospheres. Pluto does not appear to fit any picture that includes the planets. Some have suggested that Pluto was not originally a planet.

With little or no atmosphere, there is little or no weathering on Mercury, Mars and the Moon. They do show evidence of many craters caused by meteorites or comets smashing into their surface. About 4 billion years ago, early in the history of the Solar System, the newly forming planets and moons were bombarded by objects from space. They blasted down with explosive force, creating secondary craters with material thrown up by the initial blast. It is believed that meteorites that crashed into Earth at a later time may have caused the extinction of animals like the dinosaurs.

# MODERN TELESCOPES

Imagine being better able to look out at a distant star or nebula with amazing clarity. With such a telescope, one could peer billions of light years away and see things that happened billions of years ago. Astronomers are doing just that with telescopes in space. The major problem with using ground-based telescopes is that the light must pass through Earth's atmosphere. Besides clouds and the weather, Earth's atmosphere contains dust, water, and currents of cold air falling and warm air rising. All of these factors produce fuzzy images of the stars and limit the usefulness of ground-based telescopes. In the 1940's, it was proposed that a telescope in space would produce much clearer images.

In 1990, the **Hubble Space Telescope** went into orbit. Its resolution was reported to be 50 times more sensitive than ground-based telescope with 10 times more clarity. It was named after the American astronomer, Edwin Hubble, whose observations of variable stars in distant galaxies confirmed that the Universe was expanding, giving support to the Big Bang Theory of the Universe. The Hubble Space Telescope cannot observe the Sun because the intense light and heat would fry the instruments. It also cannot observe the planets Mercury and Venus because they are too close to the Sun.

NASA has had plans for four "Great Observatories" to be put into orbit. The first two were the Hubble Space Telescope, launched in 1990, and the **Compton Ray Observatory** that was in orbit from 1991 to 2000. The third is the **Chandra X-ray Observatory** deployed into space in 1999. The fourth Great Observatory is the **Space Infrared Telescope Facility** scheduled for launch in 2002.

Chandra is designed to observe X-rays eminating from high energy regions of the Universe. For example, the hot gases in the remnants of exploded stars emit such X-rays. Chandra detects and images X-ray sources that are billions of light years away. The imaging mirrors on Chandra are some of the largest, most precisely shaped and aligned, and smoothest mirrors ever constructed. The focusing power of Chandra makes it possible to read a newspaper at a distance of half a mile. Chandra will increase our understanding of the origin, evolution, and destiny of the Universe.

Plans are underway for the Next Generation Space Telescope, that will not simply replace the Hubble Space Telescope, but will be even more sensitive, providing better images of even more distant objects. It may be launched as early as 2007.

The age of optical space telescopes, started by the Hubble Space Telescope promises to revolutionize astronomy as much as, or more than, Galileo's first use of the telescope did long ago.

## The Future

Eventually, advanced shuttle craft will carry workers and materials high above Earth to travel to another planet for purposes of colonization. Exploration of other worlds will help us to understand how we can provide greater life benefits to humans.

## QUESTIONS

1. Mercury's surface is still riddled with craters millions of years after the craters formed because

   (1) There is no atmosphere to weather them.
   (2) There is no water to erode them.
   (3) The temperatures are too high because they are so close to the Sun.
   (4) The greenhouse effect has too great an impact on the temperature.

2. Which is the only planet that has all the conditions necessary to support life?

   (1) Mercury        (2) Venus        (3) Earth        (4) Mars

3. The region surrounding the Sun that supports life is the

   (1) photosphere                     (2) ecosphere
   (3) greenhouse effect               (4) atmosphere

4. Life first appeared in Earth's

   (1) atmosphere        (2) oceans        (3) interior        (4) sky

**5.** Free oxygen formed on Earth after

    (1) photosynthesis occurred
    (2) much of the iron in the oceans had oxidized
    (3) two phase changes of water
    (4) surface temperatures vaporized all the water

**6.** There is a small amount of weathering on Mars because

    (1) there is no liquid water          (2) there is no atmosphere
    (3) there is too much dust          (4) it is too cold

**7.** Why are seasons on Mars almost twice as long as on Earth?

    (1) Mars takes twice as long to revolve around the Sun.
    (2) Mars makes one rotation in about the same time period.
    (3) Earth revolves more slowly than Mars.
    (4) They have very different eccentricities.

**8.** If the amount of greenhouse gases were to increase for a very long time, the atmosphere on Earth would become most like the atmosphere of

    (1) Mercury          (2) Venus          (3) Jupiter          (4) Saturn

**9.** Which graph best illustrates the average temperatures of the planets in the solar system?

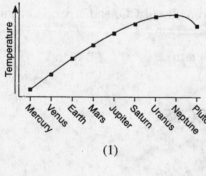

(1)

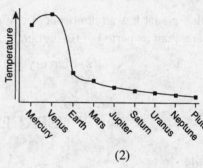

(2)

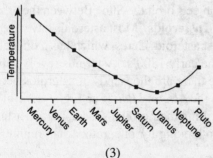

(3)

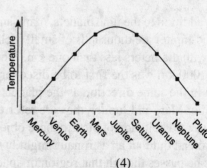

(4)

Base your answers to questions 10 and 11 on the graphs below. The graphs show the composition of the atmospheres of Venus, Earth, Mars, and Jupiter.

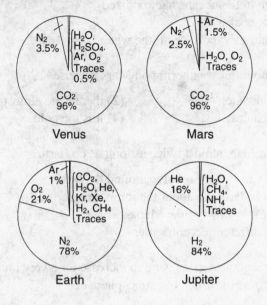

**10.** Which gas is present in the atmospheres of Venus, Earth, and Mars but is *not* present in the atmosphere of Jupiter?

(1) argon (Ar)      (2) methane ($CH_4$)    (3) hydrogen ($H_2$)     (4) water vapor ($H_2O$)

**11.** Which planet has an atmosphere composed primarily of $CO_2$ and a period of rotation greater than its period of revolution?

(1) Venus         (2) Mercury        (3) Earth        (4) Mars

# SPACE OBJECTS

## Asteroids

In addition to the nine planets, many smaller objects orbit the Sun. Between the orbits of Mars and Jupiter are thousands of small rocks called **asteroids**. Most asteroids have irregular shapes with diameters less than one km. The largest asteroid, Ceres, which has a diameter of almost 1000 km was the first to be discovered in the early 1800's. Asteroids revolve around the Sun in the same direction as the planets. Since there are thousands of asteroids between the orbit of Mars and Jupiter, they are referred to as the *Asteroid Belt* (See Fig. 9-2). But even in the asteroid belt, do not picture these objects as filling their orbital space. In fact, asteroids are so spread out that an astronaut might have to go looking for one, rather than running into them as he passes though that region of space.

Another group of asteroids have eccentric orbits around the Sun with some of them actually crossing Earth's orbital path. In 1936, the orbit of the asteroid Hermes came within $8.0 \times 10^5$ km from Earth. That is just about twice the distance from Earth to the Moon. This raises the possibility that Earth may have been hit by asteroids in the past, or that it may be hit in the future.

Astronomers generally believe that asteroids are debris left over from the formation of the solar system. A second possible source of asteroids may be comets that have broken apart.

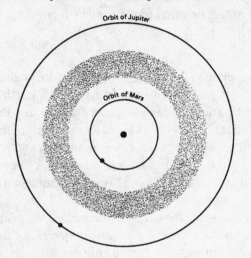

**Figure 9-2. The Asteroid Belt.** Thousands of asteroids orbit the Sun at distances between 2.3 and 3.3 Astronomical Units (AU). This region between the orbits of Mars and Jupiter is therefore called the asteroid belt.

## Comets

Far from the Sun, and well beyond the orbit of Pluto, are chunks of ice called **comets**. Most comets have very elongated orbits around the Sun. Comets with highly elongated orbits sometimes come close to the Sun (see Fig. 9-3). When this happens, the Sun's radiation vaporizes some of the comet's ices, producing a long flowing tail. One such comet is Halley's Comet which has an orbital period of about 76 years.

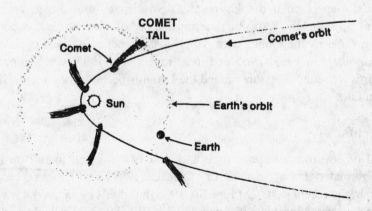

**Figure 9-3.** The highly eccentric orbit of a comet compared to the almost circular orbit of Earth. NOTE: A comet's tail always points away from the Sun.

When a comet is far from the Sun, it consists of only a *nucleus*, generally measuring about 15 km across, and is composed primarily of dust and ice (frozen ammonia, methane and water). As a comet approaches the Sun, solar heat begins to vaporize the ices. The released gases surrounding the icy nucleus begin to glow, producing a fuzzy, luminous ball called the *coma* that can eventually expand to a million kilometers in diameter. The solar wind and radiation pressure blows these luminous gases outward from the Sun into a long, flowing *tail*. A comet's tail can be as long a 1 AU, long enough to reach from Earth to the Sun. A comet's tail always points away from the Sun regardless of the direction of the comet's motion.

## Meteoroids, Meteors, and Meteorites

**Meteoroids** are fragments of rocks or ice traveling in space. **Meteors**, sometimes called "shooting stars", are streaks of light caused by meteoroids passing through Earth's atmosphere at high speed. The light is caused by friction between the meteoroid and the atoms that make up the atmosphere. The heat produced by the friction causes the atoms of the atmosphere to glow. Most meteoroids are no bigger than a grain or pebble of sand and are destroyed before they reach Earth's surface. If a piece of rock is large enough to survive its fiery descent through the atmosphere, the object that reaches the ground is called a **meteorite**. Most meteorites are made of stone.

Meteors are visible on almost any night of the year. However, on certain nights many more meteors than usual will be seen in the sky. We are seeing a *meteor shower*, or the entering of many particles into Earth's atmosphere within a short period of time. An analysis of the orbits of meteoroids producing a shower reveals that they are associated with a comet that passed along the same path at an earlier time. The particles are very likely debris left from the comet itself. The best known annual meteor showers occur in the second half of the year: the *Perseids*, August 10-14; the *Orionids*, October 18-23; the *Taurids*, Nov. 1-15; and the *Geminids*, December 10-16.

A given shower may be more impressive one year than in another because the particles that produce showers tend to travel in swarms. When Earth in its orbit passes through a *swarm of meteoroids*, a spectacular display results. Swarms of meteoroids are associated with constellations and comets. An outstanding display of the *Leonids*, occurs in a cycle of 33 years, the same as the comet with which it is associated. This cycle was verified by spectacular showers in 1932, 1965 and most recently in 1998, when approximately 1,000 meteors/hour were seen. They are named the Leonids because they seem to come out of the constellation Leo.

## Impact Events

A total of 300 tons of space rock and dust is estimated to fall on Earth each day. Although most materials that reach Earth's surface are very small, there is evidence of comets hitting Earth in the recent past. On June 30, 1908, hundreds of square kilometers of forest in Siberia were devastated in a blast that was audible 1000 km (600 miles) away. The explosion was equivalent to the detonation of a small nuclear warhead. The most likely explanation for this event was that a small comet collided with Earth. No impact crater was formed and the trees at "ground zero" were left standing upright, but were completely stripped of leaves and branches. Most meteoroids are no bigger than a grain or pebble of sand and are destroyed before they reach Earth.

There is fossil evidence that the dinosaurs met a rather sudden extinction about 65 million years ago. In fact, at that time a staggering 65 percent of all the species on Earth disappeared within a relatively brief span of time. One theory for explaining this catastrophe is that an asteroid or comet slamming into Earth would have thrown enough dust into the atmosphere to block out the Sun for several years. The dust may have obscured much of the radiation of the Sun and triggered a temporary change in Earth's climate. As plants died for lack of sunshine, the dinosaurs would have starved to death along with many other creatures in the vegetation food chain. Although scientists are not sure if this event is related to an asteroid, many agree that the hypothesis fits the available evidence better than any other explanation that has been offered.

## Impact Craters

On rare occasions, large meteoroid fragments collide with the surface of our planet. The result is an **impact crater** whose diameter depends on the mass and speed of the impinging object. One of the most impressive and best-preserved terrestrial impact craters is the famous Barringer Crater in Arizona. The crater measures 1.2 km across and is 200 m deep. The crater was formed about 30,000 years ago when an iron-rich object measuring roughly 50 m across struck the ground with a speed estimated at 11 km/sec (25,000 miles per hour). The resulting blast was equal to the detonation of a 2-megaton hydrogen bomb.

Our Moon and other planets and satellites in space have been pocketed by meteoroid impacts to their surfaces. But unlike the Moon, Earth has only a very limited amount of sites that resemble impact craters. Perhaps many eroded craters lie unfound. Some less obvious sites can be revealed by satellite photography or by very careful study of topographic maps showing the contours of a given region. A certain site which looks flat today may have been an obvious crater at an earlier time. The change would have taken place gradually as a result of erosion, atmospheric variations in wind, rain, and temperature removing the most obvious features. The Moon craters, on the other hand, have been subjected to almost no erosion because of a lack of atmosphere and therefore remain almost unchanged for thousands of years.

The age of an impact crater can be inferred from its appearance today. The Barringer Crater is believed to be no more than 30,000 years old because of its lack of erosion. The 10 km Vredefort Crater of South Africa is almost imperceptible now and is believed to be over 250 million years old. The impact which produced the Vredefort Crater is believed to be more than 500,000 times greater than that which produced the Barringer Crater.

There have been two major collisions with Earth in the 20th century, the one in 1908 and one in 1947, both in Siberia. If there were 2 major collisions/century, in a million years, Earth would have been hit 20,000 times, yet there is no evidence of that many craters on Earth. If only one major collision occurred every 1000 years there would be only 1000 craters, but there is no evidence of even that few.

# QUESTIONS

1. On which planet do large amounts of water exist in all three states of matter?

   (1) Venus        (2) Earth        (3) Mars        (4) Saturn

2. Which three planets are known as terrestrial planets because of their high density and rocky composition?

   (1) Venus, Neptune, and Pluto        (2) Venus, Saturn, and Neptune
   (3) Jupiter, Saturn, and Uranus        (4) Mercury, Mars and Venus

3. The presence of which atmospheric gas causes the high temperature of Venus?

   (1) carbon dioxide ($CO_2$)        (2) nitrogen ($N_2$)
   (3) oxygen ($O_2$)        (4) hydrogen ($H_2$)

4. Planetary temperatures were recorded by the Voyager I space probe as it traveled from Earth past the outer planets Jupiter, Saturn, and Uranus before leaving the solar system. Which graph best represents the relationship between the temperature of the planets and their distances from Earth?

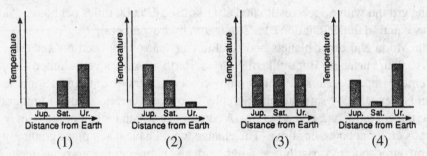

      (1)            (2)            (3)            (4)

5. In which list are celestial features correctly shown in order of increasing size?

   (1) galaxy → solar system → Universe → planet
   (2) solar system → galaxy → planet → Universe
   (3) planet → solar system → galaxy → Universe
   (4) Universe → galaxy → solar system → planet

6. Because Venus has greater atmospheric carbon dioxide ($CO_2$) content than Earth has, the surface temperature of Venus is

   (1) warmer, due to absorption of long-wave (infrared) radiation by a greenhouse gas
   (2) warmer, due to absorption of short-wave (ultraviolet) radiation by a greenhouse gas
   (3) cooler, due to absorption of long-wave (infrared) radiation by a greenhouse gas
   (4) cooler, due to absorption of short-wave (ultraviolet) radiation by a greenhouse gas

# ORIGIN AND FATE OF THE UNIVERSE

In the late 1920's, Edwin Hubble began investigating the visible spectra of galaxies and arrived at one of the most important astronomical discoveries of the twentieth century. Hubble discovered that nearby galaxies are moving away from us slowly while more distant galaxies are rushing away from us much more rapidly.

## Doppler Effect

The evidence that the galaxies are actually rushing away from us lies in their **spectra** (colors produced when wavelengths of light are separated). Such spectra show two dark lines (H & K) produced by the element calcium. Photographs of three different galaxies are shown on the left in Figure 9-4. The largest appearing galaxy (top) is the nearest and the smallest appearing galaxy (bottom) is the farthest. The spectra of the galaxies are shown to the right. In these illustrations, the actual spectra of the galaxies are the fuzzy bands of light in the middle of each spectrum. The line above and below are reference markers so that comparisons can be made. Notice that in the spectra of the galaxies, only the two dark spectral lines of calcium (H & K) are easily seen. In lab experiments, these two lines normally appear in the blue colors of the spectrum. In the spectrum of the nearest galaxy (Virgo), the two spectral lines are shifted only slightly toward the red end (the right) of the spectrum. Notice that the lines in the more distant galaxies have shifted even further toward the red end (right) of the spectrum. In the most distant galaxy (Hydra), the two lines have shifted all the way across the spectrum and are among the red colors.

The spectra of galaxies have shown a shift to the red end of the spectrum. That's because of the **Doppler effect** - a change of light or sound wavelengths as a source moves toward or away from the observer. Light waves of an object speeding away through space will *stretch* into longer wavelengths, or **red-shift**. Light waves speeding toward us will be squeezed into shorter wavelengths, or **blue-shift**. A red-shift in the spectra of a galaxy indicates that the galaxy is moving away from us. The greater the red-shift, the higher the speed. Since all galaxies have red-shifts, they are all moving away from us. From the Doppler effect, Hubble concluded that nearby galaxies are moving away from us slowly, while more distant galaxies are moving away from us much more rapidly. This relationship between distance and speeds of galaxies is **Hubble's law**. The galaxies themselves are not expanding, just the space between the galaxies.

To better understand Hubble's law, imagine someone blowing up a balloon with a number of spots on the balloon (See Figure 9-5). As the balloon expands, the spots become more distant from one another. Further, as seen from any spot, the other spots are moving away with a speed that increases with an increase in distance. Nearby spots are moving away slowly, while the distant spots are moving away more rapidly. By analogy, the real meaning of Hubble's Law is that *the Universe is expanding*.

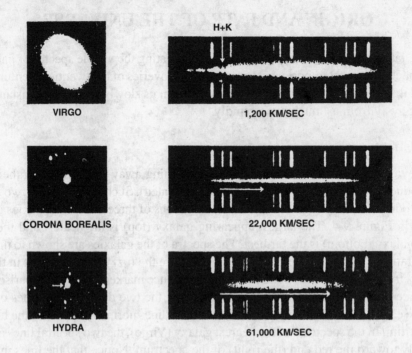

**VIRGO**

H+K

**1,200 KM/SEC**

**CORONA BOREALIS**

**22,000 KM/SEC**

**HYDRA**

**61,000 KM/SEC**

**Figure 9-4**. The red-shifts of galaxies. Photographs of three galaxies are shown on the left. Their corresponding spectra are shown on the right. Nearby galaxies (which look big) have low red-shifts. Distant galaxies (which look small) have higher red-shifts.

**Figure 9-5**. An expanding balloon. As a balloon expands, all points on the balloon move away from any given point with a speed that is proportional to their distances. By analogy, the true meaning of the Hubble law is that the Universe is expanding.

# DEEP SPACE PHENOMENA

From the observed rate of expansion, it follows that approximately 15 to 20 billion years ago, all the matter in the Universe must have been concentrated into an incredibly dense "primeval atom." This "atom" exploded with tremendous force and all matter and space began expanding at speeds nearly that of light. This was the **Big Bang**. Between 100,000 and a million years after the Big Bang, huge clouds of hydrogen and helium began to form. These clouds became the beginnings of galaxies. Eventually stars began to form. It is theorized that all galaxies formed during this first few billion years, because all the galaxies appear to be at least 10 billion years old. Residual radiation from the Big Bang can still be detected in space.

Astronomers believe that stars begin as **nebula**, huge masses of dust and gas (hydrogen) that condense in space. As the nebula is compressed by gravitational forces, its temperature rises, and a thermonuclear reaction called **nuclear fusion** begins. Hydrogen is fused into helium and energy is released. Some of the energy is given off as light and a star is born. Gradually other heavier elements evolve. Eventually, most of the hydrogen in the core of the star is used up and the star's gravity squeezes it. As the core contracts, it gets hotter and unused hydrogen is forced outward to the shell where it fuses to helium. The shell expands, eventually producing a hundredfold increase in the star's diameter. Soon, the temperature of the star's expanded surface cools and its gases glow with a reddish hue (**red giants**). The core of the red giant continues to collapse and gravity fuses helium to carbon and oxygen and finally, to iron. Now it is a small star, incredibly dense, white-hot and about the size of a planet, called a **white dwarf**. A white dwarf can either cool to a dense black cinder or continue to collapse. Pressure squeezes the electrons into atomic nuclei to produce neutrons. The result is a **neutron star** about 15 km in diameter. The outer portion of a neutron star may explode with incredible force producing a **supernova**, the brightest known object in space. Material from the explosion may form a new star called a **pulsar**, a rapidly spinning neutron star emitting pulsating signals in the radio portion of the electromagnetic spectrum. Gravity might continue to collapse the star inwardly on itself and disappear, producing a **black hole**, a region of black surrounded by stars.

## Comparing Temperature, Color and Luminosity

A pattern was discovered among stars that allows them to be compared by brightness and color. Figure 9-6 is a typical such diagram. Each point represents a star whose brightness (absolute magnitude) and color temperature (spectral type) have been determined. Bright stars are near the top, dim stars near the bottom. Hot stars are to the left (0 and B) and cool stars are to the right (m). The band stretching diagonally across the H-R diagram represents the majority of stars and is called the **Main Sequence**. Stars start out in the Main Sequence and as the core cools, they move into the giant category. A few rare stars are bigger and brighter than the typical red giant and are called **supergiants**. Betelgeuse in Orion is a supergiant. In fact, it is so big, that if it were our Sun, Earth would be engulfed inside it. As the stars continue to collapse, they become very small and very hot white dwarfs.

## Luminosity and Temperature of Stars
### (Name in italics refers to star shown by a ⊕)

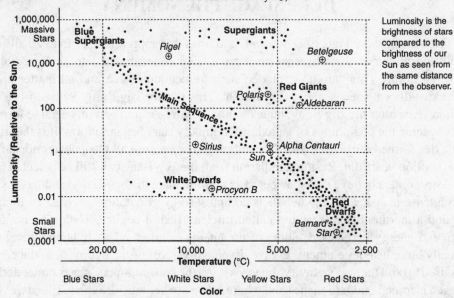

**Figure 9-6.** Luminosity is the brightness of stars compared to the brightness of our Sun as seen from the same distance from the observer.

# QUESTIONS

1. Stars produce different spectra mainly because of differences in their

    (1) temperature and size
    (2) chemical composition and temperature
    (3) size and chemical composition
    (4) mass and size

2. Diagram I below represents a normal spectrum. Diagram II represents the spectrum of a star.

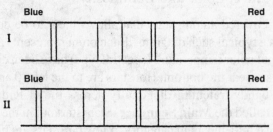

    If you compare the two diagrams, you conclude that the star is
    (1) moving toward Earth       (2) moving away from Earth
    (3) not moving                (4) changing color

**3.** The red-shift depends on the fact that

  (1) all sources emit light at the same rate
  (2) the nature of the source determines the speed of light
  (3) a light source is always constant
  (4) some light waves travel faster than others

**4.** According to Hubble's law, the Universe is

  (1) collapsing      (2) pulsating      (3) expanding      (4) shrinking

**5.** The sequence most stars go through in their "life" is best described as

  (1) main sequence, white dwarf, red giant
  (2) white dwarf, red giant, main sequence
  (3) red giant, white dwarf, main sequence
  (4) main sequence, red giant, white dwarf

**6.** The diagram below shows the brightness and temperature of stars.

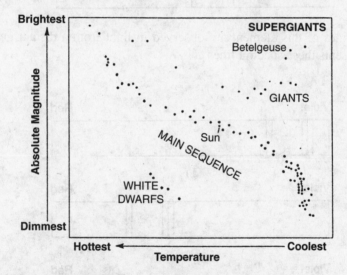

Compared to the Sun Betelgeuse is

  (1) hotter and dimmer          (2) hotter and brighter
  (3) cooler and brighter        (4) cooler and dimmer

**7.** Dense, dim stars the size of Earth are

  (1) supergiants                  (2) red giants
  (3) white dwarfs            (4) main sequence stars

8. If the expansion of the Universe were reversed, it would shrink to a point in about

   (1) 5 billion years          (2) 15 billion years
   (3) 5 years               (4) 100,000 years

9. According to the big bang theory, the Universe began as an explosion and is still expanding. This theory is supported by observations that the stellar spectra of distant galaxies show a

   (1) concentration in the yellow portion of the spectrum
   (2) concentration in the green portion of the spectrum
   (3) shift toward the blue end of the spectrum
   (4) shift toward the red end of the spectrum

10. The diagram below represents a standard dark-line spectrum for an element.

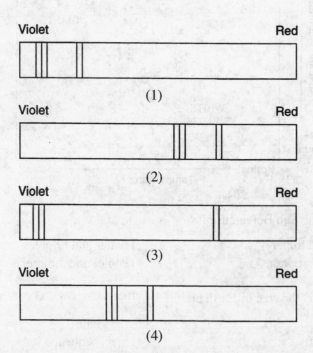

The spectral lines of this element are observed in light from a distant galaxy. Which diagram represents these spectral lines

# CELESTIAL OBSERVATIONS

## Celestial Sphere

It is very difficult for an observer on Earth's surface to explain the motions of Earth and the motions of celestial objects, such as the Sun, stars, Moon, and planets. All these objects appear to be located on the surface of a sphere that encircles Earth. This imaginary sphere is called the **celestial sphere** (see Figure 9-7). The line around the edge of Earth where the celestial sphere meets Earth is called the **horizon**. The Sun rises and sets at the horizon. The point on the celestial sphere that is directly above an observer's position on Earth's surface is called the **zenith** of the observer. An observer at the North Pole would have Polaris at his or her zenith.

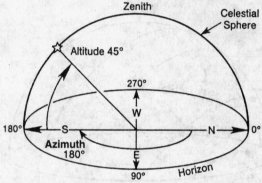

**Figure 9-7**. The celestial sphere. To an observer at point W, the star appears on the sphere at an altitude of 45° above the southern horizon.

A system known as the altitude-azimuth system can be used to describe positions of celestial objects in relation to an observer's position on Earth. The **altitude** of a celestial object is its distance in degrees, above the horizon. The **azimuth** of a celestial object is the distance, in degrees, measured clockwise from the due north position (due north is 0° azimuth). For example, a star that is halfway between the horizon and the zenith and is due south of the observer would have an altitude of 45 degrees and an azimuth of 180 degrees. From New York, the north star (Polaris), is due north, almost half way up to the Zenith.

## Star Paths

All celestial objects appear to move from east to west across the sky. The apparent daily motion of these objects describe an **arc**, which is a portion of a circular path. The apparent path of the Sun through the sky is an arc. Since Earth rotates through 360 degrees in 24 hours, the rate of apparent motion of celestial objects across the sky is constant at 15 degrees per hour. Long-exposure photos of stars show that the stars form arcs called **star trails**. Stars located between the northern horizon and Polaris never set, move in counterclockwise circles, and are called **circumpolar stars** (see Figure 9-8). Stars that rise in the east and set in the west describe long, circular arcs across the sky (see Figure 9-9). A one-hour time-lapse photo of a star will show an arc that is 15 degrees long, indicating that objects on the celestial sphere appear to move 15 degrees per hour.

**Figure 9-8.** Star trails formed by circumpolar stars.

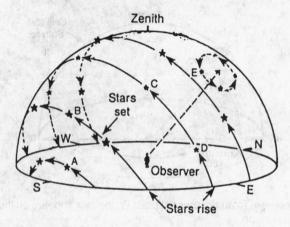

**Figure 9-9.** Stars appear to move across the sky from east to west during the night. Star E represents a circumpolar star.

In the United States, the Sun appears to rise in the eastern sky, move through the southern sky, and set in the west. The Sun is highest in the sky at noon, but it is *never* directly overhead (at our zenith) anywhere in the continental United States. In New York State, the altitude of the noon Sun ranges from about 23° in December and 72° in June.

The apparent daily motion of celestial objects is due to Earth's rotation. **Rotation** is the turning of an object on its axis. Celestial objects are not actually moving from east to west across the sky. Earth is rotating *under* them. If you observe certain stars at the same time every day, you will note that the positions of the stars appear to shift slightly to the west each day. After one year, they appear back at the positions where they were observed a year earlier. The annual westward shifting of celestial objects is due to Earth's revolution around the Sun.

**Revolution** is the movement of one celestial object around another. The path along which an object travels during a revolution is called an **orbit**.

# CONSTELLATIONS

Few people ever notice the magnificent pageant of stars in the sky each night. Although the number of stars in the Universe has been compared to the number of grains in all of Earth's beaches, the stars visible to the unaided eye number less than 3000. Ancient man first imagined pictures among groupings of stars. Stars that appear to be grouped in patterns forming the outlines of people, animals and physical objects in the sky are called **constellations**. Two thousand years ago, the Greeks recognized 48 constellations.

You may already be familiar with some of these patterns in the sky such as the Big Dipper, which is actually part of a large constellation called Ursa Major (the Great Bear). Many of these constellations, such as Orion, have names from ancient myths and legends. Modern star charts divide the entire sky into 88 constellations of which about 70 are visible in New York State. The **circumpolar constellations** are visible every night (see Figure 9-10) never set below the horizon.

## Star Shifts

The constellations you see in the sky change slowly from one night to the next. This shift occurs as Earth orbits the Sun. Earth takes a full year to go once around the Sun, and thus the darkened nighttime side of Earth is gradually turned toward different parts of the heavens. If you follow specific constellation on successive evenings, you will note that it rises approximately 4 minutes earlier each night. Each month, the night side of Earth faces different constellations.

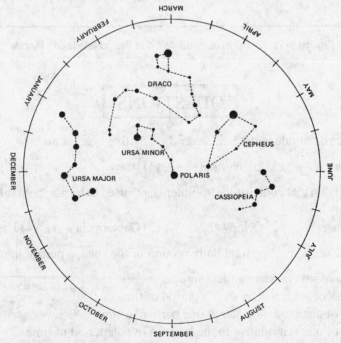

**Figure 9-10**. North circumpolar constellations at 42° of Latitude.

If we accept that Earth revolves around the Sun, then the Sun appears to pass in front of constellations on the side of the Sun away from Earth. We cannot see these constellations because the Sun is too bright. This apparent path of the Sun against the background stars is called the **ecliptic** (see Figure 9-11). These are twelve constellations centered approximately on the ecliptic. They are called the constellations of the *zodiac*.

## Planetary Motions

When viewed from Earth during the course of an evening, planets, like stars, appear to move from east to west on the celestial sphere. Over longer periods of time, however, the planets seem to change position relative to the stars around them. Like the stars, the planets appear to shift slightly westward each evening, but their shift is not as great as that of the stars. Thus, the planets actually move eastward relative to the star fields behind them.

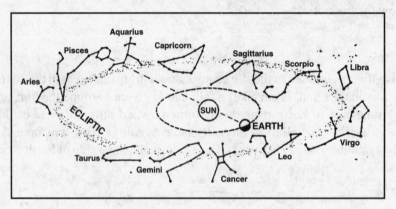

Figure 9-11. The Sun appears to be in the constellation Pisces.

# QUESTIONS

1. At which Earth latitude is the Sun never directly overhead at noon?

   (1) 42°North      (2) 20°North      (3) 0°      (4) 5°South

2. The constellation that contains the "pointer stars" used to locate the star Polaris in the sky is
   (1) Ursa Minor      (2) Orion      (3) Casseopeia      (4) Ursa Major

3. In order to describe the apparent daily motion of the stars, a person must observe the

   (1) locations of several stars at the same time
   (2) brightness of several stars over a period of time
   (3) position of one particular star at one particular time
   (4) position of one star relative to the horizon over a period of time

**4.** Observations of a planet moving among the stars over the course of a year provide evidence that the planet

(1) rotates on its axis        (2) gives off light

(3) tilts toward Polaris        (4) revolves around the Sun

**5.** Why do stars appear to move through the night sky at the rate of 15 degrees per hour?

(1) Earth actually moves around the Sun at a rate of 15° per hour.

(2) The stars actually move around the center of the Universe at a rate of 15° per hour.

(3) Earth actually rotates at a rate of 15° per hour.

(4) The stars actually revolve around Earth at a rate of 15° per hour.

**6.** How would a three-hour time exposure photograph of stars in the northern sky appear if Earth did not rotate?

  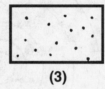 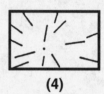

**(1)**       **(2)**       **(3)**       **(4)**

(1) Diagram 1     (2) Diagram 2     (3) Diagram 3     (4) Diagram 4

**7.** Earth rotates on its axis at a rate of approximately

(1) 1° per hour    (2) 15° per hour    (3) 23½° per hour    (4) 360° per hour

**8.** An observer in New York State sees different constellations in the winter nighttime sky than she sees in the summer nighttime sky. Which statement best explains the reason for this difference?

(1) Earth rotates on its axis.       (2) Earth revolves around the Sun.

(3) Constellations revolve around Earth.       (4) Constellations revolve around the Sun.

# MODELS TO EXPLAIN CELESTIAL MOTIONS

## Geocentric Model

The early Greeks felt that Earth was at rest at the center of the Universe. Observations of the daily rising and setting of the Sun, Moon, planets, and stars indicated that the heavens revolve around the stationary Earth.

One of the earliest models developed to explain the motions of celestial objects was the **geocentric (Earth-centered) model** suggested by Ptolemy over 2000 years ago. In this model, Earth is stationary-not rotating or revolving-and all celestial objects move around it at fixed distances from it (see Figure 9-12).

This model was readily accepted, because it explained all of the daily motions of the Sun, planets, and stars across the sky. The **retrograde (backward) motion** of some of the planets was explained by showing that they moved in small circles, called epicycles, during their travels around Earth. The Ptolemaic system worked so well and seemed so reasonable that it completely dominated all of astronomy for over a thousand years. By the early 1500's, the geocentric model contained no less than 79 separate circles when the planets "backed up" and was very complicated.

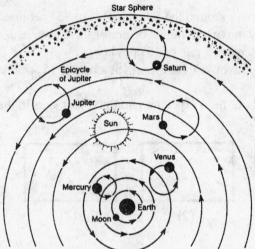

**Figure 9-12**. Geocentric (Earth-centered) model of celestial objects. The circular epicycles shown for the planets were necessary in order to explain the retrograde motion of some planets.

## Heliocentric Model

Early in the 16th century, Nicholas Copernicus suggested a more simple model to explain the motions of celestial objects that would satisfy the shortcomings of the geocentric model. This new model was the **heliocentric (Sun-centered) model**, and is the model used at the present time. In this model, Earth and the planets revolve around the Sun and Earth rotates on its axis. Retrograde motion of the planets is explained by the idea that the further a planet is from the Sun, the slower its orbital velocity (see Figure 9-13). The diagram illustrates that retrograde motion is only apparent. The planets are actually moving eastward in their orbits. The apparent retrograde motion of some planets is caused by the fact that each planet revolves around the Sun at a different speed. The closer a planet is to the Sun, the faster it moves in its orbit. Retrograde motion is most easily seen in the planets outside Earth's orbit.

The heliocentric model accounts for the phase changes of Venus and the apparent changes in diameter of the Moon and planets.

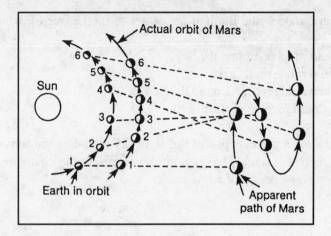

**Figure 9-13**. The apparent west-to-east movement of Mars across the sky is called retrograde motion.

---

## QUESTIONS

1. The diagram below shows the orbits of planets A and B in the star-planet system.

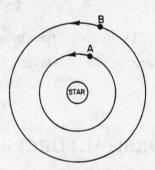

The period of revolution for planet B is 40 days. The period of revolution for planet A most likely is

(1) less than 40 days      (2) greater than 40 days      (3) 40 days

2. Which observation cannot be explained by a geocentric model?

(1) Stars follow circular paths around Polaris
(2) The Sun's path through the sky is an arc
(3) A planet's apparent diameter varies
(4) Winds shift to the right in the Northern Hemisphere

3. In the geocentric model (the Earth at the center of the Universe), which motion would occur?
   (1) Earth would revolve around the Sun.
   (2) Earth would rotate on its axis.
   (3) The Moon would revolve around the Sun.
   (4) The Sun would revolve around Earth.

4. The diagram below represents part of the night sky including the constellation Leo. The black circles represent stars. The open circles represent the changing positions of one celestial object over a period of a few weeks.

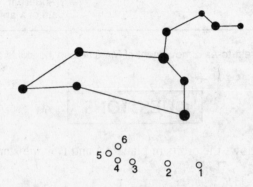

The celestial object represented by the open circles most likely is

(1) a galaxy      (2) a planet      (3) Earth's Moon      (4) another star

# ORBITAL FORCES

## Modern Celestial Model

Once the idea of a heliocentric model was established, the work of many scientists most notably Johann Kepler and Sir Isaac Newton served to modify and simplify the model and to strengthen many of the weaknesses of Copernicus' original model.

## Orbital Geometry

In 1600, Johann Kepler began work on what were to become his "Laws of Planetary Motion". He observed that the planets traveled, not in circular paths, but in closed curves called **ellipses**.

The center of an ellipse consists of two fixed points, called **foci**. Kepler's first law states that: **the orbits of the planets around the Sun are ellipses, with the Sun at one of the foci** (see Figure 9-14).

The out-of-roundness of an ellipse, its **eccentricity**, can be calculated using the following formula:

$$\text{eccentricity} = \frac{\text{distance between foci}}{\text{length of major axis}} \quad \text{or} \quad e = \frac{d}{L}$$

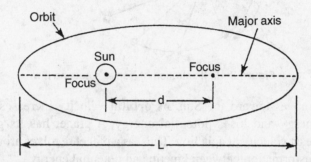

**Figure 9-14.** The elliptical orbit of a planet. Distance d is the distance between the two foci of the ellipse. L is the length of the major axis of the ellipse.

The orbital eccentricity of each planet is given in Table 9-2.

| Planet | Eccentricity |
|---------|--------------|
| Mercury | 0.206 |
| Venus | 0.007 |
| Earth | 0.017 |
| Mars | 0.093 |
| Jupiter | 0.048 |
| Saturn | 0.056 |
| Uranus | 0.047 |
| Neptune | 0.009 |
| Pluto | 0.250 |

**TABLE 9-2. ORBITAL ECCENTRICITIES**

Notice that the smaller the eccentricity, the more circular the orbit. Therefore, Venus and Neptune, with the smallest eccentricities, have the most circular orbits. Pluto, with the greatest eccentricity, has the least circular (most eccentric) orbit.

Kepler's second law of motion related the orbital velocity of a planet to its orbital position in relation to the Sun. This law states that: **an imaginary line joining a planet to the Sun will sweep over equal areas in equal periods of time** (see Figure 9-15). This means that a planet travels fastest and farthest each day when it is near position 1. Conversely, it will travel slowest and cover the least distance when it is near position 2. Note that the greatest orbital velocity occurs when the planet is closest to the Sun (**perihelion**) and its slowest velocity occurs when it is farthest from the Sun (**aphelion**). For Earth, these positions occur on January 3 and July 4 respectively.

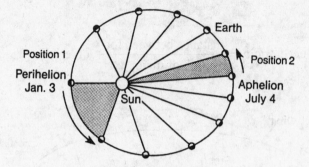

**Figure 9-15**. Illustration of Kepler's second law.

As a planet moves toward the Sun, its **orbital velocity** increases (see Figure 9-16). It gains kinetic energy and loses potential energy. A planet has its greatest velocity at perihelion and its least velocity at aphelion. Thus, as a planet revolves around the Sun, there is a cyclic energy transformation between kinetic and potential energy.

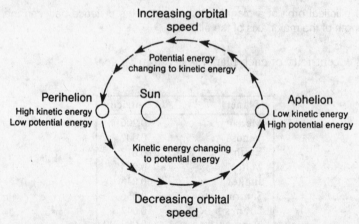

**Figure 9-16**. Changing speed and cyclic energy transformations of a planet as it orbits the Sun.

Kepler's third law relates the orbital period of a planet with the planet's distance from the Sun. The **period** of a planet equals its year, which is the time it takes for the planet to complete one revolution around the Sun. The farther a planet is from the Sun, the larger its orbit and the longer its period. Kepler's Harmonic Law states that: **the square of any planet's orbital period ($T^2$) is proportional to the mean radius of its orbit cubed ($R^3$).** This relationship can be expressed as: $T^2 \propto R^3$. T is usually expressed in Earth years, and R is expressed in the number of astronomical units between the planet and the Sun. An **Astronomical Unit (A.U.)** is the average distance between Earth and the Sun. Its numerical value is about 150 million kilometers.

# Gravitation

Sir Isaac Newton showed that every object in the Universe is attracted to every other object in the Universe. He called this force of attraction **gravitation**. It is this force that prevents the solar system from flying apart. Newton's Universal Law of Gravitation states that the **gravitational force** between any two objects in the Universe is directly proportional to the products of their masses and inversely proportional to the square of the distance between their centers. This proportion can be written as: $F$ is the gravitational force, $m_1$ and $m_2$ are the masses of the two objects, and $d$ is the distance between the centers of the, two objects. Thus, as the masses of the objects increase, gravitational force increases; as distance between the objects increases, gravitational force between them decreases.

$$F \propto \frac{m_1 m_2}{d^2}$$

## QUESTIONS

1. The equation for the gravitational force between two objects is

$$\text{Force} \propto G \frac{\text{mass}_1 \times \text{mass}_2}{\text{distance}^2}$$

   Doubling which factor would bring about the greatest change in force?
   (1) mass$_1$          (2) mass$_2$          (3) distance

2. As Earth moves in orbit from its July position to its position in January, the Sun's apparent diameter increases. This observation indicates that during this time Earth-Sun distance is
   (1) decreasing          (2) increasing          (3) remaining the same

Base your answers to questions 3 through 7 on your knowledge of Earth Science, the *Earth Science Reference Tables*, and the diagram below. The diagram is a model of the orbit of an imaginary planet Q around a star. Points A, B, C, and D indicate four orbital positions of planet Q.

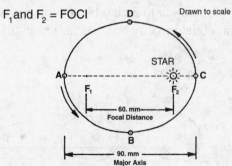

3. At which position in its orbit does planet Q have the greatest velocity?
   (1) A          (2) B          (3) C          (4) D

4. Which graph best approximates the gravitational force between the star and planet Q at positions A through D?

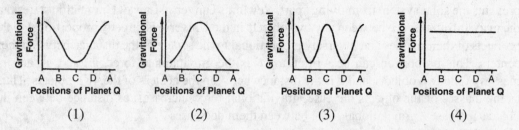

| (1) | (2) | (3) | (4) |

5. What is the approximate eccentricity of planet Q's orbit? [Use the *Earth Science Reference Tables*]

(1) 0.06         (2) 0.15         (3) 0.67         (4) 1.50

6. The diagram below represents a planet in orbit around a star. Which statement best describes how the planet's energy is changing as it moves from point A to point B?

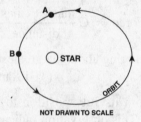

NOT DRAWN TO SCALE

(1) Kinetic energy is increasing and potential energy is decreasing.
(2) Kinetic energy is decreasing and potential energy is increasing.
(3) Both kinetic and potential energy are decreasing.
(4) Both kinetic and potential energy are increasing.

7. The top views of four possible orbits for a planet revolving around a star are shown below. The distances from the star to each orbit are drawn to scale. In which orbit would the greatest changes in orbital velocity occur as the planet makes one revolution?

KEY
• Planet
✿ Star

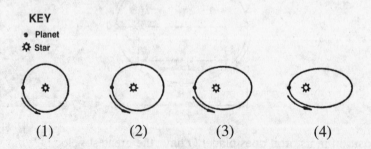

| (1) | (2) | (3) | (4) |

8. During which season in the Northern Hemisphere does Earth reach its greatest distance from the Sun?

(1) winter        (2) summer        (3) spring        (4) fall

9. Which planetary model allows a scientist to predict the exact positions of the planets in the night sky over many years?

(1) The planets' orbits are circles in a geocentric model.
(2) The planets' orbits are ellipses in a geocentric model.
(3) The planets' orbits are circles in a heliocentric model.
(4) The planets' orbits are ellipses in a heliocentric model.

10. According to the following table, which planet's orbit would most closely resemble a circle?

| Planet | Eccentricity of Orbit |
|---|---|
| Mercury | 0.206 |
| Venus | 0.007 |
| Earth | 0.017 |
| Mars | 0.093 |
| Jupiter | 0.048 |
| Saturn | 0.056 |
| Uranus | 0.047 |
| Neptune | 0.008 |
| Pluto | 0.250 |

(1) Mercury        (2) Venus        (3) Saturn        (4) Pluto

11. Planet A has a greater mean distance from the Sun than planet B. On the basis of this fact, which further comparison can be correctly made between the two planets?

(1) Planet A is larger.        (2) Planet A's revolution period is longer.
(3) Planet A's speed of rotation is greater.        (4) Planet A's day is longer.

Base your answers to questions 12 and 13 on your knowledge of Earth Science and the diagram below.

The diagram shows the path of an Earth Satellite. Earth is at one focus and the second focus is at $F_2$. Numbers 1-12 indicate the satellite's positions.

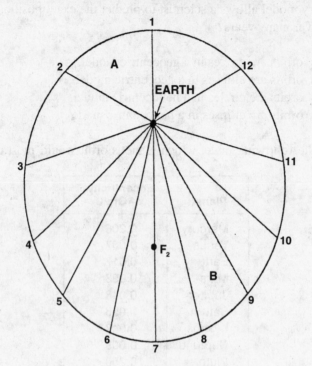

12. What is the approximate eccentricity of the satellite's orbit?

    (1) 0.31          (2) 0.40          (3) 0.70          (4) 2.5

13. Earth satellite takes 24 hours to move between each numbered position on the orbit. How does area A (between positions 1 and 2) compare to area B (between positions 8 and 9)?

    (1) Area A is smaller than area B.
    (2) Area A is larger than area B.
    (3) Area A is equal to area B.

# EARTH'S ROTATION

Earth is literally spinning like a top. It spins, or rotates, on its axis in a counterclockwise (west to east) direction through 360° in 24 hours. Thus, the angular rate of travel of Earth due to its rotation is 15° per hour. It is this rotation that accounts for the apparent motion of celestial objects across the sky from east to west.

Every point on Earth's surface travels at an *angular* rate of 15° per hour. However, different points on Earth's surface travel at different rotational speeds. The speed depends on the latitude of the point. The greater the latitude, the slower the speed. Look at Figure 9-17. Think of latitude lines, or parallels, as being circles that connect all points at the same latitude. The equator connects all points at 0° latitude. The circumference of the equator is about 40,080 kilometers. A point on the equator travels this distance in 24 hours. Thus, the point travels at a rotational speed of 40,080 km 24 hours, or 1670 km/hr. At the same time, a point on the 60° latitude travels a distance of 20,140 kilometers, which computes to a speed of about 839 km/hr.

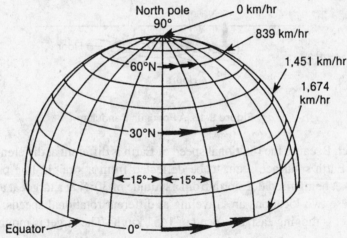

**Figure 9-17.** The rotational speed of travel of Earth's surface decreases as latitude increases.

## Evidence of Earth's Rotation

There is a considerable body of evidence indicating that Earth does rotate on its axis.

**Foucault Pendulum.** Once set in motion, a free-swinging pendulum will continue to swing along the same path unless acted upon by some outside force. Jean Foucault, a French scientist, was the first to use this principle to demonstrate that Earth does rotate on its axis. He suspended a pendulum on a long wire and set it swinging freely. After a period of time, it appeared that the direction of the pendulum's path had changed (Figure 9-18). Since no outside force had affected the pendulum, Foucault concluded that the apparent change in direction of the pendulum's swing was due to Earth's rotation. Earth had rotated beneath the pendulum. This pendulum was therefore named the **Foucault Pendulum.** There are many Foucault Pendulums set up in the United States that illustrate this principle (e.g. the United Nations Building, New York City, and the Smithsonian Institute, Washington, D.C.). The apparent change in direction of a pendulum's swing is related to the latitude of the pendulum. The greater the latitude, the greater the change in direction per hour. At the equator, there is no change in the direction of a pendulum's swing.

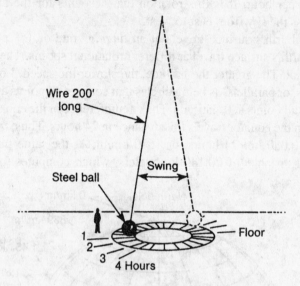

**Figure 9-18**. A Foucault Pendulum.

**Coriolis Effect.** Because the rotational speed of Earth is different at different latitudes, matter moving over Earth's surface seem to be deflected from a straight-line path. To illustrate, imagine a rocket being fired due north from a latitude of 30°N at a target at a latitude of 60°N. Recall that these two locations are traveling at different rotational speeds. Even before it is fired, the rocket is moving east at a speed of 1451 km/hr. The target is moving east at a speed of 839 km/hr.

When the rocket is fired, it will continue to move east at 1451 km/hr, even as it moves north. This means that the rocket will be traveling in an easterly direction at a faster rate than the target is moving in that direction. The net effect will be that the rocket will land east of the target. As shown in Figure 9-19, the path of the rocket appears to be deflected to the right of its intended path, which was due north.

The tendency of matter moving across Earth's surface to be deflected from a straight-line path is called the **Coriolis Effect**, and is caused by Earth's rotation. Deflection is to the right in the Northern Hemisphere and to the left in the Southern Hemisphere. The Coriolis Effect is responsible for the circular patterns of ocean currents, the global wind patterns, and the motion of the Foucault Pendulum.

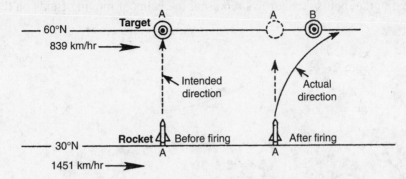

**Figure 9-19.** A rocket fired due north will appear to follow a curved path. The rocket will be deflected to the right in the Northern Hemisphere.

**Other evidence.** A satellite placed in a polar orbit can show that Earth is rotating, because different locations pass under the cameras every hour. Other indirect evidence of Earth's rotation includes the cycle of day and night and star-trail photos.

The geocentric model does not explain such apparent terrestrial motions as the Coriolis Effect and rotation of the Foucault Pendulum. Also, the need for epicycles to explain retrograde motion makes the model very complex.

The heliocentric model accounts for apparent terrestrial motions, such as the Foucault Pendulum and the Coriolis Effect, and is simpler than the geocentric model in many respects.

## QUESTIONS

1. The following diagram represents a Foucault Pendulum in a building in New York State. Points A and A¹ are fixed points on the floor. As the pendulum swings for six hours, it will

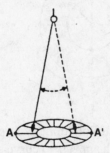

    (1) appear to change position due to Earth's rotation
    (2) appear to change position due to Earth's revolution
    (3) continue to swing between A and A¹ due to inertia
    (4) continue to swing between A and A¹ due to air pressure

**2.** In the diagram below, the arrows represent the paths of moving fluids on the surface of Earth.

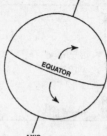

Which statement best explains why the fluid is deflected?

(1) Earth is rotating on its axis.
(2) The axis of Earth is tilted.
(3) Earth is revolving around the Sun.
(4) Earth is moving away from the Sun.

Base your answers to questions 3 and 4 on your knowledge of Earth Science and the diagram below. The diagram represents the entire Northern Hemisphere of Earth, as viewed by an observer directly over the North Pole.

The letters represent positions on the surface of Earth.
The numbers represent stationary positions in space directly above Earth's surface.

The curved arrows indicate the direction of Earth's rotation on its axis.

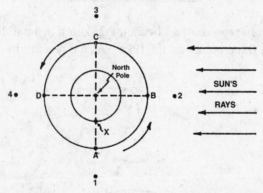

**3.** A rocket is fired from the North Pole directly at point A. To an observer at point X on Earth's surface, the rocket's path appears to curve and it misses point A. This is evidence that

(1) gravitational attraction varies over the surface of Earth
(2) Earth rotates on its axis
(3) Earth orbits around the Sun in an elliptical path
(4) differences in air pressure exist between the North Pole and point A

4. A Foucault Pendulum is set in motion at the North Pole so that it traces a path along line D-B. After six hours, an observer in space directly over the North Pole would see the pendulum tracing a path between positions

(1) 1 and 2          (2) 1 and 3          (3) 2 and 4          (4) 3 and 4

5. As one moves from the poles toward the equator, the velocity of Earth's surface caused by Earth's rotation

(1) decreases          (2) increases          (3) remains the  same

6. The Coriolis Effect would be influenced most by a change in Earth's

(1) rate of rotation                    (2) period of revolution
(3) angle of tilt                       (4) average surface temperature

7. Planet X is similar in all respects to Earth except that it does *not* rotate on its axis. A Foucault Pendulum is allowed to swing freely on planet X. After 6 hours of swinging, the path of the pendulum's swing, as seen by an observer on planet X, will be

(1) the same as the original path
(2) 90° to the right of the original path
(3) 90° to the left of the original path
(4) 180° to the right of the original path

8. Which diagram best represents a heliocentric model of a portion of the solar system? [Key: E = Earth, P = Planet, S = Sun. Diagrams are not drawn to scale.]

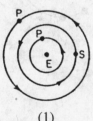
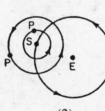
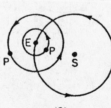
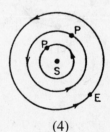

(1)                    (2)                    (3)                    (4)

9. In the geocentric model (Earth at the center of the Universe), which motion would occur?

(1) Earth would revolve around the Sun.
(2) Earth would rotate on its axis.
(3) The Moon would revolve around the Sun.
(4) The Sun would revolve around Earth.

Base your answers to question 10 on the diagrams below, which represent two views of a swinging Foucault Pendulum with a ring of 12 pegs at its base.

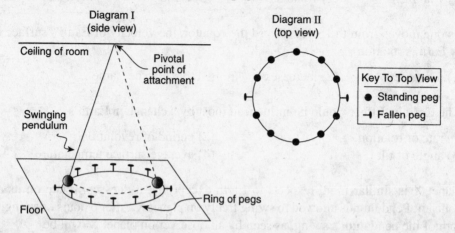

10. Diagram II shows two pegs tipped over by the swinging pendulum at the beginning of the demonstration. Which diagram shows the pattern of standing pegs and fallen pegs after several hours?

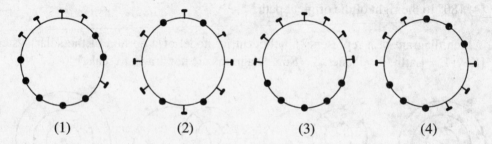

**11.** The diagram below shows some examples of how surface winds are deflected in the Northern and Southern Hemispheres because of Earth's rotation.

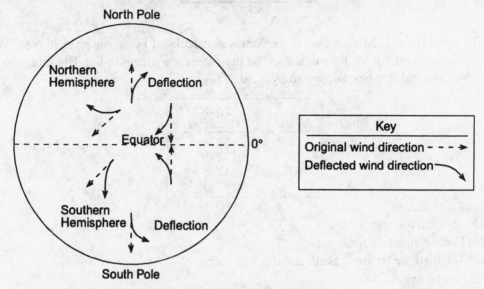

Earth's rotation causes winds to be deflected to the

(1) right in both the Northern and Southern Hemispheres
(2) right in the Northern Hemisphere and left in the Southern Hemisphere
(3) Left in the Northern Hemisphere and right in the Southern Hemisphere
(4) left in both the Northern and Southern Hemispheres

## Apparent Diameter

When observed through a telescope, the diameters of the planets seem to change in a cyclic manner. These changes are *apparent*. The **apparent diameter** of an object is the diameter the object *appears* to have, not its actual diameter. As with any object, the closer the planet is to the observer, the larger it appears to be. As the planets revolve in their orbits around the Sun, their distances from Earth vary. The closer a planet is to Earth, the larger its apparent diameter; the more distant the planet, the smaller its apparent diameter. Several of the planets have identifiable objects on their surfaces, the most notable being the Great Red Spot on the surface of Jupiter. When observed over a period of time, these identifiable objects appear to change positions on the surfaces of the planets. These apparent changes in position occur in a cyclic fashion and indicate that the planets are rotating.

# QUESTIONS

1. The apparent angular diameter of the Sun was calculated by an observer in New York State once a month for four months. The diameters are shown in the data table below. Which statement is best supported by the data?

| Month | Apparent Diameter |
|-------|-------------------|
| 1 | 32'16" |
| 2 | 32'30" |
| 3 | 32'35" |
| 4 | 32'31" |

(1) Earth rotates
(2) The Sun rotates
(3) Earth is tilted $23\frac{1}{2}$ degrees
(4) The distance between Earth and the Sun varies

2. Diagrams A through D below represent phases of a planet as seen by an observer on Earth using a telescope. The diagram is drawn to scale.

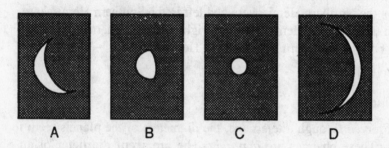

A          B          C          D

Which is the most logical conclusion about this planet?

(1) The planet has a slower orbital velocity than Earth.
(2) The planet is closest to Earth at position C.
(3) The apparent diameter of the planet varies throughout the year.
(4) The planet does not rotate on its axis

# Motions of the Sun

Due to Earth's rotation, the Sun, like all celestial objects, appears to move in an arc across the sky from east to west at a rate of 15 degrees per hour. Because Earth's axis is tilted at an angle of $23^1/_2°$ from the vertical, the location (latitude) at which the direct rays of the Sun strike Earth's surface changes in a cyclic pattern. This pattern is responsible for the seasons. Three factors cause the seasonal changes on Earth - the revolution of Earth around the Sun, the tilt of Earth's axis, and the **parallelism** of Earth's axis (the axis remains parallel to its previous position as Earth revolves around the Sun). As Earth revolves around the Sun, different portions of its surface are tilted toward the Sun at different times of the year (see Figure 9-20). For example, during its summer, the Northern Hemisphere is tilted toward the Sun, and thus receives its most direct rays. During this same period, the Southern Hemisphere is tilted away from the Sun and is experiencing winter. In the Northern Hemisphere, the first day of summer is June 21. On this date, called the Summer Solstice, the noon Sun is directly overhead at $23^1/_2°$ degrees north latitude. Approximately six months later, Earth has traveled to the other end of its elliptical orbit, and the Northern Hemisphere is tilted away from the Sun. The first day of winter, December 21, is called the *Winter Solstice*. On this date, the noon Sun is directly overhead at $23^1/_2°$ south latitude. (This is the first day of summer in the Southern Hemisphere.)

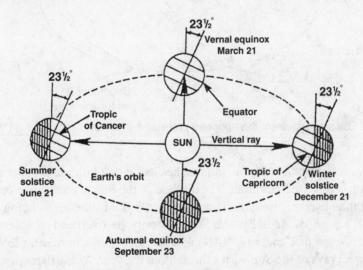

**Figure 9-20**. Earth's positions relative to the Sun on the dates of the seasonal changes.

On two days of the year, the noon Sun is directly overhead at the equator (0° latitude). These days are called *equinoxes*, because the hours of daylight and darkness are equal (12 hours) at all latitudes. The dates of the equinoxes are March 21 and September 23. These dates mark the first day of spring (Vernal Equinox) and the first day of fall (Autumnal Equinox), respectively, in the Northern Hemisphere.

The daily path traced by the Sun across the sky changes with the seasons. The Sun always rises in the east and sets in the west, but its position on the horizon at Sunrise and Sunset changes every day (see Figure 9-21). The position of the arc traced by the Sun's daily path across the sky also changes. When viewed from any position on Earth's surface, the longer the Sun's daily path across the sky, the longer the period of daylight. The day with the longest period of daylight in the Northern Hemisphere is June 21; that with the shortest period is December 21. At the equator, there are always approximately 12 hours of daylight and 12 hours of darkness.

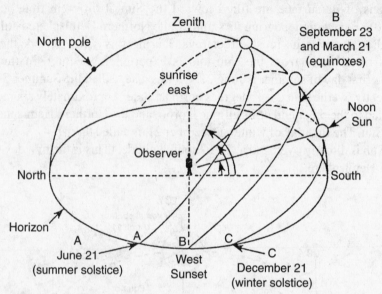

**Figure 9-21.** The arcs represent the apparent paths of the Sun across the sky on the dates indicated.

At any location on Earth, the Sun reaches its highest altitude at **solar noon**, the moment when the Sun crosses the meridian. The altitude of the Sun at solar noon depends on the time of year and the observers latitude. People often think of the Sun as being directly overhead (altitude 90°) at noon. Actually, the Sun can only be overhead at solar noon at latitudes between the Tropic of Cancer (23$\frac{1}{2}$°N) and the Tropic of Capricorn (23$\frac{1}{2}$°S). The latitude receiving direct rays of the Sun varies throughout the year. As Earth revolves around the Sun, the tilt of Earth's axis causes the Sun to migrate between 23$\frac{1}{2}$°N (on June 21) to 23$\frac{1}{2}$°S (on December 21). It takes the Sun about 4 days to migrate one degree of latitude. In other words, the Sun moves through about one-quarter of a degree of latitude per day. This information can be used to help calculate the latitude of the Sun's direct rays on any given day.

Seasonal variations in several observations of the Sun as viewed from locations in the Northern Hemisphere are listed in Table 9-3.

## Seasonal Observations of the Sun from The Northern Hemisphere

| Approximate Date | Latitude of Sun's Direct Ray | Direction of Sunrise and Sunset | Altitude of Noon Sun | Period of Daylight |
|---|---|---|---|---|
| September 23 (Autumnal Equinox) | Equator (0°) | Rises due E Sets due W | About 45° | 12 hours |
| December 21 (Winter Solstice) | Tropic of Capricorn (23 1/2°S) | Rises S of E Sets S of W | Smallest angle (lowest in sky) | less than 12 hours (shortest day) |
| March 21 (Vernal Equinox) | Equator (0°) | Rises due E Sets due W | About 45 | 12 hours |
| June 21 (Summer Solstice) | Tropic of Cancer (23 1/2°N) | Rises N of E Sets N of W | Largest angle (highest in sky) | More than 12 hours (longest day) |

TABLE 9-3

## QUESTIONS

1. From September to November, the Sun's altitude at noon in the Northern Hemisphere

   (1) decreases      (2) increases      (3) remains the same

2. Earth's axis of rotation is tilted 23½° from a line perpendicular to the plane of its orbit. What would be the result if the tilt were only 13½°?

   (1) shorter days and longer nights at the equator
   (2) colder winters and warmer summers in New York State
   (3) less difference between winter and summer temperatures in New York State
   (4) an increase in the amount of solar radiation received by Earth

3. New York State has several more hours of daylight in summer than in winter. Which statement helps explain this observation?

   (1) Earth is tilted on its axis.
   (2) The distance between Earth and the Sun varies.
   (3) The diameter of the Sun appears to change.
   (4) The speed of Earth in its orbit changes.

Base your answers to questions 4 through 6 on your knowledge of Earth Science and on the diagrams below. The diagrams represent plastic hemisphere models. Lines have been drawn to show the apparent path of the Sun across the sky on June 21 for observers at four different Earth locations. The zenith (Z) is the point in the sky directly over the observer.

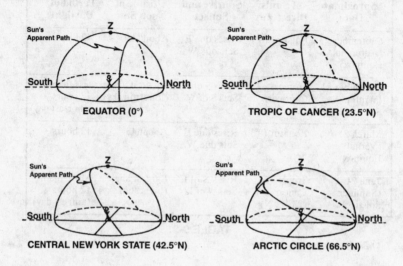

4. At which location will the longest noontime shadow be observed?

   (1) Equator                    (2) Tropic of Cancer
   (3) central New York State     (4) Arctic Circle

5. Which location will receive the greatest intensity of insolation at solar noon?

   (1) Equator                    (2) Tropic of Cancer
   (3) central New York State     (4) Arctic Circle

6. In three months, the length of a day in central New York State will be

   (1) shorter, because the Sun will rise and set farther south
   (2) shorter, because the Sun will rise and set farther north
   (3) longer, because the Sun will rise and set farther south
   (4) longer, because the Sun will rise and set farther north

Base your answers to questions 7 through 9 on your knowledge of Earth Science and the diagram below. The diagram represents Earth at a specific time in its orbit with dash lines indicating radiation from the Sun and points A through H, locations on Earth's surface.

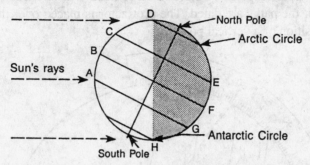

7. What is the season in the Northern Hemisphere when the Earth is in the position shown in the diagram?

   (1) spring          (2) summer        (3) fall             (4) winter

8. When the Sun is in the position shown in the diagram, how many hours of daylight would occur at the North Pole during one complete rotation?

   (1) 0              (2) 8              (3) 12            (4) 24

9. Six months after the date indicated by the diagram, which point would receive the Sun's vertical rays at noon?

   (1) A             (2) B             (3) C            (4) D

10. The diagram below represents four positions of Earth as it revolves around the Sun.

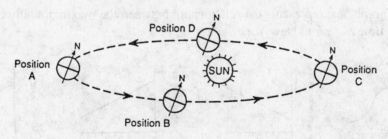

(NOT DRAWN TO SCALE)

At which position is Earth located on December 21?

   (1) A             (2) B             (3) C            (4) D

Base your answers to questions 11 through 12 on your knowledge of Earth Science and the diagram below. The diagram represents a plastic hemisphere upon which lines have been drawn to show the apparent paths of the Sun on four days at one location in the Northern Hemisphere. Two of the paths are dated. The protractor is placed over the north-south line. X represents the position of a vertical post.

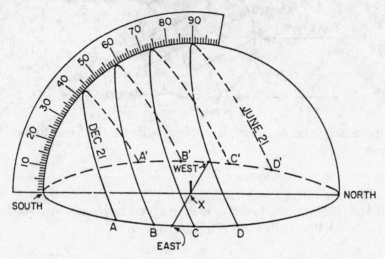

**11.** How many degrees does the altitude of the Sun change from December 21 to June 21?

    (1) 43°            (2) 47°            (3) 66½°            (4) 74°

**12.** What is the latitude of this location?

    (1) 0°            (2) 23½°N          (3) 66½°N         (4) 90°N

**13.** Which graph best represents the relationship between the maximum altitude of the Sun and the time of year in New York State?

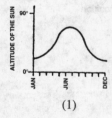
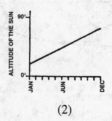
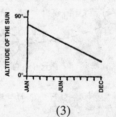
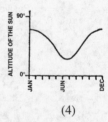

       (1)                    (2)                    (3)                    (4)

Base your answers to questions 14 through 16 on your knowledge of Earth Science and the diagram below. The diagram represents the apparent angular diameter of the Sun as measured by an observer on Earth during one year.

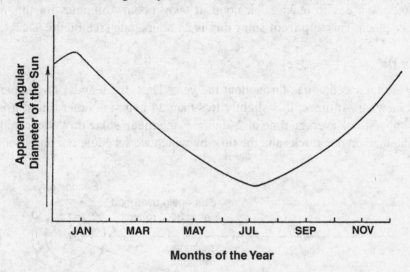

**14.** How did the apparent angular diameter of the Sun change from June to September?

(1) It decreased steadily.       (2) It decreased, then increased.
(3) It increased steadily.        (4) It remained the same.

**15.** The apparent diameter of the Sun decreases as the distance between the observer and the Sun

(1) decreases        (2) increases        (3) remains the same

**16.** The cyclic change in the apparent angular diameter of the Sun is a result of the

(1) Sun's daily rotational pattern        (2) Earth's daily rotational pattern
(3) Earth's circular orbit                      (4) Earth's slightly elliptical orbit

# TIME AND EARTH MOTIONS

Rotation and revolution of Earth provide the framework for measuring time. One revolution of Earth around the Sun takes 365¼ days, or one year. One rotation of Earth on its axis constitutes one day.

## Apparent Solar Day

Using the position of a given star on two successive nights, Earth makes one complete rotation on its axis in 23 hours, 56 minutes, and 4 seconds. This time period is called a **sidereal day** (see Figure 9-22). If Earth did not revolve around the Sun, this time period would represent one day. However, Earth does revolve. Because it is more convenient to use the Sun's position in the sky as a reference, one day is considered to be the time between two successive *solar noons* (when the Sun crosses the meridian). Thus, Earth must rotate a little more than 360° each day to reach solar noon. It takes about 4 minutes for this additional rotation to take place. This **apparent solar day** is 24 hours long (see Figure 9-22)

## Mean Solar Day

Earth's orbital speed varies throughout the year. Thus, the length of an apparent solar day varies somewhat. At times, it is slightly less than 24 hours; at other times, it is slightly more than 24 hours. The average time of 24 hours is the **mean solar day**. Mean solar time is the time maintained on our clocks and the time by which we schedule our daily activities.

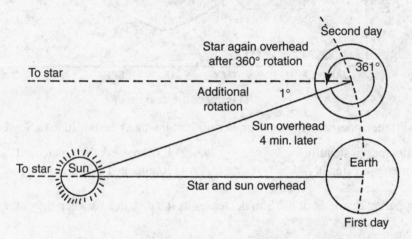

**Figure 9-22**. Because of Earth's motion in its orbit around the Sun, it must rotate through about 361° in order to complete a solar day. A solar day is almost 4 minutes longer than a sidereal day.

## QUESTIONS

1. As one moves from the equator toward the poles, the velocity of Earth's surface, in km/hr caused by Earth's rotation

   (1) decreases      (2) increases      (3) remains the same

2. The star Sirius is observed in the evening sky during the month of January. At the end of three hours, Sirius will appear to have moved

   (1) 60°      (2) 45°      (3) 3°      (4) 0°

3. What is the total number of degrees that Earth rotates on its axis during a 12-hour period?

   (1) 1°      (2) 15°      (3) 180°      (4) 360°

4. When does local solar noon always occur for an observer in New York State?

   (1) when the clock reads 12 noon
   (2) when the Sun reaches its maximum altitude
   (3) when the Sun is directly overhead
   (4) when the Sun is on the Prime Meridian

5. Which measurements would have the same values if taken at the same moment by one observer at 42°N, 74°W and another observer at 44°N, 74°W?

   (1) the altitude of Polaris          (2) the angle of insolation
   (3) the age of the surface bedrock   (4) the time of solar noon

6. What is the relationship between apparent solar time and mean solar time?

   (1) Apparent solar time is always ahead of mean solar time by a constant amount.
   (2) Apparent solar time is always behind mean solar time by a constant amount.
   (3) The difference between apparent solar time and mean solar time varies with the seasons.
   (4) There is no difference between apparent solar time and mean solar time.

7. A Sundial measures time based upon the position of the Sun in the sky. This time called

   (1) apparent solar time    (2) standard time
   (3) Greenwich time         (4) mean time

8. Upon which frame of reference is time based?

   (1) the motions of Earth    (2) the longitude of an observer
   (3) the motions of the Moon (4) the real motions of the Sun

# MOON AND ITS EFFECTS

## Moon Motions

When viewed from Earth on a daily basis, the Moon, like all celestial objects appears to move across the sky from east to west. When viewed against the background of stars over an extended period, the Moon appears to move eastward in an orbit around Earth, completing one orbit every 27$\frac{1}{3}$ days.

In reality, Earth and the Moon act like twin planets that revolve around a common center of gravity called the **barycenter** (see Figure 9-23). The barycenter of this Earth-Moon system is actually located about 1700 kilometers beneath Earth's surface. As the Moon makes one revolution around Earth, it also makes one rotation on its axis. Thus, the same side of the Moon is always facing Earth. The far side of the Moon has only been seen through satellite studies and manned space flights. Because the Moon does wobble a bit over a period of time, 59% of its surface has been seen from Earth.

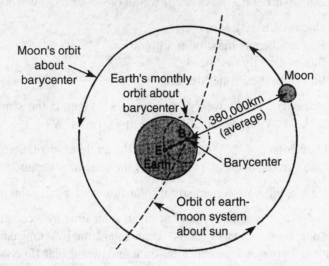

**Figure 9-23.** The Earth-Moon system rotates around the barycenter.

The Moon revolves around Earth in an elliptical orbit with a period of approximately one month. The word "month" has an origin in "moon-th". Because Earth moves in its orbit around the Sun as the Moon revolves around Earth, the Moon must actually travel farther than one revolution to complete a cycle of phases. It takes the Moon only $27\frac{1}{3}$ days to complete one revolution around Earth. This is called a **sidereal month**. The time required for the Moon to complete a cycle of phases is $29\frac{1}{2}$ days. This is called a **synodic month**.

The position of the Moon with respect to the Sun and Earth is responsible for Earth tides, Moon phases, and the occurrence of eclipses of both the Moon and the Sun.

The shape of the Moon's orbit around Earth is elliptical. Thus, the Earth-Moon distance does change as the Moon makes a revolution around Earth. Its closest, or **perigee**, distance is about 356,000 kilometers; its farthest, or **apogee**, distance is about 407,000 kilometers (see Figure 9-24). The Moon's apparent diameter changes with distance from Earth, appearing largest at perigee and smallest at apogee.

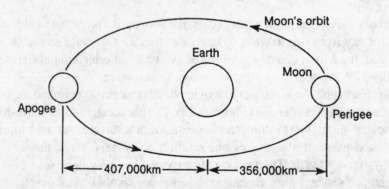

**Figure 9-24.** The Moon's orbit around Earth.

## Tides

The cyclic changes in Earth-Moon-Sun alignments are responsible for cyclic fluctuations in the **high** and **low tides** of oceans and other large bodies of water (see Figure 9-25). When Earth, Moon, and Sun are positioned in a straight line (new and full Moon phases), **spring tides** occur. Spring tides feature the largest range in ocean levels between high and low tides. When Earth, Moon, and Sun are at right angles to one another (quarter phases) **neap tides** occur. These tides show the smallest range of ocean levels between high and low tides.

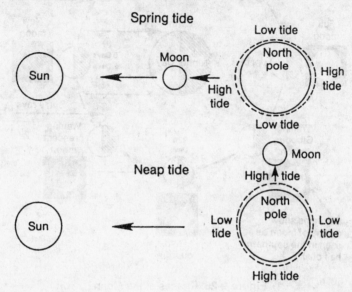

**Figure 9-25**. The relative positions of Earth, Moon, and Sun during spring tides and neap tides.

## Phases of the Moon

At any given time, half of the Moon's surface is illuminated by the Sun. As described earlier, the same side of the Moon always faces Earth. As the Moon revolves around Earth, the amount of the illuminated portion of the Moon that faces Earth varies in a cyclic fashion called **phases**. At the **new moon** phase, the entire illuminated portion of the Moon is facing away from Earth. During the **waxing** period, the right-hand portion of the Moon seems to grow, as more and more of the lighted portion becomes visible from Earth. At **full moon** phase, the entire lit portion of the Moon is facing Earth. During the **waning** period, the left-hand portion of the Moon seems to shrink, as less and less of the illuminated portion becomes visible from Earth. The new Moon phase marks the end of the waning period and the beginning of the waxing period once again (see Figure 9-26).

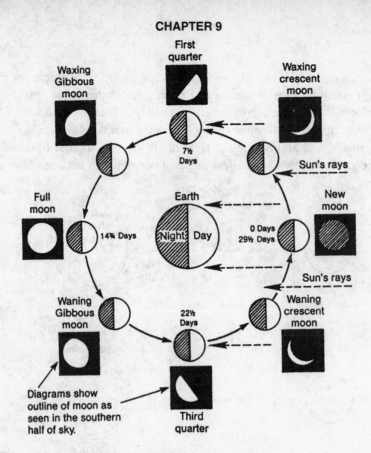

**Figure 9-26**. Phases of the Moon.

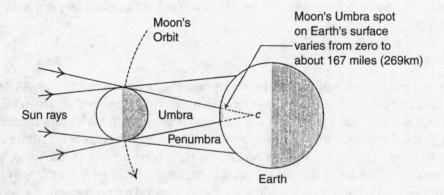

**Figure 9-27**. To observe a total solar eclipse, the observer must be in the Moon's umbra spot on Earth's surface, which varies from zero to about 167 miles. A partial solar eclipse will be observed when the observer is in the penumbral circle.

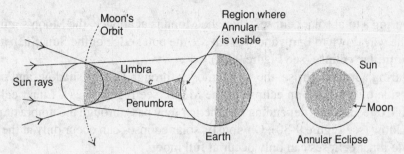

Figure 9-28. When the Moon's umbra does not reach Earth's surface, an annular eclipse is produced, because the Moon's apparent diameter is smaller than the Sun's.

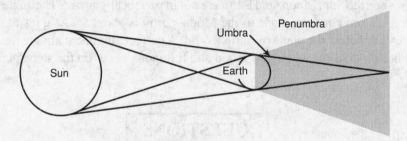

Figure 9-29. The umbra and penumbra of the shadow cones produced by the Sun's illumination of Earth and Moon.

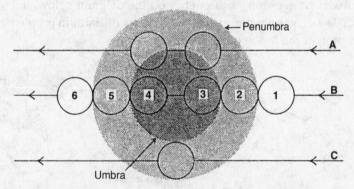

Figure 9-30. Cross-sectional view of Earth's shadow cone (umbra and penumbra), showing the Moon's paths for a partial eclipse (A), central total eclipse (B), and penumbral eclipse (C).

## Eclipses

For ancient man, <u>**eclipses**</u>, when "day turned into night", were certainly among the most terrifying of all natural phenomena. During a **solar eclipse**, the Moon passes directly between Earth and the Sun, and people standing in the path of the Moon's shadow see an eclipse of the Sun (see Figure 9-27). Because the Sun is a sphere and not a point of light, there are two parts of the Moon's shadow, the **umbra** (total darkness) and the **penumbra** (partial darkness). Only the very tip of the darkest part of the Moon's shadow touches Earth during a solar eclipse.

During a total solar eclipse, when the Moon is at apogee, the Moon's umbra does not reach all the way down to Earth and we will see the outer edge of the Sun. Such and eclipse is called an **annular eclipse** (see Figure 9-28).

During a **lunar eclipse**, the Moon moves through Earth's shadow, and people on the nighttime side of Earth see an eclipse of the Moon (see Figure 9-29). Lunar eclipses can be total, partial, or penumbra, depending on whether they pass through the umbra or penumbra of Earth's shadow (see Figure 9-30). Obviously, solar eclipses can occur only at the time of new moon while lunar eclipses can only occur at full moon.

With a full moon or a new moon every two weeks, we might wonder why we do not see an eclipse every 14 days. Most of the time, new moon and full moon phases occur under conditions when the Sun, Moon, and Earth are not in perfect alignment. The angle between the plane of Earth's orbit and the plane of the Moon's orbit is about 5°. As a result, the Moon is usually above or below the plane of Earth's orbit. A perfect alignment among the Sun, Moon, and Earth is only possible when new moon and full moon occur on the same plane as Earth.

## QUESTIONS

Base your answers to questions 1 through 4 on the diagram below and your knowledge of Earth Science. The diagram represents nine positions of Earth in orbit around the Sun during one complete orbit of the Moon on around Earth.

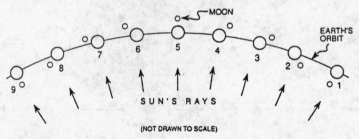

1. Which phase of the Moon will be seen from Earth at position 5?

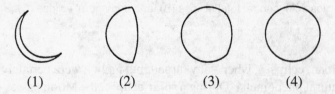

(1)          (2)          (3)          (4)

2. At which position might the Moon block part of the Sun, making a solar eclipse visible from Earth?

(1) 7          (2) 2          (3) 9          (4) 4

**3.** During the time that Earth travels from position 1 to position 9, an observer on Earth will see the illuminated portion of the Moon

(1) decrease, only

(2) increase, only

(3) decrease, then increase

(4) increase, then decrease

**4.** Earth rotates on its axis, causing the Moon to appear to rise each day. Moonrise occurs about 52 minutes later each day because as Earth completes one rotation, the Moon also

(1) completes one rotation on its axis

(2) wobbles on its axis

(3) is inclined $23\frac{1}{2}°$

(4) revolves part way around Earth

**5.** The phases of the Moon are caused by the

(1) Earth's revolution around the Sun

(2) the Moon's revolution around Earth,

(3) Moons varying distance from Earth

(4) Sun's varying distance from the Moon

**6.** The diagram below shows the relative positions of Earth, Moon, and Sun for a 1-month period.

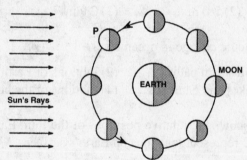

Which diagram best represents the appearance of the Moon at position P when viewed from Earth?

(1)　　　　(2)　　　　(3)　　　　(4)

Base your answers to questions 7 and 8 on the graph below. The graph shows changes in ocean level (tides) at a beach.

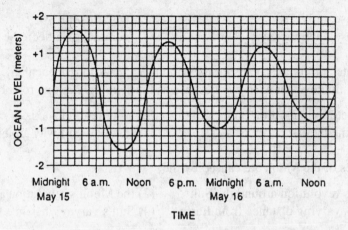

7. On May 15, what is the difference in ocean level between low tide at 10 a.m. and high tide at 4 p.m.?

(1) 1.0 m        (2) 2.0 m        (3) 2.9 m        (4) 3.9 m

8. What causes this periodic change in ocean level?

(1) changing wind and storm paths        (2) motions of Earth and Moon
(3) frequent earthquakes and tsunamis        (4) motions of the crust and mantle

9. The diagram below shows the relative positions of the Sun, Earth, and Moon in space. Letters A, B, C and D represent locations on Earth's surface.

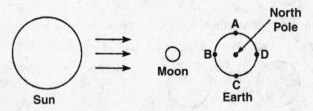

(not drawn to scale)

At which location would an observer on Earth have the best chance of seeing a total solar eclipse?

(1) A        (2) B        (3) C        (4) D

**10.** The diagram below shows Earth, the Moon, and the Sun's rays as viewed from space.

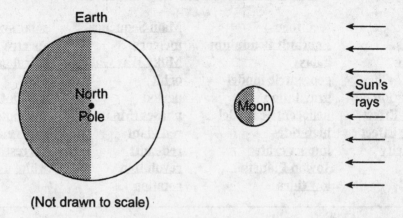

**(Not drawn to scale)**

For observers on Earth, which phase of the Moon is represented by the diagram?

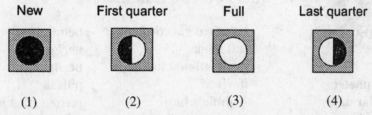

**New**          **First quarter**          **Full**          **Last quarter**

(1)                    (2)                    (3)                    (4)

**11.** Why are impact structures more obvious on the Moon than on Earth?

(1) The Moon's gravity is stronger than Earth's gravity
(2) The Moon has little or no atmosphere.
(3) The rocks on the Moon are weaker than those on Earth.
(4) The Moon rotates at a slower rate than Earth does.

**12.** The diagram below shows Earth as viewed from above the North Pole (NP). Points A and B are locations on Earth's surface.

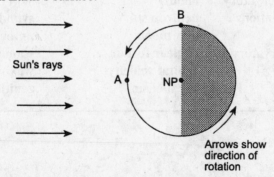

Sun's rays

Arrows show
direction of
rotation

At location A, the time is 12 noon. What is the time at location B?

(1) 6 a.m.          (2) 6 p.m.          (3) 3 p.m.          (4) 12 midnight

# CHAPTER 9 - CORE VOCABULARY

| | | | |
|---|---|---|---|
| altitude | foci (focus) | Main Sequence | solar system |
| asteroids | Foucault Pendulum | meteors | spectra |
| Big Bang | galaxy | Milky Way Galaxy | spiral galaxies |
| comets | geocentric model | orbit | Sun |
| constellation | gravitation | period | sunspot cycle |
| Coriolis Effect | heliocentric model | phases (Moon) | sunspots |
| Doppler Effect | high tides | red giant | supergiant |
| eccentricity | impact crater | red-shift | Terrestrial Planets |
| eclipses | Jovian Planets | revolution | white dwarf |
| ellipse | low tides | rotation | |

# HELPFUL VOCABULARY

| | | |
|---|---|---|
| annular eclipse | elliptical galaxies | penumbra |
| aphelion | full moon | perigee |
| apogee | gravitational force | perihelion |
| apparent diameter | horizon | pulsar |
| apparent solar day | Hubble's Law | retrograde motion |
| arc | Hubble Space Telescope | siderial day |
| Astronomical Unit (AU) | irregular galaxies | siderial month |
| astronomy | light year | solar eclipse |
| azimuth | lunar eclipse | solar noon |
| barycenter | mean solar day | Space Infrared Telescope |
| black hole | meteorites | Facility |
| blue shift | meteoroids | spring tide |
| celestial sphere | neap tide | star trails |
| Chandra X-ray Observatory | nebula | supernova |
| circumpolar constellations | neutron star | synodic month |
| circumpolar stars | new moon | umbra |
| Compton Ray Observatory | nuclear fusion | waning |
| ecliptic | orbital velocity | waxing |
| ecosphere | parallelism | zenith |

## PRACTICE FOR CONSTRUCTED RESPONSE

Base your a answers to questions 1 and 2 on the diagram below, your knowledge of Earth Science and the *Earth Science Reference Tables*. The diagram represents Earth's tilt on its axis and shows the directions to the Sun and to the Moon on a particular day of the year. The shaded portion represents the nighttime side of Earth.

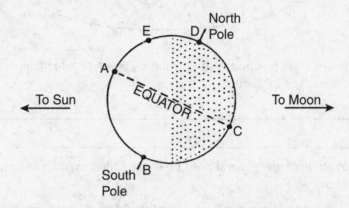

1. Describe why an observer at Point B would be unable to photograph the Moon at any time during the following 24 hours.

   _____

   _____

   _____

   _____

2. **a.** On the date represented by the diagram, how do the number of daylight hours at location A compare to the number of daylight hours at location E?

   _____

   _____

   **b.** Describe how the answer to (a) above was determined.

   _____

   _____

   _____

   _____

Base your answers to questions 3 through 5 on the diagram below and your knowledge of Earth Science. The diagram shows four positions of Earth in its orbit around the Sun. The diagram indicated relative positions of Earth to the Sun, but *the diagram has not been drawn to scale.*

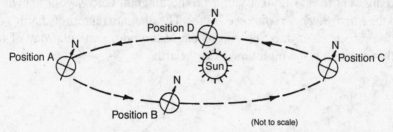

(Not to scale)

3. As Earth moves from position B to position C, describe what happens to the intensity of insolation received by Earth.

_____

_____

4. On the diagram, draw the general position of the Moon in order to create a solar eclipse on Earth at Position C.

5. On the diagram, draw the general position of the Moon in order for someone on Earth at Position A to see a full moon.

Base your answers to questions 6 through 8 on the diagram below and your knowledge of Earth Science. The diagram represents the apparent path of the Sun at three different dates during the year as it appears to an observer in New York State. The paths are labeled I, II, III and letters A through G are points on the paths. Path II occurs on March 21.

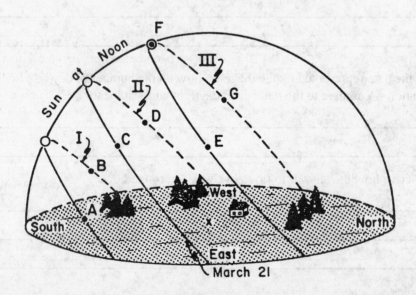

**6.** Describe the causes that change the apparent path of the sun across the sky on a daily basis.

_____

_____

_____

**7.** Of paths I, II, and III, describe the evidence which indicates that path AB has the shortest period of daylight, and path EG as the longest.

_____

_____

**8.** The Sun is at point F, which is the maximum altitude of the Sun for the next year. A vertical stick is placed at location X and the stick's shadow is measured each noon for the next 30 days. (Describe what causes the length of the shadow to become longer each day.)

_____

_____

**a.** What happens to the length of the sticks shadow?

_____

**b.** What causes the length of the shadow to change each day?

_____

_____

Base your answers to questions 9 and 10 on the data table below and on your knowledge of Earth Science. The table lists some information about the planets in the solar system. The revolution period of the planet Uranus has been deliberately left blank.

### DATA TABLE OF SOLAR SYSTEM

| | MERCURY | VENUS | EARTH | MARS | JUPITER | SATURN | URANUS | NEPTUNE | PLUTO |
|---|---|---|---|---|---|---|---|---|---|
| Mean Distance from Sun (millions of kilometers) | 57.9 | 108.2 | 149.6 | 227.9 | 778.3 | 1,427 | 2,869 | 4,496 | 5,900 |
| Period of Revolution | 88 days | 224.7 days | 365.26 days | 687 days | 11.86 years | 29.46 years | | 164.8 years | 247.7 years |
| Rotation Period | 59 days | 243 days | 23 hours 56 minutes 4 seconds | 24 hours 37 minutes 23 seconds | 9 hours 50 minutes 30 seconds | 10 hours 14 minutes | 11 hours | 16 hours | 6 days 9 hours |
| Eccentricity of Orbit | .206 | .007 | .017 | .093 | .048 | .056 | .047 | .009 | .250 |
| Equatorial Diameter (kilometers) | 4,880 | 12,104 | 12,756 | 6,787 | 142,800 | 120,000 | 47,100 | 48,400 | 2,400(?) |

**9.** What is the period of revolution for Uranus (left blank on, the chart).

_____

_____

**10. a.** On the orbital paths below, draw the relative positions of the 4 planets nearest the Sun.

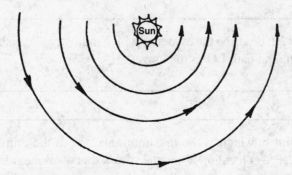

   **b.** Of the nine planets listed, which one is most Earth like? Justify your answer with the information from the Data Table.

_____

_____

Base your answers to questions 11 through 13 on the diagram below and your knowledge of Earth Science. The diagram represents the elliptical orbit of a weather satellite around Earth. Letters A through D represent locations on the satellite's orbit. $F_1$ and $F_2$ are the foci of the satellite's orbit.

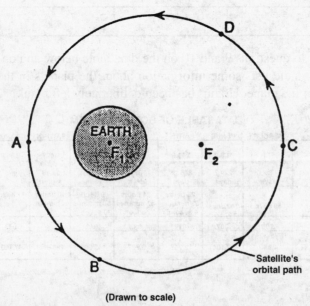

(Drawn to scale)

**11.** Why is the satellite's orbit speed the greatest at point A?

_____

_____

**12.** Calculate the eccentricity of the satellite's orbit using the following directions:

    **a.** Write the equation for eccentricity.

    **b.** Substitute data from the diagram into the equation

    **c.** Calculate the eccentricity.

    **d.** Label your answer with the proper units (if any)

**13.** Describe what happens to the gravitational attraction between Earth and the satellite as the satellite travels from A, through B, C and D, and returns to A.

_____

_____

_____

**14.** In its orbit around the Sun, Earth revolves just under 1° per day. Describe how the value of just under 1° per is determined.

_____

_____

_____

**15.** In the Northern Hemisphere, Earth is farthest from the Sun in summer. Explain how at that time in the Northern Hemisphere Earth's temperatures are the highest.

_____

_____

_____

16. The group of stars known as the Big Dipper can be used to locate the North Star (Polaris) in the night sky. On the diagram of the Big Dipper below, draw a straight arrow passing through two stars to indicate the direction to Polaris.

Base your answers to questions 17 through 19 on the tables below. Table 1 shows the average distance from the Sun in Astronomical Units (AU) and the average orbital speed in kilometers per second (km/s) of the nine planets in our solar system. Table 2 lists five large asteroids and their average distances from the Sun.

Table 1

| Planet | Average Distance from Sun (AU) | Average Orbital Speed (km/s) |
|---|---|---|
| Mercury | 0.4 | 48.0 |
| Venus | 0.7 | 35.0 |
| Earth | 1.0 | 30.0 |
| Mars | 1.5 | 24.0 |
| Jupiter | 5.2 | 13.0 |
| Saturn | 9.6 | 10.0 |
| Uranus | 19.0 | 7.0 |
| Neptune | 30.0 | 5.1 |
| Pluto | 39.0 | 4.7 |

Table 2

| Asteroid | Average Distance from Sun (AU) |
|---|---|
| Ceres | 2.8 |
| Pallas | 2.8 |
| Vesta | 2.4 |
| Hygiea | 3.2 |
| Juno | 2.7 |

**17.** On the grid below, plot the average distance from the Sun and the average orbital speed for each of the nine planets listed in Table 1. Connect the nine points with a line.

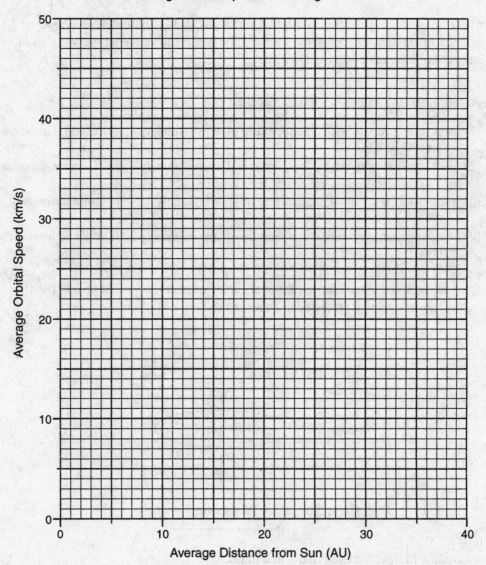

Planets' Average Orbital Speed vs. Average Distance from Sun

**18.** State the relationship between a planet's average distance from the Sun and the planet's average orbital speed.

_____

_____

**19.** The orbits of the asteroids listed in table 2 are located between two adjacent planetary orbits. State the names of the two planets.

_____ and _____

Base your answers to questions 20 and 21 on the "Luminosity and Temperature of Stars" graph in the *Earth Science Reference Tables*. The graph shows the temperature and relative brightness of many stars observed from Earth.

**20.** According to the graph, the Sun is classified as a _____

(1) main sequence star with a temperature of approximately 4,000°C and a luminosity of 100
(2) main sequence star with a temperature of approximately 6,000°C and a luminosity of 1
(3) white dwarf star with a temperature of approximately 10,000°C and luminosity of 0.01
(4) blue supergiant star with a temperature of approximately 20,000°C and luminosity of 700,000

**21.** Stars are believed to undergo evolutionary changes over millions of years. The flowchart below shows stages of predicted changes in the Sun.

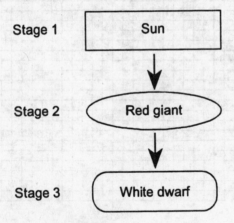

According to this flowchart, the Sun will become _____

(1) hotter and brighter in stage 2, then cooler and dimmer in stage 3
(2) cooler and dimmer in stage 2, then hotter and brighter in stage 3
(3) hotter and dimmer in stage 2, then cooler and brighter in stage 3
(4) cooler and brighter in stage 2, then hotter and dimmer in stage 3

Base your answers to questions 22 through 24 on the diagram below, which represents Mars' orbit around the Sun.

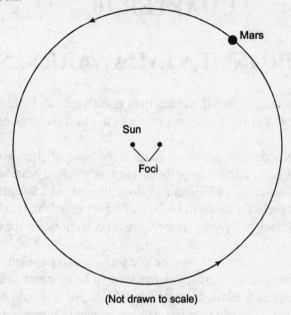

(Not drawn to scale)

**22.** On the diagram above

   **a.** Draw and label the major axis of Mars' orbit.
   **b.** Place an X on the orbit to show the location of Mars' greatest orbital velocity.

**23.** State the difference between the shape (not size) of Earth's orbit and the shape of Mars' orbit.

_____

_____

**24.** The bar graph to the right shows the equatorial diameter of Earth. On the grid below, construct the bar that represents the equatorial diameter of Mars.

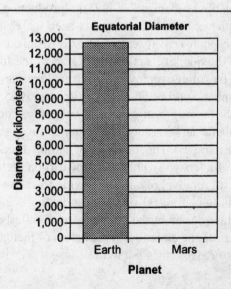

# CHAPTER 10

# ENVIRONMENTAL AWARENESS

Good science often raises more questions than it answers. But these questions can be used to guide our attempts to investigate and preserve the best possible environment for us here on Earth.

One of the most hotly debated topics on Earth is the issue of climate change. Scientists can point out many changes in climate over the last few years. And what about the future? It has been reported that: the snows of Kilimanjaro may be gone in 15 years; that by the year 2025, ninety percent of the glacier ice on the Alps may have melted; and that a glacier in South America is retreating 500 feet every year. Some climate projections for the next century show warming of 1° to 3.5°C.

Overall, the impacts of climate change on our forests, fish population, and agriculture could be extreme. For example the growing seasons might be longer, but it would also bring risks such as moisture deficits, pests, diseases, and fires. There would be changes in fish populations, up in some places, down in others. Higher temperatures would mean lower water levels in the St. Lawrence River which would affect shipping and navigation on the Great Lakes. Coastal New York would be vulnerable to rising sea levels, which would possibly cause increased flooding, coastal erosion and coastal sedimentation

Some point to the greenhouse effect as the problem. Yet, without the natural greenhouse effect, the temperature of Earth would be about zero degrees F (-18°C) instead of its present 58°F (15°C). The concern, however, is not with the fact that we have a greenhouse effect, but the question is whether human activities are enhancing it.

Temperature and precipitation patterns are altered by human influences including deforestation, urbanization, and the production of greenhouse gases such as carbon dioxide and methane. Human activity has been increasing the concentration of greenhouse gases in the atmosphere (mostly carbon dioxide from combustion of fossil fuels) as well as other gases. Carbon dioxide levels prior to the start of the Industrial Revolution were about 280 parts per million by volume (ppmv), and current levels are about 370 ppmv. According to some experts, this number could be doubled by the year 2065.

The amounts of greenhouse gases, such as carbon dioxide and methane in the atmosphere can be reduced by either controlling emissions or by increasing the rate at which they are removed. The reduction of carbon dioxide emissions could be achieved by improving energy efficiency; switching to low carbon fuels or switching to non-carbon fuels. Increasing the rate of removal of carbon dioxide from the atmosphere through the growth of terrestrial biomass (e.g. forests) or biomass in the oceans would also reduce the concentration of greenhouse gases in the atmosphere. Similarly, there is a range of measures which would reduce methane emissions. Production of methane could be limited, leakage better controlled and captured and then put to use.

Global surface temperatures have increased about 0.6°C. since the late 19th century, and about one half degree over the past 25 years. The recent warmth in the northeast has been assisted by the El Niño of 1997-98. Although El Niños are not caused by global warming, it has been hypothesized that warmer global sea surface temperatures enhance El Niño effects. A rather abrupt change in El Niño behavior occurred in about 1976 and the new behavior has continued. For example, there have been more frequent episodes since that time.

Global mean sea level has been rising at an average rate of 1 to 2 mm/year over the past 100 years, which is significantly larger than the rate averaged over the last thousand years. Some scientists project that there will be as much as a 0.5 meter sea level rise in the 21st century, but estimates vary widely.

# INTERDEPENDENCE OF EARTH'S LIVING AND NON-LIVING SYSTEMS

The planet Earth stands out as a bright blue ball in the black void of space. Its surface is like a kaleidoscope–constantly changing color as Earth turns and the clouds move over its surface. Radiation from the Sun flooding it supports life on Earth, not so far away from the Sun to be too cold and not so close that the heat is intolerable for life to survive. Earth is protected from ultraviolet radiation by an atmosphere unlike no other in the solar system.

Move in close and the outlines of deserts, flatlands, mountains and seas transform into grasslands, forests, croplands, rivers, lakes, estuaries and oceans. Each is different physically and biologically. Each is inhabited by different organisms and uniquely adapted to the environments in which they live; however, they are all interdependent on each other. The energy and nutrients in one area may find their way to another so that all parts of Earth are interrelated.

Man is a part of the natural systems. Every decision we make in social, economic and political life affects these systems, one way or another. Whatever we do–build a road, construct a city, dam up a river, cut a forest, develop an industry, reduce the ozone in the atmosphere, pollute the air, water or land–we influence or change the systems supporting life on Earth.

Our planet consists of a great variety of living and nonliving systems related through the environmental changes. Changing any part of the natural environment can cause dramatic effects on other parts of the environment. Technology increases our quality of life while it causes stress on the natural environment. We need to use our technology to observe, monitor and understand our planet.

## Pollution

**Pollution** is the concentration of any material or energy form that is ultimately harmful to humans. We can classify contamination as ground, water or air pollution. Pollution and other environmental changes are more dramatic in places of industrialization and high population density. In general, our cities have experienced the greatest severity of environmental problems. Air and water contamination are most severe in these places.

# Land Pollution

Garbage, refuse, and sludge products from agriculture, forestry, mining, and municipalities are all examples of **solid wastes** which can pollute the land. Waste created by most communities consists of paper and paper products such as newspapers and packaging materials. Other solid wastes include food remains, plastics, glass, metals, textiles and yard wastes. As populations grow, more garbage is produced which must be disposed of properly. At first, dumping occurred in open land sites. But open dumping supported large populations of rats, insects and other unwanted organisms. Foul odors filled the air close to these dumps and rainfall carried pollutants from the garbage into the ground water.

To solve this problem, **sanitary landfills**, sites where wastes are disposed of by burying them have been established. In a sanitary landfill, wastes are spread in layers about 3 meters deep and compacted. About 15 centimeters of soil is then spread on top of the refuse and compacted. This process is repeated until the mountain of garbage reached a predetermined height. The landfill is then closed and a final layer of soil, about 1 meter thick is placed over the entire area. Grass and trees are planted in the soil. To keep the methane gas which forms from building up the landfill, ventilation pipes are placed in to the ground to enable the methane gas to escape. At some landfills, the methane is collected and sold.

**Hazardous Wastes.** Solid, liquid or gaseous wastes that are potentially harmful to humans and the environment are **hazardous wastes**. In upstate New York, homes were built next to an old chemical waste dump called the Love Canal community. An elementary school and playground were built on top of the dump. After several years, an abnormally large number of cases of birth defects and cancer-related illnesses were reported by residents of the Love Canal community. Over 1,000 families were forced to evacuate and re-locate. Hazardous wastes can be classified into specific categories (see Table 10-1).

**Soil Erosion.** Overgrazing, deforestation, irrigation and excessive cultivation can cause soil erosion. These activities damage the land by disturbing the balance between living organisms and the soil. Soil protection methods used to prevent soil erosion include stripcropping, contour farming and terracing. With this, it is estimated that 2.5 billion tons of topsoil in the United States are washed away by water each year.

| WASTES | DESCRIPTION |
|---|---|
| reactive wastes | gunpowder or other wastes which can explode |
| corrosive wastes | battery acid, lye or other wastes that can eat through steel and many other materials |
| ignitable wastes | paints and other materials that can burst into flames at relatively low temperatures |
| toxic wastes | chemicals that are poisonous to people causing health problems such as birth-defects or cancer |
| radioactive wastes | radiation from materials in the Earth that can burn skin, destroy body cells and cause other problems |
| medical wastes | medicines, their containers, and lab specimens and equipment |

**TABLE 10-1**

# POLLUTION OF EARTH'S WATER

**Water pollution** is anything that makes the water unfit, harmful or undesirable for use.

## Sources of Water Pollutants

Pollutants are added to the hydrosphere through the activities of individuals, communities, and industrial processes. As the population density grows and the nation becomes more industrialized, the pollution of water becomes an increasingly greater problem, particularly near population centers.

In New York State, harmful toxic wastes placed in landfill dumps have contaminated the water supplies of a number of communities. Acid rains have lowered the pH of many New York lakes to the point that fish and other aquatic animals can no longer survive. In some locations, detergents have polluted the ground water due to inadequate disposal methods, making the water undrinkable. Although excessive radiation or an explosion are the major fears associated with nuclear power plants, a constant problem is the heated waste water, or **thermal pollution**, they add to the ground water and surface water.

It was once believed that large bodies of water, such as rivers, lakes, and even the oceans, could not be seriously polluted. The truth is that these waters can be drastically altered. Although the oceans are huge and can absorb many pollutants, most pollution occurs along the edges of the continents, where human activities are centered and pollutants concentrated.

## Types of Pollutants

Water pollutants include dissolved and suspended materials, Such as organic and inorganic wastes, thermal (heat) energy effluent (wastes) from industrial processes, radioactive substances, and the abnormal concentration of various organisms.

**Organic pollution**. Sewage is one of the most critical water pollution problems contaminating rivers, lakes and ground water. It is a major source of infectious organisms transmitted in human wastes, and, if the water is left untreated, they enter a community's water supply.

**Inorganic pollution**. Some detergents are **biodegradable**–easily decomposed by bacteria. However, detergents that are not biodegradable continue to produce suds and foam in the water of rivers and lakes, making it unfit to use.

Inorganic fertilizers add large amounts of nitrates to the soil. When these nitrates are dissolved in water used to prepare food, they can cause diseases such as anemia in infants. Lead and mercury wastes released into water have destroyed fish populations and caused such health problems as cancer and poisoning in humans and other animals. Oil spills have been a major cause of fish and bird destruction. Pesticides and herbicides have serious adverse effects on birds and marine life.

**Thermal pollution.** The major source of thermal pollution is the heated waste water released into the environment by electric power plants and industrial plants. The associated increase in water temperature adversely affects aquatic life directly, by killing or driving off organisms that cannot tolerate the higher temperatures and indirectly, by lowering the concentrations of dissolved oxygen in the water without which fish cannot survive.

**Radioactive substances.** Many radioactive substances retain high levels of radioactivity for millions of years. Thus, the safe storage and/or disposal of radioactive wastes presents a major problem. Most radioactive wastes are products of nuclear power plants and research facilities.

**Abnormal concentration of various organisms.** Certain disease causing organisms are often concentrated in toxic dumps. If these organisms find their way into the ground water, they can produce serious pollution of sources of drinking water.

## Aerobic and Anaerobic Bacteria

**Aerobic** bacteria are oxygen consuming organisms found in all bodies of water. If the temperature of a body of water is increased, the activity of these bacteria is also increased. This results in the dissolved oxygen being used up at a faster rate. As the oxygen is used up, other aquatic organisms including fish, that need oxygen to survive die out. Eventually, the aerobic bacteria are replaced by **anaerobic** bacteria, which can live without oxygen. These bacteria and their waste products become forms of pollutants.

## Eutrophication

Sewage effluents and fertilizers contain large amounts of phosphates and nitrates. When these substances are released into a lake or pond, they serve as nutrients for algae. The rapid increase in algae growth uses up dissolved oxygen, making the lake unfit for fish and other animals to survive. This process, known as **eutrophication**, usually takes hundreds or thousands of years under natural conditions. The addition of phosphates and nitrates as pollutants greatly speeds up this aging of a body of water.

## Concentration of Pollutants

Concentration of water pollutants increases in the vicinity of population centers. Human activities at all levels individual, community, and industry all contribute to the problem of pollution. Thus, as population density increases, the amount of pollution in rivers, lakes, ground water, and shore areas increases.

## Long-range Effects

If left uncontrolled, the increase of pollution in the hydrosphere would eventually create a situation in which most of Earth's water would be unfit for human use. In recent years, legislation at all levels of government has been directed toward cleaning up polluted water and keeping unpolluted water clean. Obtaining and maintaining clean water supplies is both complex and expensive. But it is much more expensive to clean up a polluted body of water than it is to keep it clean in the first place. The longer a pollution situation is allowed to continue unchecked, the more costly and time consuming it is to correct.

# AIR POLLUTION

Harmful materials released into the atmosphere are collectively called **air pollution**. Most pollutant entering Earth's atmosphere are produced from natural sources such as sand and dust storms, volcanoes and forest fires. Human activities have become a major source of air pollution. Air pollution became a widespread problem over hundreds of years when people died of everyday industrial pollution. Air pollutants are classified as either gases or **particulates** (tiny solids suspended in the atmosphere). Common air pollution includes smog (a yellow-brown haze produced when sunlight reacts with pollutants from cars), chlorofluorocarbons (compounds of carbon, chlorine and fluorine) and radon (a colorless, odorless radioactive gas).

## Health Problems

Air pollution has been linked with many health problems. Carbon monoxide causes stress on the heart, headaches, dizziness and even death. Ozone and sulfur and nitrogen oxides irritate the eyes and respiratory tract, causing discomfort and difficulty breathing. They may trigger asthma or allergy attacks. Ozone and oxides can cause bronchitis and emphysema. Particulates in the atmosphere have been linked to cancer. Ozone and sulfur oxides are harmful to plants. They damage trees and industrial crops as well. Animals also suffer from air pollution.

## Pollution On A Global Scale

On a global scale, pollution can even change the climate. Three major air pollution problems threatening the environment are acid precipitation, ozone depletion and global warming.

## Acid Rain

**Acid rain** (**acid precipitation**) is rain or snow that is more acidic than normal precipitation. Water in the air becomes acidic when it reacts with carbon dioxide, forming weak carbonic acid. When fossil fuels burn, they produce oxides of sulfur and nitrogen which combine with water to form sulfuric and nitric acids. These acids are highly corrosive and can be harmful to life. In lakes, they kill fish and plant life.

## Ozone Depletion

Ozone in the stratosphere absorbs almost all the ultraviolet radiation (UV) given off by the Sun. This prevents the dangerous ultraviolet radiation from reaching Earth's surface and causing damage to living organisms. During the 1980's, scientists discovered a "hole" in the ozone layer over the south pole, and more recently another hole over the north pole. Scientists fear damage to the ozone layer because it would increase the amount of exposure people would have to UV radiation. UV radiation can cause sunburn, blindness and cancer. It can cause crop damage and destroy the microorganisms that form the foundation of the aquatic food chain. The main cause of ozone depletion are Chlorofluorocarbons or CFCs, compounds of carbon, chlorine and fluorine once used in refrigerators, air conditioners, aerosol cans and the production of styrofoam and other plastic foams. In the stratosphere, the UV radiation breaks down the CFCs, releasing chlorine and fluorine atoms. These atoms combine with ozone to destroy the ozone.

## Global Warming

The third major impact of air pollution is **global warming**, an increase in Earth's average surface temperature caused by an increase in the greenhouse effect. Ice cores show an increase in carbon dioxide after an ice age. Scientists believe that the carbon dioxide increase after the last ice age caused the temperature to rise several degrees. As Earth's temperature rises, the ice caps will melt and the water in the oceans will expand. The sea level will rise several feet, flooding coastal areas, farmlands and lowlands - in many areas with salt water.

Air pollution is a global problem. Governments and industry must *work together* to control and reduce air pollution. Fortunately, some natural processes such as precipitation continuously reduce some of the pollutants from the air.

## Population Growth

At present, the human population is increasing at an exponential rate. Simply stated, the human population doubles every 30 years or so. Should the population continue to grow at this same rate, by the year 2030 there will be 14 billion people on Earth. The main question is, what irreversible changes in the environment will result as the essential needs of the increasing population are met?

# QUESTIONS

**1.** The graph below compares erosion caused by changes in the discharge of a stream before and after a period of population growth.

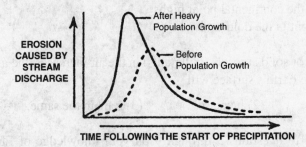

The best interpretation of the graph is that the total amount of erosion
(1) decreases with an increase in population
(2) increased with an increase in population
(3) is not affected by an increase in population

**2.** The graph below shows the growth of the world's human population in the past 400 years.

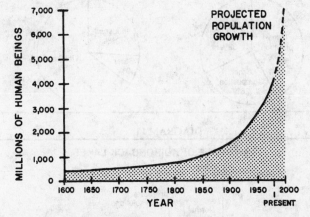

Compared to the rate at which the world's population increased between 1600 and 1700, the rate of increase from 1900 to the present has been

(1) slower, only
(2) faster, only
(3) the same
(4) first faster, then slower

3. Some scientists believe that high-flying airplanes and the discharge of fluorocarbons from the spray cans are affecting the atmosphere. Which characteristic of the atmosphere do they believe is affected?

(1) composition of the ozone layer of the stratosphere
(2) wind velocity of the tropopause
(3) location of the continental polar highs
(4) air movement in the doldrums

4. As the amount of solid aerosols (pollutants) in the air increases, the amount of insolation that reaches the Earth's surface will

(1) decrease      (2) increase      (3) remain the same.

Base your answers to questions 5 through 9 on your knowledge of Earth Science, *Earth Science Reference Tables*, the diagrams below and the map on the next page. The graphs in diagram I show the sources of nitrogen and sulfur dioxide emissions in the United States. Diagram 11 give information about the acidity of Adirondack lakes. The map shows regions of the United States affected by acid rain.

### DIAGRAM I

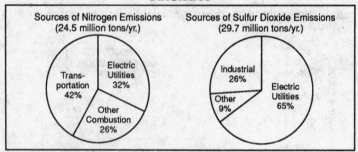

### DIAGRAM I I

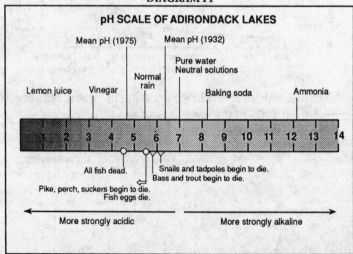

## REGIONS OF THE UNITED STATES SENSITIVE TO ACID RAIN

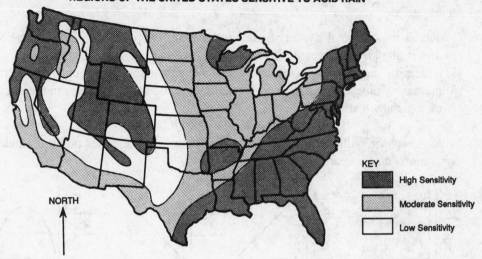

**KEY**

High Sensitivity

Moderate Sensitivity

Low Sensitivity

NORTH

**5.** Which pH level of the lake water would not support any fish life?

(1) 7.0        (2) 6.0        (3) 5.0        (4) 4.0

**6.** Which graph best shows the acidity (pH) of Adirondack lakes since 1930?

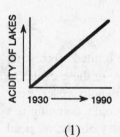
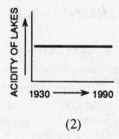
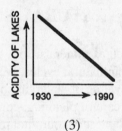
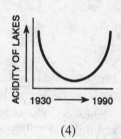

    (1)                   (2)                   (3)                   (4)

**7.** The primary cause of acid rain is the

(1) weathering and erosion of limestone rocks
(2) decay of plant and animal organisms
(3) burning of fossil fuels by humans
(4) destruction of the ozone layer

**8.** Acid rain can be reduced by

(1) increasing the use of high-sulfur coal     (2) controling the pollutants at the source
(3) reducing the cost of petroleum           (4) eliminating all use of nuclear energy

9. In addition to its effects on living organisms, acid rain may cause changes in the landscape by

   (1) decreasing chemical weathering due to an increase in destruction of vegetation

   (2) decreasing physical weathering due to less frost action

   (3) increasing the breakdown of rock material due to an increase in chemical weathering

   (4) increasing physical weathering of rock material due to an increase in the circulation of ground water

10. Which graph best illustrates the relationship between lake water pollution and human population density near the lake?

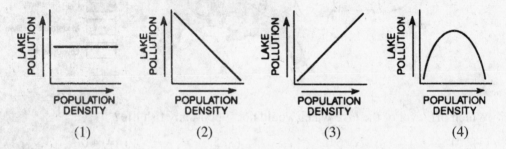

       (1)             (2)             (3)             (4)

# LIVING IN BALANCE WITH OUR NATURAL ENVIRONMENT

Our resources, such as minerals, soil, clean water and fresh air are limited. Terrestrial resources are a part of our natural cycles. We need to apply our knowledge of these cycles to preserve resources. Recycling of materials such as aluminum and paper will help preserve our resources. Technology, careful planning, conservation and guidance of people, communities and industry will help to preserve our vital resources. While we must think globally, we need to act locally.

## Technology

Technology is the application of scientific discoveries to meet the demands of humans to attain and maintain a certain standard of living. With the technology presently available, we can bring about very rapid and dramatic changes in our environment. Many of these changes are undesirable, and may be irreversible. For example, many products developed for the good of humans, such as pesticides and fertilizers, have had such undesirable side effects that their use has been banned or seriously curtailed. Acid rain is a direct side effect of industrial pollutants being released into the atmosphere. The advent of nuclear power has been accompanied by the dangers of meltdown and nuclear explosions, along with the very real problem of how to dispose of radioactive wastes. Many other waste products of industry have been found to be toxic. Their disposal in the environment has proved to be a very serious problem.

The addition of pollutants to the atmosphere alters the rate of energy absorption and reradiation which, in turn, may result in dramatic climate changes. These changes, in turn, could modify many landscape regions. A warming trend could result in the melting of icecap glaciers, thus raising sea level and flooding many coastal regions. A cooling trend could result in the development of another ice age.

## Conservation

All of our natural resources, such as soil, land, water, air, minerals and fuels can all be conserved through a program of careful planning and legislative action. In order for such programs to be successful, they must develop positive attitudes in all the people. Only society as a whole can decide "acceptable" levels of risk. Only society, and each individual as members of that society, can make and enforce decisions concerning the environment.

## The Future

As we deplete some of our resources, we often find other ways to meet our needs. Although we have run low on many resources, our quality of life has improved. How can we maintain this improved quality while using our resources is the question facing us in the present and the future. Many of the environmental problems require continued research as we undertake careful remediation. Issues such as global warming and ozone depletion merit more study. Remediation of these problems may be complex, controversial and difficult to implement. The adage, "Look before you leap" has special meaning as we deal with the problems in our environment.

Societies use **ethics** to determine right and wrong. Modern industrial society has an ethic in which resources are thought to be unlimited, and people are seen as being separate from everything else. A new ethic that meets our current needs without limiting the ability of future generations to meet their needs is emerging. This ethic relies on a reduced demand for consumer goods, recycling, conservation and the wise use of resources. A society based on this type of ethic should be able to survive indefinitely.

Research and education will help to guide human activities to preserve our environmental quality while we improve our lives. As we become more informed about environmental issues we need to change our behavior. Everyone, young and old, scientist and nonscientist can help. Now is the time to begin.

# QUESTIONS

1. An ethic is a set of rules in a society that determines

   (1) government rules      (2) human resources
   (3) right and wrong      (4) mass production

2. The competition for more resources will intensify because

   (1) agriculture is improving      (2) the climate is improving
   (3) materials are becoming scarce      (4) technology is making advances

3. A way to reduce resources use through decreased demand and increased efficiency is

   (1) recycling      (2) increased insulation
   (3) conservation      (4) technology

4. The people of an area defeated legislation that would have allowed the sale of a large section of a public owned forest preserve for the purpose of an industrial park. They also passed a bond issue providing funds for an additional sewage treatment plant for the city. These actions are an indication that a majority of the voters

   (1) are opposed to higher taxes for any reason
   (2) feel technology can solve all the problems of the environment
   (3) are aware of the delicate balance in nature
   (4) feel that nature can take care of itself

5. The process of developing and implementing environmental conservation programs is most dependent on

   (1) the availability of the most advanced technology
   (2) Earth's ability to restore itself
   (3) public awareness and cooperation
   (4) stricter environmental laws.

---

## CHAPTER 10 - CORE VOCABULARY

**global warming**
**pollution**

---

## HELPFUL VOCABULARY

| | | |
|---|---|---|
| **acid rain (acid precipitation)** | **ethics** | **sanitary landfills** |
| **aerobic** | **eutrophication** | **solid wastes** |
| **air pollution** | **hazardous wastes** | **thermal pollution** |
| **anaerobic** | **particulates** | **water pollution** |
| **biodegradable** | | |

## PRACTICE FOR CONSTRUCTED RESPONSE

Base your answers to questions 1 through 3 on the graphs below and your knowledge of Earth Science. Graph I shows the average temperature change on Earth between the years 1870 and 1955. Graph II shows the amount of carbon dioxide in the atmosphere between the years 1870 and 1962.

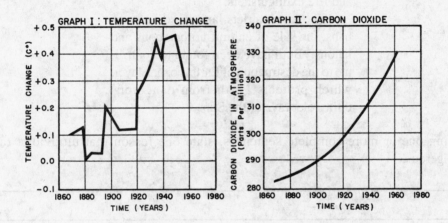

1. Describe the best interpretation that can be made from the graphs between the years 1870 and 1955.

   _____

   _____

2. Describe the relationship between the changes in carbon dioxide and temperature as shown by the graphs?

   _____

   _____

3. If the trend shown in graph II continued into 1980, the amount of carbon dioxide in the atmosphere in 1980 was probably _____.

Base your answer to question 4 on the newspaper article below and your knowledge of Earth Science.

### Legislation Protects Ozone

The governor of New York signed environmental legislation that restricted the use of ozone-depleting chemicals employed in refrigeration systems, air-conditioners, and fire extinguishers.

The law restricts, and in some cases bans, the sale of chlorofluorocarbons and halons. Both have been found to contribute to the destruction of Earth's ozone layer, which protects Earth from dangerous ultraviolet rays of the Sun.

**4.** Using one or more complete sentences, state one reason that ultraviolet rays are dangerous.

_____

_____

_____

Base your answers to questions 5 and 6 on the graph below. The graph shows the average water temperature and the dissolved oxygen levels of water in a stream over a 12-month period. The level of dissolved oxygen is measured in parts per million (ppm).

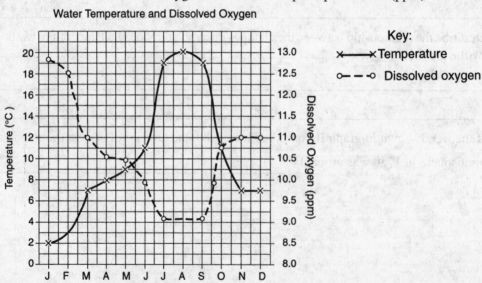

Water Temperature and Dissolved Oxygen

**5.** State the difference in average water temperature, in degrees Celsius, between January and August. _____ °C

**6.** State the relationship between the temperature of the water and the level of dissolved oxygen in the water.

_____

_____

_____

**7.** Below is a list of some mineral resources and the number of years that supplies are estimated to last (supply time) if use continues at the current rate.

**Mineral Resources' Future**

| Mineral Resource | Estimated Supply Time |
|---|---|
| Salt, magnesium metal | almost infinite |
| Lime, silicon | thousands of years |
| Potash, cobalt | 200+ years |
| Manganese ore | 200+ years |
| Iron ore | 100 to 200 years |
| Chromite, feldspar | 100 to 200 years |
| Bauxite (aluminum ore) | 50 to 100 years |
| Phosphate rock, nickel | 50 to 100 years |
| Copper, mercury | less than 50 years |
| Zinc, lead | less than 50 years |

State *one* way humans could increase the estimated supply time for many of these resources.

_____

_____

Base your answers to questions 8 and 9 on the data table below, which shows the percent and uses of different types of salt in the United States.

**Uses of Salt in the United States**

| Salt Usage | Percent | How Used |
|---|---|---|
| Water softening | 9 | Sodium ions from salt replace calcium and magnesium ions in water. |
| Highways | 69 | Salt keeps highways free of ice in the winter. |
| Agriculture | 6 | Salt is provided for livestock and poultry to balance their diet. |
| Foods | 5 | Humans use salt in their diet. |
| Industry | 11 | Many industrial processes, such as paper-making, use salt. |

8. On the pie graph below complete the graph to show the percent of *each* salt usage. (The percent of salt used in industry has been drawn and labeled.) Label *each* section of the pie graph to indicate the salt usage.

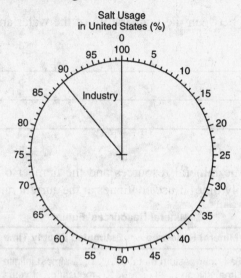

9. Shaded areas on the map below represent some counties in New York State where salt is mined.

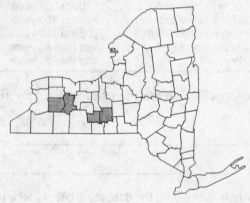

State the name of *one* New York State landscape region in which all or part of these counties are located.

_____

# ENVIRONMENTAL AWARENESS

Base your answers to questions 10 through 13 on the reading passage and maps below. The reading passage discusses acid rain. Map I shows the locations of some major United States producers of nitrogen oxide and sulfur dioxide that are released into Earth's atmosphere. Map II shows the pH concentration of acid rain in the United States.

### Acid Rain

Acid deposition consists of acidic substances that fall to Earth. The most common type of acid deposition is rain containing nitric acid and sulfuric acid. Acid rain forms when nitrogen oxide and sulfur dioxide gases combine with water and oxygen in the atmosphere.

Human-generated sulfur dioxide results primarily from coal-burning electric utility plants and industrial plants. Human-generated nitrogen oxide results primarily from burning fossil fuels in motor vehicles and electric utility plants.

Natural events, such as volcanic eruptions, forest fires, hot springs, and geysers, also produce nitrogen oxide and sulfur dioxide.

Acid rain affects trees, human-made structures, and surface water. Acid damages tree leaves and decreases the tree s ability to carry on photosynthesis. Acid also damages tree bark and exposes trees to insects and disease. Many statues and buildings are composed of rocks containing the mineral calcite, which reacts with acid and chemically weathers more rapidly than other common minerals. Acid deposition lowers the pH of surface water. Much of the surface water of the Adirondack region has pH values too acidic for plants and animals to survive.

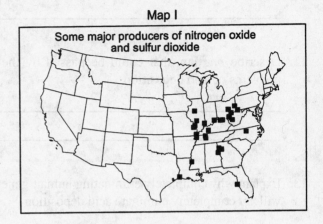

Map I

Some major producers of nitrogen oxide and sulfur dioxide

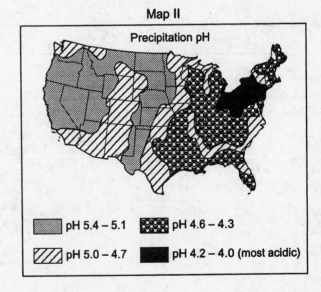

Map II

Precipitation pH

pH 5.4 – 5.1    pH 4.6 – 4.3

pH 5.0 – 4.7    pH 4.2 – 4.0 (most acidic)

**10.** State *one* reason why the northeastern part of the United States has more acid deposition than other regions of the country.

_____

_____

_____

11. State *one* sedimentary or *one* metamorphic rock that is most chemically weathered by acid rain.

    _____

    _____

12. Describe *one* law that could be passed by the government to prevent some of the problems of acid deposition.

    _____

    _____

13. Explain why completely eliminating human-generated nitrogen oxide and sulfur dioxide will *not* completely eliminate acid deposition.

    _____

    _____

    _____

# Earth Science Reference Tables

## PHYSICAL CONSTANTS

### Radioactive Decay Data

| RADIOACTIVE ISOTOPE | DISINTEGRATION | HALF-LIFE (years) |
|---|---|---|
| Carbon-14 | $C^{14} \rightarrow N^{14}$ | $5.7 \times 10^{3}$ |
| Potassium-40 | $K^{40} \begin{array}{l} \nearrow Ar^{40} \\ \searrow Ca^{40} \end{array}$ | $1.3 \times 10^{9}$ |
| Uranium-238 | $U^{238} \rightarrow Pb^{206}$ | $4.5 \times 10^{9}$ |
| Rubidium-87 | $Rb^{87} \rightarrow Sr^{87}$ | $4.9 \times 10^{10}$ |

### Specific Heats of Common Materials

| MATERIAL | | SPECIFIC HEAT (calories/gram • C°) |
|---|---|---|
| Water | solid | 0.5 |
| | liquid | 1.0 |
| | gas | 0.5 |
| Dry air | | 0.24 |
| Basalt | | 0.20 |
| Granite | | 0.19 |
| Iron | | 0.11 |
| Copper | | 0.09 |
| Lead | | 0.03 |

### Properties of Water

| | |
|---|---|
| Energy gained during melting | 80 calories/gram |
| Energy released during freezing | 80 calories/gram |
| Energy gained during vaporization | 540 calories/gram |
| Energy released during condensation | 540 calories/gram |
| Density at 3.98°C | 1.00 gram/milliliter |

## EQUATIONS

| | |
|---|---|
| Percent deviation from accepted value | $\text{deviation (\%)} = \dfrac{\text{difference from accepted value}}{\text{accepted value}} \times 100$ |
| Eccentricity of an ellipse | $\text{eccentricity} = \dfrac{\text{distance between foci}}{\text{length of major axis}}$ |
| Gradient | $\text{gradient} = \dfrac{\text{change in field value}}{\text{distance}}$ |
| Rate of change | $\text{rate of change} = \dfrac{\text{change in field value}}{\text{time}}$ |
| Density of a substance | $\text{density} = \dfrac{\text{mass}}{\text{volume}}$ |

### 2001 EDITION

This edition of the Earth Science Reference Tables should be used in the classroom beginning in the 2000–2001 school year. The first examination for which these tables will be used is the January 2001 Regents Examination in Earth Science.

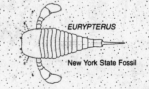

EURYPTERUS

New York State Fossil

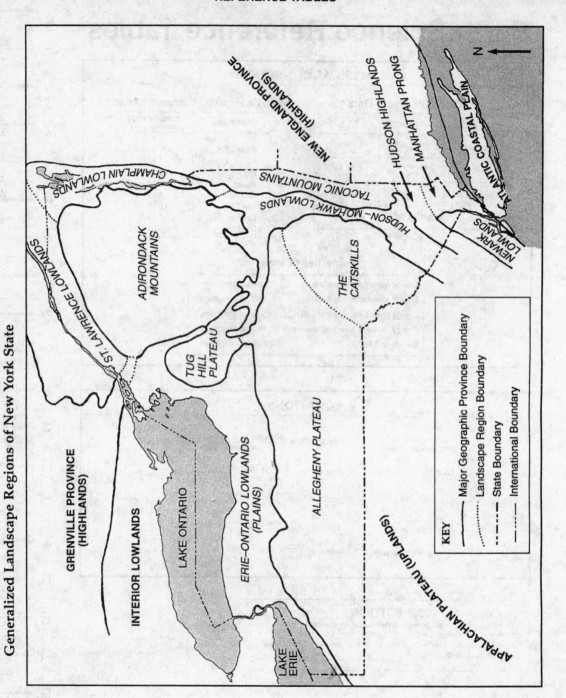

Generalized Landscape Regions of New York State

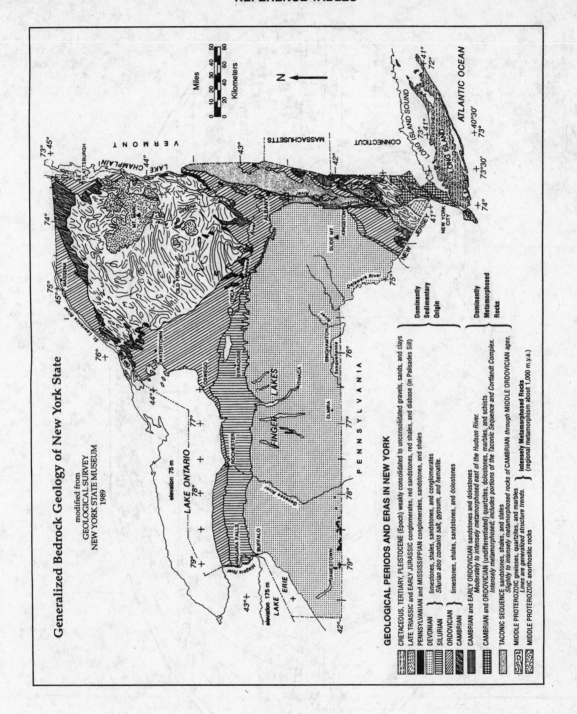

## Generalized Bedrock Geology of New York State

modified from
GEOLOGICAL SURVEY
NEW YORK STATE MUSEUM
1989

### GEOLOGICAL PERIODS AND ERAS IN NEW YORK

CRETACEOUS, TERTIARY, PLEISTOCENE (Epoch) weakly consolidated to unconsolidated gravels, sands, and clays

LATE TRIASSIC and EARLY JURASSIC conglomerates, red sandstones, red shales, and diabase (in Palisades Sill)

PENNSYLVANIAN and MISSISSIPPIAN conglomerates, sandstones, and shales

DEVONIAN — limestones, shales, sandstones, and conglomerates

SILURIAN — *Silurian also contains salt, gypsum, and hematite.*

ORDOVICIAN — limestones, shales, sandstones, and dolostones

CAMBRIAN

CAMBRIAN and EARLY ORDOVICIAN sandstones and dolostones
*Moderately to intensely metamorphosed east of the Hudson River.*

CAMBRIAN and ORDOVICIAN (undifferentiated) quartzites, dolostones, marbles, and schists
*Intensely metamorphosed; includes portions of the Taconic Sequence and Cortlandt Complex.*

TACONIC SEQUENCE sandstones, shales, and slates
*Slightly to intensely metamorphosed rocks of CAMBRIAN through MIDDLE ORDOVICIAN ages.*

MIDDLE PROTEROZOIC gneisses, quartzites, and marbles
*Lines are generalized structure trends.*

MIDDLE PROTEROZOIC anorthositic rocks

Intensely Metamorphosed Rocks
*(regional metamorphism about 1,000 m.y.a.)*

Dominantly Sedimentary Origin

Dominantly Metamorphosed Rocks

Surface Ocean Currents

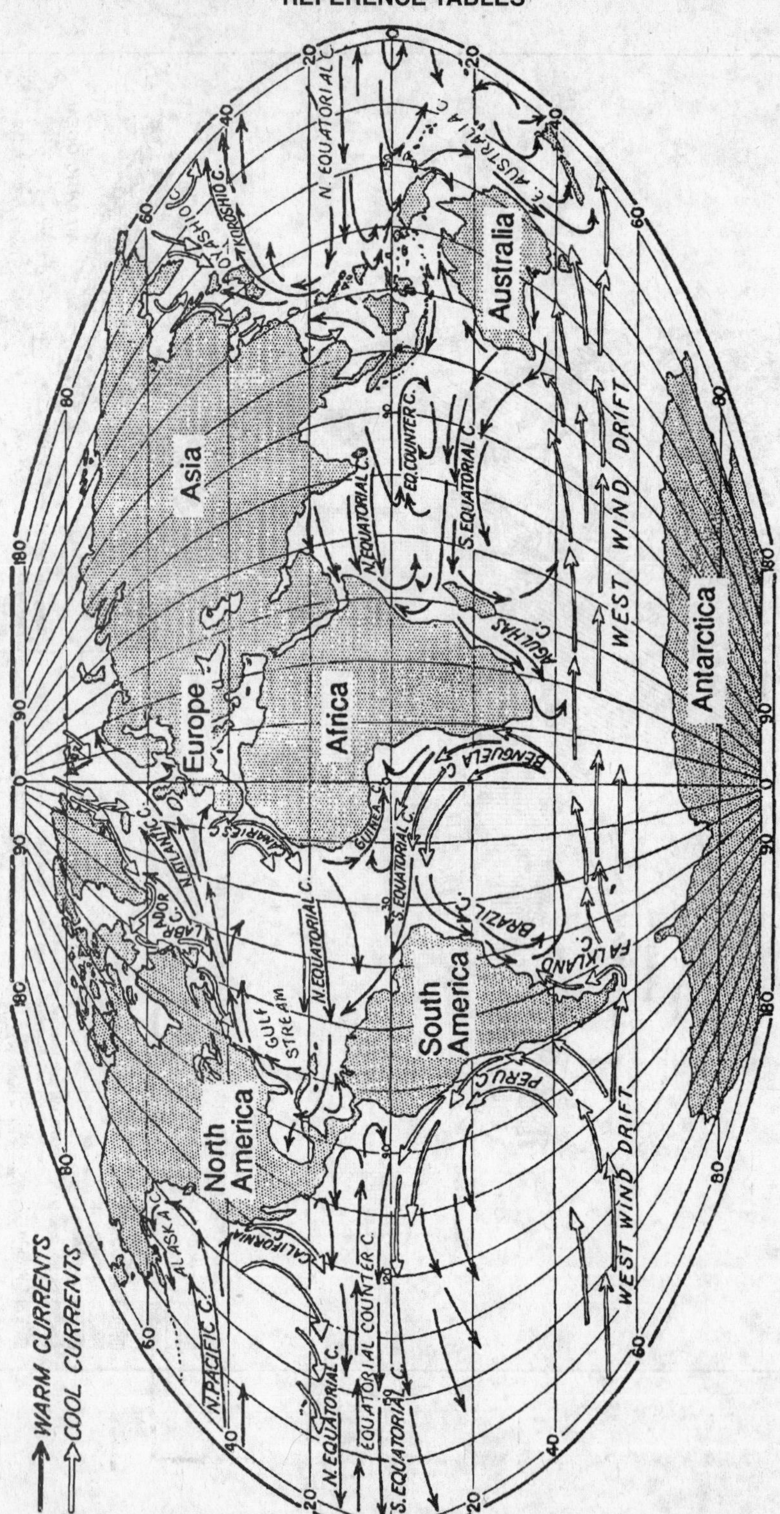

WARM CURRENTS
COOL CURRENTS

# Tectonic Plates

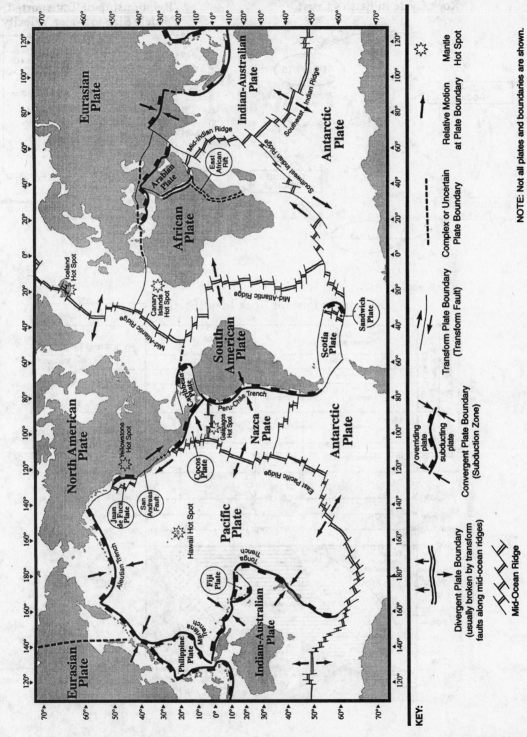

KEY:

Divergent Plate Boundary
(usually broken by transform
faults along mid-ocean ridges)

Mid-Ocean Ridge

Convergent Plate Boundary
(Subduction Zone)

Transform Plate Boundary
(Transform Fault)

Complex or Uncertain
Plate Boundary

Relative Motion
at Plate Boundary

Mantle
Hot Spot

NOTE: Not all plates and boundaries are shown.

## Rock Cycle in Earth's Crust

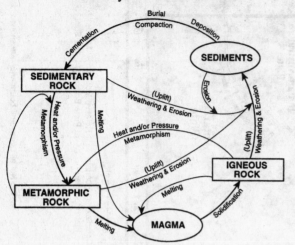

## Relationship of Transported Particle Size to Water Velocity

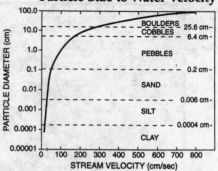

*This generalized graph shows the water velocity needed to maintain, but not start, movement. Variations occur due to differences in particle density and shape.

## Scheme for Igneous Rock Identification

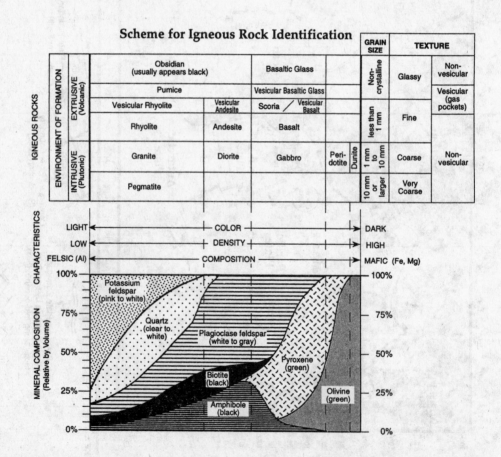

## Scheme for Sedimentary Rock Identification

### INORGANIC LAND-DERIVED SEDIMENTARY ROCKS

| TEXTURE | GRAIN SIZE | COMPOSITION | COMMENTS | ROCK NAME | MAP SYMBOL |
|---|---|---|---|---|---|
| Clastic (fragmental) | Pebbles, cobbles, and/or boulders embedded in sand, silt, and/or clay | Mostly quartz, feldspar, and clay minerals; may contain fragments of other rocks and minerals | Rounded fragments | Conglomerate | |
| | | | Angular fragments | Breccia | |
| | Sand (0.2 to 0.006 cm) | | Fine to coarse | Sandstone | |
| | Silt (0.006 to 0.0004 cm) | | Very fine grain | Siltstone | |
| | Clay (less than 0.0004 cm) | | Compact; may split easily | Shale | |

### CHEMICALLY AND/OR ORGANICALLY FORMED SEDIMENTARY ROCKS

| TEXTURE | GRAIN SIZE | COMPOSITION | COMMENTS | ROCK NAME | MAP SYMBOL |
|---|---|---|---|---|---|
| Crystalline | Varied | Halite | Crystals from chemical precipitates and evaporites | Rock Salt | |
| | Varied | Gypsum | | Rock Gypsum | |
| | Varied | Dolomite | | Dolostone | |
| Bioclastic | Microscopic to coarse | Calcite | Cemented shell fragments or precipitates of biologic origin | Limestone | |
| | Varied | Carbon | From plant remains | Coal | |

## Scheme for Metamorphic Rock Identification

| TEXTURE | GRAIN SIZE | COMPOSITION | TYPE OF METAMORPHISM | COMMENTS | ROCK NAME | MAP SYMBOL |
|---|---|---|---|---|---|---|
| FOLIATED — MINERAL ALIGNMENT | Fine | MICA / QUARTZ / FELDSPAR / AMPHIBOLE / GARNET / PYROXENE | Regional | Low-grade metamorphism of shale | Slate | |
| | Fine to medium | | (Heat and pressure increase with depth) | Foliation surfaces shiny from microscopic mica crystals | Phyllite | |
| | | | | Platy mica crystals visible from metamorphism of clay or feldspars | Schist | |
| FOLIATED — BANDING | Medium to coarse | | | High-grade metamorphism; some mica changed to feldspar; segregated by mineral type into bands | Gneiss | |
| NONFOLIATED | Fine | Variable | Contact (Heat) | Various rocks changed by heat from nearby magma/lava | Hornfels | |
| | Fine to coarse | Quartz | Regional or Contact | Metamorphism of quartz sandstone | Quartzite | |
| | | Calcite and/or dolomite | | Metamorphism of limestone or dolostone | Marble | |
| | Coarse | Various minerals in particles and matrix | | Pebbles may be distorted or stretched | Metaconglomerate | |

# REFERENCE TABLES

# GEOLOGIC HISTORY

(Fossils not drawn to scale)

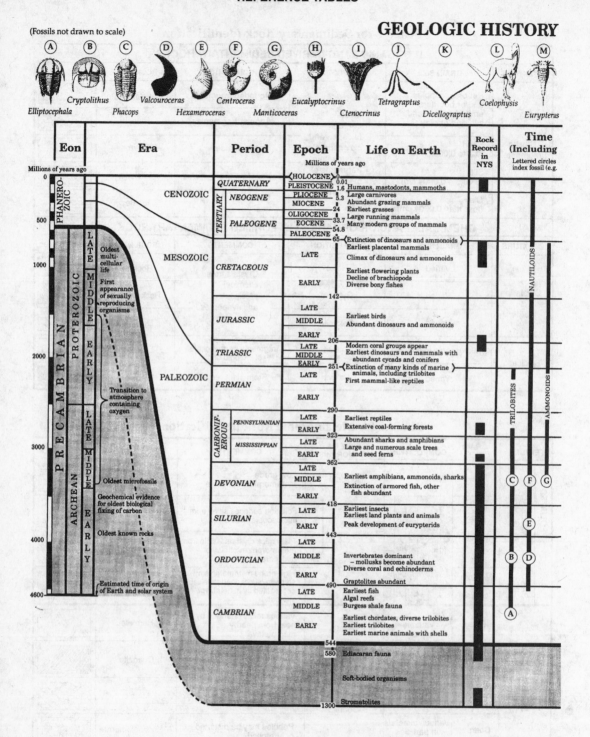

| A | B | C | D | E | F | G | H | I | J | K | L | M |

Elliptocephala — Cryptolithus — Phacops — Valcouroceras — Hexameroceras — Centroceras — Manticoceras — Eucalyptocrinus — Ctenocrinus — Tetragraptus — Dicellograptus — Coelophysis — Eurypterus

| Eon | Era | | Period | Epoch | Life on Earth | Rock Record in NYS | Time (Including Lettered circles index fossil (e.g. |
|---|---|---|---|---|---|---|---|
| Millions of years ago | | | | Millions of years ago | | | |
| PHANEROZOIC | CENOZOIC | | QUATERNARY | HOLOCENE 0.01 | Humans, mastodons, mammoths | | NAUTILOIDS |
| | | | | PLEISTOCENE 1.6 | | | |
| | | | NEOGENE | PLIOCENE 5.3 | Large carnivores | | |
| | | | | MIOCENE 24 | Abundant grazing mammals | | |
| | | TERTIARY | PALEOGENE | OLIGOCENE 33.7 | Earliest grasses / Large running mammals | | |
| | | | | EOCENE 54.8 | Many modern groups of mammals | | |
| | | | | PALEOCENE 65 | Extinction of dinosaurs and ammonoids | | |
| | MESOZOIC | | CRETACEOUS | LATE | Earliest placental mammals / Climax of dinosaurs and ammonoids | | |
| | | | | EARLY 142 | Earliest flowering plants / Decline of brachiopods / Diverse bony fishes | | |
| | | | JURASSIC | LATE | Earliest birds | | |
| | | | | MIDDLE | Abundant dinosaurs and ammonoids | | |
| | | | | EARLY 206 | | | |
| | | | TRIASSIC | LATE | Modern coral groups appear | | |
| | | | | MIDDLE | Earliest dinosaurs and mammals with | | |
| | | | | EARLY 251 | abundant cycads and conifers / Extinction of many kinds of marine animals, including trilobites | | |
| | PALEOZOIC | | PERMIAN | LATE | First mammal-like reptiles | | TRILOBITES AMMONOIDS |
| | | | | EARLY 290 | | | |
| | | | CARBONIF-EROUS PENNSYLVANIAN | LATE | Earliest reptiles | | |
| | | | | EARLY 323 | Extensive coal-forming forests | | |
| | | | MISSISSIPPIAN | LATE | Abundant sharks and amphibians | | |
| | | | | EARLY 362 | Large and numerous scale trees and seed ferns | | |
| | | | DEVONIAN | LATE | | | C F G |
| | | | | MIDDLE | Earliest amphibians, ammonoids, sharks | | |
| | | | | EARLY 418 | Extinction of armored fish, other fish abundant | | |
| | | | SILURIAN | LATE | Earliest insects / Earliest land plants and animals | | E |
| | | | | EARLY 443 | Peak development of eurypterids | | |
| | | | ORDOVICIAN | LATE | | | B D |
| | | | | MIDDLE | Invertebrates dominant — mollusks become abundant | | |
| | | | | EARLY 490 | Diverse coral and echinoderms / Graptolites abundant | | |
| | | | CAMBRIAN | LATE | Earliest fish / Algal reefs | | A |
| | | | | MIDDLE | Burgess shale fauna | | |
| | | | | EARLY 544 | Earliest chordates, diverse trilobites / Earliest trilobites / Earliest marine animals with shells | | |
| PRECAMBRIAN PROTEROZOIC ARCHEAN | | | | 580 | Ediacaran fauna | | |
| | | | | | Soft-bodied organisms | | |
| | | | | 1300 | Stromatolites | | |

LATE / MIDDLE / EARLY (PROTEROZOIC)
LATE / MIDDLE / EARLY (ARCHEAN)

Oldest multi-cellular life

First appearance of sexually reproducing organisms

Transition to atmosphere containing oxygen

Oldest microfossils

Geochemical evidence for oldest biological fixing of carbon

Oldest known rocks

Estimated time of origin of Earth and solar system

# OF NEW YORK STATE

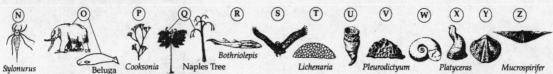

Stylonurus — N
Mastodont — O
Beluga Whale
Cooksonia — P
Aneurophyton — Q
Naples Tree
Bothriolepis
Condor — R
Lichenaria — S
Cystiphyllum — T
Pleurodictyum — U
Maclurites — V
Platyceras — W
Eospirifer — X
Mucrospirifer — Y, Z

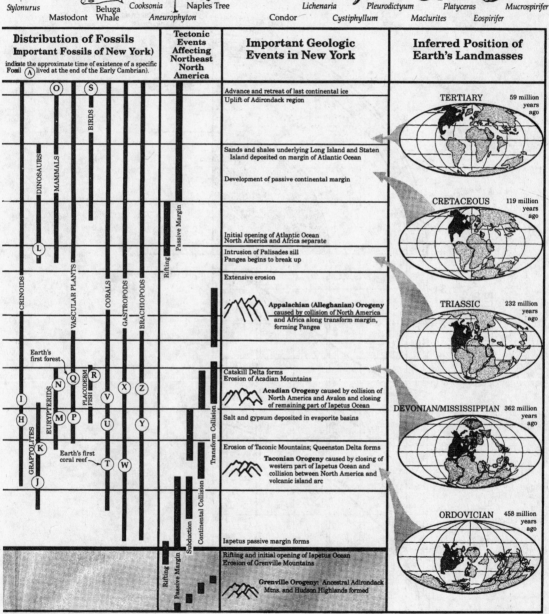

## Distribution of Fossils
### (Important Fossils of New York)
indicate the approximate time of existence of a specific Fossil (A) lived at the end of the Early Cambrian).

## Tectonic Events Affecting Northeast North America

## Important Geologic Events in New York

## Inferred Position of Earth's Landmasses

**Important Geologic Events in New York:**

- Advance and retreat of last continental ice
- Uplift of Adirondack region
- Sands and shales underlying Long Island and Staten Island deposited on margin of Atlantic Ocean
- Development of passive continental margin
- Initial opening of Atlantic Ocean North America and Africa separate
- Intrusion of Palisades sill Pangea begins to break up
- Extensive erosion
- **Appalachian (Alleghanian) Orogeny** caused by collision of North America and Africa along transform margin, forming Pangea
- Catskill Delta forms Erosion of Acadian Mountains
- **Acadian Orogeny** caused by collision of North America and Avalon and closing of remaining part of Iapetus Ocean
- Salt and gypsum deposited in evaporite basins
- Erosion of Taconic Mountains; Queenston Delta forms
- **Taconian Orogeny** caused by closing of western part of Iapetus Ocean and collision between North America and volcanic island arc
- Iapetus passive margin forms
- Rifting and initial opening of Iapetus Ocean Erosion of Grenville Mountains
- **Grenville Orogeny:** Ancestral Adirondack Mtns. and Hudson Highlands formed

**Inferred Position of Earth's Landmasses:**

- TERTIARY — 59 million years ago
- CRETACEOUS — 119 million years ago
- TRIASSIC — 232 million years ago
- DEVONIAN/MISSISSIPPIAN — 362 million years ago
- ORDOVICIAN — 458 million years ago

**Fossil distribution labels:** CRINOIDS, DINOSAURS, MAMMALS, BIRDS, VASCULAR PLANTS, CORALS, GASTROPODS, BRACHIOPODS, EURYPTERIDS, PLACODERM FISH, GRAPTOLITES, Earth's first forest, Earth's first coral reef

**Tectonic events:** Passive Margin, Rifting, Transform Collision, Continental Collision, Subduction

90-169 CDC(rev) 8/2000

# Inferred Properties of Earth's Interior

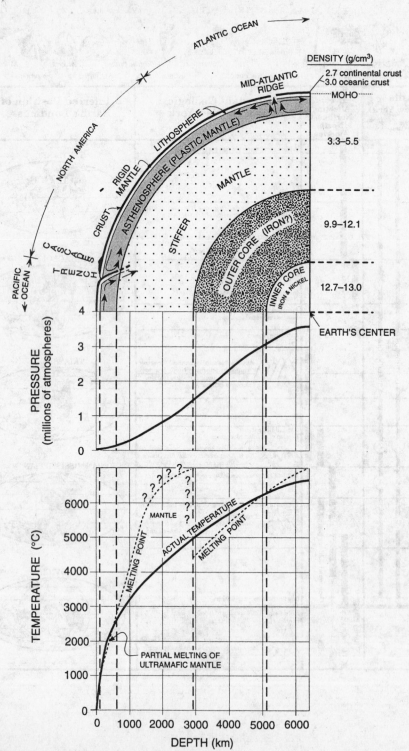

# REFERENCE TABLES

## Average Chemical Composition
## of Earth's Crust, Hydrosphere, and Troposphere

| ELEMENT (symbol) | CRUST | | HYDROSPHERE | TROPOSPHERE |
| --- | --- | --- | --- | --- |
| | Percent by Mass | Percent by Volume | Percent by Volume | Percent by Volume |
| Oxygen (O) | 46.40 | 94.04 | 33.0 | 21.0 |
| Silicon (Si) | 28.15 | 0.88 | | |
| Aluminum (Al) | 8.23 | 0.48 | | |
| Iron (Fe) | 5.63 | 0.49 | | |
| Calcium (Ca) | 4.15 | 1.18 | | |
| Sodium (Na) | 2.36 | 1.11 | | |
| Magnesium (Mg) | 2.33 | 0.33 | | |
| Potassium (K) | 2.09 | 1.42 | | |
| Nitrogen (N) | | | | 78.0 |
| Hydrogen (H) | | | 66.0 | |
| Other | 0.66 | 0.07 | 1.0 | 1.0 |

## Earthquake P-wave and S-wave Travel Time

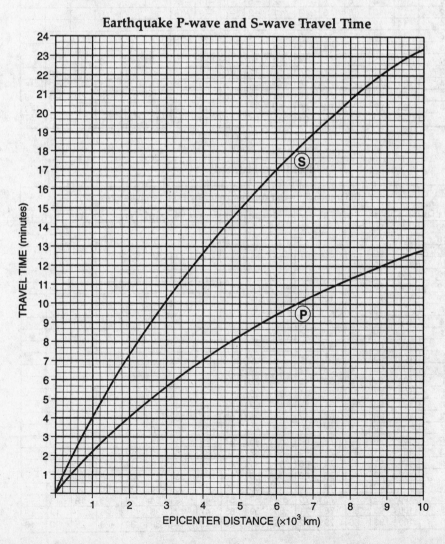

TRAVEL TIME (minutes)

EPICENTER DISTANCE (×10³ km)

## REFERENCE TABLES
## Dewpoint Temperatures (°C)

| Dry-Bulb Temperature (°C) | Difference Between Wet-Bulb and Dry-Bulb Temperatures (C°) | | | | | | | | | | | | | | | |
|---|---|---|---|---|---|---|---|---|---|---|---|---|---|---|---|---|
| | 0 | 1 | 2 | 3 | 4 | 5 | 6 | 7 | 8 | 9 | 10 | 11 | 12 | 13 | 14 | 15 |
| −20 | −20 | −33 | | | | | | | | | | | | | | |
| −18 | −18 | −28 | | | | | | | | | | | | | | |
| −16 | −16 | −24 | | | | | | | | | | | | | | |
| −14 | −14 | −21 | −36 | | | | | | | | | | | | | |
| −12 | −12 | −18 | −28 | | | | | | | | | | | | | |
| −10 | −10 | −14 | −22 | | | | | | | | | | | | | |
| −8 | −8 | −12 | −18 | −29 | | | | | | | | | | | | |
| −6 | −6 | −10 | −14 | −22 | | | | | | | | | | | | |
| −4 | −4 | −7 | −12 | −17 | −29 | | | | | | | | | | | |
| −2 | −2 | −5 | −8 | −13 | −20 | | | | | | | | | | | |
| 0 | 0 | −3 | −6 | −9 | −15 | −24 | | | | | | | | | | |
| 2 | 2 | −1 | −3 | −6 | −11 | −17 | | | | | | | | | | |
| 4 | 4 | 1 | −1 | −4 | −7 | −11 | −19 | | | | | | | | | |
| 6 | 6 | 4 | 1 | −1 | −4 | −7 | −13 | −21 | | | | | | | | |
| 8 | 8 | 6 | 3 | 1 | −2 | −5 | −9 | −14 | | | | | | | | |
| 10 | 10 | 8 | 6 | 4 | 1 | −2 | −5 | −9 | −14 | −28 | | | | | | |
| 12 | 12 | 10 | 8 | 6 | 4 | 1 | −2 | −5 | −9 | −16 | | | | | | |
| 14 | 14 | 12 | 11 | 9 | 6 | 4 | 1 | −2 | −5 | −10 | −17 | | | | | |
| 16 | 16 | 14 | 13 | 11 | 9 | 7 | 4 | 1 | −1 | −6 | −10 | −17 | | | | |
| 18 | 18 | 16 | 15 | 13 | 11 | 9 | 7 | 4 | 2 | −2 | −5 | −10 | −19 | | | |
| 20 | 20 | 19 | 17 | 15 | 14 | 12 | 10 | 7 | 4 | 2 | −2 | −5 | −10 | −19 | | |
| 22 | 22 | 21 | 19 | 17 | 16 | 14 | 12 | 10 | 8 | 5 | 3 | −1 | −5 | −10 | −19 | |
| 24 | 24 | 23 | 21 | 20 | 18 | 16 | 14 | 12 | 10 | 8 | 6 | 2 | −1 | −5 | −10 | −18 |
| 26 | 26 | 25 | 23 | 22 | 20 | 18 | 17 | 15 | 13 | 11 | 9 | 6 | 3 | 0 | −4 | −9 |
| 28 | 28 | 27 | 25 | 24 | 22 | 21 | 19 | 17 | 16 | 14 | 11 | 9 | 7 | 4 | 1 | −3 |
| 30 | 30 | 29 | 27 | 26 | 24 | 23 | 21 | 19 | 18 | 16 | 14 | 12 | 10 | 8 | 5 | 1 |

## Relative Humidity (%)

| Dry-Bulb Temperature (°C) | Difference Between Wet-Bulb and Dry-Bulb Temperatures (C°) | | | | | | | | | | | | | | | |
|---|---|---|---|---|---|---|---|---|---|---|---|---|---|---|---|---|
| | 0 | 1 | 2 | 3 | 4 | 5 | 6 | 7 | 8 | 9 | 10 | 11 | 12 | 13 | 14 | 15 |
| −20 | 100 | 28 | | | | | | | | | | | | | | |
| −18 | 100 | 40 | | | | | | | | | | | | | | |
| −16 | 100 | 48 | | | | | | | | | | | | | | |
| −14 | 100 | 55 | 11 | | | | | | | | | | | | | |
| −12 | 100 | 61 | 23 | | | | | | | | | | | | | |
| −10 | 100 | 66 | 33 | | | | | | | | | | | | | |
| −8 | 100 | 71 | 41 | 13 | | | | | | | | | | | | |
| −6 | 100 | 73 | 48 | 20 | | | | | | | | | | | | |
| −4 | 100 | 77 | 54 | 32 | 11 | | | | | | | | | | | |
| −2 | 100 | 79 | 58 | 37 | 20 | 1 | | | | | | | | | | |
| 0 | 100 | 81 | 63 | 45 | 28 | 11 | | | | | | | | | | |
| 2 | 100 | 83 | 67 | 51 | 36 | 20 | 6 | | | | | | | | | |
| 4 | 100 | 85 | 70 | 56 | 42 | 27 | 14 | | | | | | | | | |
| 6 | 100 | 86 | 72 | 59 | 46 | 35 | 22 | 10 | | | | | | | | |
| 8 | 100 | 87 | 74 | 62 | 51 | 39 | 28 | 17 | 6 | | | | | | | |
| 10 | 100 | 88 | 76 | 65 | 54 | 43 | 33 | 24 | 13 | 4 | | | | | | |
| 12 | 100 | 88 | 78 | 67 | 57 | 48 | 38 | 28 | 19 | 10 | 2 | | | | | |
| 14 | 100 | 89 | 79 | 69 | 60 | 50 | 41 | 33 | 25 | 16 | 8 | 1 | | | | |
| 16 | 100 | 90 | 80 | 71 | 62 | 54 | 45 | 37 | 29 | 21 | 14 | 7 | 1 | | | |
| 18 | 100 | 91 | 81 | 72 | 64 | 56 | 48 | 40 | 33 | 26 | 19 | 12 | 6 | | | |
| 20 | 100 | 91 | 82 | 74 | 66 | 58 | 51 | 44 | 36 | 30 | 23 | 17 | 11 | 5 | | |
| 22 | 100 | 92 | 83 | 75 | 68 | 60 | 53 | 46 | 40 | 33 | 27 | 21 | 15 | 10 | 4 | |
| 24 | 100 | 92 | 84 | 76 | 69 | 62 | 55 | 49 | 42 | 36 | 30 | 25 | 20 | 14 | 9 | 4 |
| 26 | 100 | 92 | 85 | 77 | 70 | 64 | 57 | 51 | 45 | 39 | 34 | 28 | 23 | 18 | 13 | 9 |
| 28 | 100 | 93 | 66 | 78 | 71 | 65 | 59 | 53 | 47 | 42 | 36 | 31 | 26 | 21 | 17 | 12 |
| 30 | 100 | 93 | 86 | 79 | 72 | 66 | 61 | 55 | 49 | 44 | 39 | 34 | 29 | 25 | 20 | 16 |

# REFERENCE TABLES

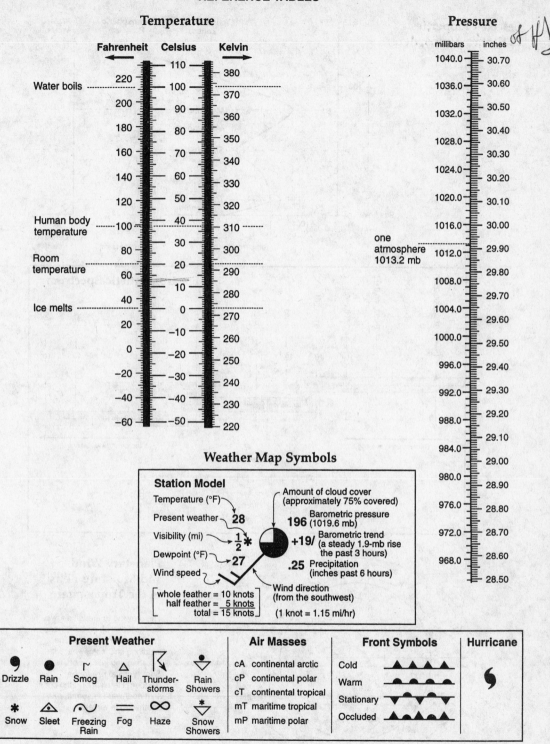

## Temperature

**Fahrenheit  Celsius  Kelvin**

Water boils — 220, 100°C, 370–380 K

Human body temperature — 100°F, 40°C, 310 K

Room temperature — 60°F, 20°C, 290 K

Ice melts — 40°F, 0°C, 270 K

## Pressure

millibars    inches

one atmosphere 1013.2 mb

## Weather Map Symbols

### Station Model

Temperature (°F) — **28**
Present weather
Visibility (mi) — **½** *
Dewpoint (°F) — **27**
Wind speed

Amount of cloud cover (approximately 75% covered)
**196** Barometric pressure (1019.6 mb)
**+19/** Barometric trend (a steady 1.9-mb rise the past 3 hours)
**.25** Precipitation (inches past 6 hours)

Wind direction (from the southwest)
(1 knot = 1.15 mi/hr)

whole feather = 10 knots
half feather = 5 knots
total = 15 knots

### Present Weather

| | | | | | |
|---|---|---|---|---|---|
| Drizzle | Rain | Smog | Hail | Thunderstorms | Rain Showers |
| Snow | Sleet | Freezing Rain | Fog | Haze | Snow Showers |

### Air Masses

cA  continental arctic
cP  continental polar
cT  continental tropical
mT  maritime tropical
mP  maritime polar

### Front Symbols

Cold
Warm
Stationary
Occluded

### Hurricane

## Selected Properties of Earth's Atmosphere

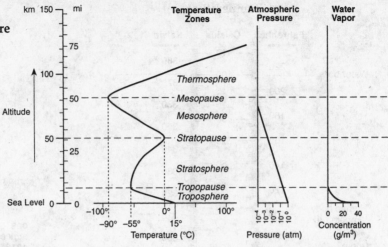

| km 150 | mi | Temperature Zones | Atmospheric Pressure | Water Vapor |

Thermosphere
Mesopause
Mesosphere
Stratopause
Stratosphere
Tropopause
Troposphere

Altitude

Sea Level 0

Temperature (°C)   −100°  −90°  −55°  0°  15°  100°

Pressure (atm)

Concentration (g/m³)   0  20  40

## Electromagnetic Spectrum

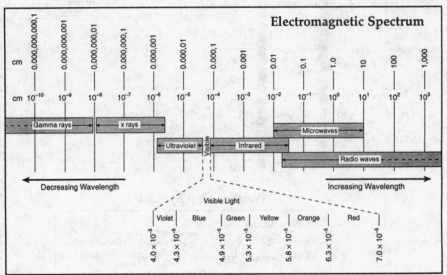

Gamma rays     x rays     Ultraviolet   Visible   Infrared   Microwaves   Radio waves

Decreasing Wavelength                          Increasing Wavelength

Visible Light

| Violet | Blue | Green | Yellow | Orange | Red |

$4.0 \times 10^{-5}$   $4.3 \times 10^{-5}$   $4.9 \times 10^{-5}$   $5.3 \times 10^{-5}$   $5.8 \times 10^{-5}$   $6.3 \times 10^{-5}$   $7.0 \times 10^{-5}$

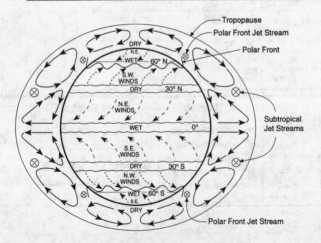

Tropopause
Polar Front Jet Stream
Polar Front
DRY
N.E.
WET  60° N
S.W. WINDS
DRY  30° N
N.E. WINDS
WET  0°
S.E. WINDS
DRY  30° S
N.W. WINDS
WET  60° S
S.E.
DRY
Subtropical Jet Streams
Polar Front Jet Stream

## Planetary Wind and Moisture Belts in the Troposphere

The drawing to the left shows the locations of the belts near the time of an equinox. The locations shift somewhat with the changing latitude of the Sun's vertical ray. In the Northern Hemisphere, the belts shift northward in summer and southward in winter.

# REFERENCE TABLES

## Luminosity and Temperature of Stars

(Name in italics refers to star shown by a ⊕)

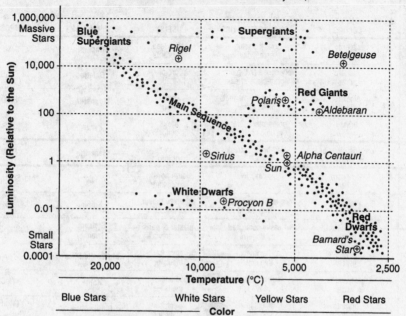

Luminosity is the brightness of stars compared to the brightness of our Sun as seen from the same distance from the observer.

## Solar System Data

| Object | Mean Distance from Sun (millions of km) | Period of Revolution | Period of Rotation | Eccentricity of Orbit | Equatorial Diameter (km) | Mass (Earth = 1) | Density (g/cm³) | Number of Moons |
|---|---|---|---|---|---|---|---|---|
| SUN | — | — | 27 days | — | 1,392,000 | 333,000.00 | 1.4 | — |
| MERCURY | 57.9 | 88 days | 59 days | 0.206 | 4,880 | 0.553 | 5.4 | 0 |
| VENUS | 108.2 | 224.7 days | 243 days | 0.007 | 12,104 | 0.815 | 5.2 | 0 |
| EARTH | 149.6 | 365.26 days | 23 hr 56 min 4 sec | 0.017 | 12,756 | 1.00 | 5.5 | 1 |
| MARS | 227.9 | 687 days | 24 hr 37 min 23 sec | 0.093 | 6,787 | 0.1074 | 3.9 | 2 |
| JUPITER | 778.3 | 11.86 years | 9 hr 50 min 30 sec | 0.048 | 142,800 | 317.896 | 1.3 | 16 |
| SATURN | 1,427 | 29.46 years | 10 hr 14 min | 0.056 | 120,000 | 95.185 | 0.7 | 18 |
| URANUS | 2,869 | 84.0 years | 17 hr 14 min | 0.047 | 51,800 | 14.537 | 1.2 | 21 |
| NEPTUNE | 4,496 | 164.8 years | 16 hr | 0.009 | 49,500 | 17.151 | 1.7 | 8 |
| PLUTO | 5,900 | 247.7 years | 6 days 9 hr | 0.250 | 2,300 | 0.0025 | 2.0 | 1 |
| EARTH'S MOON | 149.6 (0.386 from Earth) | 27.3 days | 27 days 8 hr | 0.055 | 3,476 | 0.0123 | 3.3 | — |

# REFERENCE TABLES

## Properties of Common Minerals

| LUSTER | HARD-NESS | CLEAVAGE | FRACTURE | COMMON COLORS | DISTINGUISHING CHARACTERISTICS | USE(S) | MINERAL NAME | COMPOSITION* |
|---|---|---|---|---|---|---|---|---|
| **Metallic Luster** | 1–2 | ✔ | | silver to gray | black streak, greasy feel | pencil lead, lubricants | **Graphite** | C |
| | 2.5 | ✔ | | metallic silver | very dense (7.6 g/cm³), gray-black streak | ore of lead | **Galena** | PbS |
| | 5.5–6.5 | | ✔ | black to silver | attracted by magnet, black streak | ore of iron | **Magnetite** | $Fe_3O_4$ |
| | 6.5 | | ✔ | brassy yellow | green-black streak, cubic crystals | ore of sulfur | **Pyrite** | $FeS_2$ |
| **Either** | 1–6.5 | | ✔ | metallic silver or earthy red | red-brown streak | ore of iron | **Hematite** | $Fe_2O_3$ |
| **Nonmetallic Luster** | 1 | ✔ | | white to green | greasy feel | talcum powder, soapstone | **Talc** | $Mg_3Si_4O_{10}(OH)_2$ |
| | 2 | | ✔ | yellow to amber | easily melted, may smell | vulcanize rubber, sulfuric acid | **Sulfur** | S |
| | 2 | ✔ | | white to pink or gray | easily scratched by fingernail | plaster of paris and drywall | **Gypsum** (Selenite) | $CaSO_4 \cdot 2H_2O$ |
| | 2–2.5 | ✔ | | colorless to yellow | flexible in thin sheets | electrical insulator | **Muscovite Mica** | $KAl_3Si_3O_{10}(OH)_2$ |
| | 2.5 | ✔ | | colorless to white | cubic cleavage, salty taste | food additive, melts ice | **Halite** | NaCl |
| | 2.5–3 | ✔ | | black to dark brown | flexible in thin sheets | electrical insulator | **Biotite Mica** | $K(Mg,Fe)_3$ $AlSi_3O_{10}(OH)_2$ |
| | 3 | ✔ | | colorless or variable | bubbles with acid | cement, polarizing prisms | **Calcite** | $CaCO_3$ |
| | 3.5 | ✔ | | colorless or variable | bubbles with acid when powdered | source of magnesium | **Dolomite** | $CaMg(CO_3)_2$ |
| | 4 | ✔ | | colorless or variable | cleaves in 4 directions | hydrofluoric acid | **Fluorite** | $CaF_2$ |
| | 5–6 | ✔ | | black to dark green | cleaves in 2 directions at 90° | mineral collections | **Pyroxene** (commonly Augite) | $(Ca,Na)\ (Mg,Fe,Al)$ $(Si,Al)_2O_6$ |
| | 5.5 | ✔ | | black to dark green | cleaves at 56° and 124° | mineral collections | **Amphiboles** (commonly Hornblende) | $CaNa(Mg,Fe)_4\ (Al,Fe,Ti)_3$ $Si_6O_{22}(O,OH)_2$ |
| | 6 | ✔ | | white to pink | cleaves in 2 directions at 90° | ceramics and glass | **Potassium Feldspar** (Orthoclase) | $KAlSi_3O_8$ |
| | 6 | ✔ | | white to gray | cleaves in 2 directions, striations visible | ceramics and glass | **Plagioclase Feldspar** (Na-Ca Feldspar) | $(Na,Ca)AlSi_3O_8$ |
| | 6.5 | | ✔ | green to gray or brown | commonly light green and granular | furnace bricks and jewelry | **Olivine** | $(Fe,Mg)_2SiO_4$ |
| | 7 | | ✔ | colorless or variable | glassy luster, may form hexagonal crystals | glass, jewelry, and electronics | **Quartz** | $SiO_2$ |
| | 7 | | ✔ | dark red to green | glassy luster, often seen as red grains in NYS metamorphic rocks | jewelry and abrasives | **Garnet** (commonly Almandine) | $Fe_3Al_2Si_3O_{12}$ |

*Chemical Symbols:

| | | | | |
|---|---|---|---|---|
| Al = aluminum | Cl = chlorine | H = hydrogen | Na = sodium | S = sulfur |
| C = carbon | F = fluorine | K = potassium | O = oxygen | Si = silicon |
| Ca = calcium | Fe = iron | Mg = magnesium | Pb = lead | Ti = titanium |

✔ = dominant form of breakage

# GLOSSARY

**abrade:** When a glacier slides over a rock, and the rock beneath the glacier is scratched.

**abrasion:** The physical wearing down of rocks as they rub or bounce against each other.

**absolute age:** The age, in years, of an object or event.

**absolute humidity:** The amount of water vapor actually present in the air.

**absolute zero:** The coldest possible temperature

**absorbed:** Taken in

**abyssal plains:** Flat regions of the deep ocean floor, found at the base of the continental rise

**acid rain:** Rain or snow more acidic than normal precipitation

**actual evapotranspiration:** The amount of moisture that actually evaporates.

**adiabatic temperature change:** A change in temperature that is not accompanied by the addition or removal of heat.

**advance:** Downslope movement of glaciers due to gravity and their own weight.

**aerobic:** Oxygen consuming bacteria found in bodies of water.

**aerosol:** Small particles suspended in a gas, usually air.

**air mass:** A large body of air in the troposphere having similar pressure, moisture, wind, and temperature characteristics throughout.

**air pollution:** Harmful materials released into the air.

**air pressure:** (atmospheric pressure) The force, or weight, of the air pushing down on a unit area of surface.

**arid:** Climate in which the total annual precipitation is less than the potential evapotranspiration.

**alluvial fan:** A deposit of sediment formed where the velocity of a river slows as it flows out of the mountains onto the flatland.

**Alpine glacier:** See: valley glacier

**altitude:** The angle of a celestial body above the observer's horizon.

**amount of deviation:** The difference between the measured value and the accepted value.

**amplitude:** The height of the wave

**anaerobic:** Bacteria which live without oxygen.

**anomaly:** A deviation from what is expected.

**angle of insolation:** The angle at which the Sun's rays strike Earth's surface.

**angular unconformity:** Tilted, folded, or faulted rocks which have been eroded and then covered again.

**annular eclipse:** When the Moon is at apogee, the Moon's shadow covers most of the Sun.

**anticyclone:** A high-pressure system in which the winds circle around the center in a clockwise direction in the Northern Hemisphere.

**aphelion:** The point in a planet's orbit that is farthest to the Sun.

**apogee:** The greatest distance between a satellite and its planet.

**apparent diameter:** The diameter an object appears to have, not its actual diameter.

**apparent solar day:** The average time it takes Earth to rotate on its axis, 24 hours.

**aquifer:** Water-bearing rock between two non-water bearing rocks.

**arete:** A jagged, knife-edge ridge formed when two cirques "eat" into the ridge from both sides.

**arc:** A portion of a circular path.

**arches:** Bridges of rock left above openings like caves, sometimes joining two stacks.

**arid:** When the annual total precipitation is less than the potential evapotranspiration.

**asteroid:** Rocks with irregular shapes which orbit the Sun.

**asthenosphere:** The upper part of the mantle which behaves like a thick, plastic fluid.

**Astronomical Unit (AU):** The average distance between Earth and the Sun. (about 150 million kilometers)

**astronomy:** The study of the sky and the objects in the sky; study of the universe.

**atmosphere:** The envelope of gases that surround Earth.

**atmospheric pressure:** The pressure exerted on Earth's surface by the weight of atmosphere.

**atmospheric variable:** Temperature, air pressure, wind and atmospheric transparency are variables that describe weather changes.

**azimuth:** The distance in degrees measured clockwise from the due north position.

**backwash:** Water running back down the beach and under the next waves.

**banding:** The concentrating of minerals into discrete layers in some metamorphic rocks.

**barchan dunes:** Crescent-shaped dunes with the horns of the dune pointing downwind.

**barometer:** An instrument used to measure air pressure.

**barometric pressure:** See atmospheric pressure

**barrier islands:** Sandbars that reach above sea level.

**barycenter:** The common center of gravity of the Earth-Moon system.

**base flow:** Stream discharge which is being fed from the ground water beneath the water table.

**baymouth bar:** Ridge of sediment that cuts off an earlier open bay from the ocean.

**batholith:** The largest of all intrusions, they form the cores of many mountain ranges.

**beach:** A strip of sediment (usually sand or gravel) that extends from the low tide line to a cliff or zone of permanent vegetation.

**beach face:** The steepest part of the beach.

**beds:** (or strata) Layering seen in sedimentary rocks.

**bedrock:** The solid, unweathered portion of the lithosphere.

**bench mark:** A permanent marker indicating the exact elevation above sea level of a location at the time of placement.

**berm:** The wave deposited upper part of the beach which is usually dry and covered by waves only during severe storms.

**Big Bang:** The tremendously powerful explosion of an incredibly dense mass about 15-20 billion years ago that produced the expanding universe that exists today.

**bioclastic:** Rocks formed from the remains of plants and animals.

**biodegradable:** Materials easily decomposed by bacteria.

**black hole:** A region of black surrounded by stars caused when gravity collapses a star inward on itself and it disappears.

**blowout:** A depression of the ground surface caused by wind erosion.

**blue-shift:** When a light source approaches, wavelengths decrease and shift toward the blue end of the visible spectrum.

**breaks:** The collapse of the steep wave front.

**breezes:** Small local horizontal movements of air near Earth's surface.

**calorie:** A unit of heat energy.

**capacity:** The amount of water vapor the atmosphere can hold.

**capillarity:** The ability of water to rise in small openings.

**carbon-14:** A radioactive isotope of carbon used in dating fossils less than 40,000 years old.

**carbonates:** Combinations of carbon and oxygen with other elements.

**carbonation:** Occurs when carbon dioxide unites chemically with minerals.

**carrying power:** The ability of a stream to move particles of different sizes.

**celestial sphere:** The imaginary sphere on which all objects in the sky seem to be located.

**cementation:** The process by which minerals "glue" particles together to form sedimentary rocks.

**Cenozoic Era:** This era represents the most recent 3% of Earth's geologic history.

**change:** The occurrence of an event.

**channel (stream channel):** A long narrow depression eroded by a stream into rock or sediment.

**chemical properties:** The chemical composition of minerals.

**chemical weathering:** Any action that results in a change in the chemical composition of a rock.

**chlorofluorocarbons:** Compounds of carbon, chlorine and fluorine found in refrigerators, air conditioners and aerosol cans that is the main cause of ozone depletion.

**chronometer:** An accurate clock which keeps the time at the Prime Meridian and the solar time at any other meridian.

**cinder cone:** A type of volcano that is steep and composed of volcanic ash.

**circumference:** Distance around Earth

**circum-Pacific belt:** The area circling the rim of the Pacific ocean.

**circumpolar constellations and stars:** Constellations and stars which never set below the horizon.

**circumpolar stars:** constellations and stars that move in a counterclockwise direction around Polaris and never set below the horizon. They are located between the northern horizon and Polaris.

**cirque:** A bowl shaped erosional scar on the side of a mountain formed by frost action and headword erosion of a glacier.

**cirrus:** (high clouds) Associated with fair weather

**clastic:** Fragmental particles of rocks (see: particles)

**classification:** Grouping of objects and events based on observable properties.

**cleavage:** The tendency of a mineral to split along one or more smooth, flat surfaces, or planes.

**climate:** The average weather of a region over an extended period of time.

**closed energy system:** One in which no energy from outside the system can get in and no energy from the inside can get out.

**clouds:** Collections of tiny water droplets or ice crystals suspended in the atmosphere.

**coast:** All the land near the sea including the beach and a strip of land inland from it.

**coastal blowout dune:** (Parabolic Dunes) Dunes the depth of which are controlled by the water table.

**cold front:** leading edge of a cold air mass.

**collision boundary:** The boundary between two continental plates.

**colloids:** Extremely small particles suspended in a medium, usually a gas or a liquid.

**color:** One of the properties of minerals used in their identification.

**comets:** Chunks of ice with elongated orbits around the Sun having flowing tails which always point away from the Sun regardless of the direction of its motion.

**composition:** The components of which materials are formed.

**compression:** The process by which sedimentary rock is formed by pressure of overlying sediments.

**compressional waves:** (or P-waves) Are like sound waves, and they cause particles of rock through with they travel to vibrate in a back -and-forth motion in the same direction as the wave is traveling.

**condensation:** Change in phase from gas to liquid.

**condensation nuclei:** Particles of dust or salt from the ocean.

**conduction:** The transfer of heat from molecule to molecule.

**conservation of energy:** The principle which states that energy can neither be created nor destroyed, but can be transformed from one type to another without any loss of energy within a closed system.

**constellation:** Stars that appear to be grouped in patterns forming the outlines of people, animals and physical objects in the sky.

**contact metamorphism:** The changing of an existing rock through contact with hot, liquid rock (magma or lava).

**continental:** Air masses that develop over land.

**continental climate:** The climate of areas far removed from the moderating effects of large bodies of water.

**continental crust:** The granitic rock that makes up the continental portion of the lithosphere.

**continental drift:** The idea that the continents are moving across Earth's surface.

**continental shelf** Gently sloping surface which extends under the ocean from the shoreline to a depth of about 100-200 meters.

**continental slope:** Relatively steep, extending downward as deep as 2 kilometers from the shelf.

**continental rise:** Wedge of sediment that extends from the lower part of the continental slope to the deep sea floor.

**contour line:** A line on a map connecting points of equal elevation.

**contour map:** A map which shows elevations of the surface it depicts.

**contour plowing:** Crops are planted in rows parallel to the contours of the land.

**convection:** The transfer of heat energy by currents.

**convection cell:** A circulatory flow of energy set in motion by unequal heating of a fluid

**convection current:** Convection cell

**convergence zone:** A region where two streams of air come together at Earth's surface.

**convergent boundaries:** When two plates collide

**coordinate system:** A system of intersecting lines used to determine locations on Earth's surface.

**core:** The innermost region of Earth.

**Coriolis effect:** The tendency of matter moving across Earth's surface to be deflected from a straight-line path.

**correlation:** The matching of rock units or events in separate rock formations.

**creep:** (soil creep) A slow movement of soil or weathered material which is so slow that it is difficult to measure over a period of days or weeks

**crest:** The top of a wave

**crevasse:** Fissures or cracks in the ice which formed as the glacier moved.

**crop rotation:** The alternation of crops on the same soil from year to year.

**cross-bedding:** The result of sediments being deposited at an angle to the horizontal.

**crust:** The thin, outermost layer of the lithosphere.

**crystal:** A solid with a definite shape and whose atoms are arranged in a definite, repeating pattern.

**crystalline:** has crystals

**cumulonimbus clouds:** Large vertical development thunder head clouds.

**cumulus:** Fluffy clouds associated with fair weather.

**currents:** Vertical movements of air or movements of the ocean due to differences in density

**cycles:** Wavelengths

**cyclic change:** Any change that repeats itself in some predictable pattern.

**cyclone:** A low-pressure system in which the winds circle around the center in a counterclock-wise direction in the Northern Hemisphere.

**deficit:** When all the water in the soil is used up and more is needed.

**deflation:** Removal of clay, silt, and sand particles from the ground surface by wind.

**degrees:** A unit division of a temperature scale or a unit of angular measure.

**delta:** A deposit of sediment at the mouth of a river where the river loses its carrying power as it enters a quiet body of water.

**dendritic pattern:** Drainage characterized by branching similar to that of the limbs or roots of trees.

**density:** The quantity of matter contained in a given amount of space; density = mass per unit volume.

**depletion:** Occurs when too many nutrients are removed from the soil for a crop to grow.

**deposition:** The release of sediments from an erosional system; also called sedimentation

**depressions:** Holes dug into Earth's surface.

**desertification:** destruction of marginal land resulting from overgrazing and removal of native vegetation by cropping.

**dew:** Water vapor which condenses directly onto a cold surface.

**dewpoint:** The temperature at which condensation occurs.

**dike:** Slabs of intrusive igneous rocks that cut across the rock layers they intrude.

**direct rays:** Rays of sunlight that strike Earth's surface at an angle of 90'; perpendicular rays.

**distorted structure:** The bending and warping of the bands in a metamorphic rock.

**divergence zone:** A region where two streams of air move apart at Earth's surface.

**diverging boundaries:** Occur when two ocean plates are moving apart.

**Doppler effect:** The apparent change in wave frequency as an energy source moves toward or away from the observer.

**downstream:** direction in which the water is flowing.

**drainage basin:** The area drained by a stream or a system of streams.

**drainage patterns:** Patterns formed by streams in a drainage basin.

**drift:** Sediment carried by glaciers or meltwater of glaciers.

**drizzle:** Fine drops of water which gently float to Earth's surface.

**drumlin:** Ground moraine reshaped, by later glaciers, into stream lined hills of till.

**dry adiabatic lapse rate:** When a sample of dry air rises or descends, its temperature changes adiabatically at a rate of 10°C per kilometer.

**duration of insolation:** The length of time insolation is received at a location in a day; the number of hours of sunlight.

**dune:** A mound or ridge of sand deposited by the wind.

**dynamic equilibrium:** A condition in which opposing processes are balanced.

**earthquake:** Shaking of Earth's crust caused by rapid displacement of rocks, usually along a fault.

**eccentricity:** The out-of-roundness of an ellipse

**eclipse:** When either the Moon passes between Earth and the Sun or the Moon is in Earth's shadow.

**ecliptic:** The apparent path of the Sun against the background stars.

**ecosphere:** Region surrounding the Sun in which the temperatures of a planet are suitable to support life.

**electromagnetic energy:** Energy that has the properties of transverse waves.

**electromagnetic spectrum:** The entire range of electromagnetic wavelengths.

**ellipse:** A closed curve around two fixed points, called foci. The orbits of all planets around the Sun are ellipses.

**elliptical galaxies:** Blobs or non spirals which can be circular or flattened.

**El Niño:** Periods of ocean warming along the Pacific coast of South America.

**end moraine:** A ridge of till at the front end of a glacier which has remained stationary-for a period of years.

**energy:** The ability to do work.

**energy sink:** An object which takes in energy.

**energy source:** An object which gives off energy.

**entrenched:** When a stream gradient is steepened and the stream cuts a deeper channel into an older stream bed.

**environmental equilibrium:** Balance of changes within our environment.

**environmental factors:** Include forces of uplift and erosion, the effects of climate changes etc.

**epicenter:** The point on Earth's surface directly above the focus of an earthquake.

**equinox**: A time of year when the noon Sun is directly overhead at the equator, the hours of daylight and darkness are equal, and the entire Earth views the sunrise directly in the east and sunset directly in the west. The vernal equinox occurs on/or about March 21 and marks the first day of spring in the Northern Hemisphere. The autumnal equinox occurs on/or about September 23 and marks the first day of autumn in the Northern Hemisphere.

**equilibrium**: The condition of balance between opposite forces.

**erratic**: Large rock deposited by a glacier that is different from the rock type beneath it.

**erosion**: The carrying away, or transporting, of weathered rock materials by agents such as water, wind, glacial ice or gravity.

**erosional-depositional system**: Combines the erosional process, the transporting agents, and the process of deposition.

**escarpment**: A steep slope or cliff formed in sedimentary rocks due to the presence of competent (weather-resistant) rocks.

**esker**: The sinuous deposits from the rivers of glacial meltwater.

**estuaries**: Drowned river valleys

**ethics**: Principles of right and wrong established by society or individuals.

**eutrophication**: The process of increasing the growth of algae by adding sewage effluents and sewage to a pond or lake which uses up dissolved oxygen making the pond unfit for fish or other animals.

**evaporation**: The process of changing from a liquid to a gas.

**evaporites**: Rocks formed due to the evaporation of water.

**evapotranspiration**: The combined processes of evaporation and transpiration.

**event**: When the properties of matter or a system are altered

**extrusion**: A body of igneous rock that forms when lava cools at Earth's surface

**extrusive igneous rock**: Igneous rock that forms at Earth's surface.

**faceted**: Pebbles and boulders dragged by a glacier are abraded, giving them a flat surface

**fault**: A crack or zone of weakness in Earth's crust along which movement occurs during an earthquake.

**felsic**: Igneous rocks rich in potassium feldspar and quartz and light in color.

**fetch**: The distance that the wind has travelled across the open water.

**field**: Any region of space that has some measurable value at every point in that region.

**fjords**: Long, steep sided bays carved by glaciers, filled with water.

**firn (neve)**: Snowflakes reformed under the pressure of the snow above into granular snow.

**flood plain**: The land between the stream and the steep walls of the valley that is usually covered by the stream during floods.

**focus**: (1) One of the two fixed points in an ellipse; (2) The point within the crust where an earthquake originates.

**fog**: A cloud resting on Earth's surface.

**folded strata**: Layers of sedimentary rock that have been bent or warped by crustal forces.

**foliated**: When the minerals are aligned in rocks such that they are easy to split.

**fossil:** Any evidence of former life.

**fossil fuels:** Energy resources formed from the remains of plants and animals that lived long ago.

**Foucault Pendulum:** A freely swinging pendulum whose path appears to change over time in a predictable manner; provides evidence of Earth's rotation.

**fracture:** Minerals which break with rough or uneven surfaces.

**fracture zones:** Ocean or land ridges broken into segments by faults.

**frame of reference:** Any quantity or characteristic that can be used as a basis for comparison. Time and space are frames of reference for studying change.

**free oxygen:** Oxygen not combined with other elements.

**freezing:** Liquid to solid phase change requiring the removal of heat.

**frequency:** The number of waves that pass a particular point in a given period of time.

**frictional drag:** Friction at the interface of Earth's surface and the atmosphere caused by the Coriolis effect.

**front:** The interface between two different air masses.

**frontal wedging:** The action of cool air creating a barrier over which warmer, lighter air rises.

**frost:** Water vapor which has come in contact with a freezing surface and had sublimated. (frost is *not* frozen dew)

**galaxy:** A system of billions of stars.

**geocentric model:** Any celestial model that has Earth at its center.

**Geologic history:** Study and interpretation of Earth's past.

**geologic time scale:** The division of geologic time into intervals in chronological order, based largely on fossil evidence and on evidence of significant geologic events.

**geosyncline:** A large, shallow region near a shoreline that receives vast amounts of sedimentary deposits; (theory) It is believed that these basins sink under the weight of accumulated sediments and eventually undergo uplift to form mountains and continental margins.

**glacial erosion:** Processes including the formation of U-shaped valleys and other features.

**glacial lakes:** Lakes formed when melting ice sheets released huge volumes of water, flooding lowlands.

**glacier:** A large, long-lasting mass of ice which formed on the land and moves downslope due to gravity.

**global warming:** An increase in Earth's average surface temperature caused by an increase in the greenhouse effect.

**graded:** Having a smooth gradient.

**graded bedding:** A layering of sediment that shows a gradual change in particle size, from smallest at the top to largest at the bottom.

**gradient:** The rate of change from location to location within a field.

**graphic models:** The use of graphs to illustrate certain relationships.

**gravitation:** The force of attraction that is present between any two objects in the universe.

**gravity:** The force that pulls objects toward the center of Earth.

**greenhouse effect:** Transmission of shortwave solar radiation by the atmosphere combined with selective absorption of longer wavelength terrestrial radiation, especially by water vapor and carbon dioxide, causing warming of the atmosphere.

**groins:** They are built perpendicular to the shore to trap moving sand and widen a beach to protect beaches that are losing sand from longshore drifting.

**ground moraine:** As ice melts, rock material carried by the glacier is deposited on the ground.

**ground water:** Liquid water that enters the regolith by infiltration.

**guyots:** Volcanic islands that have stopped growing and have been flattened by wave action.

**hail: (hail stones)** Ice pellets which may be repeatedly forced up into colder air and allowed to fall into warmer air having an onion-like appearance of layers of ice .

**half-life:** The time required for one-half of the unstable atoms in a radioactive sample to decay to a different isotope.

**hanging valley:** Valleys formed by glaciers high above the main valley.

**hardness:** The resistance of a mineral to being scratched.

**hazardous wastes:** Solid, liquid or gaseous materials in the ground which are potentially harmful to humans and the environment.

**headlands:** Points of land between coastal valleys.

**heat energy:** Energy that is transferred from one body to another because of a difference in temperature between the two bodies.

**heliocentric model:** Any celestial model that has the Sun at its center.

**hiatus:** A break or gap in the rock record.

**high:** A high-pressure system, or anticyclone, in which winds move in a clockwise direction around the center in the Northern Hemisphere.

**high tides:** see tides

**hook:** A spit with a curved end.

**horizon:** The line around the edge of Earth where the celestial sphere meets Earth.

**horizontal sorting:** The sorting of particles of sediments into layers in which the particles are sorted horizontally, ranging from largest to smallest in the direction of travel of the transporting agent.

**horn:** A sharp peak that remains after ice has cut back into sides of a mountain on three or more sides.

**Hubble's Law:** The relationship between distance and speeds of galaxies in space. The farther the galaxy, the faster it is moving away from us.

**Hubble Space Telescope:** A telescope sent into orbit in 1990 having a resolution reported to be 50 times more sensitive than ground-based telescopes with 10 times more clarity.

**human activities:** Activities such as lands stripped of trees and vegetation to accommodate agricultural needs which have changed the environment.

**humid:** When the annual total precipitation is greater than the potential evapotranspiration.

**humid climate:** A climate where precipitation is equal to or greater than potential evaporation during most of the year.

**hurricane:** A doughnut shaped ring of strong counterclockwise winds over 115 kilometers per hour surrounding an extremely low pressure at the center.

**hydration:** Occurs when water unites chemically with minerals.

**hydrolic cycle:** See water cycle

**hydrosphere:** All of the water that rests on and in the lithosphere.

**iceberg:** Blocks of ice that break off a glacier and float free.

**ice sheet:** A thick mass of ice that covers over 50,000 square kilometers.

**igneous rock:** A nonsedimentary rock formed by the cooling and solidifying of liquid rock (magma or lava).

**impact crater:** The result of a collision of a large meteorite with Earth's surface.

**impermeable:** Materials that do not allow water to pass through.

**index fossil:** A fossil that is useful in correlating and dating rocks because of its wide geographic distribution and small range of existence.

**inference:** An interpretation of one or more observations.

**inferring:** Making inferences

**infiltration:** The seeping of water into the regolith, where it becomes ground water.

**inner core:** The innermost "layer" of Earth, believed to consist of iron and nickel.

**insolation:** Incoming solar radiation; that part of the Sun's radiation that is received at Earth's surface.

**instruments:** Objects which improve our ability to observe and make measurements.

**interface:** The boundary between regions having different properties.

**intensity:** Refers to a rate of energy.

**intensity of insolation:** The rate at which solar energy is received by a given area of Earth's surface in a unit of time.

**intensity of radiation:** The rate at which energy is radiated from an object.

**International Date Line:** Roughly follows the 180° meridian and is a continuation of the Prime meridian on the other side of the globe.

**intrusion:** A body of igneous rock formed by the cooling of magma beneath Earth's surface

**intrusive igneous rock:** Igneous rock formed beneath Earth's surface.

**iron oxides:** compound formed when iron combines with oxygen.

**iron sulfides:** compound formed when iron combines with sulfur.

**irregular galaxies:** They have no definite shape.

**isobar:** An isoline that connects points of equal atmospheric pressure on a weather map.

**isoline:** A line used on a model of a field, such as a map, that connects points of equal value within that field.

**isostasy:** A principle that states that Earth's crust is in a state of equilibrium and that any change in the mass of one part will be neutralized by a change in the mass of some other part This principle is used to explain why mountains "rise" as they are eroded.

**iso-surface:** A surface in a model of a three-dimensional field in which all points on the surface have the same value.

**isotherm:** An isoline that connects points of equal temperature on a weather map.

**isotopes:** Atoms of the same element that have the same number of protons in their nuclei but different numbers of neutrons; isotopes of the same element have different masses.

**jet stream:** A narrow band of very fast moving westerly winds at high levels in the middle latitudes.

**jetties:** Rock walls designed to protect the entrance of a harbor from sediment deposition and storm waves.

**joint:** A crack in a rock along which there is no displacement.

**Jovian planets:** Planets which are similar to Jupiter.

**kame:** Short, steep sided hills of outwash that began as a meltwater stream or lake deposit.

**karst topography:** A limestone area pitted with sink holes and caves.

**kettle:** A steep hole left behind when an ice block melts.

**kinetic energy:** Energy of motion

**laboratory models:** Constructs that are used to simulate natural events.

**laccolith:** An intrusive igneous rock that forms between two rock layers, bulging up to form domelike masses.

**lagoon:** A body of water separating the barrier island from the mainland.

**land breeze:** When the air blows from the land out to sea due to difference in air temperature

**landlocked lakes:** Lakes that do not drain into the ocean.

**landscape:** The characteristics of Earth's surface resulting from the interaction of hydrosphere, atmosphere, and lithosphere.

**landscape region:** An area of Earth's surface that has characteristics that distinguish it from other areas.

**landslides:** Rapid downhill movements, primarily of soil and weathered debris.

**La Nina:** Conditions of unusually cold ocean temperatures in the Equatorial Pacific following an El Nino.

**latent heat:** Energy taken in or given off by a substance during a change of phase; such transfers of energy do not involve any change in temperature of the substance.

**lateral fault:** One section of rock moves horizontal relative to the section on the other side of the fault.

**lateral moraine:** Piles of till along the sides of a glacier.

**latitude:** Angular distance north or south of the equator.

**Laurentide Ice Sheet:** The glacier that covered Eastern North America during the Ice Ages

**lava:** Magma that reaches Earth's surface.

**lava plateau:** Lava that has spread over the surface for up to thousands of miles and solidifies

**length:** Measure of a distance between two points.

**leveling forces:** Forces that tend to lower the surface of the land; these forces include weathering, erosion, deposition, and subsidence.

**light year:** The distance light travels in one year.

**lithosphere:** The rigid crust and uppermost part of the mantle.

**load:** The material carried by an agent of erosion.

**loess:** Fine-grained, wind blown deposits of dust

**longitude:** Angular distance east or west of the Prime Meridian.

**longshore drift:** The movement of sediment parallel to the shore as waves strike the shoreline at an angle.

**low:** A low-pressure, or cyclone, in which the winds move in a counterclockwise direction in the Northern Hemisphere.

**low tides:** See tides

**lunar eclipse:** When the moon moves into Earth's shadow during a full moon.

**luster:** The way in which light is reflected from the surface of a mineral.


**mafic:** Igneous rocks rich in dark plagioclase feldspar and pyroxene and dark in color.

**magma:** Molten rock beneath Earth's surface.

**magnitude:** Measure of the amount of energy released during an earthquake.

**main sequence:** The band stretching diagonally across the Hertsprung-Russell diagram representing the majority of stars.

**mantle:** The solid "layer" of Earth's interior directly below the crust.

**marine climate:** A climate that displays the moderating effect of a large body of water.

**marine terrace:** A wide gently sloping platform (offshore from the beach face) that may be exposed at low tide.

**maritime:** Air masses that develop over water.

**mass:** The amount of matter in a body.

**mass movement:** (mass wasting) Movement of earth materials downslope under the influence of gravity.

**mathematical model:** Formulas and equations

**mature landscape:** One that has low rounded hills and broad flat valleys.

**maturity:** A stage of the development of a river during which side cutting becomes greater than down cutting and a flood plain forms.

**mean solar day:** The day consisting of exactly 24 hours.

**meander:** The bend in a river.

**measurement:** A means of describing observations using numbers.

**medial moraine:** Forms where two glaciers come together -the lateral moraines join and are carried as a single ridge of till.

**melting:** Changing a solid to a liquid.

**meltwater:** Water from the melting snow in a glacier.

**mental models:** Representations of ideas or images of something one in one's mind which one is trying to understand.

**meridian:** Imaginary semicircles on Earth's surface representing longitude which converge at the poles.

**mesopause:** The top of the mesosphere.

**mesosphere:** The layer of the atmosphere above the stratosphere.

**Mesozoic Era:** This time period represents about 3.5% of Earth's geologic history.

**metallic:** Shines like polished metal.

**metamorphic rock:** A nonsedimentary rock formed as a result of intense heat and pressure within the lithosphere.

**meteorite:** A rock that is large enough to survive its descent through the atmosphere and reach the ground.

**meteoroids:** Fragments of rocks or ice traveling in space.

**meteorology:** The study of weather.

**meteors:** Streaks of light caused by meteoroids passing through Earth's atmosphere at high speed.

**mid-ocean ridges:** Chains of mountains under the oceans that are associated with ocean-floor spreading and plate formation.

**mid-latitude cyclone:** A cyclone where a cold front catches up with the warm front They tend to last about seven days.

**Milky Way Galaxy:** Visible as a band of light across the dark night sky.

**millibar:** A unit used to measure atmospheric pressure; 1013.2 millibars is equivalent to a pressure of 29.92 inches of mercury, which is known as one atmosphere of pressure.

**mineral:** A naturally occurring, inorganic solid with a crystalline structure.

**modified Mercalli scale:** A description of an earthquake by the measure of a earthquakes effect on people and buildings.

**models:** Smaller copies or representations of a given system.

**Moho interface:** A shorthand term for the Mohorovicic discontinuity, the interface between the crust and mantle.

**Mohorovicic discontinuity:** See Moho interface

**moist adiabatic lapse rate:** When a sample of moist air rises, latent heat is released to the surrounding air during condensation, and the cooling rate slows to 6°C per kilometer.

**monominerallic:** Rocks composed of only one mineral.

**moraine:** A mass of glacial till left behind after a glacier has melted.

**mountain:** A landscape feature of high elevation.

**monsoon:** Large-scale seasonal changes in winds due to differences in heating and cooling of land and water similar to the smaller-scale local daily land and sea breezes

**mouth:** The end of a river

**mudflows:** Downhill movements of fine-grained surface material that has been saturated with water.

**natural levees:** Broad low ridges along both sides of the stream that form during times of flooding.

**natural bridges:** Formations created when a stream breaks through the wall of two entrenched meanders on opposite sides of a ridge.

**neap tide:** Tides occurring during quarter phases with lowest range between high and low tide.

**nebula:** Huge masses of dust and hydrogen gas that condense in space producing energy and forming a star.

**neutron star:** Pressure squeezes the electrons into atomic nuclei to produce neutrons.

**neve (firn):** See firn

**new moon:** The entire illuminated portion of the Moon is facing away from Earth.

**nimbostratus:** Low rain clouds

**non-metallic:** Having no metallic shine.

# GLOSSARY

**nonconformity:** Interfaces formed when sedimentary rocks are deposited on top of an eroded surface of igneous and/or metamorphic rocks.

**nonrenewable:** When energy resources are used faster than they can be replaced.

**nonsedimentary rock:** Rock that is not formed directly from sediments.

**normal fault:** One section of rock moves down relative to the section on the other side of the fault.

**North Star:** See Polaris

**nuclear fusion:** Thermonuclear reaction resulting from the compression of a nebula by gravitational forces.

**neutron star:** Created when a white dwarf collapses.

**oblate spheroid:** A sphere that is slightly flattened at the poles; Earth is an oblate spheroid.

**observation:** An interaction of one or more of the senses - sight, hearing, touch, taste, or smell - with the environment or surroundings.

**occluded front:** A weather front that forms when a cold front moves into a warm front, forcing the warm air to rise.

**ocean-floor spreading:** The idea that the oceanic crust spreads outward from the mid-ocean ridges.

**ocean currents:** Water beneath and at the surface of oceans that flow like great rivers without solid banks.

**oceanic crust:** The basaltic crustal rock beneath the oceans.

**off shore breeze:** Air blowing from the land to sea.

**old age:** A stage in the development of a river when the valley floor becomes wider than the river meanders can fill.

**old landscape:** Ones in which uplands have been eroded almost to sea level.

**on shore breeze:** Air blowing from the sea onto land.

**oozes:** Sediments of microscopic shells

**orbit:** The path of a planet around the Sun or a satellite around Earth.

**orbital speed:** The speed of an orbiting body in its orbit at a given time.

**ore:** Minerals that contain a high percentage of some commercially valuable substance

**original horizontality:** A principle that states that sedimentary rocks are originally formed in horizontal layers.

**organic:** Related to plants and animals; e.g. organic sedimentary rocks which form from the remains of plants and animals.

**organic decay:** Occurs when acids, which are formed when plants and animals decay, dissolve in water .

**orographic effects:** The effects that mountains have on climates.

**orographic lifting:** The action of mountains which act as barriers to the flow of air forcing the air to rise to get to the other side.

**outcrop:** Bedrock exposed at Earth's surface.

**outer core:** The "layer" of Earth's interior between the mantle and the inner core; believed to be a liquid.

**outgassing:** The release of gasses from the interior of Earth due to internal heat and chemical reaction.

**outwash:** Rock material deposited by the meltwater of a glacier.

**outwash plain:** A body of outwash that forms a broad plain beyond a moraine.

**oxbow lake:** The curved section of river channels that have been abandoned by the river .

**oxidation:** Occurs when oxygen unites chemically with minerals.

**P-waves:** See primary waves.

**Paleozoic Era:** This time period represents about 5% of Earth's geologic history.

**parallel:** (of latitude) Circles on which all points are the same angular distance from the equator and have the same latitude.

**parallelism:** The axis remains parallel to its previous position as Earth revolves around the Sun.

**parallel unconformities:** (disconformities) Occur when parallel rock layers of different ages are separated by en erosional surface.

**particles:** (fragmental, or clastics) Rocks formed from sediments made up of rock fragments held together by cement.

**particulates:** Tiny solids suspended in the atmosphere.

**pelagic:** Fine-grained clay and ocean sediments that include skeletons of microscopic organisms.

**peneplane:** Region that has been reduced by erosion to a nearly flat surface.

**penumbra:** The partial darkness created during an eclipse.

**percentage error:** The amount of error in a measurement expressed as a percent.

**percent deviation from accepted value:** The difference between the measured value and the accepted value divided by the accepted value and multiplied by 100%.

**perigee:** The closest distance of a satellite and its planet.

**perihelion:** The point in a planet's elliptical orbit that is closest to the Sun.

**period:** (1) The time required for a planet to complete one revolution around the Sun; a planet's year; (2) a division of the geologic time scale.

**permeability:** The ability of the regolith to allow water to pass through.

**permeable:** Materials that allow water to pass through.

**phase:** (1) Another term for the state of a sample of matter; (2) the shape formed by the lighted portion of the Moon's surface.

**phase change:** A change in state of solids, liquids or gases.

**photosynthesis:** The manufacture of sugars and starches from carbon dioxide and **water in the presence of sunlight.**

**physical weathering:** Occurs when rocks are cracked, split or broken into smaller pieces.

**physiographic provinces:** Landscape regions with similar characteristics.

**physical model:** Uses observations of sight to provide information.

**physical properties:** The properties of minerals which are largely due to the internal arrangement of their atoms.

**physical weathering:** Is the condition where rock is cracked, split, or broken into smaller pieces called sediments with no change in the rock composition.

**plain:** A landscape of low elevation and gentle slopes, usually underlain by horizontal bedrock.

**planetary wind system:** The belts of prevailing winds found between Earth's pressure zones.

**plateau:** A landscape of relatively high elevation and horizontal sedimentary rocks.

**plate tectonic theory:** The theory stating that Earth's crust is made up of several crustal sections called plates; these plates are slowly "floating" across Earth's surface, driven by giant convection currents in the asthenosphere.

**pluton:** Large masses of intrusive igneous rock.

**plutonic rock:** See intrusive igneous rocks.

**polar:** Air masses that develop over higher latitudes, tend to be cool.

**Polaris:** The North Star, which is located almost directly above Earth's geographic North Pole

**pollutants:** Substances or forms of energy that pollute the environment.

**polluted:** The condition wherein the concentration of any substance or form of energy reaches a proportion that adversely affects humans.

**pollution:** The presence of pollutants in the environment to such a degree as to have an adverse effect on plant and animal life.

**polyminerallic:** Rocks composed of more than one mineral.

**porosity:** The amount of open pore space between particles of a material.

**potential energy:** Stored energy; energy an object or system has due to its position or state.

**potential evapotranspiration:** The amount of water that would evaporate if sufficient water were available.

**Precambrian:** This time period represents the first 85% of Earth history.

**precipitation:** (1) The falling of liquid or solid water from clouds; (2) the process by which dissolved substances come out of solution to form solids.

**prediction:** An inference based on observations that indicate what will happen in the future.

**pressure gradient:** The rate of change in air pressure over a specific distance

**Prime Meridian:** The reference line for longitude, which passes through Greenwich, England.

**primary waves:** Compression waves produced by an earthquake; also called P-waves.

**Principle of Original horizontality:** See Original Horizontality.

**Principle of Supreposition:** See Superposition.

**Principle of Uniformitarianism:** See Uniformitarianism.

**probability of occurrence:** The relationships among atmospheric variables as they relate to predictions.

**profile:** A side view of Earth's surface.

**psychrometer:** An instrument used to measure the amount of moisture in the atmosphere.

**pulsar:** A rapidly spinning neutron star.

**radial pattern:** Drainage pattern found where streams radiate out from a central point on a large single peak that looks like the spokes of a wheel.

**radiation:** The emission of energy in the form of electromagnetic waves.

**radiative balance:** A condition in which a body gives off as much heat as it receives.

**radioactive dating:** Use of radioactive isotopes to determine absolute age of an object.

**radioactive decay:** The breakdown of the nuclei of unstable atoms into more stable atoms of the same or other elements.

**radioactivity:** See radioactive decay.

**rain:** Large drops of water which fall to Earth's surface.

**rain shadow:** An area where very little precipitation falls, often on the leeward side of mountains.

**rate of change:** How long it takes for a given change to occur; change in field value divided by time.

**recessional moraine:** Forms when a glacier recedes for a while and then becomes stationary -part of the end moraine.

**recede:** Ice in a glacier melts back faster than the ice sheet moves downslope; the glacier appears to move backward.

**rectangular pattern:** Drainage pattern which develops where the rock is strongly jointed or faulted and the streams tend to follow the pattern.

**recharge:** The addition of water to the soil storage; recharge occurs when precipitation exceeds potential evapotranspiration.

**recrystallization:** A process in which rocks undergo change without true melting.

**red giant:** Large stars that are produced when the shell expands, its surface cools and the gases glow with a reddish hue.

**red-shift:** As the source of visible light moves away from the observer, the wavelengths increase, creating a shift toward the red end of the visible spectrum.

**reflection:** A change in direction of waves when they strike the surface of a material; a reflected wave leaves the reflecting surface at the same angle at which it arrived.

**refraction:** The "bending" of a wave as it crosses the interface of two materials of different density.

**regolith:** All the loose, unconsolidated material at Earth's surface.

**regional metamorphism:** occurs when large areas of rock are under intense heat and pressure.

**relative age:** The age of rocks or events in relation to the age of some other rocks or events.

**relative humidity:** The ratio of the amount of water vapor in the air to the maximum amount of water vapor the air could hold at the given conditions of temperature and pressure.

**residual sediment:** Weathered material that is resting on the bed rock from which it formed

**residual soil:** Soil formed from the rock material beneath the soil.

**retrograde motion:** The apparent backward movement of the planets with respect to the stars beyond.

**reverse fault:** One section of rock moves upward relative to the section on the other side of the fault.

**reversed polarity:** When Earth's magnetic polarity was opposite from what it is at present.

**revolution:** The movement of one body around another.

**Richter scale:** A numerical description of an earthquake's magnitude.

**ridges:** Undersea mountain ranges in the ocean basins.

**rift valleys:** Valleys that develop in mid-ocean ridges.

**rip currents:** Strong narrow currents that flow straight out to sea through the surf zone.

# GLOSSARY

**rock:** A naturally formed mass that is usually composed of two or more minerals.

**Rock Cycle:** the model that describes how rocks of all types can be constantly "recycled" or changed into other types of rocks.

**rock flour:** Powder produced by rocks grinding against each other.

**rock forming minerals:** minerals which form rocks, (about ten to fifteen of the 2500 minerals classified).

**rotation:** The turning of an object on its own axis.

**runoff:** The moving of liquid water on Earth's surface.

**S-waves:** See secondary waves.

**saltation:** The bouncing of material along a stream bed.

**salinity:** The saltiness of the ocean.

**sandbars:** Ridges of sand parallel to the shoreline, usually underwater.

**sanitary landfills:** Sites where wastes are disposed of by burying them.

**saturation:** The condition of being filled-to capacity.

**saturation vapor pressure:** The vapor pressure of a sample of air when it is filled to capacity

**sea arches:** Bridges of rock left above openings like caves.

**sea breezes:** When the air blows from the sea onto the land due to differences in air temperature over the land and water.

**sea cliffs:** Steep slopes that erode as waves undercut them.

**seamounts:** Volcanic mountains, found at hot spots, rising 1,000 m above the ocean floor.

**seasons:** Periods of the year with characteristic weather conditions.

**scalar quantity:** An amount which has magnitude (size), but no direction.

**scattered:** Refracted and reflected

**secondary wave:** A transverse earthquake wave, also called an S-wave.

**sediment:** Weathered rock particles; particles carried by a transporting agent.

**sedimentary rocks:** Rocks formed as a result of compaction and cementation of sediments.

**sedimentation:** Particles carried by an agent of erosion that are dropped and deposited.

**sediment laden flow:** Transporting medium with sediments.

**seeding:** Placing condensation nuclei into the atmosphere where there is some available water vapor in an attempt to make it rain.

**seismic waves:** The energy waves set in motion by an earthquake.

**seismogram:** The product of the seismograph.

**seismograph:** An instrument used to record seismic waves.

**shadow zone:** A zone on Earth's surface where no seismic waves are received when an earthquake occurs.

**shield cone:** A type of volcano with gentle slopes composed of volcanic lava.

**sidereal day:** The time it takes Earth to complete one rotation on its axis (23 hours, 56 minutes, and 4 seconds).

**sidereal month:** The time it takes for a satellite to complete one revolution around the planet.

**silicates:** Combinations of silicone and oxygen with other elements.

**silicon-oxygen tetrahedron:** The structural unit of minerals composed largely of oxygen and silicon, which is made up of four oxygen atoms and one silicon atom.

**sill:** Slabs of intrusive igneous rock parallel to the rocks they intrude.

**sink holes:** saucer-shaped holes left on the surface of the land when carbonic acid dissolves limestone in the ground.

**slip face:** The steep slope of a dune.

**sleet:** Rain which freezes as it falls.

**slope:** The inclined surface of a land feature.

**slump:** Downward slipping of rock material, usually with a backward rotation.

**smog:** A combination of aerosols and water vapor in stagnant air.

**snow:** Ice crystals that form as a result of sublimation and grow large enough to fall to Earth's surface.

**snow line:** The boundary between the upper glacier where snow accumulates and the lower glacier where the ice melts.

**soil:** The part of the regolith that will support plants that have roots.

**soil association:** A unit of soil classification made up of soils with similar characteristics.

**soil horizon:** A layer of soil with given characteristics.

**soil profile:** A cross section view of the soil horizons of a given sample.

**soil solution:** Ground water containing ions.

**solar eclipse:** when the moon's shadow moves across Earth's surface during a new moon.

**solar energy:** Energy from the Sun.

**solar noon:** The moment when the Sun crosses the meridian.

**solar system:** Includes our Sun, the nine planets, and many Moons, and all the other objects that revolve around the Sun.

**Solar time:** Time set by when the Sun passes directly over the observer's meridian.

**solid:** A state of matter in which the material has a given shape and volume.

**solid wastes:** Garbage, refuse and sludge from agriculture, forestry, mining and municipalities which pollute the land.

**solstices:** The two times of the year when the noon Sun is directly overhead at an angular distance of 23 $\frac{1}{2}$ degrees from the equator In the Northern Hemisphere. The summer solstice occurs about June 21st and marks the first day of summer. The winter solstice occurs on about December 21st and marks the first day of winter.

**solution:** The manner in which dissolved particles are carried in a stream.

**sorting:** The separating of a sample of sediment by particle size; the more similar the particles are in size, the greater the degree of sorting.

**source:** The place where a river begins.

**source region:** The area of Earth's surface over which an air mass originates.

**species:** A group of organisms that can mate and produce offspring.

**specific heat:** The quantity of heat, the calories, needed to raise the temperature of 1 gram of a substance 1°C.

**spectra:** Colors produced when wavelengths of light are separated.

**spiral galaxies:** group of billions of stars in a swirled pattern

**spit:** Finger-like ridge of sediment that extends out into the open water.

**spring tide:** Tides occurring during the full moon phases with the highest range between high and low tides.

**squall line:** Moving lines of thunderstorms.

**stacks:** Erosional remnants of headlands.

**stalactites:** Icicle-like limestone deposits which "grow down" from the ceiling.

**stalagmites:** Limestone deposits which, "grow up" from the ground.

**star trails:** Long exposure photos of stars show that the stars form arcs as they move through the sky.

**state:** See Phase.

**station model:** Weather observations for a particular location are recorded.

**stationary front:** A weather condition in which the boundary between two different air masses remains in the same position.

**storm surge:** A dome of water 65 to 80 kilometers wide that sweeps across the coast near where the eye makes landfall.

**strata:** (see: beds) Layers of sedimentary rock.

**stratified:** Rocks deposited in layers - usually well-sorted.

**stratopause:** The top of the stratosphere.

**stratosphere:** The layer of the atmosphere above the troposphere.

**streak:** The color of a mineral in its powdered form.

**stream bed:** The floor of a stream channel.

**stream discharge:** The volume of water passing a given spot in a given amount of time.

**stream draining pattern:** The pattern formed by the stream courses in an area.

**striations:** Long grooves scratched in bedrock by rocks dragged by glaciers.

**strip cropping:** Planting strips of low cover crops between strips of other crops.

**structure:** The arrangement of atoms in a mineral.

**subduction:** One Tectonic plate plunging or sliding under another.

**subduction boundary:** active edge of a subducting plate.

**sublimation:** The change of phase from solid to gas (or gas to solid) with no intermediate liquid phase.

**submarine canyons:** V-shaped valleys that run across continental shelves and down continental slopes.

**sunspots:** Patches on the surface of the Sun.

**sunspot cycle:** The periodic changes of the number of sunspots over a period of years.

**supergiants:** A few stars bigger than the red giants.

**supernova:** The outer portion of a neutron star explodes producing the brightest known object in space.

**surf:** The turbulent water caused by breaking waves.

**surface currents:** Broad, slow movements of surface water.

**sublimation:** The change of phase from solid to gas (or gas to solid) with no intermediate liquid phase.

**subsidence:** The gradual sinking of part of Earth's surface.

**superposition:** The principle that states that, in layered rocks, the youngest layer is on top and the age of the other layers increases with depth.

**surplus:** Excess water that results when storage is at capacity and precipitation exceeds potential evapotranspiration; most surplus water becomes runoff.

**suspension:** The manner in which fine sediments of clay, silt and colloids are carried in a stream.

**swash:** The motion of the water up the beach.

**synodic month:** The time required for the Moon to complete a cycle of phases (29 1/2 days).

**synoptic weather map:** Maps that provide a summary of weather conditions all over the country.

**synopsis:** The summary of weather conditions provided by Synoptic Weather Maps.

**talus:** Angular deposits of broken rocks along the base of a cliff.

**technology:** The application of scientific discoveries to the methods of producing goods and services.

**tectonics:** study of the movement of the solid rock of Earth's crust.

**temperature:** A measure of the average kinetic energy of the particles of a substance.

**temperature inversion:** When a layer of warm, less dense air is above a layer of colder, denser air.

**terraced:** A series of level steps on which crops are grown.

**terminal moraine:** A moraine indicating the farthest advance of a glacier-part of the end moraine.

**terrestrial:** Things that relate to the land.

**terrestrial planets:** Planets which are most similar to Earth.

**terrestrial radiation:** Electromagnetic energy given off by the surface of Earth.

**terrigenous:** Land sediment that has settled on the ocean floor.

**tetrahedron:** A four-sided solid,, each side being a triangle.

**texture:** The "feel" of a rock due to the size, shape and arrangement of mineral crystals or sediments in a rock.

**thermal pollution:** Heated waste water added to the ground water.

**thermometer:** An instrument used to measure temperature.

**thermosphere:** The outer upper layer of the atmosphere.

**tides:** cyclic fluctuations in coastal water levels caused by the gravitational forces between Earth, Sun and Moon.

**till:** Unsorted rock material deposited directly by glaciers.

**tilted strata:** Formerly horizontal rock layers that have been tilted at some angle from the horizontal by some crustal activity.

**time:** The instant at which something happens or the period during which a change occurs.

**topographic map:** See contour map.

**top soil:** The top layer of mature soil.

**tombolo:** A bar of sediment connecting a former island to the mainland.

**tornado:** Violent windstorms that take the form of a rotating funnel of air that extends downward from a cumulonimbus cloud.

**track:** The path followed by an air mass.

**transform boundaries:** They occur when one plate slides horizontally past another along a single fault of a group of parallel faults.

**transformation:** The changing of energy from one form to another.

**transition zone:** An area where a mass of rock changes from one class (igneous, sedimentary, metamorphic) to another class.

**transpiration:** The process by which plants release water vapor into the atmosphere.

**transported sediment:** Sediment that has been moved from one location to another by some erosional agent.

**transported soil:** Soil that has been moved from its place of origin.

**transporting agents:** Forces which move sediments from one place to another.

**transporting system:** A system that carries out erosion.

**transverse wave:** A wave that vibrates at right angles to its direction of travel.

**trellis pattern:** Drainage pattern which develops in a valley-and-ridge terrain, where rocks of different hardnesses are folded.

**trenches:** Deep ocean chasms parallel to the edge of a continent or island arc.

**tropical:** Air masses that develop over lower latitudes, tend to be warm.

**tropopause:** The top of the troposphere.

**troposphere:** The layer of the atmosphere closest to Earth's surface.

**trough:** The lower part of a wave .

**Tsunamis:** Very large tidal waves caused by the sudden movement of the sea floor during an earthquake (at or near the water) .

**turbidites:** Deposits made by turbidity currents .

**turbidity currents:** Mixtures of water and sediment that are pulled downslope by gravity like huge avalanches.

**U-shaped:** The shape of valleys carved by glaciers.

**ultraviolet radiation:** A form of electromagnetic radiation of shorter wavelength than visible light.

**umbra:** The total darkness created during an eclipse.

**unconformity:** A gap in the rock record caused by the burial of an erosional surface by younger rocks or sediments.

**uniformitarianism:** A principle stating that the geological processes in action today are the same as those that acted in the past, thus allowing us to interpret the events of the past by studying events currently taking place.

**unsorted:** The presence of particles of different sizes.

**uplifting forces:** Forces that originate within or beneath Earth's crust and have the effect of raising Earth's surface.

**uranium 238:** A radioactive isotope of uranium that is very useful for dating very old rocks.

**usage:** The removal of water from the soil; usage occurs whenever precipitation is less than potential evapotranspiration.

**V-shaped:** the general shape of valleys carved by streams.

**valley glacier (alpine glacier):** A glacier that is confined to a valley and flows from higher to lower elevations.

**vapor pressure:** The pressure exerted by water vapor in a given volume of air.

**variations:** Natural changes within species.

**vector field:** A field that must be described in terms of both magnitude and direction.

**vein:** A mineral deposit formed from a solution that filled a crack or permeable zone in previously formed rocks.

**ventifacts:** Rocks with flat, wind-abraded surfaces which may have greasy or polished surfaces.

**vertical rays:** See direct rays.

**visibility:** The farthest distance that a person can see a prominent object on the horizon with the unaided eye.

**visible spectrum:** The different color wavelengths of visible light.

**volcanic ash:** Small pieces of volcanic rock dispersed into the air during a volcanic eruption.

**volcanic rock:** See extrusive igneous rocks.

**volcano:** A vent in Earth through which molten magma erupts, producing a mountain of the material.

**volcanic neck:** The harder part of a volcano left behind when the volcano erodes.

**volume:** The amount of space an object takes up.


**walking the outcrop:** A method of correlation that involves actually following the relationships of layers or formations in out-crops of bedrock.

**waning moon:** The sequence of phases during which progressively less of the lighted left side of the moon is seen from Earth.

**warm front:** When a warm air mass overtakes a colder air mass.

**water budget:** The numerical model of a area's water supply.

**water cycle:** A model used to show the movement and phase changes of water at Earth's surface; the continuous interchange of water between the atmosphere and Earth's surface.

**water pollution:** Anything that makes the water unfit, harmful or undesirable for use.

**water table:** The upper surface of the zone of saturation of ground water.

**water vapor:** Water in the gaseous state.

**waterspout:** A tornado over the water.

**wave action:** The movement of water toward and away from shores.

**wave height:** The vertical distance between the crest and the trough.

**wavelength:** The distance between two successive crests or troughs, or between corresponding points on successive cycles of a wave.

**wave refraction:** The bending of a wave.

**waxing moon:** The sequence of phases during which progressively more of the lighted right side of the moon is seen from Earth.

**weather:** The condition of the atmosphere at a given time and place.

**weather forecasting:** Methods used to determine the future state of the atmosphere, knowing current weather patterns.

**weathering:** The chemical and physical breakdown of rocks at or near Earth's surface by weathering agents.

**weathering agents:** The hydrosphere, atmosphere, plants and animals which change the characteristics of rocks.

**white dwarf:** A small, incredibly dense, white-hot star about the size of a planet.

**wind:** The horizontal movement of air.

**wind break:** Belts of trees along the edge of farming areas.

**year:** The time it takes a planet to complete one revolution of the Sun. Earth's year is 365 ¼ days.

**young landscape:** One in which a cycle of erosion is beginning.

**youthful:** stage of stream development characterized by a straight channel, steep vee shaped valley, steep gradient, fast current, rapids with erosion dominant over deposition.

**zenith:** The point on the celestial sphere that is directly above an observer's position on Earth's surface.

**Zone of Accumulation:** The upper part of a glacier where more snow falls than melts.

**Zone of Aeration:** The part of Earth's surface above the water table.

**zones of divergence:** Descending air in high pressure regions which spreads out and moves away from the region (dry).

**zones of convergence:** Air which comes together in low pressure regions where it rises (moist).

**Zone of Saturation:** The part of Earth's surface that is filled with ground water.

# INDEX

# W

waning 478
Warm fronts 349
warming, Global 201
Warning, Hurricane 360
Warning, Tropical Storm 360
wasting, mass 212
Watch, Tropical Storm 360
Water 431
water budget 404
water cycle 124
water , ground 124
Water, Erosion and Running 139
water table 125
watershed 139
Waterspouts 362
Watch, Hurricane 360
wave action 169
wave height 180
wave refraction 185
wavelength 180, 293
Wavelength Reradiation 303
waves 180
waves, Compressional 83
Waves, Earthquake 83
waves, Long 83
waves, primary 83
waves, secondary 83
waves, seismic 83
waves, Shear 83
waxing 478
Weather 292
weather forecasting 341
weather variables, atmospheric 292
Weathering 130
weathering agents 130
weathering, Chemical 131
Weathering, Climate and 132
weathering, Physical 131
Weathering Rates 132
wedging, Frontal 331
white dwarf 442
Wind 140
Wind and Ice Erosion 140
Wind breaks 135
winds 322

Winds, Planetary 324
wind system, planetary 325

# X

X-ray, Chandra Observatory, 432

# Y

year, light 425
young landscape 223
youthful 149

# Z

zenith 445
Zero, Absolute 292
Zone of Accumulation 190
zone of aeration 125
zones, fracture 98
zone of saturation 125
zones of convergence 324
Zones of Crustal Activity 91
zones of divergence 324
zone, shadow 86
Zones, Transition 67

# REGENTS
# EXAMINATIONS

The University of the State of New York

REGENTS HIGH SCHOOL EXAMINATION

# PHYSICAL SETTING
# EARTH SCIENCE

**Thursday,** June 14, 2001 — 9:15 a.m. to 12:15 p.m., only

The answer sheet for Part A and Part B–1 is the last page of this examination booklet. Turn to the last page and fold it along the perforations. Then, slowly and carefully, tear off the answer sheet and fill in the heading.

The answer booklet for Part B–2 and Part C is stapled in the center of this examination booklet. Open the examination booklet, carefully remove the answer booklet, and close the examination booklet. Then fill in the heading of your answer booklet.

You are to answer *all* questions in all parts of this examination according to the directions provided in the examination booklet. Record your answers to the Part A and Part B–1 multiple-choice questions on your separate answer sheet. Write your answers to the Part B–2 and Part C questions in your answer booklet. All work should be written in pen, except for graphs and drawings, which should be done in pencil. You may use scrap paper to work out the answers to the questions, but be sure to record all your answers on the answer sheet and in the answer booklet.

The *Earth Science Reference Tables*, which you may need to answer some questions in this examination, are supplied separately. Be certain you have a copy of the *2001 edition* of these reference tables before you begin the examination.

When you have completed the examination, you must sign the statement printed at the end of your separate answer sheet, indicating that you had no unlawful knowledge of the questions or answers prior to the examination and that you have neither given nor received assistance in answering any of the questions during the examination. Your answer sheet and answer booklet cannot be accepted if you fail to sign this declaration.

**DO NOT OPEN THIS EXAMINATION BOOKLET UNTIL THE SIGNAL IS GIVEN.**

# PHYSICAL SETTING - Earth Science
# June 14, 2001

## Part A

**Answer all questions in this part.**

*Directions* (1–35): For *each* statement or question, write on the separate answer sheet the *number* of the word or expression that, of those given, best completes the statement or answers the question. Some questions may require the use of the *Earth Science Reference Tables*.

1 The diagram below shows the Moon in different positions as it revolves around Earth, as observed from above the North Pole (NP).

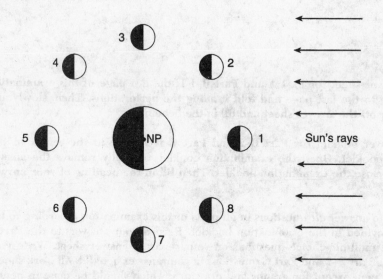

Which image correctly represents the Moon at position 8, as observed from Earth?

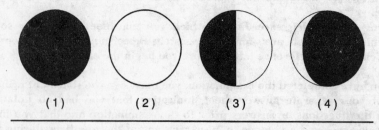

    (1)       (2)       (3)       (4)

2 The Sun's position in space is best described as the approximate center of

(1) a constellation
(2) the universe
(3) the Milky Way galaxy
(4) our solar system

3 Compared to Pluto, Mercury moves more rapidly in its orbit because Mercury

(1) is larger
(2) is more dense
(3) is closer to the Sun
(4) has a more elliptical orbit

4 The diagram below represents two planets in our solar system drawn to scale, Jupiter and planet A.

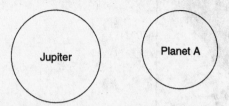

Planet A most likely represents

(1) Earth        (3) Saturn
(2) Venus        (4) Uranus

5 The graph below represents the brightness and temperature of stars visible from Earth.

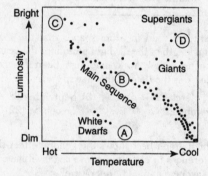

Which location on the graph best represents a star with average brightness and temperature?

(1) A        (3) C
(2) B        (4) D

6 The length of an Earth year is based on Earth's

(1) rotation of 15°/hr
(2) revolution of 15°/hr
(3) rotation of approximately 1°/day
(4) revolution of approximately 1°/day

7 Earth's hydrosphere is best described as the

(1) solid outer layer of Earth
(2) liquid outer layer of Earth
(3) magma layer located below Earth's stiffer mantle
(4) gaseous layer extending several hundred kilometers from Earth into space

8 The passage of the Moon into Earth's shadow causes a

(1) lunar eclipse        (3) new Moon
(2) solar eclipse        (4) full Moon

9 The diagram below shows the latitude-longitude grid on an Earth model. Points A and B are locations on the surface.

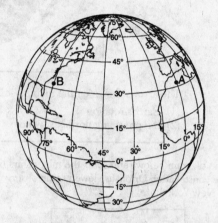

On Earth, the solar time difference between point A and point B would be

(1) 1 hour        (3) 12 hours
(2) 5 hours       (4) 24 hours

10 The diagram below represents part of Earth's latitude-longitude system.

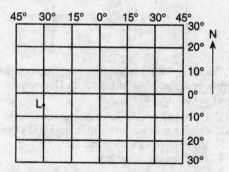

What is the latitude and longitude of point L?

(1) 5° E 30° N        (3) 5° N 30° E
(2) 5° W 30° S        (4) 5° S 30° W

11 The map below shows part of North America.

The arrows shown on the map most likely represent the direction of movement of

(1) Earth's rotation
(2) the prevailing northeast winds
(3) ocean conduction currents
(4) Atlantic Ocean hurricanes

12 The diagram below represents the major stars of the constellation Orion, as viewed by an observer in New York State.

Which statement best explains why Orion can be observed from New York State on December 21 but not on June 21?

(1) Orion has an eccentric orbit around Earth.
(2) Orion has an eccentric orbit around the Sun.
(3) Earth revolves around the Sun.
(4) Earth rotates on its axis.

13 Which type of air mass usually contains the most moisture?

(1) mT          (3) cT
(2) mP          (4) cP

14 A student read in a newspaper that the maximum length of the daylight period for the year in Syracuse, New York, had just been reached. What was the date of this newspaper?

(1) March 22        (3) September 22
(2) June 22         (4) December 22

15 Which graph best shows the general effect that differences in elevation above sea level have on the average annual temperature?

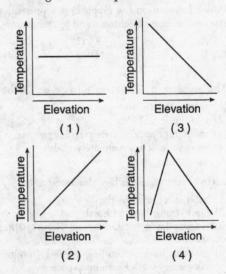

16 Ozone is concentrated in Earth's atmosphere at an altitude of 20 to 35 kilometers. Which atmospheric layer contains the greatest concentration of ozone?

(1) mesosphere      (3) troposphere
(2) thermosphere      (4) stratosphere

17 Halite has three cleavage directions at 90° to each other. Which model best represents the shape of a broken sample of halite?

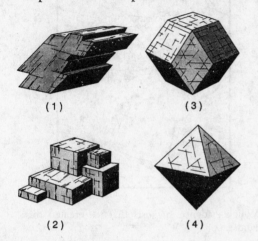

(1)               (3)

(2)               (4)

18 Which geologic feature is caused primarily by chemical weathering?

(1) large caves in limestone bedrock
(2) a pattern of parallel cracks in a granite mountain
(3) blocks of basalt at the base of a steep slope
(4) the smooth, polished surface of a rock in a dry, sandy area

19 Ocean tides are best described as

(1) unpredictable and cyclic
(2) unpredictable and noncyclic
(3) predictable and cyclic
(4) predictable and noncyclic

20 Where is the most deposition likely to occur?

(1) on the side of a sand dune facing the wind
(2) at the mouth of a river, where it enters an ocean
(3) at a site where glacial ice scrapes bedrock
(4) at the top of steep slope in a streambed

21 The map below shows the area surrounding a meandering stream.

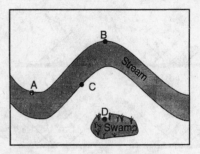

At which point is erosion greatest?

(1) *A*      (3) *C*
(2) *B*      (4) *D*

22 What is the largest particle that can be kept in motion by a stream that has a velocity of 100 centimeters per second?

(1) silt      (3) pebble
(2) sand      (4) cobble

23 An extrusive igneous rock with a mineral composition of 35% quartz, 35% potassium feldspar, 15% plagioclase feldspar, 10% biotite, and 5% amphibole is called

(1) rhyolite      (3) gabbro
(2) granite      (4) basaltic glass

24 During which process does heat transfer occur because of density differences?

(1) conduction      (3) radiation
(2) convection      (4) reflection

25 Carbon-14, an isotope used to date recent organic remains, would most likely be useful in determining the age of a fossil

(1) trilobite      (3) armored fish
(2) *Coelophysis*      (4) Beluga whale

26 Which diagram best represents visible light rays after striking a dark, rough surface?

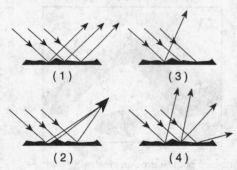

( 1 )   ( 3 )

( 2 )   ( 4 )

27 The cartoon below illustrates possible interaction between humans and mammoths.

The primitive game of "Pull the mammoth's tail and run"

During which geologic timespan could this "game" have occurred?

(1) Pleistocene Epoch
(2) Pennsylvanian Epoch
(3) Precambrian Era
(4) Paleozoic Era

28 The apparent shift in the direction of swing of a Foucault pendulum is caused by Earth's

(1) revolution       (3) spherical shape
(2) rotation         (4) tilted axis

29 The diagram below shows a glacial landscape.

Which evidence suggests that ice created this landscape?

(1) U-shaped valleys
(2) many stream valleys
(3) sorted sediment on the valley floor
(4) the landslide near the valley floor

30 An earthquake's P-wave arrived at a seismograph station at 02 hours 40 minutes 00 seconds. The earthquake's S-wave arrived at the same station 2 minutes later. What is the approximate distance from the seismograph station to the epicenter of the earthquake?

(1) 1,100 km       (3) 3,100 km
(2) 2,400 km       (4) 4,000 km

31 When small particles settle through water faster than large particles, the small particles are probably

(1) lighter        (3) better sorted
(2) flatter        (4) more dense

32 The diagram below shows the abundance of organisms called crinoids, blastoids, and echinoids throughout different geologic periods. The number of species living at any given time is represented by the width of the blackened areas.

Phylum Echinodermata

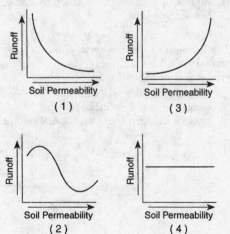

Which statement about crinoids, blastoids, and echinoids is best supported by the diagram?

(1) They are now extinct.
(2) They came into existence during the same geologic period.
(3) They existed during the Devonian Period.
(4) They have steadily increased in number since they first appeared.

---

33 Which graph shows the effect of soil permeability on the amount of runoff in an area?

34 In a Doppler red shift, the observed wavelengths of light from distant celestial objects appear closer to the red end of the spectrum than light from similar nearby celestial objects. The explanation for the red shift is that the universe is presently

(1) contracting, only
(2) expanding, only
(3) remaining constant in size
(4) alternating between contracting and expanding

35 Which sequence of change in rock type occurs as shale is subjected to increasing heat and pressure?

(1) shale → schist → phyllite → slate → gneiss
(2) shale → slate → phyllite → schist → gneiss
(3) shale → gneiss → phyllite → slate → schist
(4) shale → gneiss → phyllite → schist → slate

## Part B–1

### Answer all questions in this part.

*Directions* (36–51): For *each* statement or question, write on the separate answer sheet the *number* of the word or expression that, of those given, best completes the statement or answers the question. Some questions may require the use of the *Earth Science Reference Tables*.

Base your answers to questions 36 through 38 on the weather map below. Points *A, B, C,* and *D* are locations on Earth's surface.

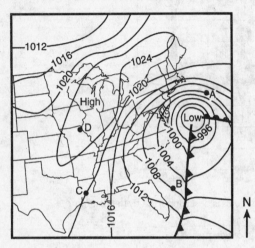

36 The isolines on the map represent values of air

    (1) density         (3) pressure

    (2) humidity      (4) temperature

37 The strongest winds are closest to location

    (1) *A*            (3) *C*

    (2) *B*           (4) *D*

38 Which type of front extends southward from the center of the low?

    (1) occluded     (3) warm

    (2) stationary    (4) cold

Base your answers to questions 39 and 40 on Moh's mineral hardness scale and on the chart below showing the approximate hardness of some common objects.

| Moh's Mineral Hardness Scale | | Approximate Hardness of Common Objects |
|---|---|---|
| Talc | 1 | |
| Gypsum | 2 | Fingernail (2.5) |
| Calcite | 3 | |
| Fluorite | 4 | Copper penny (3.5) |
| Apatite | 5 | |
| Feldspar | 6 | Iron nail (4.5) |
| Quartz | 7 | |
| Topaz | 8 | Glass (5.5) |
| Corundum | 9 | Steel file (6.5) |
| Diamond | 10 | Streak plate (7.0) |

39 Which statement is best supported by this scale?

    (1) A fingernail will scratch calcite, but not quartz.

    (2) A fingernail will scratch quartz, but not calcite.

    (3) A piece of glass can be scratched by quartz, but not by calcite.

    (4) A piece of glass can be scratched by calcite, but not by quartz.

40 The hardness of these minerals is most closely related to the

    (1) mineral's color

    (2) mineral's abundance in nature

    (3) amount of iron the mineral contains

    (4) internal arrangement of the mineral's atoms

Base your answers to questions 41 through 43 on the map below, which shows the location of the Peru-Chile Trench.

41 The Peru-Chile Trench marks the boundary between the

(1) Pacific Plate and the Antarctic Plate
(2) Nazca Plate and the South American Plate
(3) North American Plate and the Cocos Plate
(4) Caribbean Plate and the Scotia Plate

42 In which diagram do the arrows best represent the motions of Earth's crust at the Peru-Chile Trench?

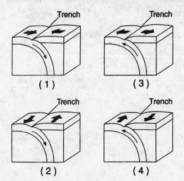

43 Which observation provides the best evidence of the pattern of crustal movement at the Peru-Chile Trench?

(1) the direction of flow of warm ocean currents
(2) the mineral composition of samples of mafic mantle rock
(3) comparison of the rates of sediment deposition
(4) the locations of shallow-focus and deep-focus earthquakes

44 The table below shows the altitude and compass direction of one planet, as viewed by an observer in New York State at 10 p.m. on the first day of each month from April through November.

| Month | Altitude | Compass Direction |
|-------|----------|-------------------|
| April | 20° | SW |
| May | 23° | SSW |
| June | 25° | S |
| July | 29° | SSE |
| August | 33° | SE |
| September | 38° | S |
| October | 42° | SW |
| November | 45° | S |

Which graph best represents a plot of this planet's apparent path, as viewed by the observer over the 7-month period?

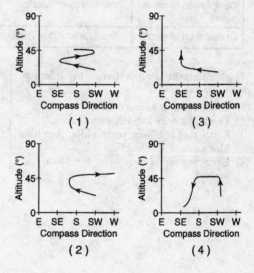

Base your answers to questions 45 and 46 on the data table below. The data table provides information about the Moon, based on current scientific theories.

**Information About the Moon**

| Subject | Current Scientific Theories |
|---|---|
| Origin of the Moon | Formed from material thrown from a still-liquid Earth following the impact of a giant object 4.5 billion years ago |
| Craters | Largest craters resulted from an intense bombardment by rock objects around 3.9 billion years ago |
| Presence of water | Mostly dry, but water brought in by the impact of comets may be trapped in very cold places at the poles |
| Age of rocks in terrae highlands | Most are older than 4.1 billion years; highland anorthosites (igneous rocks composed almost totally of feldspar) are dated at 4.4 billion years |
| Age of rocks in maria plains | Varies widely from 2 billion to 4.3 billion years |
| Composition of terrae highlands | Wide variety of rock types, but all contain more aluminum than rocks of maria plains |
| Composition of maria plains | Wide variety of basalts |
| Composition of mantle | Varying amounts of mostly olivine and pyroxene |

45 Which statement is supported by the information in the table?

(1) The Moon was once a comet.
(2) The Moon once had saltwater oceans.
(3) Earth is 4.5 billion years older than the Moon.
(4) Earth was liquid rock when the Moon was formed.

46 Which Moon feature is an impact structure?

(1) crater          (3) terrae highland
(2) maria plain     (4) mantle

Base your answers to questions 47 through 49 on the map and data table below. The map shows the locations of volcanic islands and seamounts that erupted on the seafloor of the Pacific Plate as it moved northwest over a stationary mantle hotspot beneath the lithosphere. The hotspot is currently under Kilauea. Island size is not drawn to scale. Locations X, Y, and Z are on Earth's surface.

## Map of Volcanic Features

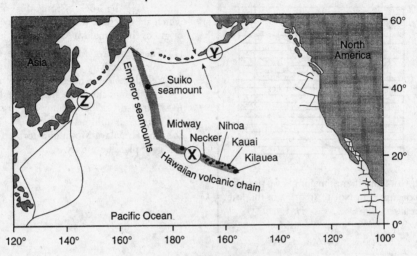

### Data Table
### Age of Volcanic Features

| Volcanic Feature | Distance from Kilauea (km) | Age (millions of years) |
|---|---|---|
| Kauai | 545 | 5.6 |
| Nihoa | 800 | 6.9 |
| Necker | 1,070 | 10.4 |
| Midway | 2,450 | 16.2 |
| Suiko seamount | 4,950 | 41.0 |

47 Approximately how far has location X moved from its original location over the hotspot?

(1) 3,600 km    (3) 1,800 km
(2) 2,500 km    (4) 20 km

48 According to the data table, what is the approximate speed at which the island of Kauai has been moving away from the mantle hotspot, in kilometers per million years?

(1) 1    (3) 100
(2) 10    (4) 1,000

49 Which lithospheric plate boundary features are located at Y and Z?

(1) trenches created by the subduction of the Pacific Plate
(2) rift valleys created by seafloor spreading of the Pacific Plate
(3) secondary plates created by volcanic activity within the Pacific Plate
(4) mid-ocean ridges created by faulting below the Pacific Plate

50 The diagram below shows trends in the temperature of North America during the last 200,000 years, as estimated by scientists.

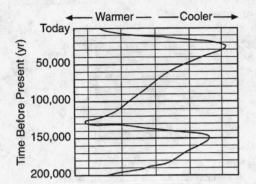

What is the total number of major glacial periods that have occurred in North America in the last 200,000 years?

(1) 5          (3) 3
(2) 2          (4) 4

51 The Himalaya Mountains are located along a portion of the southern boundary of the Eurasian Plate. At the top of Mt. Everest (29,028 feet) in the Himalaya Mountains, climbers have found fossilized marine shells in the surface bedrock. From this observation, which statement is the best inference about the origin of the Himalaya Mountains?

(1) The Himalaya Mountains were formed by volcanic activity.
(2) Sea level has been lowered more than 29,000 feet since the shells were fossilized.
(3) The bedrock containing the fossil shells is part of an uplifted seafloor.
(4) The Himalaya Mountains formed at a divergent plate boundary.

## Part B–2

### Answer all questions in this part.

*Directions* (52–64): Record your answers in the spaces provided in your answer booklet. Some questions may require the use of the *Earth Science Reference Tables*.

Base your answers to questions 52 through 56 on the diagram below. The diagram represents the apparent path of the Sun observed at four locations on Earth's surface on March 21. The present positions of the Sun, Polaris, and the zenith (position directly overhead) are shown for an observer at each location.

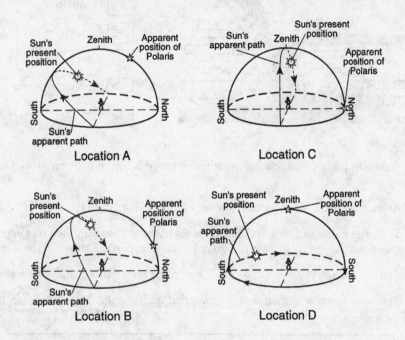

52 The observer at location *A* casts a shadow at the time represented in the diagram.

  *a* State the compass direction in which the observer at location *A* must look to view her shadow.   [1]

  *b* Describe the change in the length of the shadow that will occur between the time shown and sunset.   [1]

53 State the approximate time of day for the observer at location *B* when the Sun is at the position shown in the diagram.   [1]

54 Explain why the intensity of sunlight at noon on March 21 is greater at location *C* than at the other locations.   [1]

55 The observer at location *D* is located at a higher latitude than the other three observers. State *one* way that this conclusion can be determined from the diagram.   [1]

56 State the other day of the year when the Sun's apparent path is exactly the same as that shown for these four locations on March 21.   [1]

Base your answers to questions 57 through 61 on the diagram and information below.

The diagram shows a cross section of a portion of Earth's crust that has undergone geological processes. Overturning of rock layers has not occurred. Point A represents one location of metamorphic rock.

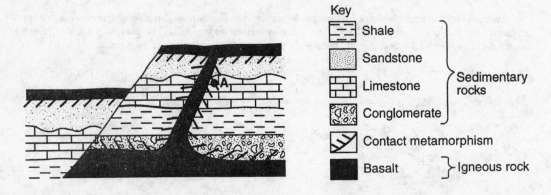

57  State *one* piece of evidence that indicates basalt is the youngest rock unit in the cross section.    [1]

58  As magma cools, what process changes it into basalt?    [1]

59  State the name of the inorganic sedimentary rock shown in the cross section that is composed of sediment with the greatest range in particle size.    [1]

60  State the name of the rock, formed by contact metamorphism, located at A.    [1]

61  State *one* piece of evidence that shows that crustal uplift has occurred in this region.    [1]

---

Base your answers to questions 62 through 64 on the weather information below.

A student using a sling psychrometer obtained a dry-bulb reading of 20°C and a wet-bulb reading of 16°C for a parcel of air outside the classroom.

62  State the dewpoint.    [1]

63  State the change in relative humidity as the air temperature and the dewpoint get closer to the same value.    [1]

64  On another day, the student determined the dewpoint was 70°F. Record the dewpoint, using the proper format, in the correct location on the weather station model provided *in your answer booklet*.    [1]

## Part C

### Answer all questions in this part.

*Directions* (65–79): Record your answers in the spaces provided in your answer booklet. Some questions may require the use of the *Earth Science Reference Tables*.

Base your answers to questions 65 through 67 on the paragraph below, which describes some factors that affect Earth's climate.

Earth's climate is in a delicate state of balance. Many factors affect climate. Any small change in the factors may lead to long-term cooling or warming of Earth's atmosphere. For example, during the last 100 years, measurements have shown a gradual increase in atmospheric carbon dioxide. This change has been linked to an increase in Earth's average atmospheric temperature. Variations in the tilt of Earth's axis have been similarly linked to the occurrence of ice ages. Both the increases in temperature and the occurrence of ice ages have been linked to changes in global sea level.

65 State *one* reason for the increase in the amount of carbon dioxide in Earth's atmosphere during the last 100 years.    [1]

66 State *one* way that the recent increase in average global temperature can cause changes in ocean water level.    [1]

67 State what would happen to the average summer and winter temperatures in New York State if the tilt of Earth's axis were to decrease from $23\frac{1}{2}°$ to 20°.    [1]

Base your answers to questions 68 through 75 on the reading passage and topographic map below.

A group of Earth science students decided to take an adventurous camping trip, so they rode bicycles to a New York State park that was located in an isolated area. They traveled up a steep hill. When they reached the top, they looked at the landscape and noticed a lake at the bottom of the hill. They named it Hidden Lake. To the left of Hidden Lake was a large field with a small stream. They decided to set up their campsite in the field near Hidden Lake. To get to the field, they cycled down a very steep slope.

The map below shows the location of the bicycle trail and the students' campsite. Points *P* and *Q* are reference points on the map.

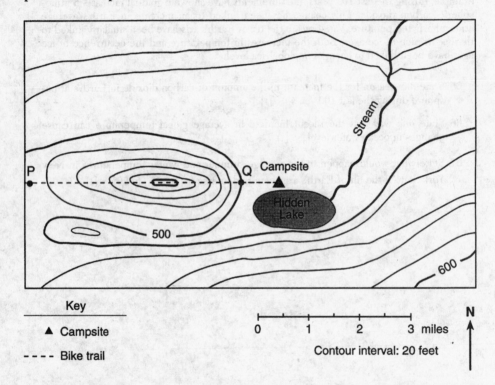

Key

▲ Campsite

- - - - Bike trail

0    1    2    3 miles

Contour interval: 20 feet

N ↑

68  State the evidence shown on the map that indicates that the area directly north of Hidden Lake is relatively flat.   [1]

69  *a*  State the general compass direction in which the stream is flowing.   [1]

    *b*  State how contour lines provide the evidence for determining this direction.   [1]

70  On the grid provided *in your answer booklet*, draw a profile of the landscape along the bicycle trail from point *P* to point *Q* by following the directions below.

    *a*  Plot the elevation along line *PQ* by marking with a dot *each* point where a contour line is crossed by line *PQ*. Point *P* and point *Q* have been plotted for you.   [2]

    *b*  Connect the dots to complete the profile.   [1]

71 The students decided to measure the speed of the stream by floating apples down a straight section of the stream. Describe the steps the students must take to determine the stream's surface rate of movement (speed) by using a stopwatch, a 10-foot rope, and several apples. Include the equation for calculating rate.   [3]

72 While exploring the stream, a student found a rock containing a trilobite fossil. Name the most likely type of rock this student found.   [1]

73 State the geologic era during which the rock containing the trilobite most likely formed.   [1]

74 The next day the students decided to move their campsite 1 mile directly east of their original campsite. On the map provided *in your answer booklet,* place another campsite symbol, ▲, to indicate the location of their second campsite.   [1]

75 The students decided to take a different route home to avoid riding their bicycles up the steep hill. Plan a return route that will take the campers back to point *P* and that will involve the *least* change in elevation during the trip. On the map provided *in your answer booklet,* draw a line from the second campsite to point *P* to show the route. Place arrows on the line to show the direction that the students will be traveling.   [1]

Base your answers to questions 76 through 79 on the magazine article and diagram below.

## Lake-Effect Snow

During the cold months of the year, the words "lake effect" are very much a part of the weather picture in many locations in New York State. Snow created by the lake effect may represent more than half the season's snowfall in some areas.

In order for heavy lake-effect snow to develop, the temperature of the water at the surface of the lake must be higher than the temperature of the air flowing over the water. The higher the water temperature and the lower the air temperature, the greater the potential for lake-effect snow.

A lake-effect storm begins when air flowing across the lake is warmed as it comes in close contact with the water. The warmed air rises and takes moisture along with it. This moisture, which is water vapor from the lake, is turned into clouds as it encounters much colder air above. When the clouds reach the shore of the lake, they deposit their snow on nearby land. A typical lake-effect storm is illustrated in the diagram below.

The area most likely to receive snow from a lake is called a "snowbelt." Lake Ontario's snowbelt includes the counties along the eastern and southeastern ends of the lake. Because the lake runs lengthwise from west to east, the prevailing westerly winds are able to gather the maximum amount of moisture as they flow across the entire length of the lake. There can be lake-effect snowfall anywhere around the lake, but the heaviest and most frequent snowfalls occur near the eastern shore.

In parts of the snowbelt, the lake effect combines with a phenomenon known as orographic lifting to produce some very heavy snowfalls. After cold air has streamed over the length of Lake Ontario, it moves inland and is forced to climb the slopes of the Tug Hill Plateau and the Adirondack Mountains, resulting in very heavy snowfall.

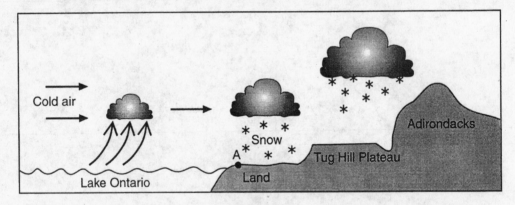

76 State the relationship that must exist between water temperature and air temperature for lake-effect snow to develop.   [1]

77 State why locations east and southeast of Lake Ontario are more likely to receive lake-effect snow than are locations west of the lake.   [1]

78 State the name of the New York State landscape region that includes location A shown in the diagram.   [1]

79 State why very heavy snowfall occurs in the Tug Hill Plateau region.   [1]

The University of the State of New York

REGENTS HIGH SCHOOL EXAMINATION

# PHYSICAL SETTING
# EARTH SCIENCE

**Thursday,** June 14, 2001 — 9:15 a.m. to 12:15 p.m., only

## ANSWER SHEET

Student ........................................... Sex:  ☐ Male  ☐ Female  Grade ........

Teacher ........................................... School ...........................

**Record your answers to Part A and Part B–1 on this answer sheet.**

| Part A | | | | Part B–1 | |
|---|---|---|---|---|---|
| 1 .......... | 13 .......... | 25 .......... | | 36 .......... | 44 .......... |
| 2 .......... | 14 .......... | 26 .......... | | 37 .......... | 45 .......... |
| 3 .......... | 15 .......... | 27 .......... | | 38 .......... | 46 .......... |
| 4 .......... | 16 .......... | 28 .......... | | 39 .......... | 47 .......... |
| 5 .......... | 17 .......... | 29 .......... | | 40 .......... | 48 .......... |
| 6 .......... | 18 .......... | 30 .......... | | 41 .......... | 49 .......... |
| 7 .......... | 19 .......... | 31 .......... | | 42 .......... | 50 .......... |
| 8 .......... | 20 .......... | 32 .......... | | 43 .......... | 51 .......... |
| 9 .......... | 21 .......... | 33 .......... | | | |
| 10 .......... | 22 .......... | 34 .......... | | | |
| 11 .......... | 23 .......... | 35 .......... | | | |
| 12 .......... | 24 .......... | | | | |

Part B–1 Score

Part A Score

**Write your answers to Part B–2 and Part C in your answer booklet.**

**The declaration below should be signed when you have completed the examination.**

I do hereby affirm, at the close of this examination, that I had no unlawful knowledge of the questions or answers prior to the examination and that I have neither given nor received assistance in answering any of the questions during the examination.

_____

**Signature**

The University of the State of New York

REGENTS HIGH SCHOOL EXAMINATION

# PHYSICAL SETTING
# EARTH SCIENCE

**Thursday,** June 14, 2001 — 9:15 a.m. to 12:15 p.m., only

### ANSWER BOOKLET

☐ Male

Student ................................... Sex: ☐ Female

Teacher ....................................................

School.................................... Grade ........

**Answer all questions in Part B–2 and Part C. Record your answers in this booklet.**

| Performance Test Score (Maximum Score: 23) | | |
| --- | --- | --- |

| Part | Maximum Score | Student's Score |
| --- | --- | --- |
| A | 35 | |
| B–1 | 16 | |
| B–2 | 14 | |
| C | 20 | |

| Total Written Test Score (Maximum Raw Score: 85) | |
| --- | --- |
| Final Score (from chart in Rating Guide) | |

Raters' Initials:

Rater 1 ......... Rater 2 .........

## Part B–2

**For Raters Only**

52 *a* _____    52*a* ☐

   *b* _____    52*b* ☐

53 _____ p.m.    53 ☐

54 _____    54 ☐

_____

55 _____    55 ☐

_____

56 _____    56 ☐

57 _____     57 ☐

_____

58 _____     58 ☐

59 _____     59 ☐

60 _____     60 ☐

61 _____     61 ☐

_____

62 _____ °C     62 ☐

63 _____     63 ☐

64     64 ☐

○

Total
Score for
Part B–2 ☐

## Part C

65 _____     65 ☐

_____

66 _____     66 ☐

_____

67 _____     67 ☐

_____

68 _____    68 [ ]

_____

69 *a* _____    69 *a* [ ]

*b* _____    69 *b* [ ]

_____

70 *a–b*    70 *a* [ ]

70 *b* [ ]

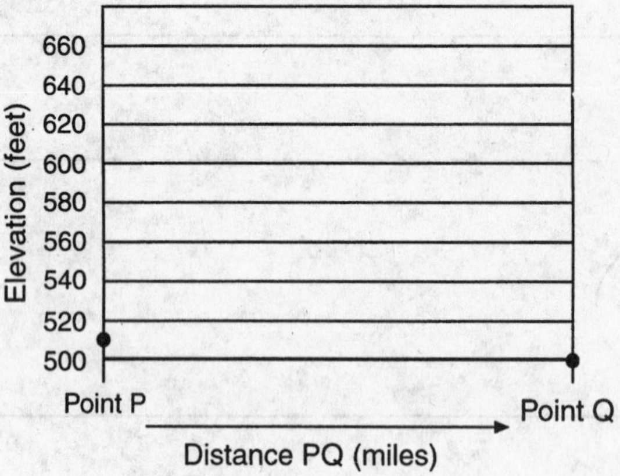

Elevation (feet): 660, 640, 620, 600, 580, 560, 540, 520, 500

Point P ● ● Point Q

Distance PQ (miles)

71 _____    71 [ ]

_____

_____

_____

_____

72 _____    72 [ ]

73 _____ Era    73 [ ]

74

75

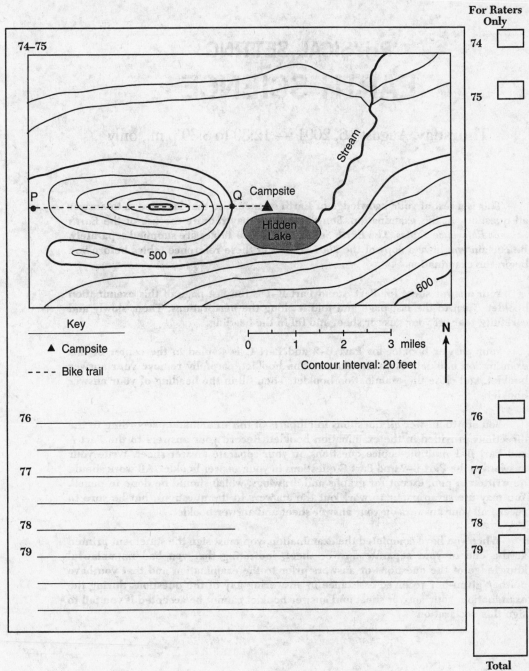

74–75

Key

▲ Campsite

---- Bike trail

0    1    2    3  miles

Contour interval: 20 feet

N

76 _____

_____

77 _____

78 _____

79 _____

_____

_____

76

77

78

79

The University of the State of New York

REGENTS HIGH SCHOOL EXAMINATION

# PHYSICAL SETTING
# EARTH SCIENCE

**Thursday,** August 16, 2001 — 12:30 to 3:30 p.m., only

This is a test of your knowledge of Earth science. Use that knowledge to answer all questions in this examination. Some questions may require the use of the *Earth Science Reference Tables*. The *Earth Science Reference Tables* are supplied separately. Be certain you have a copy of the *2001 edition* of these reference tables before you begin the examination.

Your answer sheet for Part A and Part B–1 is the last page of this examination booklet. Turn to the last page and fold it along the perforations. Then, slowly and carefully, tear off your answer sheet and fill in the heading.

Your answer booklet for Part B–2 and Part C is stapled in the center of this examination booklet. Open the examination booklet, carefully remove your answer booklet, and close the examination booklet. Then fill in the heading of your answer booklet.

You are to answer *all* questions in all parts of this examination according to the directions provided in the examination booklet. Record your answers to the Part A and Part B–1 multiple-choice questions on your separate answer sheet. Write your answers to the Part B–2 and Part C questions in your answer booklet. All work should be written in pen, except for graphs and drawings, which should be done in pencil. You may use scrap paper to work out the answers to the questions, but be sure to record all your answers on your answer sheet and answer booklet.

When you have completed the examination, you must sign the statement printed at the end of your separate answer sheet, indicating that you had no unlawful knowledge of the questions or answers prior to the examination and that you have neither given nor received assistance in answering any of the questions during the examination. Your answer sheet and answer booklet cannot be accepted if you fail to sign this declaration.

**DO NOT OPEN THIS EXAMINATION BOOKLET UNTIL THE SIGNAL IS GIVEN.**

# PHYSICAL SETTING - Earth Science
## August 16, 2001

### Part A

### Answer all questions in this part.

*Directions* (1–35): For *each* statement or question, write on your separate answer sheet the *number* of the word or expression that, of those given, best completes the statement or answers the question. Some questions may require the use of the *Earth Science Reference Tables*.

1 The graph below shows the snow line (the elevation above which glaciers form at different latitudes in the Northern Hemisphere).

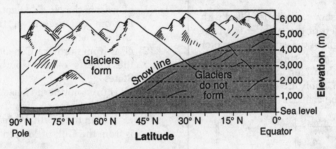

At which location would a glacier most likely form?

(1) 0° latitude at an elevation of 6,000 m
(2) 15° N latitude at an elevation of 4,000 m
(3) 30° N latitude at an elevation of 3,000 m
(4) 45° N latitude at an elevation of 1,000 m

2 The graph below shows the relationship between mass and volume for three samples, A, B, and C, of a given material.

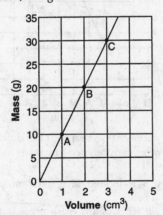

What is the density of this material?

(1) 1.0 g/cm³
(2) 5.0 g/cm³
(3) 10.0 g/cm³
(4) 20.0 g/cm³

3 The length of an Earth day is determined by the time required for approximately one

(1) Earth rotation
(2) Earth revolution
(3) Sun rotation
(4) Sun revolution

4 To an observer in Buffalo, New York, the North Star, *Polaris*, is always located above the northern horizon at an altitude of approximately

(1) $23\frac{1}{2}°$
(2) 43°
(3) $66\frac{1}{2}°$
(4) 90°

5 Which planet is approximately thirty times farther from the Sun than Earth is?

(1) Jupiter
(2) Saturn
(3) Uranus
(4) Neptune

6 Which object is located at one foci of the elliptical orbit of Mars?

(1) the Sun      (3) Earth
(2) *Betelgeuse*      (4) Jupiter

7 What is the basic difference between ultraviolet, visible, and infrared radiation?

(1) half-life      (3) wavelength
(2) temperature      (4) wave velocity

8 The diagram below shows a cylinder filled with clean water. At the left of the cylinder is a light source, and at the right of the cylinder is a meter that measures the intensity (brightness) of light as it passes through the water. One minute after the light is turned on, a mixture of sand, silt, and clay is poured into the cylinder.

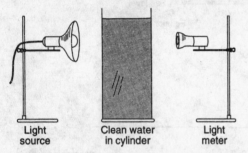

Light source     Clean water in cylinder     Light meter

Which graph shows the probable change in light intensity (brightness) recorded during the 6-minute period after the light is turned on?

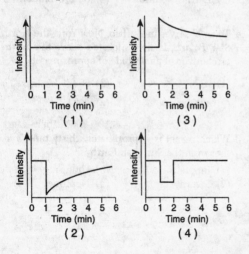

9 What is the dewpoint when the dry-bulb temperature is 24°C and the wet-bulb temperature is 15°C?

(1) 8°C      (3) 36°C
(2) –18°C      (4) 4°C

10 In New York State, dry, cool air masses (cP) often interact with moist, warm air masses (mT). Which statement correctly matches each air mass with its usual geographic source region?

(1) cP is from the North Atlantic Ocean and mT is from the deserts of the southwestern United States.
(2) cP is from northern Canada and mT is from the deserts of the southwestern United States.
(3) cP is from northern Canada and mT is from the Gulf of Mexico.
(4) cP is from the North Atlantic Ocean and mT is from the Gulf of Mexico.

11 The graph below shows the average monthly temperatures for two cities, *A* and *B*, which are both located at 41° north latitude.

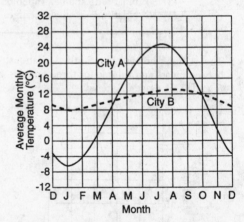

Which statement best explains the difference in the average yearly temperature range for the two cities?

(1) City *B* is located in a different planetary wind belt.
(2) City *B* receives less yearly precipitation.
(3) City *B* has a greater yearly duration of insolation.
(4) City *B* is located near a large body of water.

12 In the cartoon below, Lucy gives Linus incorrect information about pebbles.

If Lucy wanted to give Linus correct information about pebbles, which statement would be most accurate?

(1) Pebbles can become cemented together to form a rock called gabbro.
(2) Pebble is the name given to the smallest-size sediment.
(3) Any large rock that weathers could become a pebble.
(4) Magma is composed of pebbles.

Base your answers to questions 13 through 15 on the diagram below. Columns A, B, C, and D are partially filled with different sediments. Within each column, the sediment is uniform in size. A fine wire mesh screen covers the bottom of each column to prevent the sediment from falling out. The lower part of each column has just been placed in a beaker of water. Sediment sizes are not drawn to scale.

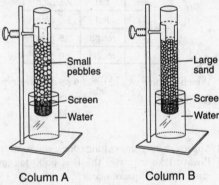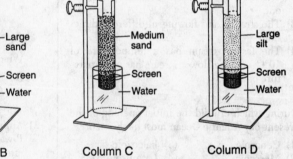

Column A  Column B  Column C  Column D

13 Which column contains sediment with an average diameter closest to 0.1 centimeter?

(1) A       (3) C
(2) B       (4) D

14 In which sediment will capillary action cause the water from the beaker to rise fastest in the column?

(1) small pebbles    (3) medium sand
(2) large sand       (4) large silt

15 In an experiment, the beakers of water were removed and replaced with empty beakers. The sediments were allowed to dry. Then water was poured into each column to compare the permeability of the sediments. The permeability rate of the medium sand sample was shown to be

(1) less than the silt and pebble samples
(2) less than the silt sample but more than the pebble sample
(3) greater than the silt sample but less than the pebble sample
(4) greater than the silt and pebble samples

16 The diagram below shows four rock samples.

Sample A

Sample B

Sample C

Sample D

Which sample best shows the physical properties normally associated with regional metamorphism?

(1) A                    (3) C
(2) B                    (4) D

17 Two streams begin at the same elevation and have equal volumes. Which statement best explains why one stream could be flowing faster than the other stream?

(1) The faster stream contains more dissolved minerals.
(2) The faster stream has a much steeper gradient.
(3) The streams are flowing in different directions.
(4) The faster stream has a temperature of 10°C, and the slower stream has a temperature of 20°C.

18 During which era did the initial opening of the present-day Atlantic Ocean most likely occur?

(1) Cenozoic            (3) Paleozoic
(2) Mesozoic            (4) Late Proterozoic

19 The absolute age of a rock is the approximate number of years ago that the rock formed. The absolute age of an igneous rock can best be determined by

(1) comparing the amounts of decayed and undecayed radioactive isotopes in the rock
(2) comparing the sizes of the crystals found in the upper and lower parts of the rock
(3) examining the rock's relative position in a rock outcrop
(4) examining the environment in which the rock is found

20 The four particles shown in the table below are of equal volume and are dropped into a column filled with water.

| Particle | Shape | Density |
|----------|-------|---------|
| A | flat | 2.5 g/cm³ |
| B | flat | 3.0 g/cm³ |
| C | round | 2.5 g/cm³ |
| D | round | 3.0 g/cm³ |

Which particle would usually settle most rapidly?

(1) A                    (3) C
(2) B                    (4) D

21 Approximately how long does an earthquake *P*-wave take to travel the first 6500 kilometers after the earthquake occurs?

(1) 6.5 min             (3) 10.0 min
(2) 8.0 min             (4) 18.5 min

22 Which two locations are in the same New York State landscape region?

(1) Albany and Old Forge
(2) Massena and Mt. Marcy
(3) Binghamton and New York City
(4) Jamestown and Ithaca

23 The diagram below is a portion of a geologic time line. Letters A through D represent the time intervals between the labeled events, as estimated by some scientists.

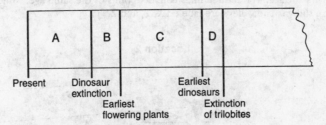

Fossil evidence indicates that the earliest birds developed during which time interval?

(1) A  (3) C
(2) B  (4) D

24 In which map does the arrow show the general direction that most low-pressure storm systems move across New York State?

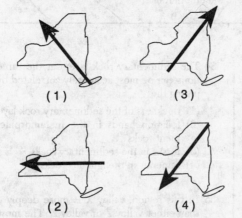

25 The apparent daily path of the Sun changes with the seasons because

(1) Earth's axis is tilted
(2) Earth's distance from the Sun changes
(3) the Sun revolves
(4) the Sun rotates

26 In general, the probability of flooding decreases when there is an increase in the amount of

(1) precipitation  (3) runoff
(2) infiltration  (4) snow melt

27 Which object orbits Earth in both the Earth-centered (geocentric) and Sun-centered (heliocentric) models of our solar system?

(1) the Moon  (3) the Sun
(2) Venus  (4) Polaris

28 Predictable changes in the direction of swing of a Foucault pendulum provide evidence that

(1) Earth is tilted on its axis
(2) Earth rotates on its axis
(3) Earth's orbit is slightly elliptical
(4) Earth's magnetic poles reverse over time

29 Compared to felsic igneous rocks, mafic igneous rocks contain greater amounts of

(1) white quartz  (3) pink feldspar
(2) aluminum  (4) iron

30 What is the age of the most abundant surface bedrock in the Finger Lakes region of New York State?

(1) Cambrian  (3) Pennsylvanian
(2) Devonian  (4) Permian

31 What are the two most abundant elements by mass found in Earth's crust?

(1) aluminum and iron
(2) sodium and chlorine
(3) calcium and carbon
(4) oxygen and silicon

Base your answers to questions 32 through 35 on the geologic cross section below, which shows a view of rock layers at Earth's surface. The dashed lines connect points of the same age. Major fossils contained within each rock layer are shown. The valleys are labeled X, Y, and Z.

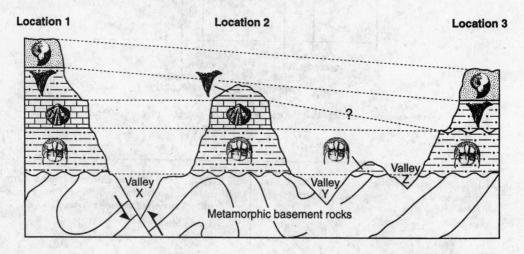

32 In which type of environment were the sediments that formed these sedimentary rock layers most likely deposited?

   (1) glacial        (3) marine
   (2) mountainous     (4) terrestrial plateau

33 Which fossil would most likely be found in the same siltstone layer as the *Cryptolithus* fossil?

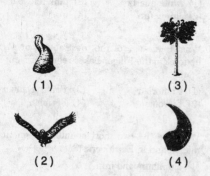

   (1)               (3)

   (2)               (4)

34 The sedimentary rock layers at the three locations can be most accurately correlated by comparing the

   (1) thickness of the sedimentary rock layers
   (2) foliation bands in the metamorphic basement rocks
   (3) fossils in the sedimentary rocks
   (4) minerals in the igneous rocks

35 In this region, valley X is more deeply eroded than either valley Y or valley Z. The most likely explanation for this occurrence is that the metamorphic rock near X has been

   (1) weakened by faulting
   (2) folded by pressure
   (3) intruded by melted rock
   (4) covered by sedimentary rocks

## Part B–1

### Answer all questions in this part.

*Directions* (36–52): For *each* statement or question, write on your separate answer sheet the *number* of the word or expression that, of those given, best completes the statement or answers the question. Some questions may require the use of the *Earth Science Reference Tables*.

Base your answers to questions 36 through 38 on the topographic map below. Points *X*, *Y*, and *Z* are locations on the map. Elevations are expressed in meters.

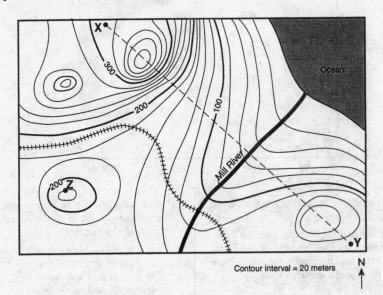

Contour interval = 20 meters

36 Which profile best represents the topography along the dashed line from point *X* to point *Y*?

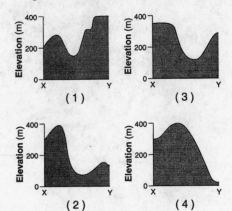

(1)

(3)

(2)

(4)

37 Mill River generally flows toward the

(1) southeast     (3) northeast
(2) southwest     (4) northwest

38 What is the elevation of point *Z*?

(1) 190 m     (3) 240 m
(2) 220 m     (4) 250 m

Base your answers to questions 39 through 41 on the map below. The map shows the locations of deep-sea core drilling sites numbered 1 through 4. The approximate location of the East Pacific Ridge is shown by a dashed line. Point A is located on the East Pacific Ridge.

**Map of Drilling Sites**

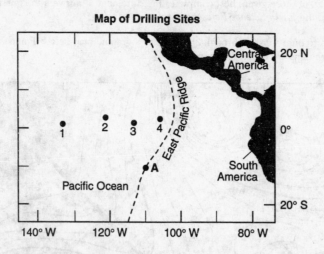

39 At point A, the East Pacific Ridge is the boundary between the

(1) Cocos Plate and the North American Plate
(2) South American Plate and the Nazca Plate
(3) Pacific Plate and the South American Plate
(4) Pacific Plate and the Nazca Plate

40 At which drilling site would the oldest igneous bedrock most likely be found?

(1) 1          (3) 3
(2) 2          (4) 4

41 Compared to the thickness and density of the continental crust of South America, the oceanic crust of the Pacific floor is

(1) thinner and less dense
(2) thinner and more dense
(3) thicker and less dense
(4) thicker and more dense

Base your answers to questions 42 and 43 on the map below. Seismic stations are located at the four cities shown on the map. Letter *X* represents the epicenter of an earthquake determined from seismic waves recorded at all four cities.

42 At which city is there a difference of approximately 3 minutes and 20 seconds between the arrival times of the *P*-waves and the *S*-waves?

    (1) New Orleans               (3) Pittsburgh
    (2) Louisville                  (4) New York City

43 Which map correctly shows how the location of the epicenter was determined?

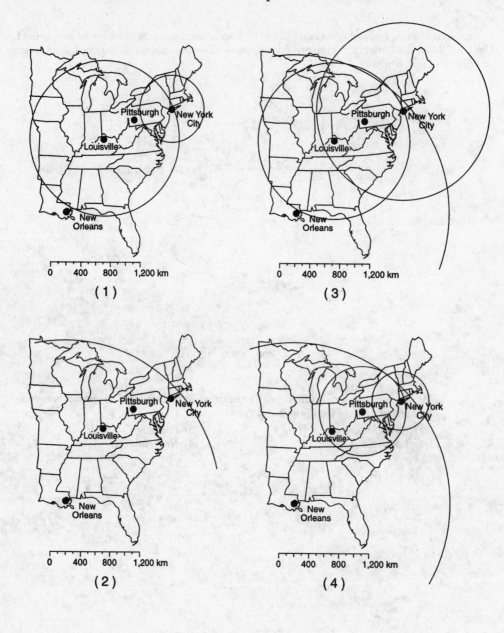

44 The diagram below illustrates three stages of a current theory of the formation of the universe.

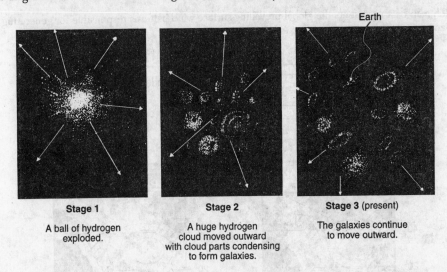

**Stage 1**

A ball of hydrogen exploded.

**Stage 2**

A huge hydrogen cloud moved outward with cloud parts condensing to form galaxies.

**Stage 3** (present)

The galaxies continue to move outward.

A major piece of scientific evidence supporting this theory is the fact that wavelengths of light from galaxies moving away from Earth in stage 3 are observed to be

(1) shorter than normal (a red shift)
(2) shorter than normal (a blue shift)
(3) longer than normal (a red shift)
(4) longer than normal (a blue shift)

45 The diagram below shows the Moon orbiting Earth as viewed from space above the North Pole. The Moon is shown at eight different positions in its orbit.

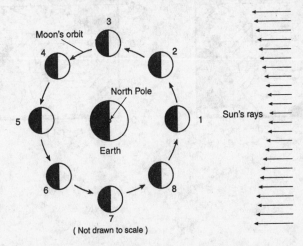

( Not drawn to scale )

At which two positions of the Moon is an eclipse of the Sun or Moon possible?

(1) 1 and 5
(2) 2 and 6
(3) 3 and 7
(4) 4 and 8

46 Which map best represents the global prevailing surface wind patterns responsible for generating Atlantic Ocean currents?

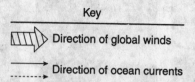

Key

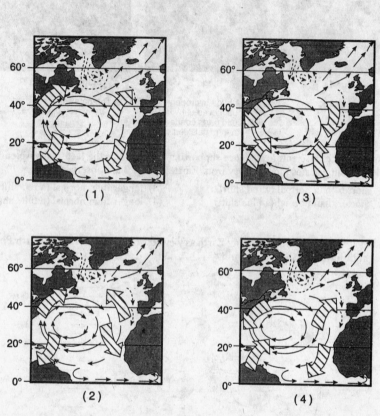

47 The map below shows some features along an ocean shoreline.

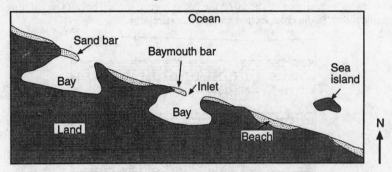

In which general direction is the sand being moved along this shoreline by ocean (long-shore) currents?

(1) northeast

(3) northwest

(2) southeast

(4) southwest

48 The block diagram below shows the bedrock age as measured by radioactive dating and the present location of part of the Hawaiian Island chain. These volcanic islands may have formed as the Pacific Plate moved over a mantle hot spot.

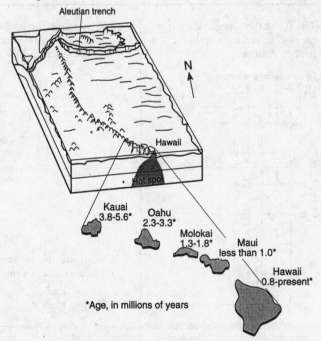

This diagram provides evidence that the Pacific Crustal Plate was moving toward the

(1) south

(3) southwest

(2) east

(4) northwest

Base your answers to questions 49 and 50 on the geologic cross section below. Overturning has not occurred. The dike and sills shown in the cross section are igneous intrusions.

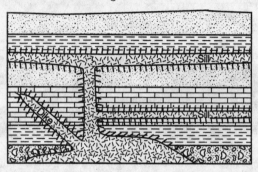

49 Which rock type is the oldest?

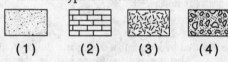

(1)  (2)  (3)  (4)

50 Which feature is represented by the symbol ╱╱╱╱ along the edges of the dike and sills?

(1) contact metamorphic rock
(2) an unconformity
(3) a glacial moraine
(4) index fossils

---

51 The graph below shows the concentration (percentage) of copper at various depths in the bedrock at a mine in Arizona.

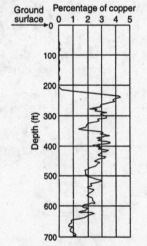

Between which depths should the bedrock be mined in order to obtain rock with the highest percentage of copper?

(1) 100–130 ft          (3) 330–360 ft
(2) 230–260 ft          (4) 650–680 ft

52 The station model below shows the weather conditions at Massena, New York, at 9 a.m. on a particular day in June.

What was the barometric pressure at Massena 3 hours earlier on that day?

(1) 997.1 mb          (3) 1003.3 mb
(2) 999.7 mb          (4) 1009.1 mb

## Part B–2

### Answer all questions in this part.

*Directions* (53–59): Record your answers in the spaces provided in your answer booklet. Some questions may require the use of the *Earth Science Reference Tables*.

Base your answers to questions 53 through 55 on the diagram below, which represents Earth at a specific position in its orbit as viewed from space. The shaded area represents nighttime. Points *A* and *B* are locations on Earth's surface.

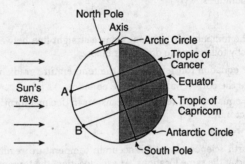

53 *a* State the month in which Earth is at the position shown in the diagram.    [1]

   *b* State the latitude that receives the most intense radiation from the Sun when Earth is at this position in its orbit.    [1]

54 Describe the length of daylight at point *A* compared to the length of daylight at point *B* on the day represented by the diagram.    [1]

55 The model of Earth provided *in your answer booklet* represents Earth in its orbit *6 months later*. On the model shown *in your answer booklet*
   • draw the position of Earth's axis and label the axis    [1]
   • label the North Pole    [1]
   • draw the position of Earth's Equator and label the Equator    [1]

Base your answers to questions 56 through 59 on the field map provided in your answer booklet. The field map shows air temperature at specific locations in an area near a school in New York State. Part of this area is a blacktop parking lot. Accurate temperature readings were taken by Earth science students at 10 a.m. on June 1. Two reference points, A and B, are shown.

56 On the field map provided, draw only the 15°C and the 20°C isotherms. Isotherms must be extended to the edge of the map.     [2]

57 Surface temperatures are higher on the east side of the field map, where the parking lot is located. Explain how a characteristic of the parking lot surface could cause these higher temperatures.   [1]

58 Calculate the temperature gradient along a straight line between point A and point B on the map by following the directions below.

   a Write the equation for determining the temperature gradient.

   b Substitute the correct values into the equation.     [1]

   c Solve the equation and record your answer in decimal form. Label the answer with the correct units.   [2]

59 Another Earth science class took accurate temperature readings at 12 noon on the same day and at the same locations. At each location, the temperature was warmer than it had been at 10 a.m. Explain why the temperature readings would normally increase between 10 a.m. and 12 noon.     [1]

## Part C

### Answer all questions in this part.

*Directions* (60–72): Record your answers in the spaces provided in your answer booklet. Some questions may require the use of the *Earth Science Reference Tables*.

Base your answers to questions 60 through 62 on the notes below written by a student during field trips to three different locations in New York State.

### NOTES

| Location A | Location B | Location C |
|---|---|---|
| Good view from this hilltop; chilly and windy. We rested to catch our breath, then collected samples. Rocks are visible everywhere. There are boulders, cobbles, and pebbles of many sizes and shapes mixed together. These surface rock fragments are composed of metamorphic rock sitting on the limestone bedrock. The teacher showed us parallel scratches in the bedrock. I saw almost no soil. | It is rocky and the streambank is steep. Where we are standing, we can see a waterfall and rapids. It is cool by the water. From the streambed we collected pebbles and cobbles — some red, some white, others a mixture of many colors. The streambed is full of rocks of all sizes. The teacher warned us to be careful of the strong stream current. | It is cool in the shade, and the rock cliff above us still has some ice on it from winter. The rocks we are sitting on have sharp edges. Rock fragments at the bottom of the cliff are the same color as the cliff. Our teacher warned us to watch out for falling rocks. |

60 *a* State the agent of erosion that deposited most of the sediment found at location *A*. [1]

*b* State *one* observation recorded by the student that supports this conclusion. [1]

61 Some samples of sediment collected from the streambed at location *B* are shown below.

Explain why these samples are smooth and have rounded shapes. [1]

62 Explain how ice in cracks on the cliff at location *C* may have helped cause weathering of the bedrock on the face of the cliff. [1]

Base your answers to questions 63 through 65 on the table below, which shows the concentration of ozone, in ozone units, in Earth's atmosphere at different altitudes. [One ozone unit is equal to $10^{12}$ molecules per cubic centimeter.]

| Concentration of Ozone | |
| --- | --- |
| Altitude (km) | Ozone Units |
| 0 | 0.7 |
| 5 | 0.6 |
| 10 | 1.1 |
| 15 | 3.0 |
| 20 | 4.9 |
| 25 | 4.4 |
| 30 | 2.6 |
| 35 | 1.4 |
| 40 | 0.6 |
| 45 | 0.2 |
| 50 | 0.1 |
| 55 | 0.0 |

63 On the grid provided *in your answer booklet,* construct a line graph of the ozone concentration in the atmosphere recorded at the different altitudes shown on the table by plotting the data from the table and connecting the points.     [3]

64 State the name of the temperature zone of the atmosphere in which the concentration of ozone is greatest.     [1]

65 State how incoming solar radiation (insolation) is affected by the ozone in the atmosphere.     [1]

Base your answers to questions 66 through 70 on the weather satellite photograph of a portion of the United States and Mexico provided in your answer booklet. The photograph shows the clouds of a major hurricane approaching the eastern coastline of Texas and Mexico. The calm center of the hurricane, the eye, is labeled.

66 This hurricane has a pattern of surface winds typical of all low-pressure systems in the Northern Hemisphere. On the satellite photograph provided, draw *three* arrows on the clouds to show the direction of the surface wind movement outside the eye of the hurricane.   [1]

67 Cloud droplets form around small particles in the atmosphere. Describe how the hurricane clouds formed from water vapor. Include the terms "dewpoint" and either "condensation" or "condense" in your answer.   [1]

68 State the latitude and longitude of the hurricane's eye. The compass directions must be included in the answer.   [1]

69 At the location shown in the photograph, the hurricane had maximum winds recorded at 110 miles per hour. Within a 24-hour period, the hurricane moved 150 miles inland and had maximum winds of only 65 miles per hour. State why the wind velocity of a hurricane usually decreases when the hurricane moves over a land surface.   [1]

70 *a* State *two* dangerous conditions, other than hurricane winds, that could cause human fatalities as the hurricane strikes the coast.   [2]

  *b* Describe *one* emergency preparation humans could take to avoid a problem caused by one of these dangerous conditions.   [1]

Base your answers to questions 71 and 72 on the rock cycle diagram below.

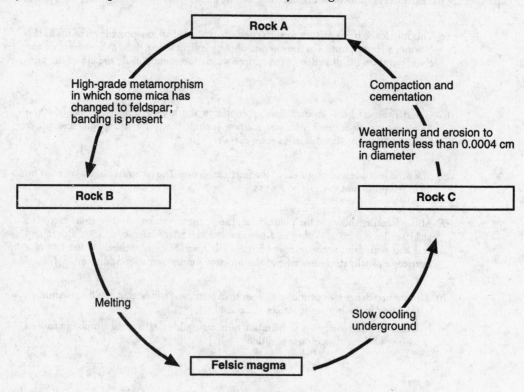

71 State the specific names of rocks *A, B,* and *C* in the diagram. Do *not* write the terms "sedimentary," "igneous," and "metamorphic."    [3]

72 State *one* condition or process that would cause the high-grade metamorphism of rock *A*.    [1]

The University of the State of New York

REGENTS HIGH SCHOOL EXAMINATION

# PHYSICAL SETTING
# EARTH SCIENCE

Thursday, August 16, 2001 — 12:30 to 3:30 p.m., only

## ANSWER SHEET

Student ............................................... Sex: ☐ Male ☐ Female  Grade .........

Teacher ........................................... School ...................................

### Record your answers to Part A and Part B–1 on this answer sheet.

| Part A | | | Part B–1 | |
|---|---|---|---|---|
| 1 .......... | 13 .......... | 25 .......... | 36 .......... | 45 .......... |
| 2 .......... | 14 .......... | 26 .......... | 37 .......... | 46 .......... |
| 3 .......... | 15 .......... | 27 .......... | 38 .......... | 47 .......... |
| 4 .......... | 16 .......... | 28 .......... | 39 .......... | 48 .......... |
| 5 .......... | 17 .......... | 29 .......... | 40 .......... | 49 .......... |
| 6 .......... | 18 .......... | 30 .......... | 41 .......... | 50 .......... |
| 7 .......... | 19 .......... | 31 .......... | 42 .......... | 51 .......... |
| 8 .......... | 20 .......... | 32 .......... | 43 .......... | 52 .......... |
| 9 .......... | 21 .......... | 33 .......... | 44 .......... | Part B–1 Score |
| 10 .......... | 22 .......... | 34 .......... | | |
| 11 .......... | 23 .......... | 35 .......... | | |
| 12 .......... | 24 .......... | Part A Score | | |

Write your answers to Part B–2 and Part C in your answer booklet.

The declaration below should be signed when you have completed the examination.

I do hereby affirm, at the close of this examination, that I had no unlawful knowledge of the questions or answers prior to the examination and that I have neither given nor received assistance in answering any of the questions during the examination.

_____

Signature

The University of the State of New York

REGENTS HIGH SCHOOL EXAMINATION

# PHYSICAL SETTING
# EARTH SCIENCE

**Thursday,** August 16, 2001 — 12:30 to 3:30 p.m., only

### ANSWER BOOKLET

Student ....................................    Sex: ☐ Male   ☐ Female

Teacher ......................................................

School ...................................    Grade ........

Answer all questions in Part B–2 and Part C. Record your answers in this booklet.

Performance Test Score
(Maximum Score: 23)  ☐

| Part | Maximum Score | Student's Score |
|------|---------------|-----------------|
| A | 35 | |
| B–1 | 17 | |
| B–2 | 13 | |
| C | 20 | |

Total Written Test Score
(Maximum Raw Score: 85)  ☐

Final Score
(from conversion chart)  ☐

Raters' Initials:

Rater 1 ......... Rater 2 .........

### Part B–2

For Raters Only

53 *a* _____   53 *a* ☐

  *b* _____   53 *b* ☐

54 _____

_____   54 ☐

55

Sun's rays

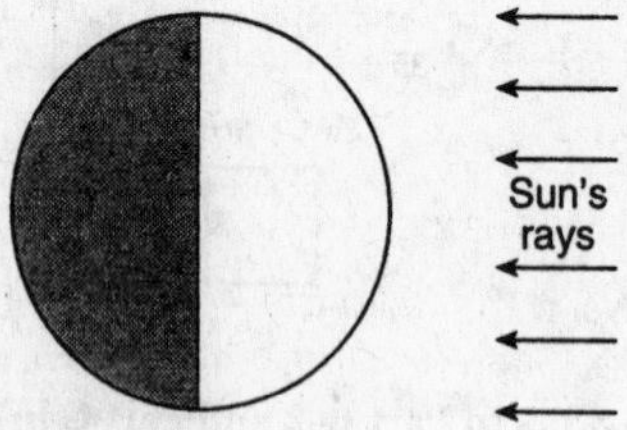

Earth's position in its
orbit 6 months later

55 ☐

**56**

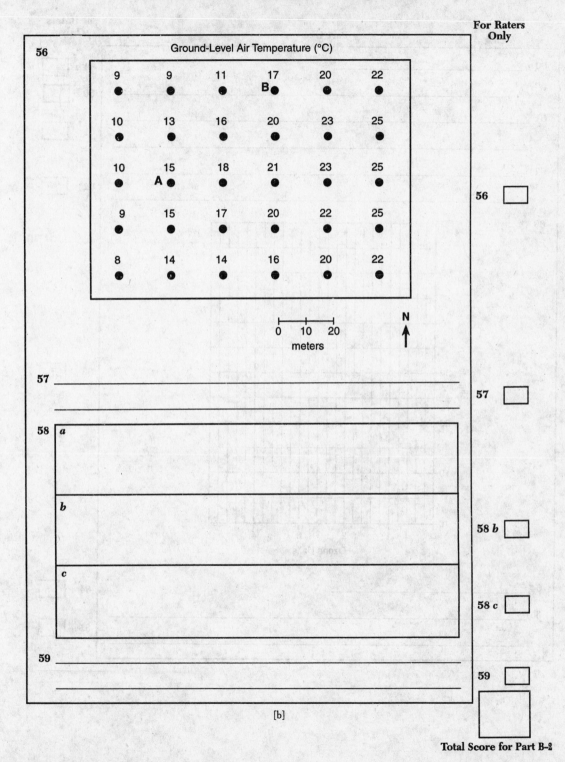

Ground-Level Air Temperature (°C)

56 ☐

**57** _____

57 ☐

**58**  *a*

*b*

*c*

58 *b* ☐

58 *c* ☐

**59** _____

59 ☐

[b]

Total Score for Part B-2 ☐

Part C

For Raters Only

60 *a* _____    60 *a* [ ]

   *b* _____    60 *b* [ ]

61 _____    61 [ ]

   _____

62 _____    62 [ ]

   _____

63 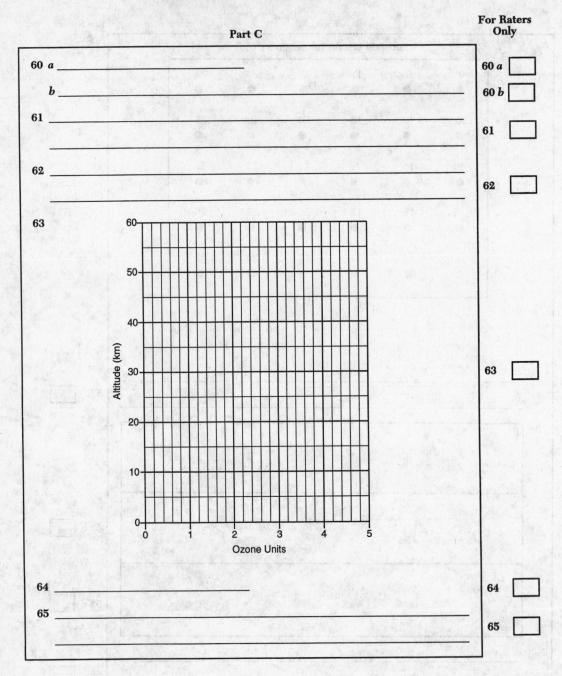    63 [ ]

64 _____    64 [ ]

65 _____    65 [ ]

   _____

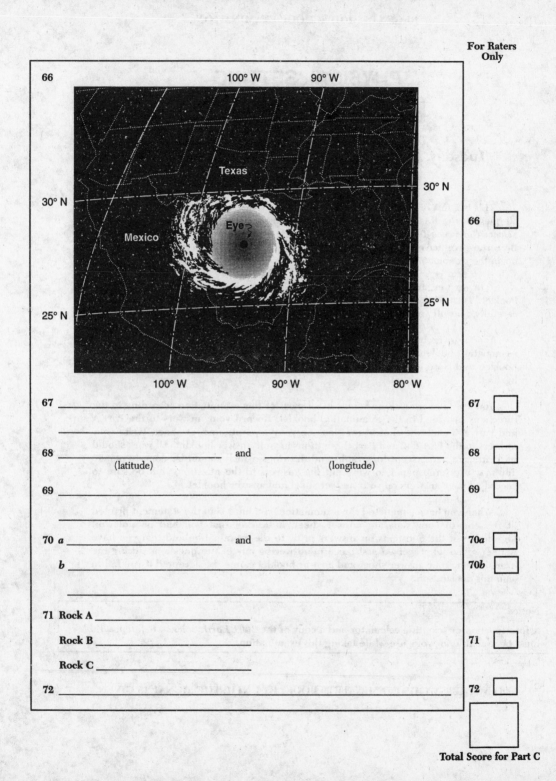

66

100° W    90° W

Texas

30° N                                    30° N

Eye

Mexico

25° N                                    25° N

100° W         90° W         80° W

66 ☐

67 _____    67 ☐
_____

68 _____ and _____    68 ☐
     (latitude)              (longitude)

69 _____    69 ☐
_____

70 a _____ and _____    70a ☐

   b _____    70b ☐
_____

71 Rock A _____
   Rock B _____                71 ☐
   Rock C _____

72 _____      72 ☐

☐

Total Score for Part C

The University of the State of New York

REGENTS HIGH SCHOOL EXAMINATION

# PHYSICAL SETTING
# EARTH SCIENCE

**Tuesday,** June 18, 2002 — 9:15 a.m. to 12:15 p.m., only

This is a test of your knowledge of Earth science. Use that knowledge to answer all questions in this examination. Some questions may require the use of the *Earth Science Reference Tables*. The *Earth Science Reference Tables* are supplied separately. Be certain you have a copy of the *2001 edition* of these reference tables before you begin the examination.

Your answer sheet for Part A and Part B–1 is the last page of this examination booklet. Turn to the last page and fold it along the perforations. Then, slowly and carefully, tear off your answer sheet and fill in the heading.

Your answer booklet for Part B–2 and Part C is stapled in the center of this examination booklet. Open the examination booklet, carefully remove your answer booklet, and close the examination booklet. Then fill in the heading of your answer booklet.

You are to answer *all* questions in all parts of this examination according to the directions provided in the examination booklet. Record your answers to the Part A and Part B–1 multiple-choice questions on your separate answer sheet. Write your answers to the Part B–2 and Part C questions in your answer booklet. All work should be written in pen, except for graphs and drawings, which should be done in pencil. You may use scrap paper to work out the answers to the questions, but be sure to record all your answers on your answer sheet and answer booklet.

When you have completed the examination, you must sign the statement printed at the end of your separate answer sheet, indicating that you had no unlawful knowledge of the questions or answers prior to the examination and that you have neither given nor received assistance in answering any of the questions during the examination. Your answer sheet and answer booklet cannot be accepted if you fail to sign this declaration.

---

Notice. . .

A four-function or scientific calculator and a copy of the *2001 Earth Science Reference Tables* must be available for your use while taking this examination.

---

**DO NOT OPEN THIS EXAMINATION BOOKLET UNTIL THE SIGNAL IS GIVEN.**

## Part A

### Answer all questions in this part.

*Directions* (1–35): For *each* statement or question, write on your separate answer sheet the *number* of the word or expression that, of those given, best completes the statement or answers the question. Some questions may require the use of the *Earth Science Reference Tables*.

1 The dashed line on the map below shows a ship's route from Long Island, New York, to Florida. As the ship travels south, the star *Polaris* appears lower in the northern sky each night.

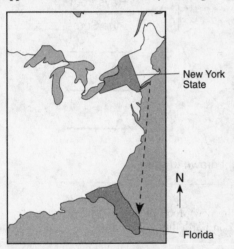

The best explanation for this observation is that *Polaris*

(1) rises and sets at different locations each day
(2) has an elliptical orbit around Earth
(3) is located directly over Earth's Equator
(4) is located directly over Earth's North Pole

2 When the dry-bulb temperature is 22°C and the wet-bulb temperature is 13°C, the relative humidity is

(1) 10%          (3) 41%
(2) 33%          (4) 59%

3 As the altitude increases within Earth's stratosphere, air temperature generally

(1) decreases, only
(2) increases, only
(3) decreases, then increases
(4) increases, then decreases

4 The diagrams below represent four rock samples. Which rock was formed by rapid cooling in a volcanic lava flow? [The diagrams are not to scale.]

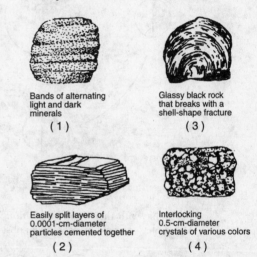

5 On June 21, some Earth locations have 24 hours of daylight. These locations are all between the latitudes of

(1) 0° and $23\frac{1}{2}$° N

(2) $23\frac{1}{2}$° N and 47° N

(3) 47° N and $66\frac{1}{2}$° N

(4) $66\frac{1}{2}$° N and 90° N

6 The Milky Way galaxy is best described as

(1) a type of solar system
(2) a constellation visible to everyone on Earth
(3) a region in space between the orbits of Mars and Jupiter
(4) a spiral-shaped formation composed of billions of stars

7 The diagram below shows the Moon at four positions in its orbit around Earth as viewed from above the North Pole.

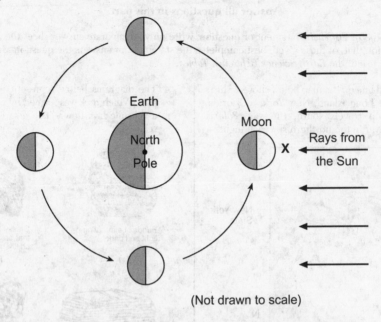

(Not drawn to scale)

Beginning with the Moon at position *X* (the new-Moon phase), which sequence of Moon phases would be seen by an observer on Earth during 1 month?

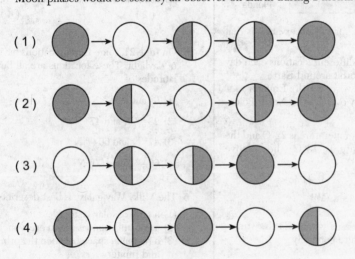

8 The diagram below represents a simple geocentric model. Which object is represented by the letter *X*?

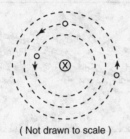

( Not drawn to scale )

(1) Earth      (3) Moon
(2) Sun        (4) *Polaris*

9 Which condition would cause surface runoff to increase in a particular location?

(1) covering a dirt road with pavement
(2) reducing the gradient of a steep hill
(3) planting grasses and shrubs on a hillside
(4) having a decrease in the annual rainfall

10 An increase in which gas would cause the most greenhouse warming of Earth's atmosphere?

(1) nitrogen      (3) carbon dioxide
(2) oxygen      (4) hydrogen

11 Scientists believe that Earth's early atmosphere changed in composition as a result of

(1) the appearance of oxygen-producing organisms
(2) the drifting of the continents
(3) the changes in Earth's magnetic field
(4) a transfer of gases from the Sun

12 Which atmospheric conditions would cause smoke from a campfire on a beach to blow toward the ocean?

(1) warm air over the land and cool air over the ocean
(2) humid air over the land and dry air over the ocean
(3) low-density air over the land and high-density air over the ocean
(4) high air pressure over the land and low air pressure over the ocean

13 Which characteristics of a building material would provide the most energy-absorbing exterior covering for a house?

(1) dark colored and smooth textured
(2) dark colored and rough textured
(3) light colored and smooth textured
(4) light colored and rough textured

14 When the time of day for a certain ship at sea is 12 noon, the time of day at the Prime Meridian (0° longitude) is 5 p.m. What is the ship's longitude?

(1) 45° W      (3) 75° W
(2) 45° E      (4) 75° E

15 The occurrence of parallel scratches on bedrock in a U-shaped valley indicates that the area has most likely been eroded by

(1) a glacier      (3) waves
(2) a stream      (4) wind

16 Which weather change usually occurs when the difference between the air temperature and the dewpoint temperature is *decreasing*?

(1) The amount of cloud cover decreases.
(2) The probability of precipitation decreases.
(3) The relative humidity increases.
(4) The barometric pressure increases.

17 In which list are the forms of electromagnetic energy arranged in order from longest to shortest wavelengths?

(1) gamma rays, x rays, ultraviolet rays, visible light
(2) radio waves, infrared rays, visible light, ultraviolet rays
(3) x rays, infrared rays, blue light, gamma rays
(4) infrared rays, radio waves, blue light, red light

18 On a clear summer day, the surface of land is usually warmer than the surface of a nearby body of water because the water

(1) receives less insolation
(2) reflects less insolation
(3) has a higher density
(4) has a higher specific heat

19 The diagram below represents the present number of decayed and undecayed atoms in a sample that was originally 100% radioactive material.

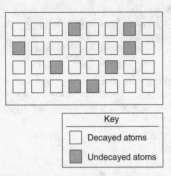

| Key | |
|---|---|
| ☐ | Decayed atoms |
| ■ | Undecayed atoms |

If the half-life of the radioactive material is 1,000 years, what is the age of the sample represented by the diagram?

(1) 1,000 yr          (3) 3,000 yr
(2) 2,000 yr          (4) 4,000 yr

20 Earth's outer core is best inferred to be

(1) liquid, with an average density of approximately 4 g/cm$^3$
(2) liquid, with an average density of approximately 11 g/cm$^3$
(3) solid, with an average density of approximately 4 g/cm$^3$
(4) solid, with an average density of approximately 11 g/cm$^3$

21 The table below shows the rate of erosion and the rate of deposition at four stream locations.

| Location | Rate of Erosion (tons/year) | Rate of Deposition (tons/year) |
|---|---|---|
| A | 3.00 | 3.25 |
| B | 4.00 | 4.00 |
| C | 4.50 | 4.65 |
| D | 5.60 | 5.20 |

A state of dynamic equilibrium exists at location

(1) A          (3) C
(2) B          (4) D

22 The diagram below shows land features that have been disrupted by an earthquake.

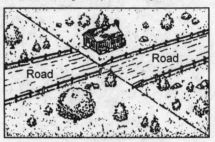

Which type of crustal movement most likely caused the displacement of features in this area?

(1) vertical lifting of surface rock
(2) folding of surface rock
(3) down-warping of the crust
(4) movement along a transform fault

23 The Coriolis effect provides evidence that Earth

(1) rotates          (3) has seasons
(2) has a tilted axis          (4) revolves

24 Which interaction between the atmosphere and the hydrosphere causes most surface ocean currents?

(1) cooling of rising air above the ocean surface
(2) evaporation of water from the ocean surface
(3) friction from planetary winds on the ocean surface
(4) seismic waves on the ocean surface

25 On a field trip 40 kilometers east of the Finger Lakes, students observed a boulder of gneiss on the surface bedrock. This observation best supports the inference that the

(1) surface sedimentary bedrock was weathered to form a boulder of gneiss
(2) surface sedimentary bedrock melted and solidified to form a boulder of gneiss
(3) gneiss boulder was formed from sediments that were compacted and cemented together
(4) gneiss boulder was transported from its original area of formation

26 The diagram below shows granite bedrock with cracks. Water has seeped into the cracks and frozen. The arrows represent the directions in which the cracks have widened due to weathering.

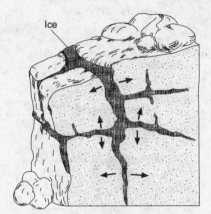

Ice

Which statement best describes the physical weathering shown by the diagram?

(1) Enlargement of the cracks occurs because water expands when it freezes.
(2) This type of weathering occurs only in bedrock composed of granite.
(3) The cracks become wider because of chemical reactions between water and the rock.
(4) This type of weathering is common in regions of primarily warm and humid climates.

27 The table below shows the density of four mineral samples.

| Mineral | Density (g/cm³) |
|---------|-----------------|
| Cinnabar | 8.2 |
| Magnetite | 5.2 |
| Quartz | 2.7 |
| Siderite | 3.9 |

If the shape and size of the four mineral samples are the same, which mineral will settle most *slowly* in water?

(1) cinnabar      (3) quartz
(2) magnetite     (4) siderite

28 Which stream-drainage pattern most likely developed on the surface of a newly formed volcanic mountain?

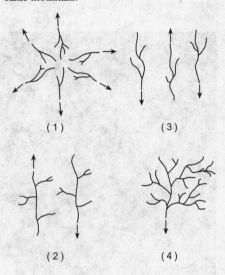

(1)          (3)

(2)          (4)

29 The cross section below shows sedimentary rocks being eroded by water at a waterfall.

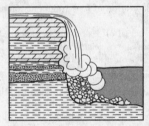

The sedimentary rock layers are being weathered and eroded at different rates primarily because the rock layers

(1) formed during different time periods
(2) contain different fossils
(3) have different compositions
(4) are horizontal

Base your answers to questions 30 and 31 on the photograph below, which shows an outcrop of sedimentary rock layers that have been tilted and slightly metamorphosed.

30 The tilted rock structure shown in the photograph is most likely the result of the

(1) deposition of rock fragments on a mountain slope
(2) reversal of past magnetic poles
(3) passage of seismic waves
(4) collision of crustal plates

31 Tilted, slightly metamorphosed rock layers such as these are typically found in which New York State landscape region?

(1) Taconic Mountains
(2) Atlantic Coastal Plain
(3) Tug Hill Plateau
(4) Erie-Ontario Lowlands

32 A stream with a water velocity of 150 centimeters per second decreases to a velocity of 100 centimeters per second. Which sediment size will most likely be deposited?

(1) pebbles          (3) boulders
(2) sand             (4) cobbles

33 The diagram below shows a stream profile before and after an earthquake. Points A and B are locations along the streambed.

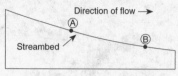

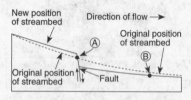

What is the probable relationship between erosion and deposition at points A and B after the earthquake?

(1) There is more deposition at point A and more erosion at point B.
(2) There is more erosion at point A and more deposition at point B.
(3) There is more deposition than erosion at points A and B.
(4) There is more erosion than deposition at points A and B.

**Note that questions 34 and 35 have only three choices.**

34 As air on the surface of Earth warms, the density of the air

(1) decreases
(2) increases
(3) remains the same

35 Compared to the average density of the terrestrial planets (Mercury, Venus, Earth, and Mars), the average density of the Jovian planets (Jupiter, Saturn, Uranus, and Neptune) is

(1) less
(2) greater
(3) the same

## Part B–1

### Answer all questions in this part.

*Directions* (36–50): For *each* statement or question, write on your separate answer sheet the *number* of the the word or expression that, of those given, best completes the statement or answers the question. Some questions may require the use of the *Earth Science Reference Tables*.

Base your answers to questions 36 through 38 on the diagram below, which represents the elliptical orbit of a planet traveling around a star. Points *A, B, C,* and *D* are four positions of this planet in its orbit.

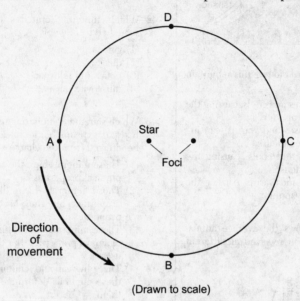

(Drawn to scale)

36 The calculated eccentricity of this orbit is approximately

(1) 0.1         (3) 0.3
(2) 0.2         (4) 0.4

37 The gravitational attraction between the star and the planet will be greatest at position

(1) *A*         (3) *C*
(2) *B*         (4) *D*

38 As the planet revolves in orbit from position *A* to position *D*, the orbital velocity will

(1) continually decrease
(2) continually increase
(3) decrease, then increase
(4) increase, then decrease

39 The cross section below shows how prevailing winds have caused different climates on the windward and leeward sides of a mountain range.

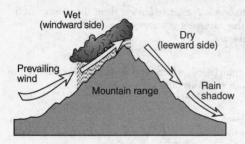

Why does the windward side of this mountain have a wet climate?

(1) Rising air compresses and cools, causing the water droplets to evaporate.
(2) Rising air compresses and warms, causing the water vapor to condense.
(3) Rising air expands and cools, causing the water vapor to condense.
(4) Rising air expands and warms, causing the water droplets to evaporate.

40 Which graph best shows the average annual amounts of precipitation received at different latitudes on Earth?

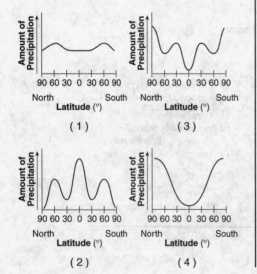

Base your answers to questions 41 through 44 on the "Properties of Common Minerals" chart in the *Earth Science Reference Tables*.

41 Which mineral leaves a green-black powder when rubbed against an unglazed porcelain plate?

(1) galena        (3) hematite
(2) graphite      (4) pyrite

42 Which mineral scratches dolomite and is scratched by olivine?

(1) galena
(2) quartz
(3) potassium feldspar
(4) muscovite mica

43 Which statement about the minerals plagioclase feldspar, gypsum, biotite mica, and talc can best be inferred from the chart?

(1) These minerals have the same chemical and physical properties.
(2) These minerals have different chemical properties, but they have similar physical properties.
(3) These minerals have different physical and chemical properties, but they have identical uses.
(4) The physical and chemical properties of these minerals determine how humans use them.

44 Minerals from this chart are found in several different rocks. Which two rocks are primarily composed of a mineral that bubbles with acid?

(1) limestone and marble
(2) granite and dolostone
(3) sandstone and quartzite
(4) slate and conglomerate

Base your answers to questions 45 through 49 on the cross sections below, which show widely separated outcrops at locations *X, Y,* and *Z.*

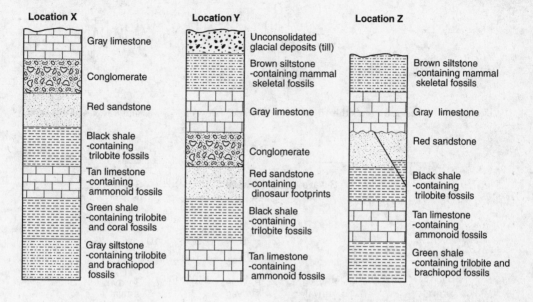

**Location X**

- Gray limestone
- Conglomerate
- Red sandstone
- Black shale -containing trilobite fossils
- Tan limestone -containing ammonoid fossils
- Green shale -containing trilobite and coral fossils
- Gray siltstone -containing trilobite and brachiopod fossils

**Location Y**

- Unconsolidated glacial deposits (till)
- Brown siltstone -containing mammal skeletal fossils
- Gray limestone
- Conglomerate
- Red sandstone -containing dinosaur footprints
- Black shale -containing trilobite fossils
- Tan limestone -containing ammonoid fossils

**Location Z**

- Brown siltstone -containing mammal skeletal fossils
- Gray limestone
- Red sandstone
- Black shale -containing trilobite fossils
- Tan limestone -containing ammonoid fossils
- Green shale -containing trilobite and brachiopod fossils

45 Which rock layer is oldest?

  (1) gray siltstone
  (2) green shale
  (3) tan limestone
  (4) brown siltstone

46 At location *Y,* the boundary between the red sandstone and the black shale marks the

  (1) beginning of the Cenozoic Era
  (2) beginning of the Mesozoic Era
  (3) end of the Cenozoic Era
  (4) end of the Mesozoic Era

47 An unconformity can be observed at location *Z.* Which rock layer was most probably removed by erosion during the time represented by the unconformity?

  (1) conglomerate    (3) black shale
  (2) gray siltstone    (4) brown siltstone

48 The fossils in the rock formations at location *X* indicate that this area was often covered by

  (1) tropical rain forests
  (2) glacial ice
  (3) desert sand
  (4) seawater

49 Which rock layer was formed by the compaction and cementation of particles that were all less than 0.0004 centimeter in diameter?

  (1) red sandstone
  (2) green shale
  (3) brown siltstone
  (4) conglomerate

50 The diagram below is a seismogram of the famous San Francisco earthquake of 1906, recorded at a seismic station located 6,400 kilometers from San Francisco.

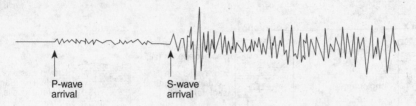

Which time scale best represents the arrival-time difference between *P*-waves and *S*-waves at this station?

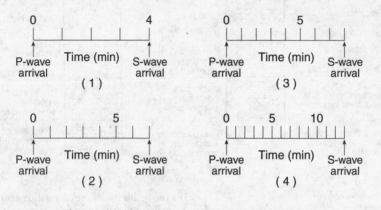

## Part B–2

### Answer all questions in this part.

*Directions* (51–60): Record your answers in the spaces provided in your answer booklet. Some questions may require the use of the *Earth Science Reference Tables*.

51 Using the proper format, place the following data on the weather station model provided *in your answer booklet*.   [2]

Dewpoint = 74°F

Cloud cover = 100%

Base your answers to questions 52 through 54 on the data table below, which shows one cycle of equinoxes and solstices for the northern hemispheres of several planets in the solar system and the tilt of each planet's axis. Data for the planets are based on Earth's time system.

**Data Table**

| Planet | Spring Equinox | Summer Solstice | Autumn Equinox | Winter Solstice | Tilt of Axis (degrees) |
|--------|----------------|-----------------|----------------|-----------------|------------------------|
| Venus | June 25 | August 21 | October 16 | December 11 | 3.0 |
| Earth | March 21 | June 21 | September 23 | December 22 | 23.5 |
| Jupiter | 1997 | 2000 | 2003 | 2006 | 3.0 |
| Saturn | 1980 | 1987 | 1995 | 2002 | 26.8 |
| Uranus | 1922 | 1943 | 1964 | 1985 | 82.0 |
| Neptune | 1880 | 1921 | 1962 | 2003 | 28.5 |

52 State the length, in years, of the spring season on Uranus.   [1]

53 Describe the relationship between a planet's distance from the Sun and the length of a season on that planet.   [1]

54 Identify *two* factors that cause seasons on Earth.   [2]

_____

Base your answers to questions 55 and 56 on the data table below, which shows the volume and mass of three different samples, *A*, *B*, and *C*, of the mineral pyrite.

| Pyrite | | |
|--------|--------------|----------|
| Sample | Volume (cm³) | Mass (g) |
| A | 2.5 | 12.5 |
| B | 6.0 | 30.0 |
| C | 20.0 | 100.0 |

55 On the grid provided *in your answer booklet,* plot the data (volume and mass) for the *three* samples of pyrite and connect the points with a line.   [2]

56 State the mass of a 10.0-cm³ sample of pyrite.   [1]

_____

Base your answers to questions 57 through 59 on the topographic map below of an area in New York State. Points $X$ and $Y$ are locations on Squab Hollow Creek.

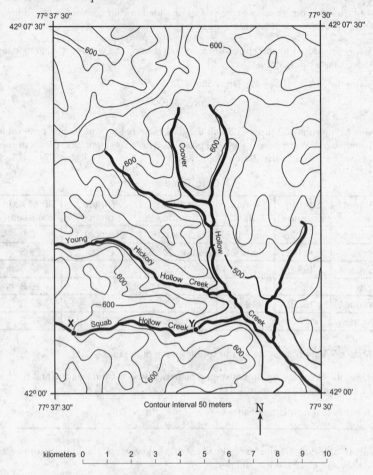

57 In the space provided *in your answer booklet,* determine the gradient of Squab Hollow Creek between point $X$ and point $Y$ by following the directions below.

   *a* Using the *Earth Science Reference Tables,* write the equation used to determine the gradient.

   *b* Substitute values into the equation.   [1]

   *c* Solve the equation and label the answer with the correct units.   [2]

58 Describe one way to determine the direction of flow of Coover Hollow Creek from information shown on the map.   [1]

59 Based on the latitude and longitude coordinates given, identify the New York State landscape region in which this map region is located.   [1]

60 Some marine organisms swim or float in the ocean, and others live on or in the sediment of the ocean floor. A group of floating organisms called graptolites were common in some ancient seas that covered New York State and are found in some New York State bedrock.

Floating graptolites

State one reason why certain species of graptolites are used as an index fossil.   [1]

_____

**Part C**

**Answer all questions in this part.**

*Directions* (61–72): Record your answers in the spaces provided in your answer booklet. Some questions may require the use of the *Earth Science Reference Tables*.

Base your answers to questions 61 and 62 on the graph below and on the "Luminosity and Temperature of Stars" graph in the *Earth Science Reference Tables*. The graph below shows the inferred stages of development of the Sun, showing luminosity and surface temperature at various stages.

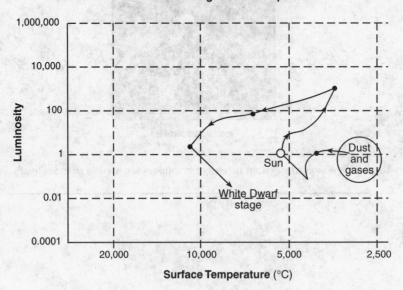

**Inferred Stages of Development**

61 Describe the changes in luminosity of the Sun that will occur from its current Main Sequence stage to its final White Dwarf stage.   [1]

62 Which star shown on the "Luminosity and Temperature of Stars" graph in the *Earth Science Reference Tables* is currently at the Sun's final predicted stage of development?   [1]

Base your answers to questions 63 and 64 in part on the news article and map below. Points *A* and *B* on the map are reference points.

### Huge Quake Possible in Oregon Valley

Scientists have warned for years that a magnitude 8 or 9 earthquake could strike about 30 miles off the Oregon coast, causing huge tsunamis (large ocean waves) and tremendous damage.

Now scientists say these earthquakes could be centered much farther inland and cause severe damage to a larger area, including cities in Oregon such as Portland, Salem, and Eugene.

Geologic evidence suggests that strong quakes in this area occur about every 400 years, plus or minus 200 years. The last one, believed to be a magnitude 9, occurred 300 years ago.

A magnitude 8 quake can cause tremendous damage. The San Francisco quake of 1906 has been estimated at 7.9. The Mexico City quake of 1985 that left thousands dead was measured at 8.1.

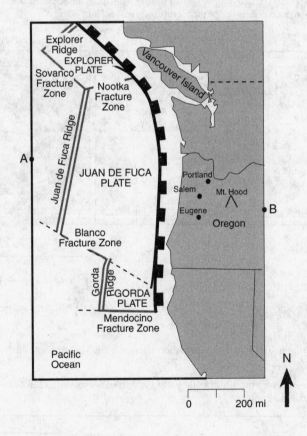

63 The cross section in your answer booklet shows the lithosphere and asthenosphere between points *A* and *B* on the map.

   *a* On the cross section provided *in your answer booklet,* draw an arrow in the Juan de Fuca Plate to indicate the direction of the relative movement of the plate.   [1]

   *b* Identify the type of tectonic plate boundary that exists at the Juan de Fuca Ridge.   [1]

   *c* Identify the name of the plate in the cross section labeled *x*.   [1]

   *d* How does the average earthquake depth beneath the Oregon coastline compare to the average earthquake depth beneath Mt. Hood?   [1]

64 An emergency management specialist in Portland, Oregon, is developing a plan that would help save lives or prevent property damage in the event of a future earthquake. Describe *two* actions or ideas that should be included in the plan.   [2]

Base your answers to questions 65 and 66 in part on the maps below, which show areas of hurricane formation and normal hurricane paths in the Atlantic Ocean during May, July, and September. The areas of hurricane formation usually have surface ocean-water temperatures greater than 80°F.

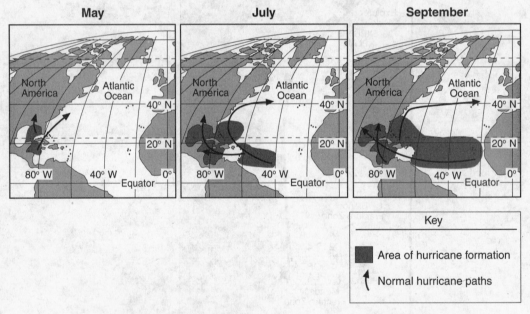

65 How does the area of hurricane formation change from May to September?   [1]

66 State one reason why most hurricane paths curve northeastward as hurricanes move north of 30° N latitude.   [1]

Base your answers to questions 67 through 69 on the weather map provided in your answer booklet. The weather map shows a low-pressure system over part of North America. Five weather stations are shown on the map. Lines *AB, BC,* and *BD* represent surface frontal boundaries. Line *AB* represents an occluded front that marks the center of a low-pressure system. Symbols cP and mT represent different air masses.

67 On the weather map provided *in your answer booklet,* place the proper front symbols on lines *AB, BC,* and *BD.* Place the front symbols on the correct side of each line to show the direction of front movement.   [3]

68 Name the geographic region over which the mT air mass most likely formed.   [1]

69 Other than low pressure, state *two* weather conditions associated with a low-pressure center.   [2]

---

Base your answers to questions 70 through 72 in part on the newspaper article shown below, taken and adapted from the *Los Angeles Times.*

### Volcanic Blast Shaped Earth

*Study finds eruption split an ancient continent,*
*creating Atlantic Ocean*

The largest volcanic eruption in Earth's history — so powerful it split an ancient supercontinent and created the Atlantic Ocean — spewed millions of square miles of searing lava that extinguished much of life on ancient Earth.

From hundreds of basalt outcrops that rim the Atlantic coasts, scientists have pieced together evidence of the titanic eruption 200 million years ago. Researchers said that the eruption set the fractured landmasses adrift and, by wedging them apart, gradually opened the gulf that created the Atlantic — giving the map of the world the form it has today.

"This is one of the biggest things that has ever happened in Earth's history. This is a gigantic, igneous event and it all seems to have occurred in an amazingly brief amount of time."

To reconstruct the ancient catastrophe, a team of scientists analyzed basalt dikes, sills, and lavas from the New Jersey Palisades, the Brazilian Amazon, Spain, and West Africa.

By studying the chemical composition and dating the residual radioisotopes in the basaltic rocks, the researchers determined that the rocks all originated from the same eruption. Once they realized the outcrops were linked, they were able to determine that, in the distant past, the rocks all had been located together at the center of an immense continent called Pangea that once stretched, unbroken, from pole to pole.

70 Name the geologic time period when this major volcanic eruption initially opened the Atlantic Ocean.   [1]

71 Scientists stated that rocks from the volcanic eruption that separated the continents are basalt. List *two* observable characteristics that are normally used to identify basaltic rock.   [2]

72 Basaltic outcrops are not the only evidence of this ancient continental splitting. Describe another piece of evidence that supports the idea that the present-day continents were once part of the large ancient continent, Pangea, that split apart.   [1]

---

The University of the State of New York

REGENTS HIGH SCHOOL EXAMINATION

# PHYSICAL SETTING
# EARTH SCIENCE

**Tuesday,** June 18, 2002 — 9:15 a.m. to 12:15 p.m., only

## ANSWER SHEET

Student ........................................ Sex: ☐ Male ☐ Female   Grade ..........

Teacher ........................................ School ..................................

**Record your answers to Part A and Part B–1 on this answer sheet.**

| Part A | | | Part B–1 | |
|---|---|---|---|---|
| 1 .......... | 13 .......... | 25 .......... | 36 .......... | 44 .......... |
| 2 .......... | 14 .......... | 26 .......... | 37 .......... | 45 .......... |
| 3 .......... | 15 .......... | 27 .......... | 38 .......... | 46 .......... |
| 4 .......... | 16 .......... | 28 .......... | 39 .......... | 47 .......... |
| 5 .......... | 17 .......... | 29 .......... | 40 .......... | 48 .......... |
| 6 .......... | 18 .......... | 30 .......... | 41 .......... | 49 .......... |
| 7 .......... | 19 .......... | 31 .......... | 42 .......... | 50 .......... |
| 8 .......... | 20 .......... | 32 .......... | 43 .......... | |
| 9 .......... | 21 .......... | 33 .......... | | |
| 10 .......... | 22 .......... | 34 .......... | | |
| 11 .......... | 23 .......... | 35 .......... | | |
| 12 .......... | 24 .......... | | | |

Part A Score ☐

Part B–1 Score ☐

**Write your answers to Part B–2 and Part C in your answer booklet.**

**The declaration below should be signed when you have completed the examination.**

I do hereby affirm, at the close of this examination, that I had no unlawful knowledge of the questions or answers prior to the examination and that I have neither given nor received assistance in answering any of the questions during the examination.

_____

Signature

The University of the State of New York

REGENTS HIGH SCHOOL EXAMINATION

# PHYSICAL SETTING
# EARTH SCIENCE

**Tuesday,** June 18, 2002 — 9:15 a.m. to 12:15 p.m., only

## ANSWER BOOKLET

Sex: ☐ Male   ☐ Female

Student . . . . . . . . . . . . . . . . . . . . . . . . . . . . . . . . .

Teacher . . . . . . . . . . . . . . . . . . . . . . . . . . . . . . . . . . . . .

School . . . . . . . . . . . . . . . . . . . . . . . . . . . . . . . . .   Grade . . . . . . . .

Answer all questions in Part B–2 and Part C. Record your answers in this booklet.

Performance Test Score
(Maximum Score: 23)

| Part | Maximum Score | Student's Score |
|---|---|---|
| A | 35 | |
| B–1 | 15 | |
| B–2 | 15 | |
| C | 20 | |

Total Written Test Score
(Maximum Raw Score: 85)

Final Score
(from conversion chart)

Raters' Initials:

Rater 1 . . . . . . . .   Rater 2 . . . . . . . .

## Part B–2

For Raters Only

51

51 ☐

52 _____ years   52 ☐

53 _____   53 ☐

_____

54 (1) _____   _____

(2) _____   54 ☐

[OVER]

**55**

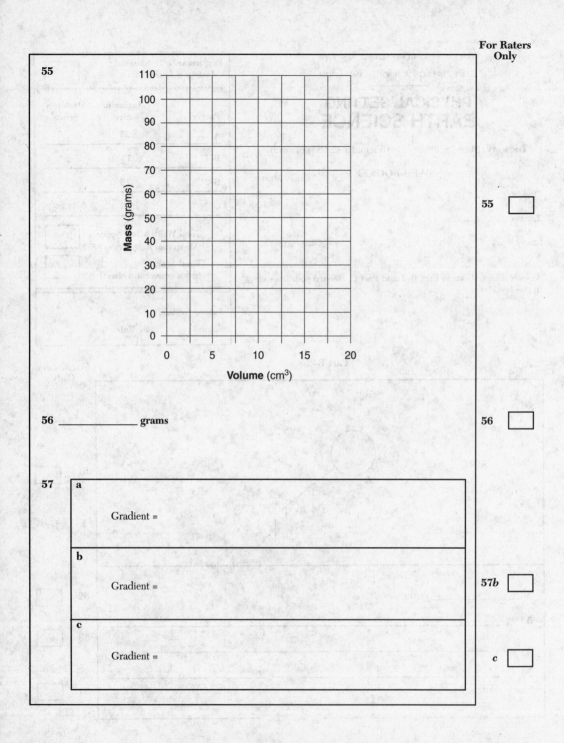

**55** ☐

**56** _____ **grams**

**56** ☐

**57**

| **a** |
| --- |
| Gradient = |

| **b** |
| --- |
| Gradient = |

| **c** |
| --- |
| Gradient = |

**57b** ☐

**c** ☐

For Raters Only

58 ______________________________________ 58 [ ]

______________________________________

59 ______________________________________ 59 [ ]

60 ______________________________________ 60 [ ]

______________________________________

[ ] Total Score for Part B–2

**Part C**

61 ______________________________________ 61 [ ]

62 ____________________ 62 [ ]

63 *a*

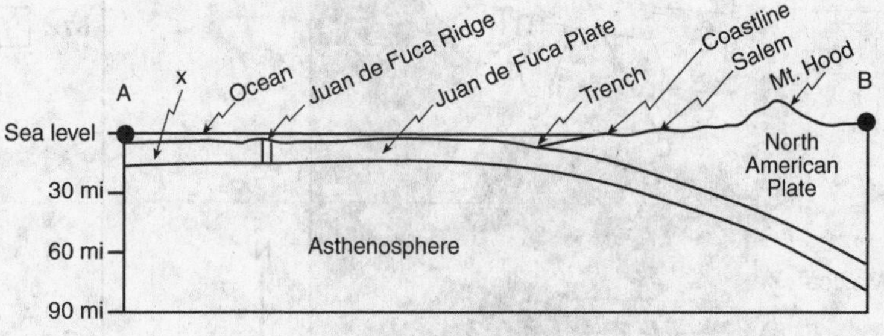


63*a* [ ]

*b* ____________________ plate boundary *b* [ ]

*c* ____________________ Plate *c* [ ]

*d* ______________________________________

______________________________________ *d* [ ]

64 (1) ______________________________________

______________________________________

(2) ______________________________________ 64 [ ]

______________________________________

For Raters Only

65 ______________________________ 65 [ ]

66 ______________________________ 66 [ ]

67 67 [ ]

68 ______________________________ 68 [ ]

69 (1) ______________________________ 69 [ ]

(2) ______________________________

70 ______________________________ Period 70 [ ]

71 (1) ______________________________ 71 [ ]

(2) ______________________________

72 ______________________________ 72 [ ]

[ ]

Total Score for Part C

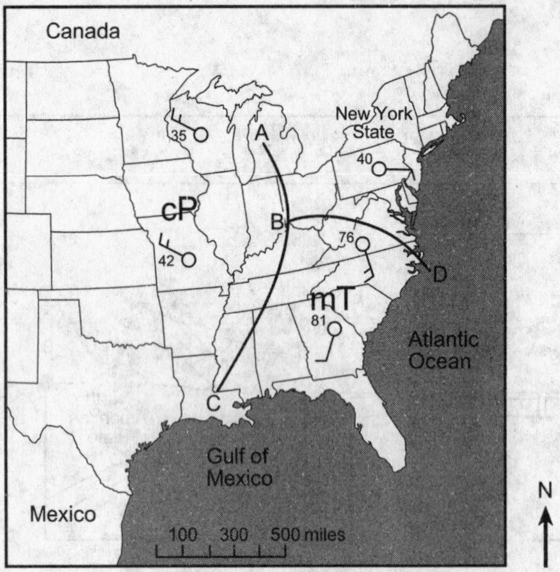

The University of the State of New York

REGENTS HIGH SCHOOL EXAMINATION

# PHYSICAL SETTING
# EARTH SCIENCE

**Tuesday,** August 13, 2002 — 12:30 to 3:30 p.m., only

This is a test of your knowledge of Earth science. Use that knowledge to answer all questions in this examination. Some questions may require the use of the *Earth Science Reference Tables*. The *Earth Science Reference Tables* are supplied separately. Be certain you have a copy of the *2001 edition* of these reference tables before you begin the examination.

Your answer sheet for Part A and Part B–1 is the last page of this examination booklet. Turn to the last page and fold it along the perforations. Then, slowly and carefully, tear off your answer sheet and fill in the heading.

Your answer booklet for Part B–2 and Part C is stapled in the center of this examination booklet. Open the examination booklet, carefully remove your answer booklet, and close the examination booklet. Then fill in the heading of your answer booklet.

You are to answer *all* questions in all parts of this examination according to the directions provided in the examination booklet. Record your answers to the Part A and Part B–1 multiple-choice questions on your separate answer sheet. Write your answers to the Part B–2 and Part C questions in your answer booklet. All work should be written in pen, except for graphs and drawings, which should be done in pencil. You may use scrap paper to work out the answers to the questions, but be sure to record all your answers on your answer sheet and answer booklet.

When you have completed the examination, you must sign the statement printed at the end of your separate answer sheet, indicating that you had no unlawful knowledge of the questions or answers prior to the examination and that you have neither given nor received assistance in answering any of the questions during the examination. Your answer sheet and answer booklet cannot be accepted if you fail to sign this declaration.

---

Notice. . .

A four-function or scientific calculator and a copy of the *2001 Earth Science Reference Tables* must be available for your use while taking this examination.

---

**DO NOT OPEN THIS EXAMINATION BOOKLET UNTIL THE SIGNAL IS GIVEN.**

## Part A

### Answer all questions in this part.

*Directions* (1–35): For *each* statement or question, write on your separate answer sheet the *number* of the word or expression that, of those given, best completes the statement or answers the question. Some questions may require the use of the *Earth Science Reference Tables*.

1 The apparent rising and setting of the Sun, as viewed from Earth, is caused by

(1) Earth's rotation
(2) Earth's revolution
(3) the Sun's rotation
(4) the Sun's revolution

2 In which direction on the horizon does the Sun appear to rise on July 4 in New York State?

(1) due north          (3) north of due east
(2) due south          (4) south of due east

3 Which graph best represents the change in gravitational attraction between the Sun and a comet as the distance between them increases?

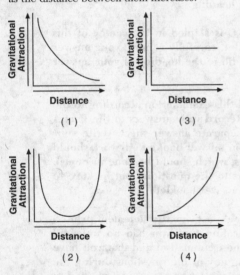

4 The best evidence that Earth spins on its axis is provided by

(1) variations in atmospheric density
(2) apparent shifts in the swing of a Foucault pendulum
(3) changes in the position of sunspots on the Sun
(4) eclipses of the Moon

5 A major belt of asteroids is located between Mars and Jupiter. What is the approximate average distance between the Sun and this major asteroid belt?

(1) 110 million kilometers
(2) 220 million kilometers
(3) 390 million kilometers
(4) 850 million kilometers

6 A cycle of Moon phases can be seen from Earth because the

(1) Moon's distance from Earth changes at a predictable rate
(2) Moon's axis is tilted
(3) Moon spins on its axis
(4) Moon revolves around Earth

7 Which diagram represents the approximate altitude of *Polaris* as seen by an observer located in Syracuse, New York?

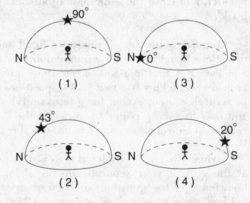

8 Compared to Earth's crust, Earth's core is believed to be

(1) less dense, cooler, and composed of more iron
(2) less dense, hotter, and composed of less iron
(3) more dense, hotter, and composed of more iron
(4) more dense, cooler, and composed of less iron

9  Which graph best represents the relative periods of rotation of Mercury, Venus, Earth, and Mars?

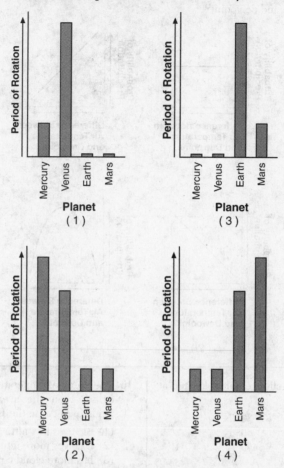

10  An environmental scientist needs to prepare a report on the potential effects that a proposed surface mine in New York State will have on the watershed where the mine will be located. In which reference materials will the scientist find the most useful data with which to determine the watershed's boundaries?

(1) topographic maps
(2) geologic time scales
(3) tectonic plate maps
(4) planetary wind maps

11  Which two kinds of adjoining bedrock would most likely have a zone of contact metamorphism between them?

(1) shale and conglomerate
(2) shale and sandstone
(3) limestone and sandstone
(4) limestone and granite

12 Which graph best shows the relationship between the probability of precipitation and the difference between air temperature and dewpoint?

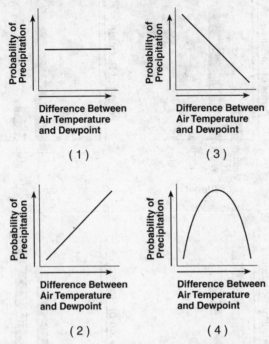

( 1 )

( 3 )

( 2 )

( 4 )

13 A high air-pressure, dry-climate belt is located at which Earth latitude?

(1) 0°                    (3) 30° N
(2) 15° N                 (4) 60° N

14 The Canaries Current along the west coast of Africa and the Peru Current along the west coast of South America are both

(1) warm currents that flow away from the Equator
(2) warm currents that flow toward the Equator
(3) cool currents that flow away from the Equator
(4) cool currents that flow toward the Equator

15 Which two gases in Earth's atmosphere are believed by scientists to be greenhouse gases that are major contributors to global warming?

(1) carbon dioxide and methane
(2) oxygen and nitrogen
(3) hydrogen and helium
(4) ozone and chlorine

16 The average temperature at Earth's North Pole is colder than the average temperature at the Equator because the Equator

(1) receives less ultraviolet radiation
(2) receives more intense insolation
(3) has more cloud cover
(4) has a thicker atmosphere

17 On a certain day, the isobars on a weather map are very close together over eastern New York State. To make the people of this area aware of possible risk to life and property in this situation, the National Weather Service should issue

(1) a dense-fog warning
(2) a high-wind advisory
(3) a heat-index warning
(4) an air-pollution advisory

18 During which geologic time period did the earliest reptiles and great coal-forming forests exist?

(1) Devonian               (3) Mississippian
(2) Quaternary             (4) Pennsylvanian

19 In the diagram below, the spectral lines of hydrogen gas from three galaxies, A, B, and C, are compared to the spectral lines of hydrogen gas observed in a laboratory.

Laboratory Hydrogen Spectral Lines

Blue          Red

Galaxy A Spectral Lines

Blue          Red

Galaxy B Spectral Lines

Blue          Red

Galaxy C Spectral Lines

Blue          Red

What is the best inference that can be made concerning the movement of galaxies A, B, and C?

(1) Galaxy A is moving away from Earth, but galaxies B and C are moving toward Earth.
(2) Galaxy B is moving away from Earth, but galaxies A and C are moving toward Earth.
(3) Galaxies A, B, and C are all moving toward Earth.
(4) Galaxies A, B, and C are all moving away from Earth.

20 What is the dewpoint temperature when the dry-bulb temperature is 16°C and the wet-bulb temperature is 11°C?

(1) 5°C          (3) 9°C
(2) 7°C          (4) –17°C

21 A strong west wind steadily blew over Lake Ontario picking up moisture. As this moist air flowed over the Tug Hill Plateau, the plateau received a 36-inch snowfall. This snow fell from clouds that formed when rising air was

(1) cooled by expansion, causing water vapor to condense
(2) cooled by compression, causing water vapor to condense
(3) warmed by expansion, causing water vapor to evaporate
(4) warmed by compression, causing water vapor to evaporate

22 The map below shows a meandering river. A–A' is the location of a cross section. The arrows show the direction of the riverflow.

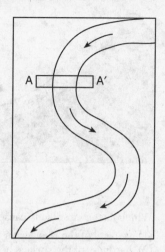

Which cross section best represents the shape of the river bottom at A–A'?

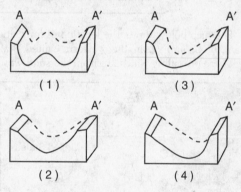

( 1 )          ( 3 )

( 2 )          ( 4 )

23 During which phase change of water is the most energy released into the environment?

(1) water freezing
(2) ice melting
(3) water evaporating
(4) water vapor condensing

24 During a rainfall, surface runoff will probably be greatest in an area that has a

(1) steep slope and a clay-covered surface
(2) steep slope and a gravel-covered surface
(3) gentle slope and a grass-covered surface
(4) gentle slope and a tree-covered surface

25 The cross section below illustrates the general sorting of sediment by a river as it flows from a mountain to a plain.

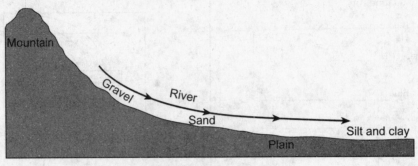

(Not drawn to scale)

Which factor most likely caused the sediment to be sorted in the pattern shown?

(1) velocity of the river water
(2) hardness of the surface bedrock
(3) mineral composition of the sediment
(4) temperature of the water

26 The map below shows the location of four cities, A, B, C, and D, in the western United States where prevailing winds are from the southwest.

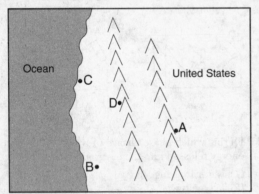

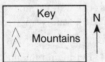

Which city most likely receives the *least* amount of average yearly precipitation?

(1) A                    (3) C
(2) B                    (4) D

27 Earth's troposphere, hydrosphere, and lithosphere contain relatively large amounts of which element?

(1) iron                 (3) hydrogen
(2) oxygen               (4) potassium

28 The long, sandy islands along the south shore of Long Island are composed mostly of sand and rounded pebbles arranged in sorted layers. The agent of erosion that most likely shaped and sorted the sand and pebbles while transporting them to their island location was

(1) glaciers             (3) wind
(2) landslides           (4) ocean waves

29 Which river is a tributary branch of the Hudson River?

(1) Delaware River       (3) Mohawk River
(2) Susquehanna River    (4) Genesee River

30 What are the largest particles that a stream can transport when its velocity is 200 centimeters per second?

(1) silt                 (3) pebbles
(2) sand                 (4) cobbles

31 The diagrams below show the relative sizes of particles from soil samples *A*, *B*, and *C*. Equal volumes of each soil sample were placed in separate containers. Each container has a screen at the bottom. Water was poured through each sample to determine the infiltration rate.

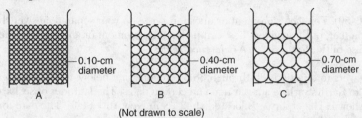

(Not drawn to scale)

Which graph best shows how the infiltration rates of the three soil samples would compare?

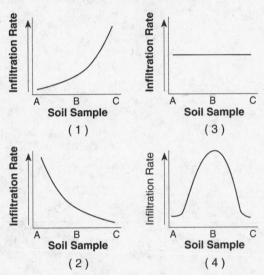

32 Which common rock is formed from the solidification of molten material?

(1) rock gypsum        (3) rhyolite
(2) slate              (4) coal

33 Rocks can be classified as sedimentary, igneous, or metamorphic based primarily upon differences in their

(1) color              (3) origin
(2) density            (4) age

34 Buffalo, New York, and Plattsburgh, New York, are both located in landscape regions called

(1) mountains          (3) plateaus
(2) highlands          (4) lowlands

35 The diagram below shows how a sample of the mineral mica breaks when hit with a rock hammer.

This mineral breaks in smooth, flat surfaces because it

(1) is very hard
(2) is very dense
(3) contains large amounts of iron
(4) has a regular arrangement of atoms

## Part B–1

### Answer all questions in this part.

*Directions* (36–50): For *each* statement or question, write on your separate answer sheet the *number* of the word or expression that, of those given, best completes the statement or answers the question. Some questions may require the use of the *Earth Science Reference Tables*.

Base your answers to questions 36 through 38 on the diagram below, which represents the position of the Sun with respect to Earth's surface at solar noon on certain dates. The latitudes of six locations on the same line of longitude are shown. The observer is located at 42° N in New York State. The date for the Sun at position *A* has been deliberately left blank.

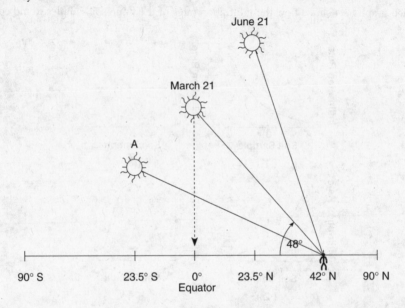

36 At which New York State location could the observer be located?

  (1) Plattsburgh      (3) New York City
  (2) Mount Marcy     (4) Slide Mountain

37 When the Sun is at position A, which latitude receives the most direct rays of the Sun?

  (1) Tropic of Cancer (23.5° N)
  (2) Tropic of Capricorn (23.5° S)
  (3) Equator (0°)
  (4) Antarctic Circle (66.5° S)

38 When the Sun is at the March 21 position, New York State will usually have

  (1) longer days than nights
  (2) 12 hours of daylight and 12 hours of darkness
  (3) the lowest annual altitude of the Sun at solar noon
  (4) the highest annual altitude of the Sun at solar noon

Base your answers to questions 39 and 40 on the graph below. The graph shows air temperature and relative humidity at a single location during a 24-hour period.

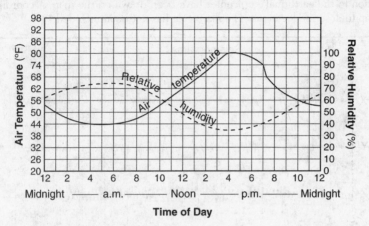

39 What was the approximate change in relative humidity from 12 noon to 4 p.m.?

(1) 10%          (3) 20%
(2) 15%          (4) 30%

40 At which time would the rate of evaporation most likely be greatest?

(1) 11 p.m.          (3) 10 a.m.
(2) 6 a.m.          (4) 4 p.m.

Base your answers to questions 41 and 42 on the map below of Iceland, a country located on the Mid-Atlantic Ridge. Four locations are represented by the letters A through D.

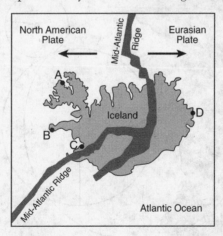

41 The fine-grained texture of most of the igneous rock formed on the surface of Iceland is due to

(1) rapid cooling of the molten rock
(2) high density of the molten rock
(3) numerous faults in the island's bedrock
(4) high pressure under the island

42 The youngest bedrock is most likely found at which location?

(1) A          (3) C
(2) B          (4) D

Base your answers to questions 43 through 46 on the diagram and map below. The diagram shows three seismograms of the same earthquake recorded at three different seismic stations, X, Y, and Z. The distances from each seismic station to the earthquake epicenter have been drawn on the map. A coordinate system has been placed on the map to describe locations. The map scale has not been included.

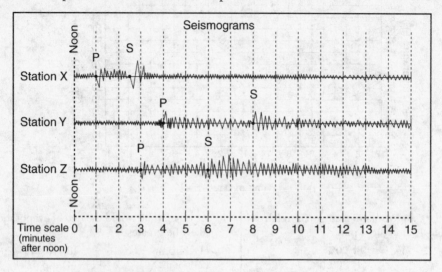

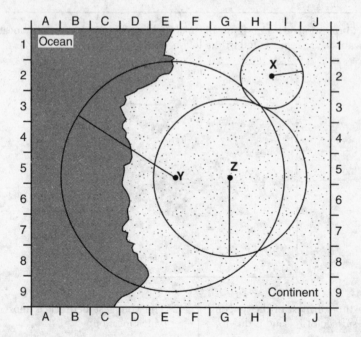

43 Approximately how far away from station *Y* is the epicenter?

(1) 1,300 km  (3) 3,900 km
(2) 2,600 km  (4) 5,200 km

44 The *S*-waves from this earthquake that travel toward Earth's center will

(1) be deflected by Earth's magnetic field
(2) be totally reflected off the crust-mantle interface
(3) be absorbed by the liquid outer core
(4) reach the other side of Earth faster than those that travel around Earth in the crust

45 Seismic station *Z* is 1,700 kilometers from the epicenter. Approximately how long did it take the *P*-wave to travel to station *Z*?

(1) 1 min 50 sec  (3) 3 min 30 sec
(2) 2 min 50 sec  (4) 6 min 30 sec

46 On the map, which location is closest to the epicenter of the earthquake?

(1) *E*–5  (3) *H*–3
(2) *G*–1  (4) *H*–8

**GO RIGHT ON TO THE NEXT PAGE** ⇨

Base your answers to questions 47 through 49 on the diagram below. The diagram shows a model of the relationship between Earth's surface and its interior.

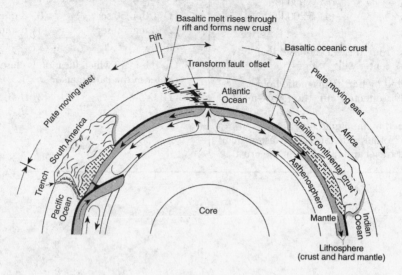

(Not drawn to scale)

47 Mid-ocean ridges (rifts) normally form where tectonic plates are

(1) converging
(2) diverging
(3) stationary
(4) sliding past each other

48 The motion of the convection currents in the mantle beneath the Atlantic Ocean appears to be mainly making this ocean basin

(1) deeper        (3) wider
(2) shallower     (4) narrower

49 According to the diagram, the deep trench along the west coast of South America is caused by movement of the oceanic crust that is

(1) sinking beneath the continental crust
(2) uplifting over the continental crust
(3) sinking at the Mid-Atlantic ridge
(4) colliding with the Atlantic oceanic crust

50 A student incorrectly measured the volume of a mineral sample as 63 cubic centimeters. The actual volume was 72 cubic centimeters. What was the student's approximate percent deviation (percentage of error)?

(1) 9.0%              (3) 14.2%
(2) 12.5%             (4) 15.3%

## Part B–2

### Answer all questions in this part.

*Directions* (51–59): Record your answers in the spaces provided in your answer booklet. Some questions may require the use of the *Earth Science Reference Tables*.

Base your answers to questions 51 and 52 on the topographic map of an island shown below. Elevations are expressed in feet. Points *A*, *B*, *C*, and *D* are locations on the island. A triangulation point shows the highest elevation on the island.

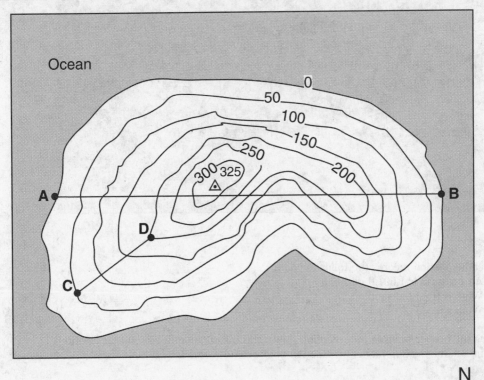

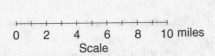

51 On the grid provided *in your answer booklet*, construct a topographic profile representing the cross-sectional view between point *A* and point *B*, following the directions below.

   *a* Plot the elevation of the land along line *AB* by marking, with a dot, the elevation of *each* point where a contour line is crossed by line *AB*.    [2]

   *b* Connect the dots with a smooth, curved line to complete the topographic profile.   [1]

52 What is the average gradient, in feet per mile, along the straight line from point *C* to point *D*?   [1]

_____

53 The photograph below shows an impact crater approximately 1 mile wide located in Diablo Canyon, Arizona. Describe the event that produced this crater.   [1]

Barringer Crater, Arizona, U.S.A. (photo courtesy of NASA)

54 A weather station records the following data:
    Air pressure is 1,001.0 millibars.
    Wind is from the south.
    Wind speed is 25 knots.

Using the proper weather map symbols, place this information in the correct locations on the weather station model provided *in your answer booklet*.   [3]

55 On the United States time zone map provided *in your answer booklet*, indicate the standard time in *each* time zone when it is 9 a.m. in the Central Time Zone. The dashed lines represent the standard-time meridians for each time zone. Be sure to indicate the time for all *three* zones.   [1]

56 The weather map below shows a typical midlatitude low-pressure system centered in Illinois.

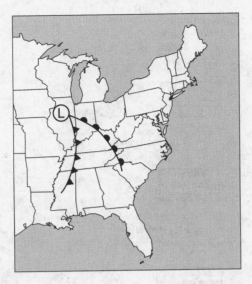

*a* On the weather map provided *in your answer booklet,* indicate which boxed area has the highest surface air temperatures by marking an **X** in one of the four boxes on the map. [1]

*b* On the weather map provided *in your answer booklet,* draw an arrow to predict the normal storm track that this low-pressure center would be expected to follow. [1]

Base your answers to questions 57 through 59 on the flowchart below, which shows a sequence of geologic processes at or near Earth's surface. Box A has been deliberately left blank. The diagrams are not drawn to scale.

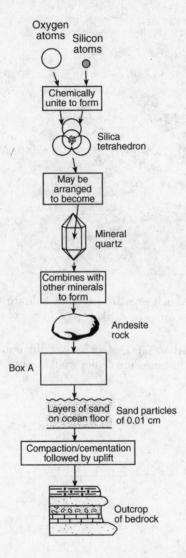

57  Identify the *three* minerals that are normally found with quartz in samples of andesite rock.    [2]

58  State one geologic process represented by box A.    [1]

59  Identify by name one type of rock layer, other than sandstone, shown in the outcrop.    [1]

## Part C

### Answer all questions in this part.

*Directions* (60–75): Record your answers in the spaces provided in your answer booklet. Some questions may require the use of the *Earth Science Reference Tables*.

60 A family wants to use rock materials as flooring in the entrance of their new house. They have narrowed their choice to granite or marble. Which of these rocks is more resistant to the physical wear of foot traffic and explain why this rock is more resistant.   [2]

Base your answers to questions 61 and 62 in part on the newspaper article below.

### Ancient human footprints found

**PARIS** — In the darkness of an underground cave lined with prehistoric paintings, French scientists believe they have discovered the oldest footprints of humans in Europe.

Embedded in damp clay, the imprints, slightly more than 8 inches long, appear to be those of a boy, 8 or 10 years old, who was walking barefoot between 25,000 and 30,000 years ago, prehistorians said Wednesday.

They said the dates are only hypothetical because there is no precise way to determine when the markings were made. But Michel-Andre Garcia, one prehistorian who has studied the site, said that the carbon datings in the cave and the context make this "a very strong hypothesis." The four footprints were found in the Ardeche region of southern France, deep inside the Chauvet cave.

— *Times Union,* June 10, 1999

61 Scientists have inferred that these "oldest" European human footprints were made during which geologic epoch?   [1]

62 Which characteristic of the radioactive isotope carbon-14 explains why carbon-14, rather than the radioactive isotope uranium-238, was used by archeologists in dating the age of their findings?   [1]

Base your answers to questions 63 through 66 on the diagram below, which represents an exaggerated model of Earth's orbital shape. Earth is closest to the Sun at one time of year (perihelion) and farthest from the Sun at another time of year (aphelion).

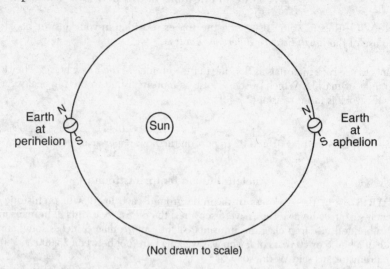

(Not drawn to scale)

63  State the actual geometric shape of Earth's orbit.    [1]

64  Identify the season in the Northern Hemisphere when Earth is at perihelion.    [1]

65  Describe the change that takes place in the apparent size of the Sun, as viewed from Earth, as Earth moves from perihelion to aphelion.    [1]

66  State the relationship between Earth's distance from the Sun and Earth's orbital velocity.    [1]

Base your answers to questions 67 and 68 on the cross section provided in your answer booklet, which represents a house at an ocean shoreline at night. Smoke from the chimney is blowing out to sea.

67 Label the *two* lines provided on the cross section *in your answer booklet* to show where air pressure is relatively "high" and where it is relatively "low."    [1]

68 Assume that the wind blowing out to sea on this night is caused by local air-temperature conditions. Label the *two* lines provided on the cross section *in your answer booklet* to show where Earth's surface air temperature is relatively "warm" and where it is relatively "cool."    [1]

**GO RIGHT ON TO THE NEXT PAGE** ⇨

Base your answers to questions 69 through 71 on data tables I and II and on the Hurricane Tracking Map below. Table I represents the storm track data for an Atlantic hurricane. Location, wind velocity, air pressure, and storm strength are shown for the storm's center at 3 p.m. Greenwich time each day. Table II shows a scale of relative storm strength. The map shows the hurricane's path.

### Data Table I

| Latitude (°N) | Longitude (°W) | Date | Wind Velocity (knots) | Air Pressure (millibars) | Storm Strength |
|---|---|---|---|---|---|
| 14 | 37 | Aug. 24 | 30 | 1006 | Tropical depression |
| 16 | 44 | Aug. 25 | 70 | 987 | Category-1 hurricane |
| 19 | 52 | Aug. 26 | 90 | 970 | Category-2 hurricane |
| 21 | 59 | Aug. 27 | 80 | 997 | Category-1 hurricane |
| 23 | 65 | Aug. 28 | 80 | 988 | Category-1 hurricane |
| 25 | 70 | Aug. 29 | 80 | 988 | Category-1 hurricane |
| 27 | 73 | Aug. 30 | 65 | 988 | Category-1 hurricane |
| 30 | 74 | Aug. 31 | 85 | 976 | Category-2 hurricane |
| 32 | 72 | Sept. 01 | 85 | 968 | Category-2 hurricane |
| 37 | 64 | Sept. 02 | 70 | 975 | Category-1 hurricane |
| 44 | 53 | Sept. 03 | 65 | 955 | Category-1 hurricane |

### Data Table II

| Storm Strength Scale | Relative Strength |
|---|---|
| Tropical depression<br>Tropical storm<br>Category 1<br>Category 2<br>Category 3<br>Category 4<br>Category 5 | Weakest<br><br>↓<br><br>Strongest |

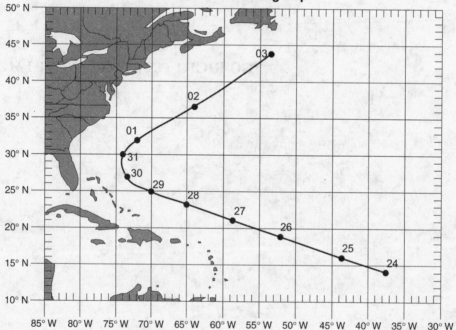

Hurricane Tracking Map

69 Describe *two* characteristics of the circulation pattern of the surface winds around the center (eye) of a Northern Hemisphere low-pressure hurricane.   [2]

70 The hurricane did not continue moving toward the same compass direction during the entire period shown by the data table. Explain why the hurricane changed direction.  [1]

71 In the space provided *in your answer booklet,* calculate the average daily rate of movement of the hurricane during the period from 3 p.m. August 24 to 3 p.m. August 28. The hurricane traveled 2,600 kilometers during this 4-day period. Follow the directions given below.

   *a* Write the equation used to determine the rate of change.
   *b* Substitute data into the equation.  [1]
   *c* Calculate the rate and label it with the proper units.  [1]

Base your answers to questions 72 through 74 on the cross section provided in your answer booklet. The cross section represents a portion of Earth's crust. Letters *A, B, C,* and *D* are rock units.

72 Igneous rock *B* was formed after rock layer *D* was deposited but before rock layer *A* was deposited. Using the contact metamorphism symbol shown in the key, draw that symbol in the proper locations on the cross section provided *in your answer booklet* to indicate those rocks that underwent contact metamorphism when igneous rock *B* was molten.   [1]

73 In relation to rock units *A* and *B* in the cross section, when was igneous rock *C* formed? [1]

74 Describe one observable characteristic of rock *A* that indicates that rock *A* is sedimentary.  [1]

75 The diagram provided in your answer booklet represents the Sun and Earth as viewed from space on a certain date.

   *a* Using a symbol for the Moon of approximately this size ($\bigcirc$), draw the position of the Moon on the diagram provided *in your answer booklet* at the time when the full-Moon phase is observed from Earth.   [1]

   *b* Draw an arrow on the diagram provided *in your answer booklet* that shows the Earth motion that causes surface ocean currents and surface winds to curve (Coriolis effect).  [1]

The University of the State of New York

REGENTS HIGH SCHOOL EXAMINATION

# PHYSICAL SETTING
# EARTH SCIENCE

**Tuesday,** August 13, 2002 — 12:30 to 3:30 p.m., only

## ANSWER SHEET

Student .............................................  Sex:  ☐ Male  ☐ Female  Grade ...........

Teacher .........................................  School ...........................................

**Record your answers to Part A and Part B–1 on this answer sheet.**

| Part A | | | Part B–1 | |
|---|---|---|---|---|
| 1 ............ | 13 ............ | 25 ............ | 36 ............ | 44 ............ |
| 2 ............ | 14 ............ | 26 ............ | 37 ............ | 45 ............ |
| 3 ............ | 15 ............ | 27 ............ | 38 ............ | 46 ............ |
| 4 ............ | 16 ............ | 28 ............ | 39 ............ | 47 ............ |
| 5 ............ | 17 ............ | 29 ............ | 40 ............ | 48 ............ |
| 6 ............ | 18 ............ | 30 ............ | 41 ............ | 49 ............ |
| 7 ............ | 19 ............ | 31 ............ | 42 ............ | 50 ............ |
| 8 ............ | 20 ............ | 32 ............ | 43 ............ | Part B–1 Score |
| 9 ............ | 21 ............ | 33 ............ | | |
| 10 ............ | 22 ............ | 34 ............ | | |
| 11 ............ | 23 ............ | 35 ............ | | |
| 12 ............ | 24 ............ | Part A Score | | |

**Write your answers to Part B–2 and Part C in your answer booklet.**

**The declaration below should be signed when you have completed the examination.**

I do hereby affirm, at the close of this examination, that I had no unlawful knowledge of the questions or answers prior to the examination and that I have neither given nor received assistance in answering any of the questions during the examination.

_____

Signature

Tear Here

Tear Here

The University of the State of New York

REGENTS HIGH SCHOOL EXAMINATION

# PHYSICAL SETTING
# EARTH SCIENCE

**Tuesday,** August 13, 2002 — 12:30 to 3:30 p.m., only

### ANSWER BOOKLET

Sex: ☐ Male  ☐ Female

Student.......................................

Teacher .......................................

School....................................... Grade .........

**Answer all questions in Part B–2 and Part C. Record your answers in this booklet.**

| | Performance Test Score (Maximum Score: 23) |
|---|---|

| Part | Maximum Score | Student's Score |
|---|---|---|
| A | 35 | |
| B–1 | 15 | |
| B–2 | 15 | |
| C | 20 | |

| | |
|---|---|
| **Total Written Test Score** (Maximum Raw Score: 85) | |
| **Final Score** (from conversion chart) | |

Raters' Initials:

Rater 1 .......... Rater 2 ..........

---

**Part B–2**

**For Raters Only**

**51** *a* and *b*

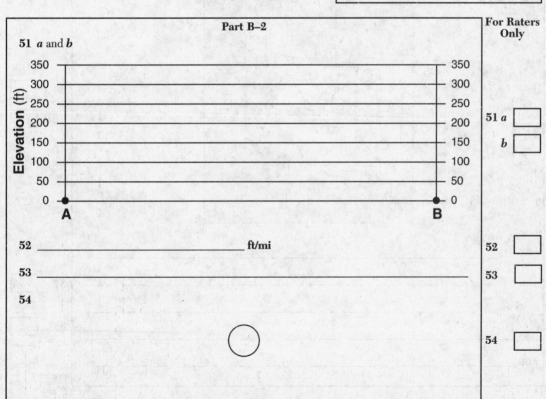

52 _____ ft/mi

53 _____

54

| | |
|---|---|
| 51 *a* | |
| *b* | |
| 52 | |
| 53 | |
| 54 | |

55

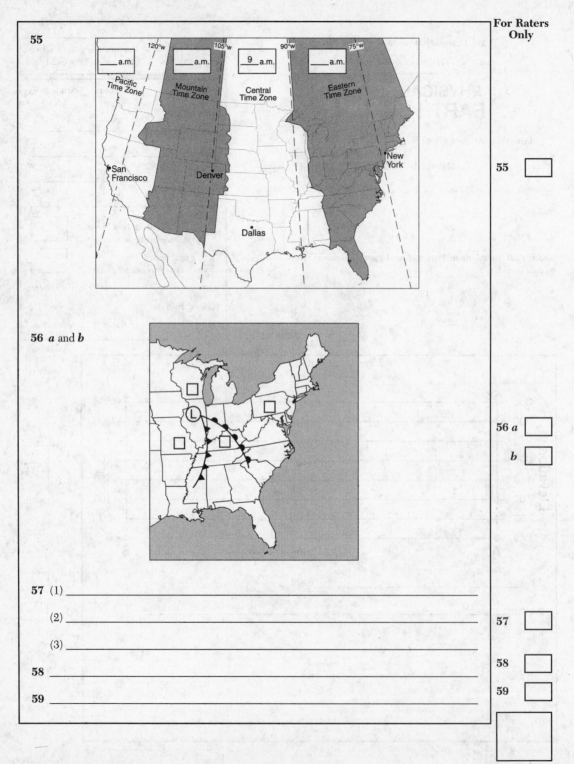

55 [ ]

56  *a* and *b*

56 *a* [ ]

*b* [ ]

57 (1) _____

(2) _____

(3) _____

58 _____

59 _____

57 [ ]

58 [ ]

59 [ ]

[ ]

**Total Score for Part B–2**

**Part C**

**60** Rock: _____

Reason: _____

_____

60 ☐

**61** _____ **epoch**

61 ☐

**62** _____

62 ☐

**63** _____

63 ☐

**64** _____

64 ☐

**65** _____

_____

65 ☐

**66** _____

_____

66 ☐

**67** and **68**

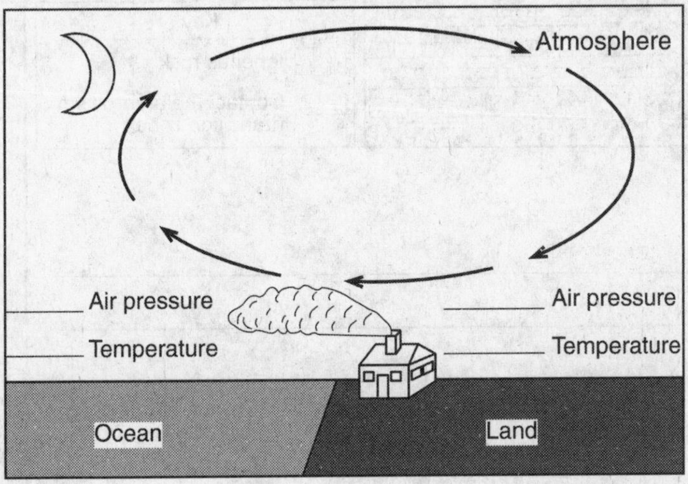

67 ☐

68 ☐

**69** _____ and _____

69 ☐

**70** _____

_____

70 ☐

**For Raters Only**

71  *a*

Rate of change =

*b*

Rate of change =                                             71*b* ☐

*c*

Rate of change =                                               *c* ☐

72

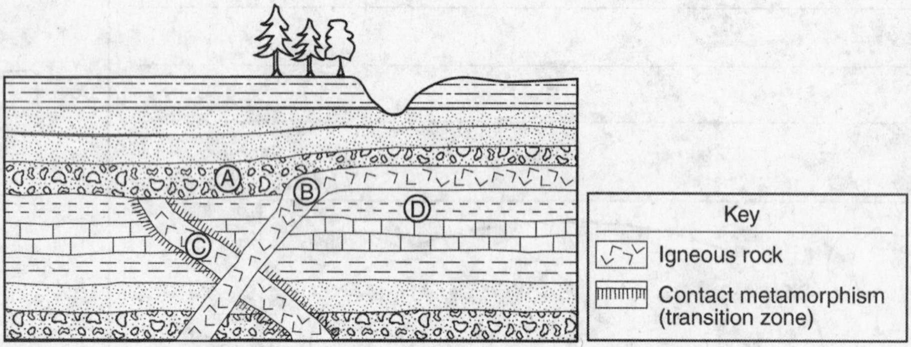

Key

〰️ Igneous rock

▦ Contact metamorphism (transition zone)                        72 ☐

73 _____                     73 ☐

74 _____                     74 ☐

75 *a* and *b*

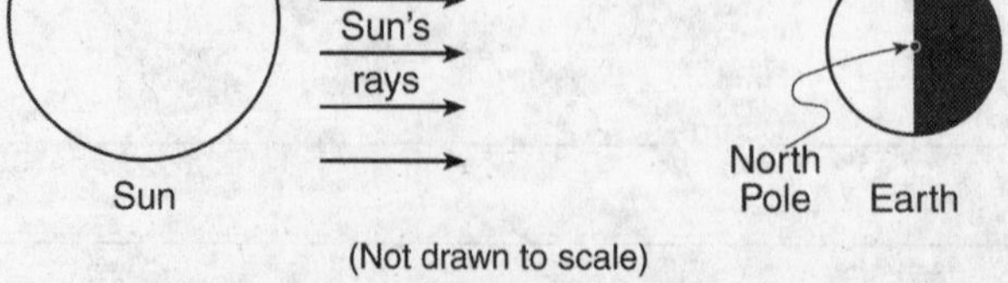

Sun's rays

Sun

North Pole   Earth

(Not drawn to scale)                                           75*a* ☐

                                                                  *b* ☐

Total Score for Part C ☐

The University of the State of New York

REGENTS HIGH SCHOOL EXAMINATION

# PHYSICAL SETTING
# EARTH SCIENCE

**Tuesday,** January 28, 2003 — 1:15 to 4:15 p.m., only

This is a test of your knowledge of Earth science. Use that knowledge to answer all questions in this examination. Some questions may require the use of the *Earth Science Reference Tables*. The *Earth Science Reference Tables* are supplied separately. Be certain you have a copy of the *2001 edition* of these reference tables before you begin the examination.

Your answer sheet for Part A and Part B–1 is the last page of this examination booklet. Turn to the last page and fold it along the perforations. Then, slowly and carefully, tear off your answer sheet and fill in the heading.

Your answer booklet for Part B–2 and Part C is stapled in the center of this examination booklet. Open the examination booklet, carefully remove your answer booklet, and close the examination booklet. Then fill in the heading of your answer booklet.

You are to answer *all* questions in all parts of this examination according to the directions provided in the examination booklet. Record your answers to the Part A and Part B–1 multiple-choice questions on your separate answer sheet. Write your answers to the Part B–2 and Part C questions in your answer booklet. All work should be written in pen, except for graphs and drawings, which should be done in pencil. You may use scrap paper to work out the answers to the questions, but be sure to record all your answers on your separate answer sheet and in your answer booklet.

When you have completed the examination, you must sign the statement printed at the end of your separate answer sheet, indicating that you had no unlawful knowledge of the questions or answers prior to the examination and that you have neither given nor received assistance in answering any of the questions during the examination. Your answer sheet and answer booklet cannot be accepted if you fail to sign this declaration.

---

Notice. . .

A four-function or scientific calculator and a copy of the *2001 Earth Science Reference Tables* must be available for your use while taking this examination.

---

**DO NOT OPEN THIS EXAMINATION BOOKLET UNTIL THE SIGNAL IS GIVEN.**

## Part A

### Answer all questions in this part.

*Directions* (1–35): For *each* statement or question, write on your separate answer sheet the *number* of the word or expression that, of those given, best completes the statement or answers the question. Some questions may require the use of the *Earth Science Reference Tables*.

1  Which diagram correctly shows the apparent motion of *Polaris* from sunset to midnight for an observer in northern Canada?

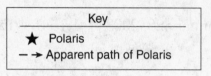

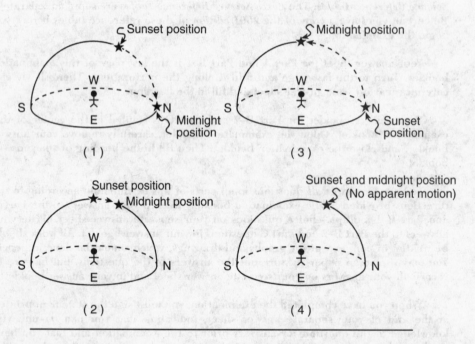

2  Earth's orbital velocity is slowest on July 5 because
   (1)  the Moon is closest to Earth
   (2)  Earth's distance from the Sun is greatest
   (3)  Earth, the Moon, and the Sun are located along a straight line in space
   (4)  the highest maximum temperatures occur in the Northern Hemisphere

3  Three planets that are relatively large, gaseous, and of low density are
   (1)  Mercury, Jupiter, and Saturn
   (2)  Venus, Jupiter, and Neptune
   (3)  Mars, Jupiter, and Uranus
   (4)  Jupiter, Saturn, and Uranus

4  Which diagram sequence correctly shows the order of Moon phases, as viewed from Earth, for a period of 1 month? [Note that some phases have been omitted.]

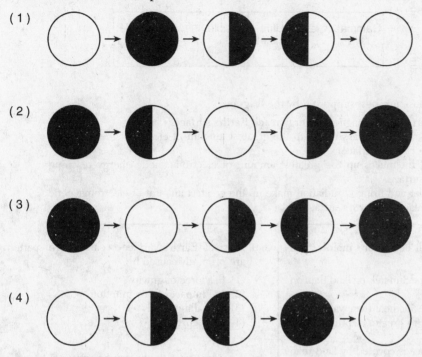

5  The diagram below shows the relative positions of the Sun, the Moon, and Earth when an eclipse was observed from Earth. Positions A and B are locations on Earth's surface.

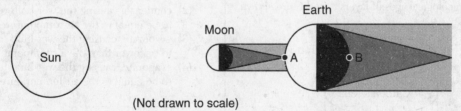

(Not drawn to scale)

Which statement correctly describes the type of eclipse that was occurring and the position on Earth where this eclipse was observed?

(1) A lunar eclipse was observed from position A.
(2) A lunar eclipse was observed from position B.
(3) A solar eclipse was observed from position A.
(4) A solar eclipse was observed from position B.

6 The diagram below shows the types of electromagnetic energy given off by the Sun. The shaded part of the diagram shows the approximate amount of each type actually reaching Earth's surface.

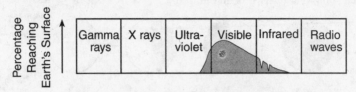

Which conclusion is best supported by the diagram?

(1) All types of electromagnetic energy reach Earth's surface.
(2) Gamma rays and x rays make up the greatest amount of electromagnetic energy reaching Earth's surface.
(3) Visible light makes up the greatest amount of electromagnetic energy reaching Earth's surface.
(4) Ultraviolet and infrared radiation make up the greatest amount of electromagnetic energy reaching Earth's surface.

7 Land surfaces of Earth heat more rapidly than water surfaces because

(1) more energy from the Sun falls on land than on water
(2) land has a lower specific heat than water
(3) sunlight penetrates to greater depths in land than in water
(4) less of Earth's surface is covered by land than by water

8 The geologic drill core below shows bedrock layers A, B, and C that have not been overturned. The geological ages of layers A and C are shown.

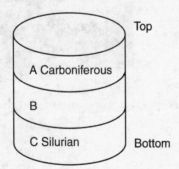

What is the geologic age of layer B?

(1) Cambrian        (3) Devonian
(2) Ordovician      (4) Permian

9 Most of Earth's surface ocean current patterns are primarily caused by

(1) the force of gravity
(2) the impact of precipitation
(3) prevailing winds
(4) river currents

10 A student uses a sling psychrometer outdoors on a clear day. The dry-bulb (air) temperature is 10°C. The water on the wet bulb will most likely

(1) condense, causing the wet-bulb temperature to be higher than the air temperature
(2) condense, causing the wet-bulb temperature to be equal to the air temperature
(3) evaporate, causing the wet-bulb temperature to be lower than the air temperature
(4) evaporate, causing the wet-bulb temperature to be equal to the air temperature

11 In which direction do surface winds around low-pressure centers in the Northern Hemisphere generally move?

(1) counterclockwise, toward the center of the low
(2) clockwise, toward the center of the low
(3) counterclockwise, away from the center of the low
(4) clockwise, away from the center of the low

12 The profile below shows the average diameter of sediment that was sorted and deposited in specific areas A, B, C, and D by a stream entering an ocean.

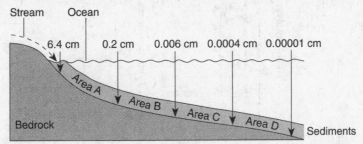

As compaction and cementation of these sediments eventually occur, which area will become siltstone?

(1) A                              (3) C
(2) B                              (4) D

13 The sequence of diagrams below represents the gradual geologic changes in layer X, located just below Earth's surface.

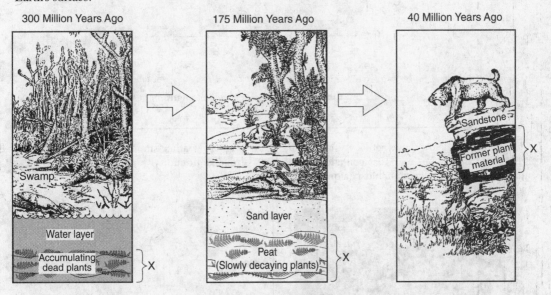

Which type of sedimentary rock was formed at layer X?

(1) conglomerate                  (3) rock salt
(2) shale                             (4) coal

14 Most water vapor enters the atmosphere by the processes of

(1) convection and radiation
(2) condensation and precipitation
(3) evaporation and transpiration
(4) erosion and conduction

15 Glaciers often form parallel scratches and grooves in bedrock because glaciers

(1) deposit sediment in unsorted piles
(2) deposit rounded sand in V-shaped valleys
(3) continually melt and refreeze
(4) drag loose rocks over Earth's surface

16  Which graph correctly represents the three most abundant elements, by mass, in Earth's crust?

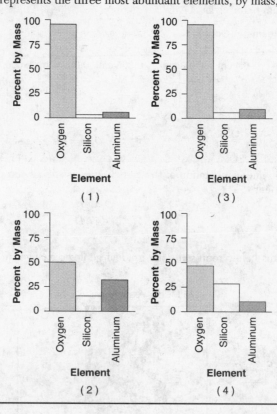

17  The photograph below shows actual crystal sizes in a light-colored igneous rock that contains several minerals, including potassium feldspar, quartz, and biotite mica.

(Shown to actual size)

The rock should be identified as

(1) granite          (3) basalt
(2) gabbro           (4) rhyolite

18  Which weather station model shows the highest relative humidity?

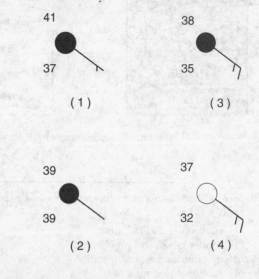

19 The graph below shows the average change in the elevation of a mountain range over time.

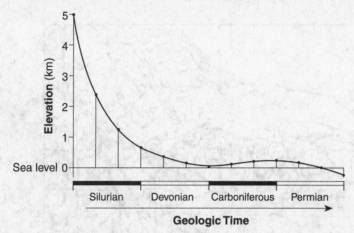

According to the graph, the rate of uplifting was greater than the rate of erosion during which geologic time period?

(1) Silurian                              (3) Carboniferous
(2) Devonian                           (4) Permian

20 The photograph below shows an eroded plateau found in the southwestern United States.

The landscape was developed by the processes of

(1) crustal uplift and stream erosion        (3) crustal folding and stream erosion
(2) crustal uplift and glacial erosion         (4) crustal folding and glacial erosion

21 At which latitude and longitude in New York State would a salt mine in Silurian-age bedrock most likely be located?

(1) 41° N 72° W            (3) 44° N 74° W
(2) 43° N 77° W            (4) 44° N 76° W

22 An unidentified mineral that is softer than calcite exhibits a metallic luster and cubic cleavage. This mineral most likely is

(1) galena               (3) halite
(2) pyrite               (4) pyroxene

23 The study of how seismic waves change as they travel through Earth has revealed that

(1) *P*-waves travel more slowly than *S*-waves through Earth's crust
(2) seismic waves travel more slowly through the mantle because it is very dense
(3) Earth's outer core is solid because *P*-waves are not transmitted through this layer
(4) Earth's outer core is liquid because *S*-waves are not transmitted through this layer

24 The map below shows major streams in the New York State area. The bold lines mark off sections *A* through *I* within New York State.

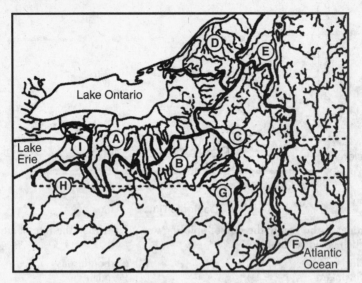

The best title for the map would be

(1) "Tectonic Plate Boundaries in New York State"
(2) "Bedrock Geology Locations of New York State"
(3) "Landscape Regions of New York State"
(4) "Watershed Areas of New York State"

---

Base your answers to questions 25 and 26 on the earthquake seismogram below.

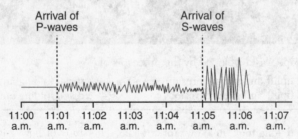

25  When did the first *P*-waves arrive at this seismic station?

(1) 3 minutes after an earthquake occurred 2,600 km away
(2) 5 minutes after an earthquake occurred 2,600 km away
(3) 9 minutes after an earthquake occurred 3,500 km away
(4) 11 minutes after an earthquake occurred 3,500 km away

26 How many additional seismic stations must report seismogram information in order to locate this earthquake?

(1) one          (3) three
(2) two          (4) four

27 The diagram below shows some features of Earth's crust and upper mantle.

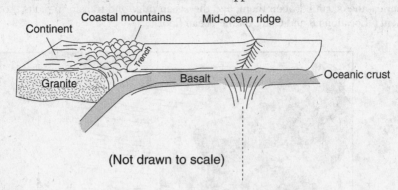

(Not drawn to scale)

Which model most accurately shows the movements (arrows) associated with the surface features shown in the diagram?

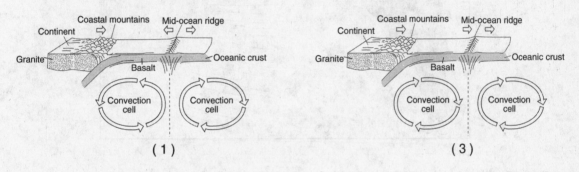

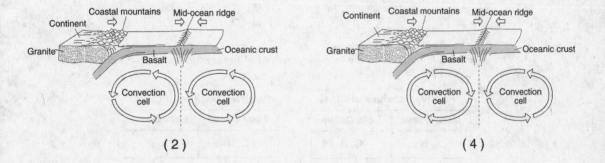

Base your answers to questions 28 through 30 on the map below. The map shows the continents of Africa and South America, the ocean between them, and the ocean ridge and transform faults. Locations *A* and *D* are on the continents. Locations *B* and *C* are on the ocean floor.

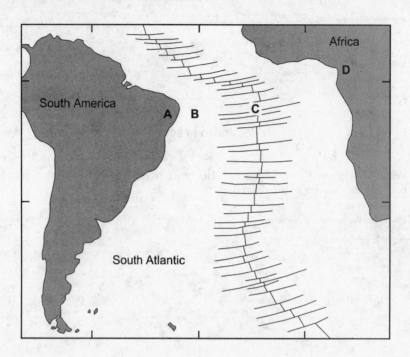

28 The hottest crustal temperature measurements would most likely be found at location

(1) *A*                    (3) *C*
(2) *B*                    (4) *D*

29 Which table best shows the relative densities of the crustal bedrock at locations *A*, *B*, *C*, and *D*?

**Relative Densities of Crust**

| More Dense | Less Dense |
|------------|------------|
| A, B | C, D |

(1)

**Relative Densities of Crust**

| More Dense | Less Dense |
|------------|------------|
| C, D | A, B |

(3)

**Relative Densities of Crust**

| More Dense | Less Dense |
|------------|------------|
| B, C | A, D |

(2)

**Relative Densities of Crust**

| More Dense | Less Dense |
|------------|------------|
| A, D | B, C |

(4)

30  Which graph best shows the relative age of the ocean-floor bedrock from location *B* to location *C*?

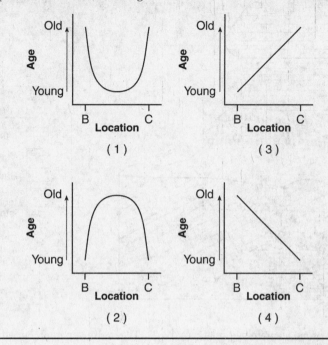

Base your answers to questions 31 and 32 on the diagram below, which shows a cross section of Earth's crust.

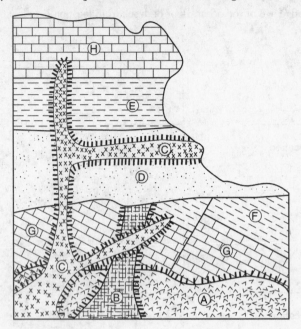

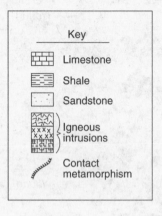

Key

| | |
|---|---|
| ▦ | Limestone |
| ▤ | Shale |
| ⬚ | Sandstone |
| ⬚⬚ | } Igneous intrusions |
| 〰 | Contact metamorphism |

31 Which statement gives an accurate age relationship for the bedrock in the cross section?

(1) Intrusion *A* is younger than intrusion *C*.
(2) Intrusion *C* is younger than intrusion *B*.
(3) Intrusion *B* is older than intrusion *A*.
(4) Intrusion *C* is older than layer *E*.

32 The most apparent buried erosional surface is found between rock units

(1) *A* and *B*          (3) *D* and *F*
(2) *C* and *D*          (4) *E* and *H*

33 During a heavy rainfall, runoff will be greatest on a soil that has an infiltration (permeability) rate of

(1) 0.1 cm/sec          (3) 0.3 cm/sec
(2) 0.2 cm/sec          (4) 1.2 cm/sec

34 Which inference is best supported by the rock and fossil record in New York State?

(1) Eurypterids lived in shallow seas near present-day Syracuse.
(2) *Coelophysis* wandered through jungles near present-day Albany.
(3) The first coral reefs formed off the shoreline of present-day Long Island.
(4) The condor nested on the peaks of the ancestral Adirondack Mountains during the Grenville Orogeny.

35 The diagram below shows a rock with deformed structure and intergrown crystals.

The rock was probably formed by

(1) sediments that were deposited on the ocean floor
(2) heat and pressure that changed a preexisting rock
(3) volcanic lava that cooled on Earth's surface
(4) a meteor impact on Earth's surface

## Part B–1

### Answer all questions in this part.

*Directions* (36–50): For *each* statement or question, write on your separate answer sheet the *number* of the word or expression that, of those given, best completes the statement or answers the question. Some questions may require the use of the *Earth Science Reference Tables*.

36  The table below shows the duration of insolation at different latitudes for three different days during the year.

| Latitude | Day 1 Duration of Insolation (hours) | Day 2 Duration of Insolation (hours) | Day 3 Duration of Insolation (hours) |
|----------|------|------|------|
| 90° N | 24 | 12 | 0 |
| 80° N | 24 | 12 | 0 |
| 70° N | 24 | 12 | 0 |
| 60° N | $18\frac{1}{2}$ | 12 | $5\frac{1}{2}$ |
| 50° N | $16\frac{1}{4}$ | 12 | $7\frac{3}{4}$ |
| 40° N | 15 | 12 | 9 |
| 30° N | 14 | 12 | 10 |
| 20° N | $13\frac{1}{4}$ | 12 | $10\frac{3}{4}$ |
| 10° N | $12\frac{1}{2}$ | 12 | $11\frac{1}{2}$ |
| 0° | 12 | 12 | 12 |

Which dates are represented most correctly by Day 1, Day 2, and Day 3, respectively?

(1)  March 21, September 22, December 21
(2)  June 21, September 22, December 21
(3)  September 22, December 21, March 21
(4)  December 21, March 21, June 21

Base your answers to questions 37 and 38 on the graph below, which shows changes in the Sun's magnetic activity and changes in the number of sunspots over a period of approximately 100 years. Sunspots are dark, cooler areas within the Sun's photosphere that can be seen from Earth.

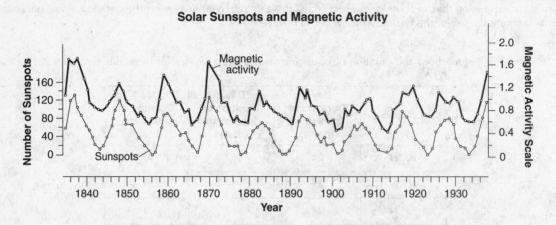

**Solar Sunspots and Magnetic Activity**

37 The graph indicates that years having the greatest number of sunspots occur

(1) randomly and unpredictably
(2) precisely at the beginning of each decade
(3) in a cyclic pattern, repeating approximately every 6 years
(4) in a cyclic pattern, repeating approximately every 11 years

38 Which graph best represents the relationship between the number of sunspots and the amount of magnetic activity in the Sun?

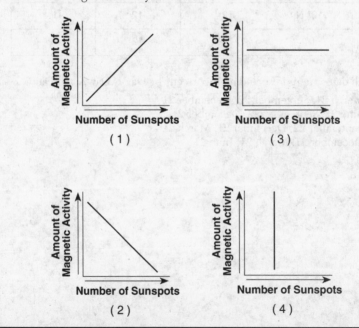

39 A student performed a laboratory activity in which water was poured slowly into four cups containing equal volumes of loosely packed sediment samples, as shown in the diagram below. All particles were spherical in shape and uniform in size within a container. After the water level reached the surface of each sample, the student determined the amount of water that had been added.

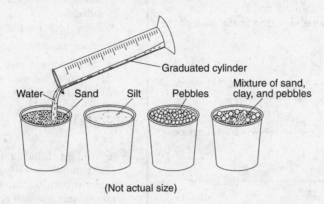

(Not actual size)

The results of the activity should have indicated that approximately equal amounts of water were added to the cups of

(1) silt and pebbles, only
(2) sand, silt, and pebbles, only
(3) pebbles and the mixture, only
(4) sand, pebbles, and the mixture, only

40 The diagram below shows the apparent path of the Sun as viewed by an observer at a certain Earth location on March 21.

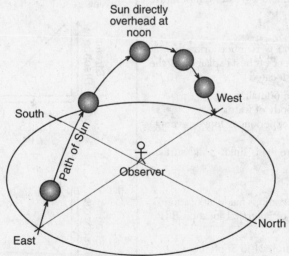

At which latitude is the observer located?

(1) the Equator (0°)

(2) $23\frac{1}{2}°$ N

(3) $66\frac{1}{2}°$ N

(4) 90° N

Base your answers to questions 41 through 43 on the map below. The map shows an imaginary continent on Earth. Arrows represent prevailing wind directions. Letters A through D represent locations on the continent. Locations A and B are at the same latitude and at the same elevation at the base of the mountains.

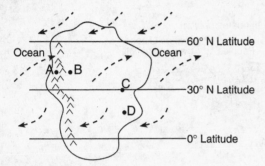

41 Over the course of a year, compared to location B, location A will have

(1) less precipitation and a smaller temperature range
(2) less precipitation and a greater temperature range
(3) more precipitation and a smaller temperature range
(4) more precipitation and a greater temperature range

42 The climate at location C is much drier than at location D. This difference is best explained by the fact that location C is located

(1) farther from any mountain range
(2) closer to a large body of water
(3) at a latitude that experiences longer average annual daylight
(4) at a latitude where air is sinking and surface winds diverge

43 Compared to the observations made at location D, the observed altitude of Polaris at location B is

(1) always less
(2) only less from March 21 to September 22
(3) only greater from March 21 to September 22
(4) always greater

44 A list of three observed relationships is shown below.

• Erosional rate = depositional rate
• Amount of insolation = amount of terrestrial radiation
• Rate of condensation = rate of evaporation

In which situation would each relationship exist?

(1) when a cyclic change occurs
(2) when a change of state occurs
(3) when dynamic equilibrium is reached
(4) when global warming ceases and global cooling begins

45 A student filled a graduated cylinder with 1,000 milliliters of water to represent a radioactive substance. After 30 seconds, the student poured out one-half of the water in the cylinder to represent the decay occurring within the first half-life. The student repeated the process every 30 seconds. How much water did the student pour from the cylinder at the 2-minute mark?

(1) 12.5 mL          (3) 125.0 mL
(2) 62.5 mL          (4) 250.0 mL

46 Which graph best represents the relationship between surface-water runoff and stream discharge?

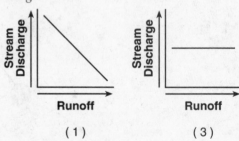

( 1 )                    ( 3 )

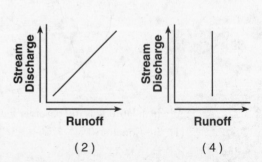

( 2 )                    ( 4 )

47 The temperature field map below represents surface air temperatures within a park. The location of a lake within the park is also indicated.

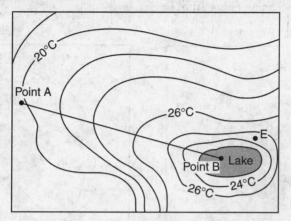

Which graph best represents the temperature profile along a straight line from point A to point B?

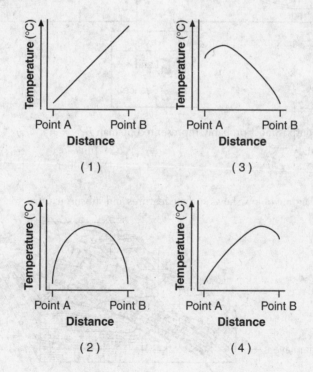

48  The maps below show the amount of sea ice surrounding the continent of Antarctica at two different times of the year. Map *A* represents late August when the area covered by sea ice approaches its greatest extent. Map *B* represents the minimum extent of sea ice.

Map A

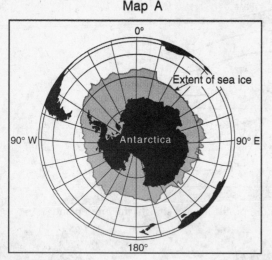

Map B

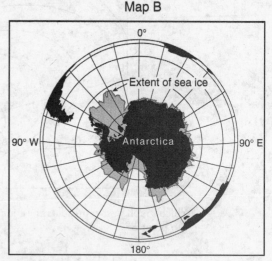

Key

■ Land

▨ Sea ice

Which month is most probably represented by map *B*?

(1) February                    (3) June
(2) May                         (4) October

49  The geologic block diagram below shows surface features and subsurface structures of a section of Montana.

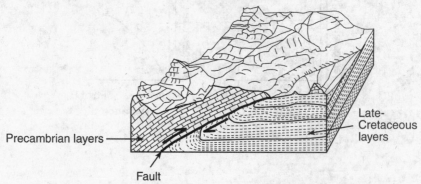

The faulting shown in the diagram could have occurred

(1) 2,100 million years ago         (3) 250 million years ago
(2) 520 million years ago           (4) 50 million years ago

50 The photograph below shows an outcrop of horizontal rock layers in New York State.

Sandstone {
Shale {

Rock outcrops like this are most commonly found in which area of New York State?

(1) Hudson Highlands      (3) Atlantic Coastal Plain
(2) Adirondack Mountains      (4) Appalachian Plateau

## Part B–2

### Answer all questions in this part.

*Directions* (51–63): Record your answers in the spaces provided in your answer booklet. Some questions may require the use of the *Earth Science Reference Tables*.

51  Identify by name the surface ocean current that cools the climate of locations on the western coastline of North America.    [1]

Base your answers to questions 52 and 53 on diagrams I through III below. Diagrams I, II, and III represent the length and direction of the shadow of a vertical stick measured at noon on three different dates at 42° N latitude.

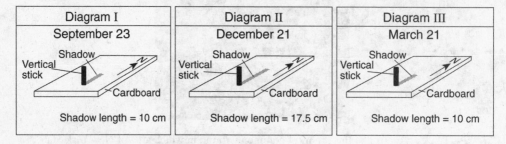

| Diagram I | Diagram II | Diagram III |
|---|---|---|
| September 23 | December 21 | March 21 |
| Shadow length = 10 cm | Shadow length = 17.5 cm | Shadow length = 10 cm |

52  Explain how the changing altitude (angle of incidence) of the noon Sun affects the length of the shadows shown in the diagrams.    [1]

53  On the diagram provided *in your answer booklet,* draw the direction and length of the shadow at noon that will most likely be observed at 42° N latitude on June 21.  [1]

54  The diagram below shows a cross section of New York State bedrock that has not been overturned. Line *X* represents an unconformity.

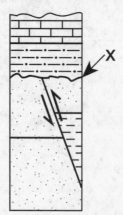

The index fossil *Eurypterus* is found in the limestone layer. What trilobite index fossil could be found in the shale layer?    [1]

Base your answers to questions 55 and 56 on the graph below, which shows a generalized sequence of rock types that form from original clay deposits at certain depths and temperature conditions within Earth's interior.

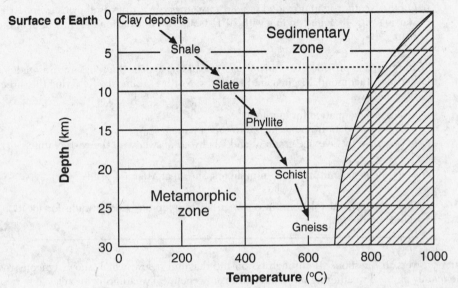

**Inferred Metamorphism of Shale**

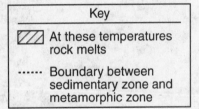

Key

At these temperatures rock melts

Boundary between sedimentary zone and metamorphic zone

55 When clay materials are buried to a depth of 14 kilometers, which type of metamorphic rock is normally formed?   [1]

56 Explain why gneiss would *not* form at a depth of 27 kilometers and at a temperature of 800°C.   [1]

Base your answers to questions 57 through 60 on the weather map provided *in your answer booklet,* which shows partial weather-station data for several cities in eastern North America.

57 On the weather map provided *in your answer booklet*, draw isotherms every 10°F, starting with 40°F and ending with 70°F. Isotherms must extend to the edges of the map.   [2]

58 In the space provided *in your answer booklet,* calculate the temperature gradient between Richmond, Virginia, and Hatteras, North Carolina, by following the directions below.

   *a* Write the equation for gradient.
   *b* Substitute data from the map into the equation.   [1]
   *c* Calculate the average gradient and label your answer with the correct units.   [1]

59 State the actual air pressure, in millibars, shown at Miami, Florida.   [1]

60 State the general relationship between air temperature and latitude for locations shown on the map.   [1]

---

Base your answers to questions 61 through 63 on the diagram below, which shows igneous rock that has undergone mainly physical weathering into sand and mainly chemical weathering into clay.

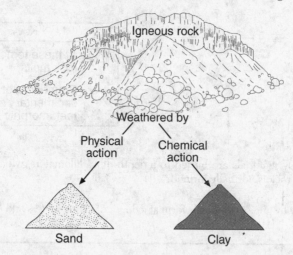

61 Compare the particle size of the physically weathered fragments to the particle size of the chemically weathered fragments.   [1]

62 Describe the change in temperature and moisture conditions that would cause an increase in the rate of chemical weathering into clay.   [1]

63 If the igneous rock is a layer of vesicular andesite, identify *three* types of mineral grains that could be found in the sand.   [1]

---

## Part C

### Answer all questions in this part.

*Directions* (64–77): Record your answers in the spaces provided in your answer booklet. Some questions may require the use of the *Earth Science Reference Tables*.

Base your answers to questions 64 and 65 on your knowledge of Earth science and on the newspaper article shown below, written by Paul Recer and printed in the *Times Union* on October 9, 1998.

### Astronomers peer closer to big bang

**WASHINGTON** — The faintest and most distant objects ever sighted — galaxies of stars more than 12 billion light years away — have been detected by an infrared camera on the Hubble Space Telescope.

The sighting penetrates for the first time to within about one billion light years of the very beginning of the universe, astronomers said, and shows that even at that very early time there already were galaxies with huge families of stars.

"We are seeing farther than ever before," said Rodger I. Thompson, a University of Arizona astronomer and the principal researcher in the study.

Thompson and his team focused an infrared instrument on the Hubble on a narrow patch of the sky that had been previously photographed in visible light. The instrument detected about 100 galaxies that were not seen in the visible light and 10 of these were at extreme distance.

He said the galaxies are seen as they were when the universe was only about 5 percent of its present age. Astronomers generally believe the universe began with a massive explosion, called the "big bang," that occurred about 13 billion years ago.

Since the big bang, astronomers believe that galaxies are moving rapidly away from each other, spreading out and becoming more distant.

64 The big-bang theory is widely believed by astronomers to explain the beginning of the universe. Why does the light from distant galaxies support the big-bang theory?   [1]

65 Compare the age of Earth and our solar system to the age of these distant galaxies of stars.   [1]

Base your answers to questions 66 and 67 on the diagram below, which shows the orbit of planet *D* around the star *Upsilon Andromedae*. The dashed lines show where the paths of the first four planets of our solar system would be located if they were going around *Upsilon Andromedae* instead of the Sun. All distances are drawn to scale.

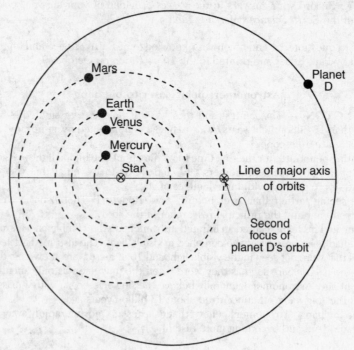

66 Describe the eccentricity of planet *D's* orbit relative to the eccentricities of the orbits of the planets shown in our solar system.    [1]

67 Describe the changes in gravitational force between planet *D* and the star *Upsilon Andromedae* during one complete orbit around the star. Be sure to describe where the force is greatest and where the force is least.    [1]

68 The photographs below show the Moon and Earth as viewed from space. It is inferred that Earth had many impact craters similar to those shown on the Moon.

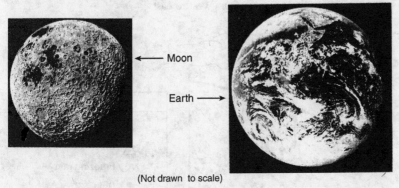

← Moon

Earth →

(Not drawn to scale)

Describe one process that has destroyed many of the impact craters that once existed on Earth.   [1]

69 Name one region of the United States that is likely to experience a major damaging earthquake. Explain why an earthquake is likely to occur in that region.   [1]

Base your answers to questions 70 through 73 on the atmospheric cross section below, which represents a winter storm system. Zones *A*, *B*, *C*, and *D* are located on a west to east line at approximately 43° N latitude across New York State. This cross section shows how solid and liquid forms of precipitation depend on the air temperature above Earth's surface. The storm is moving from west to east.

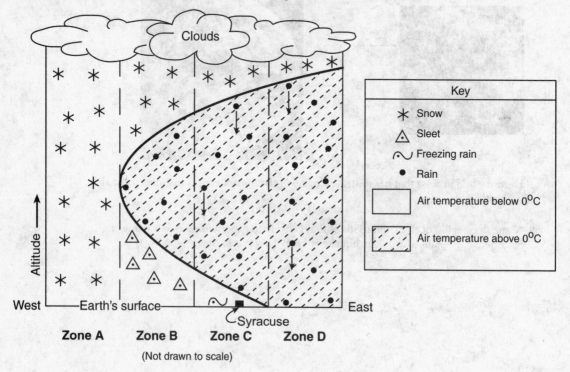

70  Explain why sleet is occurring in Zone *B*.   [1]

71  At the time of the events represented by the cross section, Syracuse, New York, is experiencing the following weather conditions:

| Cloud cover | 100% |
|---|---|
| Wind speed | 15 knots |
| Present weather | Freezing rain |
| Precipitation | 1.23 inches past 6 hours |
| Visibility | 1 mile |

The temperature, dewpoint, and wind direction are shown on the weather station model in your answer booklet. Using proper format, add the information shown in the table to the model provided *in your answer booklet.*   [2]

72  As the storm moves eastward, the type of precipitation received in Syracuse changes. State the type of precipitation that will immediately follow freezing rain.   [1]

73  Describe the general air movement and temperature change that caused the clouds associated with this storm to form.   [2]

74 An island measures 10 kilometers from east to west and 8 kilometers from north to south. A single hill on the east side of the island has a maximum elevation of 57 meters and is steepest to the north. In the box provided *in your answer booklet,* draw a simple contour map to represent this island, using a distance scale of 1 centimeter = 1 kilometer and a contour interval of 10 meters.   [4]

Base your answers to questions 75 through 77 on the information and diagram below and on the data table provided *in your answer booklet.*

A student used water, a trough, a timer, a Ping-Pong ball, and a metric ruler to investigate waterflow. The trough was set at different angles to compile the data in the data table provided *in your answer booklet.*

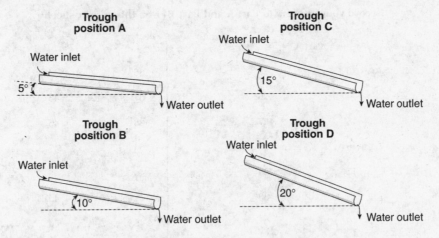

75 Calculate the average velocity of the water flowing down the trough in each position, A, B, C, and D. Record your answers in the data table provided *in your answer booklet.* Express your answers to the *nearest tenth.*   [2]

76 State the purpose of the student's investigation.   [1]

77 Based on the data and the values you calculated for average stream velocity, state an appropriate conclusion to this investigation.   [1]

The University of the State of New York

REGENTS HIGH SCHOOL EXAMINATION

# PHYSICAL SETTING
# EARTH SCIENCE

**Tuesday,** January 28, 2003 — 1:15 to 4:15 p.m., only

## ANSWER SHEET

Student ............................................... Sex: ☐ Male ☐ Female   Grade ...........

Teacher ............................................... School ...................................

Record your answers to Part A and Part B–1 on this answer sheet.

|  Part A | | | Part B–1 | |
|---|---|---|---|---|
| 1 ............ | 13 ............ | 25 ............ | 36 ............ | 44 ............ |
| 2 ............ | 14 ............ | 26 ............ | 37 ............ | 45 ............ |
| 3 ............ | 15 ............ | 27 ............ | 38 ............ | 46 ............ |
| 4 ............ | 16 ............ | 28 ............ | 39 ............ | 47 ............ |
| 5 ............ | 17 ............ | 29 ............ | 40 ............ | 48 ............ |
| 6 ............ | 18 ............ | 30 ............ | 41 ............ | 49 ............ |
| 7 ............ | 19 ............ | 31 ............ | 42 ............ | 50 ............ |
| 8 ............ | 20 ............ | 32 ............ | 43 ............ | |
| 9 ............ | 21 ............ | 33 ............ | | |
| 10 ............ | 22 ............ | 34 ............ | | |
| 11 ............ | 23 ............ | 35 ............ | | |
| 12 ............ | 24 ............ | | | |

Part A Score [ ]

Part B–1 Score [ ]

Write your answers to Part B–2 and Part C in your answer booklet.

The declaration below should be signed when you have completed the examination.

I do hereby affirm, at the close of this examination, that I had no unlawful knowledge of the questions or answers prior to the examination and that I have neither given nor received assistance in answering any of the questions during the examination.

_____

Signature

The University of the State of New York

REGENTS HIGH SCHOOL EXAMINATION

# PHYSICAL SETTING
# EARTH SCIENCE

**Tuesday,** January 28, 2003 — 1:15 to 4:15 p.m., only

### ANSWER BOOKLET

☐ Male

Student ..................................... Sex: ☐ Female

Teacher ....................................................

School .................................... Grade .........

**Answer all questions in Part B–2 and Part C. Record your answers in this booklet.**

| | Performance Test Score (Maximum Score: 23) |
|---|---|

| Part | Maximum Score | Student's Score |
|---|---|---|
| A | 35 | |
| B–1 | 15 | |
| B–2 | 15 | |
| C | 20 | |

Total Written Test Score (Maximum Raw Score: 85) ☐

Final Score (from conversion chart) ☐

Raters' Initials:

Rater 1 .......... Rater 2 ..........

---

**Part B–2**

**For Raters Only**

51 _____ **Current**          51 ☐

52 _____                    52 ☐
   _____

53                                            53 ☐

June 21

Vertical stick

54 _____                    54 ☐

55 _____                    55 ☐

56 _____                    56 ☐
   _____

57

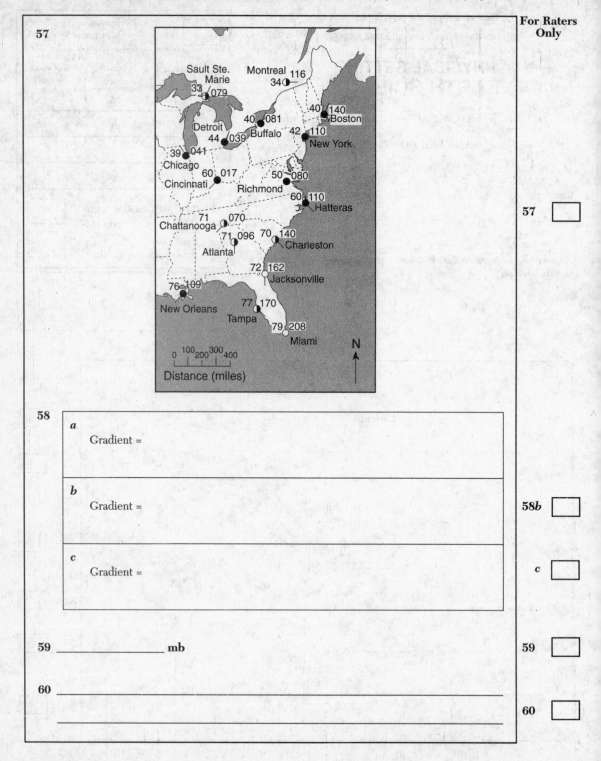

57 ☐

58

a

Gradient =

b

Gradient =                                                                    58b ☐

c

Gradient =                                                                    c ☐

59 _____ mb                                                         59 ☐

60 _____

_____                      60 ☐

**For Raters Only**

61 _____

_____

61 ☐

62 _____

_____

62 ☐

63 (1) _____

(2) _____

(3) _____

63 ☐

☐

**Total Score for Part B–2**

**Part C**

64 _____

_____

64 ☐

65 _____

_____

65 ☐

66 _____

_____

66 ☐

67 _____

_____

67 ☐

68 _____

_____

68 ☐

69 Region: _____

Explanation: _____

_____

69 ☐

70 _____

_____

70 ☐

71

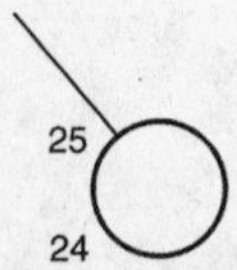

71 ☐

25

24

72 _____

72 [ ]

73 Air movement: _____

Temperature change: _____

73 [ ]

74

74 [ ]

N

75                                    **Data Table**

| Trough Position | Slope (degrees) | Length of Trough (meters) | Time (seconds) | Velocity (meters/second) |
|---|---|---|---|---|
| A | 5 | 1.5 | 4.4 | |
| B | 10 | 1.5 | 3.5 | |
| C | 15 | 1.5 | 2.7 | |
| D | 20 | 1.5 | 2.3 | |

75 [ ]

76 _____

_____

76 [ ]

77 _____

_____

77 [ ]

[ ]

**Total Score for Part C**

The University of the State of New York

REGENTS HIGH SCHOOL EXAMINATION

# PHYSICAL SETTING
# EARTH SCIENCE

**Thursday,** June 19, 2003 — 1:15 to 4:15 p.m., only

This is a test of your knowledge of Earth science. Use that knowledge to answer all questions in this examination. Some questions may require the use of the *Earth Science Reference Tables*. The *Earth Science Reference Tables* are supplied separately. Be certain you have a copy of the *2001 edition* of these reference tables before you begin the examination.

Your answer sheet for Part A and Part B–1 is the last page of this examination booklet. Turn to the last page and fold it along the perforations. Then, slowly and carefully, tear off your answer sheet and fill in the heading.

The answers to the questions in Part B–2 and Part C are to be written in your separate answer booklet. Be sure to fill in the heading on the front of your answer booklet.

You are to answer *all* questions in all parts of this examination according to the directions provided in the examination booklet. Record your answers to the Part A and Part B–1 multiple-choice questions on your separate answer sheet. Write your answers to the Part B–2 and Part C questions in your answer booklet. All work should be written in pen, except for graphs and drawings, which should be done in pencil. You may use scrap paper to work out the answers to the questions, but be sure to record all your answers on your separate answer sheet and in your answer booklet.

When you have completed the examination, you must sign the statement printed at the end of your separate answer sheet, indicating that you had no unlawful knowledge of the questions or answers prior to the examination and that you have neither given nor received assistance in answering any of the questions during the examination. Your answer sheet and answer booklet cannot be accepted if you fail to sign this declaration.

---

Notice. . .

A four-function or scientific calculator and a copy of the *2001 Earth Science Reference Tables* must be available for your use while taking this examination.

---

**DO NOT OPEN THIS EXAMINATION BOOKLET UNTIL THE SIGNAL IS GIVEN.**

## Part A

### Answer all questions in this part.

*Directions* (1–35): For *each* statement or question, write on your separate answer sheet the *number* of the word or expression that, of those given, best completes the statement or answers the question. Some questions may require the use of the *Earth Science Reference Tables*.

1 The planetary winds in Earth's Northern Hemisphere generally curve to the right due to Earth's

(1) orbit around the Sun
(2) spin on its axis
(3) magnetic field
(4) force of gravity

2 The redshift of light from distant galaxies provides evidence that the universe is

(1) shrinking, only
(2) expanding, only
(3) shrinking and expanding in a cyclic pattern
(4) remaining the same size

3 Which of these characteristics identify an Earth surface that is likely to be the best absorber of insolation?

(1) light colored and smooth
(2) light colored and rough
(3) dark colored and smooth
(4) dark colored and rough

4 Which phase change requires water to gain 540 calories per gram?

(1) solid ice melting
(2) liquid water freezing
(3) liquid water vaporizing
(4) water vapor condensing

5 The diagram below shows the positions of the Moon and the Sun at sunset during an evening in New York State. Points *A*, *B*, *C*, and *D* represent positions along the western horizon.

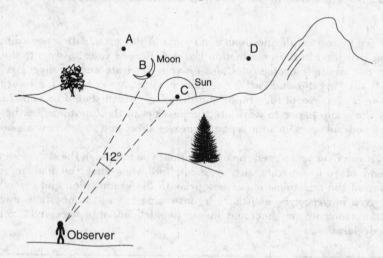

At sunset on the following evening, the Moon will be located at position

(1) *A*
(2) *B*
(3) *C*
(4) *D*

6  Which diagram best illustrates how air rising over a mountain produces precipitation?

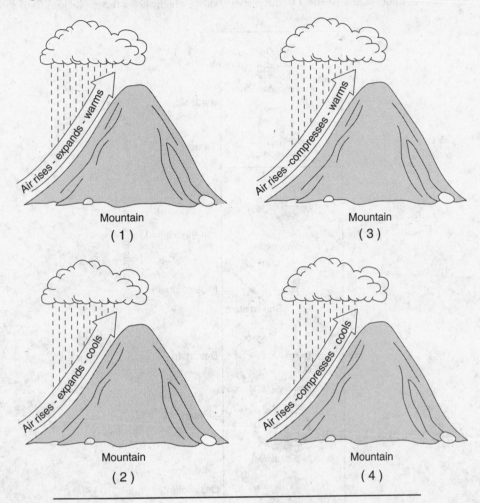

7  A student used a sling psychrometer to measure the humidity of the air. If the relative humidity was 65% and the dry-bulb temperature was 10°C, what was the wet-bulb temperature?

(1) 5°C                 (3) 3°C
(2) 7°C                 (4) 10°C

8  A gradual increase in atmospheric carbon dioxide would warm Earth's atmosphere because carbon dioxide is a

(1) poor reflector of ultraviolet radiation
(2) good reflector of ultraviolet radiation
(3) poor absorber of infrared radiation
(4) good absorber of infrared radiation

9  Why are the beaches that are located on the southern shore of Long Island often considerably cooler than nearby inland locations on hot summer afternoons?

(1) A land breeze develops due to the lower specific heat of water and the higher specific heat of land.
(2) A sea breeze develops due to the higher specific heat of water and the lower specific heat of land.
(3) The beaches are closer to the Equator than the inland locations are.
(4) The beaches are farther from the Equator than the inland locations are.

Base your answers to questions 10 and 11 on the chart below, which shows the geologic ages of some well-known fossils.

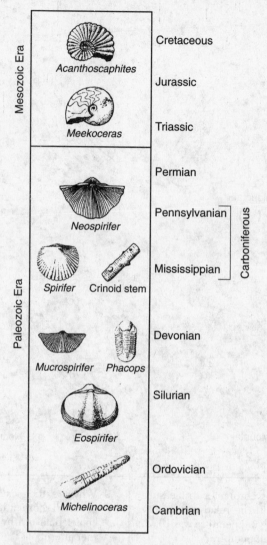

10  The *Spirifer*, Crinoid stem, and *Neospirifer* fossils might be found in some of the surface bedrock of which New York State landscape region?

(1) the Allegheny Plateau southeast of Jamestown
(2) the Catskills near Slide Mountain
(3) the Adirondack Mountains near Mt. Marcy
(4) the Erie-Ontario Lowlands northeast of Niagara Falls

11  Which New York State fossil is found in rocks of the same period of geologic history as *Meekoceras*?

(1) Condor
(2) Placoderm fish
(3) *Eurypterus*
(4) *Coelophysis*

12  The flowchart below shows part of Earth's water cycle. The question marks indicate a part of the flowchart that has been deliberately left blank.

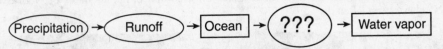

Which process should be shown in place of the question marks to best complete the flowchart?

(1) condensation
(2) deposition

(3) evaporation
(4) infiltration

---

13  Which weather-station model shows an air pressure of 993.4 millibars?

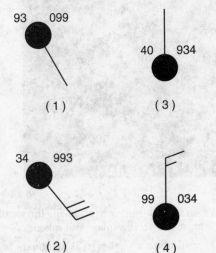

14  An Earth science student observed the following weather conditions in Albany, New York, for 2 days: The first day was warm and humid with southerly winds. The second day, the temperature was 15 degrees cooler, the relative humidity had decreased, and wind direction was northwest. Which type of air mass most likely had moved into the area on the second day?

(1) continental tropical    (3) maritime tropical
(2) continental polar       (4) maritime polar

15  A sample of wood found in an ancient tomb contains 25% of its original carbon-14. The age of this wood sample is approximately

(1) 2,800 years     (3) 11,400 years
(2) 5,700 years     (4) 17,100 years

16  Which set of conditions would produce the most runoff of precipitation?

(1) gentle slope and permeable surface
(2) gentle slope and impermeable surface
(3) steep slope and permeable surface
(4) steep slope and impermeable surface

17  Which map view best shows the movement of surface air around a low-pressure system in the Northern Hemisphere?

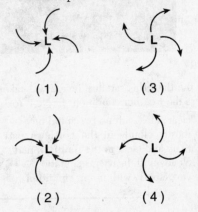

18  The surface bedrock of a region of eastern New York State is shale. Which statement best explains why the soil that covers the shale in this region contains abundant garnet and gneiss pebbles?

(1) Volcanic lava flowed over the shale bedrock.
(2) A meteor impact scattered garnet and gneiss pebbles over the area.
(3) The soil consists of rock materials transported to this region by agents of erosion.
(4) The soil formed from the chemical and physical weathering of shale.

Base your answers to questions 19 and 20 on the satellite image below, which shows cloud patterns associated with weather fronts over the United States on a certain day. The states of Nebraska (NE) and New York (NY) have been labeled.

19 At the time this satellite image was taken, what were the weather conditions in New York State?

(1) clear skies with no precipitation
(2) mostly cloudy in the northern part of the State and clear in the southern part
(3) cloudy with heavy precipitation
(4) very cloudy with no precipitation

20 Which type of front was producing the weather in Nebraska when this image was taken?

(1) cold front          (3) stationary front
(2) warm front          (4) occluded front

Base your answers to questions 21 and 22 on the graph below, which shows the changes in relative humidity and air temperature during a spring day in Washington, D.C.

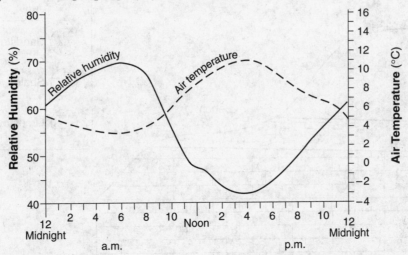

21 Which statement best describes the relationship between relative humidity and air temperature as shown by the graph?

(1) Relative humidity decreases as air temperature decreases.
(2) Relative humidity decreases as air temperature increases.
(3) Relative humidity increases as air temperature increases.
(4) Relative humidity remains the same as air temperature decreases.

22 What were the relative humidity and air temperature at noon on this day?

(1) 47% and 32°F      (3) 47% and 48°F
(2) 65% and 32°F      (4) 65% and 48°F

23 Landscapes will undergo the most chemical weathering if the climate is

(1) cool and dry      (3) warm and dry
(2) cool and wet      (4) warm and wet

24 A huge undersea earthquake off the Alaskan coastline could produce a

(1) tsunami      (3) hurricane
(2) cyclone      (4) thunderstorm

25 Which rock is foliated, shows mineral alignment but not banding, and contains medium-sized grains of quartz and pyroxene?

(1) phyllite     (3) gneiss
(2) schist       (4) quartzite

26 The cross section below shows a V-shaped valley and the bedrock beneath the valley.

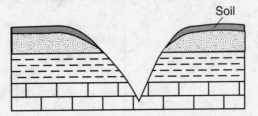

Which agent of erosion is responsible for cutting most V-shaped valleys into bedrock?

(1) surface winds     (3) glacial ice
(2) running water     (4) ocean waves

27  The geologic cross section below shows a hillslope and the rock layers that underlie it.

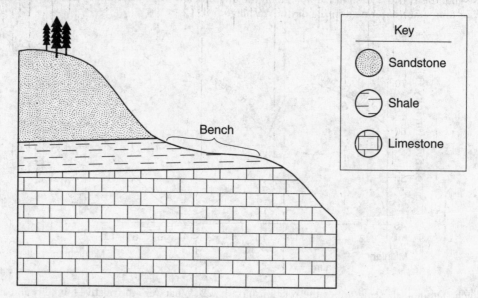

Which difference between the sandstone, shale, and limestone layers caused the formation of the relatively gently sloped section labeled "bench"?

(1)  rock age
(2)  fossil content

(3)  resistance to weathering
(4)  amount of uranium-238

28  Which graph best represents the range of particle sizes that can be carried by a glacier?

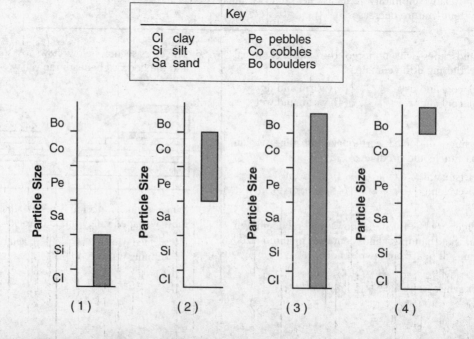

Base your answers to questions 29 and 30 on the diagram below, which shows three minerals with three different physical tests, A, B, and C, being performed on them.

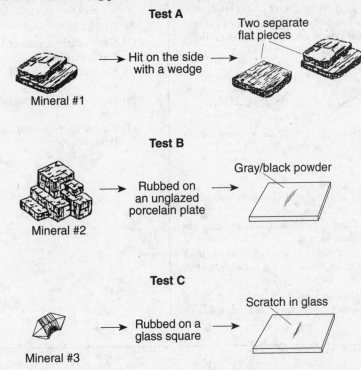

29 Which sequence correctly matches each test, A, B, and C, with the mineral property tested?

(1) A—cleavage; B—streak; C—hardness
(2) A—cleavage; B—hardness; C—streak
(3) A—streak; B—cleavage; C—hardness
(4) A—streak; B—hardness; C—cleavage

30 The results of all three physical tests shown are most useful for determining the

(1) rate of weathering of the minerals
(2) identity of the minerals
(3) environment where the minerals formed
(4) geologic period when the minerals formed

31 An air temperature of 95°C most often exists in which layer of the atmosphere?

(1) troposphere        (3) mesosphere
(2) stratosphere       (4) thermosphere

32 During the intrusion of the Palisades Sill, contact metamorphism changed sandstone and shale into

(1) diorite            (3) limestone
(2) marble             (4) hornfels

33 Which process most likely formed a layer of the sedimentary rock, gypsum?

(1) precipitation from seawater
(2) solidification of magma
(3) folding of clay-sized particles
(4) melting of sand-sized particles

34 The diagram below shows a stream flowing past points $X$ and $Y$. If the velocity of the stream at point $X$ is 100 centimeters per second, which statement best describes the sediments being transported past these points?

(1) At points $X$ and $Y$, only clay is being transported.
(2) At points $X$ and $Y$, only sand, silt, and clay are being transported.
(3) Some pebbles being transported at point $Y$ are bigger than those being transported at point $X$.
(4) Some pebbles and cobbles are being transported at points $X$ and $Y$, but not sand, silt, or clay.

35 Specific mass extinction of living organisms and global climatic changes in geologic history are inferred by most scientists to have been caused by

(1) the impact of asteroids or large meteors on Earth's surface
(2) the gravitational pull of the Sun on Earth's surface
(3) large energy surges from the surface of the Sun
(4) earthquakes occurring along crustal plate boundaries

## Part B–1

## Answer all questions in this part.

*Directions* (36–50): For *each* statement or question, write on your separate answer sheet the *number* of the word or expression that, of those given, best completes the statement or answers the question. Some questions may require the use of the *Earth Science Reference Tables*.

Base your answers to questions 36 through 38 on the data table below, which gives information collected at seismic stations *A*, *B*, *C*, and *D* for the same earthquake. Some of the data has been deliberately omitted.

| Seismic Station | P-Wave Arrival Time | S-Wave Arrival Time | Difference in Arrival Times | Distance to Epicenter |
|---|---|---|---|---|
| A | 08:48:20 | No S-waves arrived | | |
| B | 08:42:00 | | 00:04:40 | |
| C | 08:39:20 | | 00:02:40 | |
| D | 08:45:40 | | | 6,200 km |

Key for Reading Time on the Table

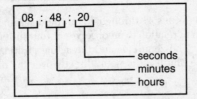

36 What is the most probable reason for the absence of *S*-waves at station *A*?

(1) *S*-waves cannot travel through liquids.
(2) *S*-waves were not generated at the epicenter.
(3) Station *A* was located on solid bedrock.
(4) Station *A* was located too close to the epicenter.

37 What is the approximate distance from station *C* to the earthquake epicenter?

(1) 3,200 km
(2) 2,400 km
(3) 1,600 km
(4) 1,000 km

38 How long did it take the *P*-wave to travel from the epicenter of the earthquake to seismic station *D*?

(1) 00:46:20
(2) 00:39:20
(3) 00:17:20
(4) 00:09:40

Base your answers to questions 39 and 40 on the map below, which shows the latitude and longitude of five observers, *A, B, C, D,* and *E,* on Earth.

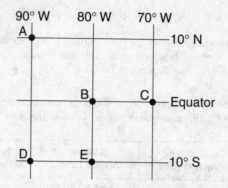

39 What is the altitude of *Polaris* (the North Star) above the northern horizon for observer *A*?

(1) 0°           (3) 80°
(2) 10°          (4) 90°

40 Which two observers would be experiencing the same apparent solar time?

(1) *A* and *C*           (3) *B* and *E*
(2) *B* and *C*           (4) *D* and *E*

Base your answers to questions 41 through 43 on the diagram below, which shows a model of the apparent path and position of the Sun in relation to an observer at four different locations, *A, B, C,* and *D,* on Earth's surface on the dates indicated. The zenith (z) and the actual position of the Sun in the model at the time of the observation are shown. [The zenith is the point directly over the observer.]

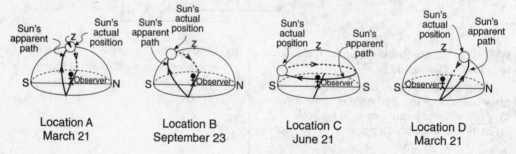

| Location A | Location B | Location C | Location D |
| March 21 | September 23 | June 21 | March 21 |

41 According to the Sun's actual position shown in the diagrams, the most intense insolation is being received by the observer at location

(1) *A*           (3) *C*
(2) *B*           (4) *D*

42 Where on Earth's surface is the observer at location *C* located?

(1) at the Equator
(2) at the South Pole
(3) at the North Pole
(4) in Oswego, New York

43 From sunrise to sunset at location *B*, the length of the observer's shadow will

(1) increase, only
(2) decrease, only
(3) increase, then decrease
(4) decrease, then increase

Base your answers to questions 44 through 46 on the map below, which shows the location of mid-ocean ridges and the age of some oceanic bedrock near these ridges. Letters *A* through *D* are locations on the surface of the ocean floor.

Age of Rocks on the Sea Bottom Relative to Ridges

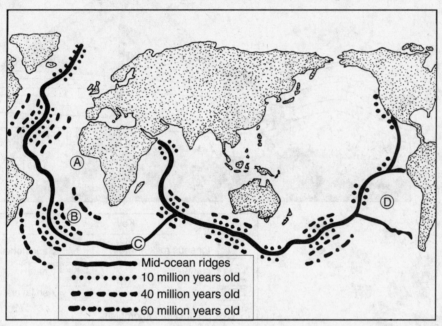

44 What is the most probable age, in millions of years, of the bedrock at location *B*?

   (1) 5             (3) 48

   (2) 12           (4) 62

45 Rising convection currents in the asthenosphere would most likely be under location

   (1) *A*           (3) *C*

   (2) *B*           (4) *D*

46 The age of oceanic bedrock on either side of a mid-ocean ridge is supporting evidence that at the ridges, tectonic plates are

   (1) diverging         (3) locked in place

   (2) converging      (4) being subducted

Base your answers to questions 47 and 48 on the geologic cross section below. The large cone-shaped mountain on Earth's surface is a volcano. Letters *A*, *B*, and *C* represent certain rocks.

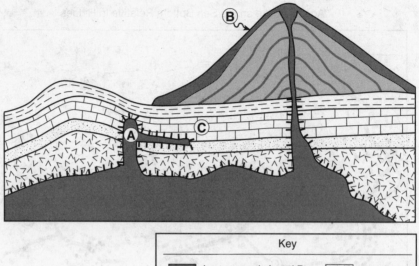

Key

■ Igneous rock A and B        ⬚ Sandstone

⟨⟨⟨ Gabbro        ⊟ Shale

▦ Limestone        ▨ Ash layers

⊥⊥⊥⊥ Contact metamorphism

47 Which statement correctly describes the relative ages of rocks *A* and *C* and gives the best supporting evidence from the cross section?

(1) *A* is younger than *C*, because *A* is a lower sedimentary rock layer.

(2) *A* is younger than *C*, because the intrusion of *A* metamorphosed part of rock layer *C*.

(3) *A* is older than *C*, because *A* has older index fossils.

(4) *A* is older than *C*, because the intrusion of *A* cuts across rock layer *C*.

48 Rock *B* is most likely which type of igneous rock?

(1) granite        (3) pegmatite

(2) peridotite        (4) basalt

Base your answers to questions 49 and 50 on the diagram below, which shows sunlight entering a room through the same window at three different times on the same winter day.

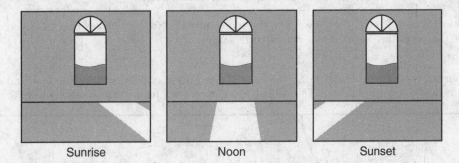

|  |  |  |
|---|---|---|
| Sunrise | Noon | Sunset |

49 The apparent change in the Sun's position shown in the diagram is best explained by

(1) the Sun rotating at a rate of 15° per hour

(2) Earth rotating at a rate of 15° per hour

(3) the Sun's axis tilted at an angle of $23\frac{1}{2}°$

(4) Earth's axis tilted at an angle of $23\frac{1}{2}°$

50 This room is located in a building in New York State. On which side of the building is the window located?

(1) north          (3) east

(2) south          (4) west

## Part B–2

### Answer all questions in this part.

*Directions* (51–60): Record your answers in the spaces provided in your answer booklet. Some questions may require the use of the *Earth Science Reference Tables*.

Base your answers to questions 51 through 54 on the topographic map below. Points *A*, *B*, *Y*, and *Z* are reference points on the topographic map. The symbol ▲533 represents the highest elevation on Aurora Hill.

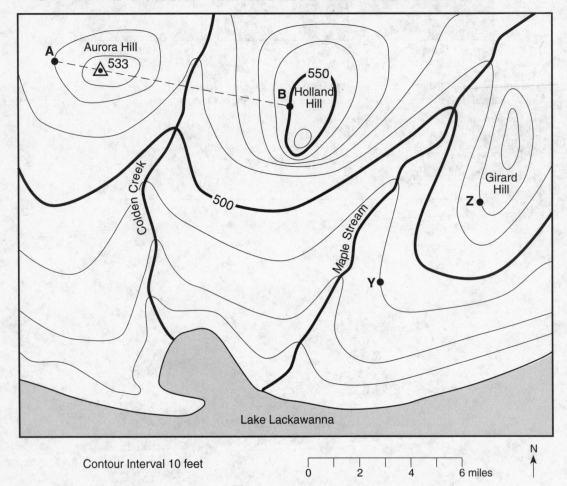

Contour Interval 10 feet

51 State the general compass direction in which Maple Stream is flowing.   [1]

52 Calculate the gradient between points *Y* and *Z* on the map, and label the answer with the correct units.   [2]

53 Describe the evidence shown on the map that indicates that the southern side of Holland Hill has the steepest slope.  [1]

54 On the grid provided *in your answer booklet,* construct a topographic profile from point *A* to point *B* by following the directions below.

   *a* Plot the elevation along line *AB* by marking with an **X** *each* point where a contour line is crossed by line *AB*. Points *A* and *B* have been plotted for you.  [2]

   *b* Complete the profile by correctly connecting the plotted points with a smooth, curved line.  [1]

55 The cross section below illustrates the normal pattern of sediments deposited where a stream enters a lake. Letter *X* represents a particular type of sediment.

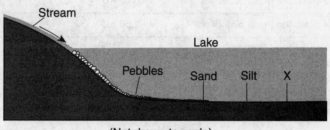

(Not drawn to scale)

   *a* Briefly explain why deposition of sediment usually occurs where a stream enters a lake.  [1]

   *b* Name the type of sediment most likely represented by letter *X*.  [1]

Base your answers to questions 56 and 57 on the temperature field map provided *in your answer booklet.* The map shows air temperatures, in degrees Fahrenheit, recorded at the same time at weather stations across North America. The air temperature at location *A* has been deliberately left blank.

56 On the map provided *in your answer booklet,* use smooth, curved solid lines to draw the 30°F, 40°F, and 50°F isotherms.  [2]

57 What is the most probable air temperature at location *A*?  [1]

Base your answers to questions 58 through 60 on the information, data table, and diagram below and on your knowledge of Earth science.

Astronomers have discovered strong evidence for the existence of three large extrasolar (outside our solar system) planets that orbit *Upsilon Andromedae*, a star located 44 light years from Earth. The three planets are called planet *B*, planet *C*, and planet *D*. Some of the information gathered about these three new planets is shown in the table below. The period of revolution for planet *C* has been deliberately left blank.

**Characteristics of Planets *B*, *C*, and *D* Orbiting Star *Upsilon Andromedae***

| Planet | Mass | Distance from Upsilon Andromedae | Period of Revolution |
|--------|------|----------------------------------|----------------------|
| *B* | $\frac{3}{4}$ of the mass of Jupiter | 0.06 AU | 4.6 Earth days |
| *C* | 2 times the mass of Jupiter | 0.83 AU | |
| *D* | 4 times the mass of Jupiter | 2.50 AU | 3.5 to 4.0 Earth years |

[1 AU = average distance of Earth from the Sun]

The diagram below compares a part of our solar system to the *Upsilon Andromedae* planetary system. Planet distances from their respective star and the relative size of each planet are drawn to scale. [The scale for planet distances is not the same scale used for planet size.]

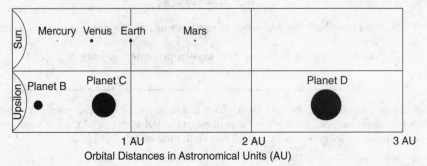

Orbital Distances in Astronomical Units (AU)

58 Planet *D*'s diameter is 10 times greater than Earth's diameter. What planet in our solar system has a diameter closest in size to the diameter of planet *D*?   [1]

59 As planet *B* travels in its orbit, describe the change in orbital velocity of planet *B* as the distance between *Upsilon Andromedae* and planet *B* *decreases*.   [1]

60 If our solar system had a planet located at the same distance from the Sun as planet *C* is from *Upsilon Andromedae*, what would be its approximate period of revolution?   [1]

## Part C

### Answer all questions in this part.

*Directions* (61–75): Record your answers in the spaces provided in your answer booklet. Some questions may require the use of the *Earth Science Reference Tables*.

Base your answers to questions 61 and 62 on the information below and on your knowledge of Earth science.

### Howe Caverns

Many scientists believe that the formation of the rocks in which Howe Caverns is now found began millions of years ago. At that time, an ocean covered the eastern region of New York State. Hundreds of feet of calcium carbonate ($CaCO_3$) sediments were deposited in layers along the edge of this ocean. These layers eventually formed the sedimentary rock limestone, which makes up the walls of today's Howe Caverns.

Much later, tectonic forces raised this region of New York State above sea level exposing the rock to weathering and erosion. These tectonic forces cracked the thick limestone, creating pathways for groundwater to infiltrate and gradually increase the size of the cracks. Eventually some of the larger cracks provided pathways for the underground stream, which carved the winding passages of Howe Caverns seen today.

61 State *two* processes that caused these sediments to become limestone.    [2]

62 Identify one method that could be used to determine that the walls of Howe Caverns are made of limestone.    [1]

Base your answers to questions 63 through 66 on the passage and map below and on your knowledge of Earth science. The passage provides some information about the sediments under Portland, Oregon, and the map shows where Portland is located.

### Bad seismic combination under Portland: Earthquake faults and jiggly sediment

Using a technique called seismic profiling, researchers have found evidence of ancient earthquake faults under Portland, Oregon. The faults may still be active, a USGS [United States Geological Survey] seismologist will announce tomorrow.

The research also turned up a 250-foot deep layer of silt and mud, deep under the city, which may have been caused by a catastrophic ice dam break some 15,000 years ago.

The two findings could together mean bad news, as soft sediment is known to amplify ground shaking during strong earthquakes. In the 1989 San Francisco earthquake, much of the damage to buildings was caused by liquefaction, a shaking and sinking of sandy, water-saturated soil along waterways. . . .

— Robert Roy Britt
excerpted from
"Bad sesimic combination under Portland:
Earthquake faults and jiggly sediment"
explorezone.com 05/03/99

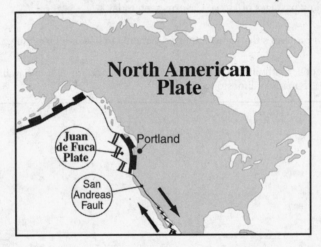

63 Explain why Portland is likely to experience a major earthquake.   [1]

64 Why is the presence of a layer of silt and mud deep under the city a danger to Portland?   [1]

65 Describe one precaution that can be taken to prevent or reduce property damage in preparation for a future earthquake in Portland.   [1]

66 What type of tectonic plate boundary is shown at the San Andreas Fault?   [1]

Base your answers to questions 67 and 68 on the diagram of the ellipse below.

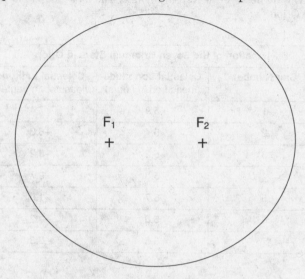

67 Calculate the eccentricity of the ellipse to the *nearest thousandth*.   [1]

68 State how the eccentricity of the given ellipse compares to the eccentricity of the orbit of Mars.   [1]

Base your answers to questions 69 through 72 on your knowledge of Earth science and on the table below, which lists the seven brightest stars, numbered 1 through 7, in the constellation Orion. This constellation can be seen in the winter sky by an observer in New York State. The table shows the celestial coordinates for the seven numbered stars of Orion.

| Location of the Seven Brightest Stars in Orion | | |
|---|---|---|
| Star Number | Celestial Longitude (measured in hours) | Celestial Latitude (measured in degrees) |
| 1 | 5.9 | +7.4 |
| 2 | 5.4 | +6.3 |
| 3 | 5.2 | −8.2 |
| 4 | 5.8 | −9.7 |
| 5 | 5.7 | −1.9 |
| 6 | 5.6 | −1.2 |
| 7 | 5.5 | −0.3 |

69 On the grid provided *in your answer booklet*, graph the data shown in the table by following the steps below.

   *a* Mark with an **X**, the position of *each* of the seven stars. Write the number of the plotted star beside each **X**. The first star has been plotted for you.    [2]

   *b* Show the apparent shape of Orion by connecting the **X**s in the following order:

   $$5 - 1 - 2 - 7 - 3 - 4 - 5 - 6 - 7 \quad [1]$$

70 Star 1 plotted on the grid is the star *Betelgeuse*. Star 3 plotted on the grid is the star *Rigel*. How do the temperature and luminosity of *Betelgeuse* compare to the temperature and luminosity of *Rigel*?    [1]

71 The seven stars of the constellation Orion that were plotted are located within our galaxy. Name the galaxy in which the plotted stars of Orion are located.    [1]

72 State one reason why an observer in New York State can never observe the constellation Orion at midnight during July but can observe the constellation Orion at midnight during January.    [1]

Base your answers to questions 73 through 75 on your knowledge of Earth science and on the data table below, which shows the industrial uses of wollastonite, a mineral mined in the eastern Adirondack Mountains of New York State.

**Industrial Uses of Wollastonite in the United States**

| Industrial Uses of Wollastonite | Percent of Total Use |
| --- | --- |
| Plastics | 37 |
| Ceramics | 28 |
| Metallurgy | 10 |
| Paint | 10 |
| Asbestos substitute | 9 |
| Miscellaneous | 6 |

73 On the pie graph provided *in your answer booklet*, complete the graph to show the percent of *each* industrial use of wollastonite. Label *each* section of the pie graph with its industrial use. The percent for Miscellaneous and for Asbestos substitute has been drawn and labeled for you.   [2]

74 Wollastonite forms during the intense metamorphism of a sandy limestone. The expression below shows part of the process that results in the formation of wollastonite.

Metamorphism

$$CaCO_3 \quad + \quad SiO_2 \quad \longrightarrow \quad CaSiO_2 \quad + \quad CO_2$$

Mineral 1       Mineral 2       Wollastonite       Carbon dioxide

a Name the *two* minerals involved in the formation of wollastonite.   [1]
b What *two* conditions normally cause intense metamorphism?   [1]

75 Identify the geologic age of the New York State Adirondack Mountain bedrock in which wollastonite deposits are found.   [1]

The University of the State of New York

REGENTS HIGH SCHOOL EXAMINATION

# PHYSICAL SETTING
# EARTH SCIENCE

**Thursday,** June 19, 2003 — 1:15 to 4:15 p.m., only

## ANSWER SHEET

Student ........................................   Sex: ☐ Male  ☐ Female  Grade ..........

Teacher ....................................   School ....................................

**Record your answers to Part A and Part B–1 on this answer sheet.**

| Part A | | | Part B–1 | |
|---|---|---|---|---|
| 1 .......... | 13 .......... | 25 .......... | 36 .......... | 44 .......... |
| 2 .......... | 14 .......... | 26 .......... | 37 .......... | 45 .......... |
| 3 .......... | 15 .......... | 27 .......... | 38 .......... | 46 .......... |
| 4 .......... | 16 .......... | 28 .......... | 39 .......... | 47 .......... |
| 5 .......... | 17 .......... | 29 .......... | 40 .......... | 48 .......... |
| 6 .......... | 18 .......... | 30 .......... | 41 .......... | 49 .......... |
| 7 .......... | 19 .......... | 31 .......... | 42 .......... | 50 .......... |
| 8 .......... | 20 .......... | 32 .......... | 43 .......... | |
| 9 .......... | 21 .......... | 33 .......... | | |
| 10 .......... | 22 .......... | 34 .......... | | |
| 11 .......... | 23 .......... | 35 .......... | | |
| 12 .......... | 24 .......... | | | |

Part B–1 Score

Part A Score

**Write your answers to Part B–2 and Part C in your answer booklet.**

**The declaration below should be signed when you have completed the examination.**

I do hereby affirm, at the close of this examination, that I had no unlawful knowledge of the questions or answers prior to the examination and that I have neither given nor received assistance in answering any of the questions during the examination.

_____

Signature

**The University of the State of New York**

REGENTS HIGH SCHOOL EXAMINATION

# PHYSICAL SETTING
# EARTH SCIENCE

**Thursday,** June 19, 2003 — 1:15 to 4:15 p.m., only

## ANSWER BOOKLET

☐ Male

Student . . . . . . . . . . . . . . . . . . . . . . . . . . . . . . . . . . . . .    Sex: ☐ Female

Teacher . . . . . . . . . . . . . . . . . . . . . . . . . . . . . . . . . . . . . . . . . . .

School . . . . . . . . . . . . . . . . . . . . . . . . . . . . . . . . . .    Grade . . . . . . . . .

Answer all questions in Part B–2 and Part C. Record your answers
in this booklet.

| | Performance Test Score (Maximum Score: 23) |
|---|---|

| Part | Maximum Score | Student's Score |
|---|---|---|
| A | 35 | |
| B–1 | 15 | |
| B–2 | 15 | |
| C | 20 | |

| | |
|---|---|
| **Total Written Test Score** (Maximum Raw Score: 85) | |
| **Final Score** (from conversion chart) | |

Raters' Initials:

Rater 1 . . . . . . . . . .    Rater 2 . . . . . . . . . .

---

| Part B–2 | For Raters Only |
|---|---|
| 51 _____ | 51 ☐ |
| 52 Gradient = _____ | 52 ☐ |
| 53 _____ <br> _____ | 53 ☐ |

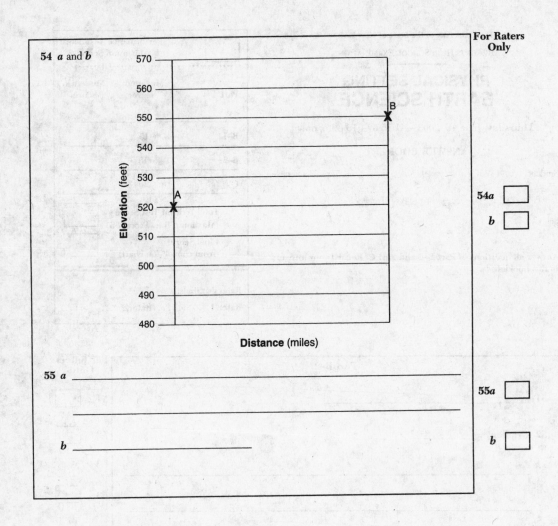

**54** *a* and *b*

Elevation (feet)

570
560
550
540
530
520
510
500
490
480

A

B

Distance (miles)

**55** *a* _____

_____

*b* _____

56

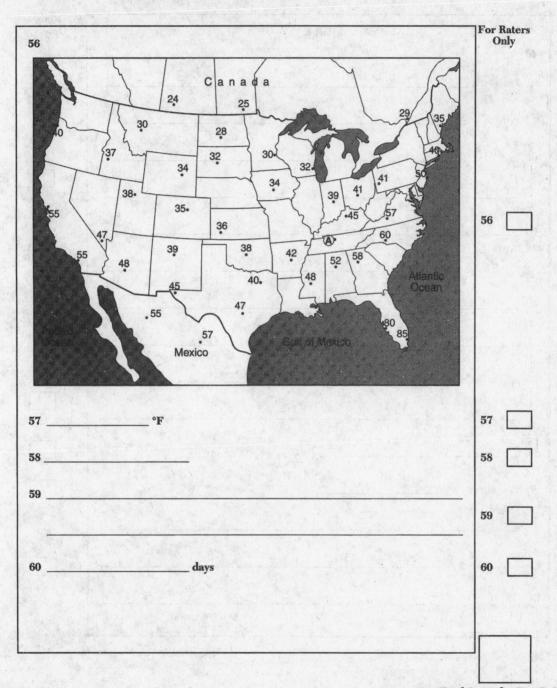

56 □

57 _____ °F          57 □

58 _____            58 □

59 _____

   _____            59 □

60 _____ days       60 □

□

**Total Score for Part B–2**

## Part C

For Raters Only

61  Process 1: _____

    Process 2: _____

61 [ ]

62 _____

   _____

62 [ ]

63 _____

   _____

63 [ ]

64 _____

   _____

64 [ ]

65 _____

   _____

65 [ ]

66 _____

66 [ ]

67  Eccentricity = _____

67 [ ]

68 _____

   _____

   _____

68 [ ]

69 *a* and *b*

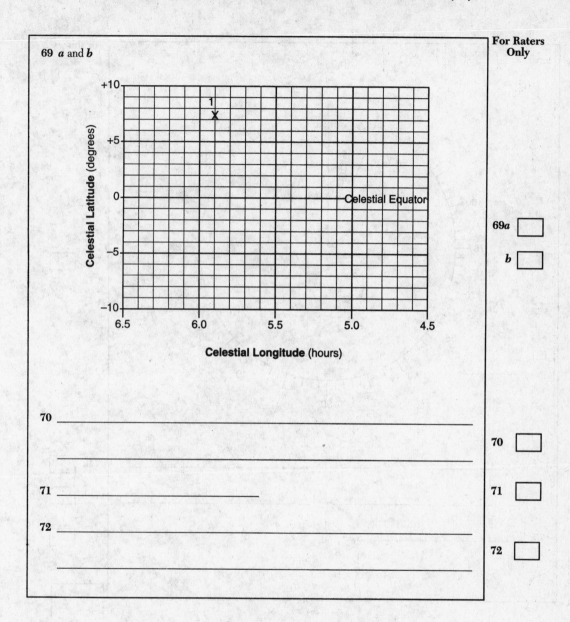

69a ☐

b ☐

70 _____

_____

70 ☐

71 _____

71 ☐

72 _____

72 ☐

_____

**73**

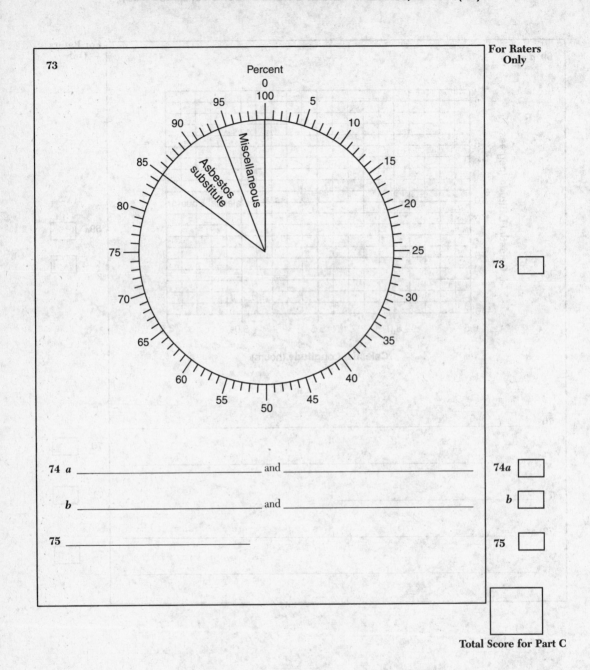

Percent

Miscellaneous

Asbestos
substitute

73 ☐

74 *a* _____ and _____    74*a* ☐

*b* _____ and _____    *b* ☐

75 _____    75 ☐

☐
**Total Score for Part C**

The University of the State of New York

REGENTS HIGH SCHOOL EXAMINATION

# PHYSICAL SETTING
# EARTH SCIENCE

**Friday,** June 18, 2004 — 1:15 to 4:15 p.m., only

This is a test of your knowledge of Earth science. Use that knowledge to answer all questions in this examination. Some questions may require the use of the *Earth Science Reference Tables*. The *Earth Science Reference Tables* are supplied separately. Be certain you have a copy of the *2001 edition* of these reference tables before you begin the examination.

Your answer sheet for Part A and Part B–1 is the last page of this examination booklet. Turn to the last page and fold it along the perforations. Then, slowly and carefully, tear off your answer sheet and fill in the heading.

The answers to the questions in Part B–2 and Part C are to be written in your separate answer booklet. Be sure to fill in the heading on the front of your answer booklet.

You are to answer *all* questions in all parts of this examination according to the directions provided in the examination booklet. Record your answers to the Part A and Part B–1 multiple-choice questions on your separate answer sheet. Write your answers to the Part B–2 and Part C questions in your answer booklet. All work should be written in pen, except for graphs and drawings, which should be done in pencil. You may use scrap paper to work out the answers to the questions, but be sure to record all your answers on your separate answer sheet and in your answer booklet.

When you have completed the examination, you must sign the statement printed at the end of your separate answer sheet, indicating that you had no unlawful knowledge of the questions or answers prior to the examination and that you have neither given nor received assistance in answering any of the questions during the examination. Your answer sheet and answer booklet cannot be accepted if you fail to sign this declaration.

---

Notice. . .

A four-function or scientific calculator and a copy of the *2001 Earth Science Reference Tables* must be available for your use while taking this examination.

---

**DO NOT OPEN THIS EXAMINATION BOOKLET UNTIL THE SIGNAL IS GIVEN.**

## Part A

### Answer all questions in this part.

*Directions* (1–35): For *each* statement or question, write on your separate answer sheet the *number* of the word or expression that, of those given, best completes the statement or answers the question. Some questions may require the use of the *Earth Science Reference Tables*.

1 The motion of a Foucault pendulum provides evidence of

(1) the Sun's rotation    (3) Earth's rotation
(2) the Sun's revolution    (4) Earth's revolution

2 Which form of electromagnetic radiation has a wavelength of $1.0 \times 10^{-3}$ centimeter?

(1) ultraviolet    (3) radio waves
(2) infrared    (4) microwaves

3 The time required for the Moon to show a complete cycle of phases when viewed from Earth is approximately

(1) 1 day    (3) 1 month
(2) 1 week    (4) 1 year

4 Which planet has an orbital eccentricity most like the orbital eccentricity of the Moon?

(1) Pluto    (3) Mars
(2) Saturn    (4) Mercury

5 On June 21, where will the Sun appear to rise for an observer located in New York State?

(1) due west    (3) north of due east
(2) due east    (4) south of due east

6 Which statement best describes sediments deposited by glaciers and rivers?

(1) Glacial deposits and river deposits are both sorted.
(2) Glacial deposits are sorted, and river deposits are unsorted.
(3) Glacial deposits are unsorted, and river deposits are sorted.
(4) Glacial deposits and river deposits are both unsorted.

7 The diagram below shows four different chemical materials escaping from the interior of early Earth.

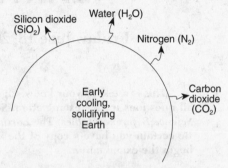

Which material contributed *least* to the early composition of the atmosphere?

(1) $SiO_2$    (3) $N_2$
(2) $H_2O$    (4) $CO_2$

8 The diagram below shows a fossil found in the surface bedrock of New York State.

Centroceras

Which other fossil is most likely to be found in the same age bedrock?

(1) *Phacops*    (3) *Coelophysis*
(2) condor    (4) *Tetragraptus*

9 Soil composed of which particle size usually has the greatest capillarity?

(1) silt    (3) coarse sand
(2) fine sand    (4) pebbles

10 Which sequence correctly shows the relative size of the nine planets of our solar system?

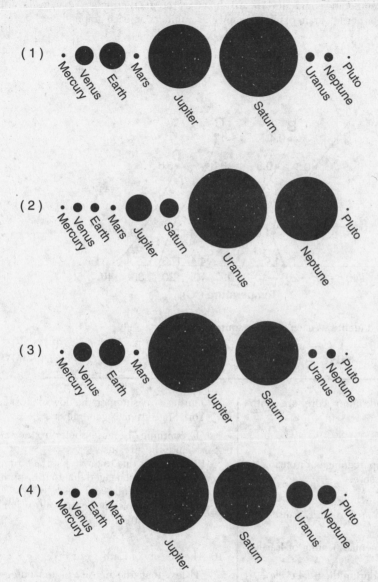

11  The graph below shows changes in the atmosphere occurring above typical air-mass source regions *A*, *B*, *C*, and *D*. Changes in air temperature and altitude are shown as the graphed lines. Changes in water-vapor content, in grams of vapor per kilogram of air, are shown as numbers on each graphed line.

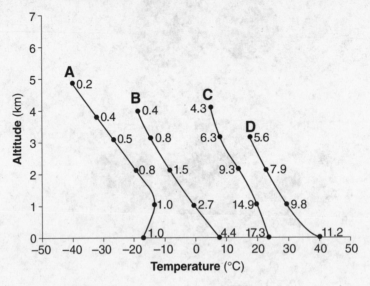

Which list best identifies each air-mass source region?

(1) *A* — cT, *B* — cP, *C* — mP, *D* — mT        (3) *A* — mP, *B* — mT, *C* — cT, *D* — cP
(2) *A* — cP, *B* — mP, *C* — mT, *D* — cT        (4) *A* — mT, *B* — cT, *C* — cP, *D* — mP

---

12  Earth's outer core and inner core are both inferred to be

(1) liquid
(2) solid
(3) composed of a high percentage of iron
(4) under the same pressure

13  Surface winds on Earth are primarily caused by differences in

(1) air density due to unequal heating of Earth's surface
(2) ocean wave heights during the tidal cycle
(3) rotational speeds of Earth's surface at various latitudes
(4) distances from the Sun during the year

14  Which nonfoliated rock forms only in a zone of contact metamorphism?

(1) conglomerate        (3) pegmatite
(2) hornfels            (4) quartzite

15  During a dry summer, the flow of most large New York State streams generally

(1) continues because some groundwater seeps into the streams
(2) increases due to greater surface runoff
(3) remains unchanged due to transpiration from grasses, shrubs, and trees
(4) stops completely because no water runs off into the streams

16  The density of Earth's crust is

(1) less than the density of the outer core but greater than the density of the mantle
(2) greater than the density of the outer core but less than the density of the mantle
(3) less than the density of both the outer core and the mantle
(4) greater than the density of both the outer core and the mantle

17  Which map best represents the direction of surface winds associated with the high- and low-pressure systems?

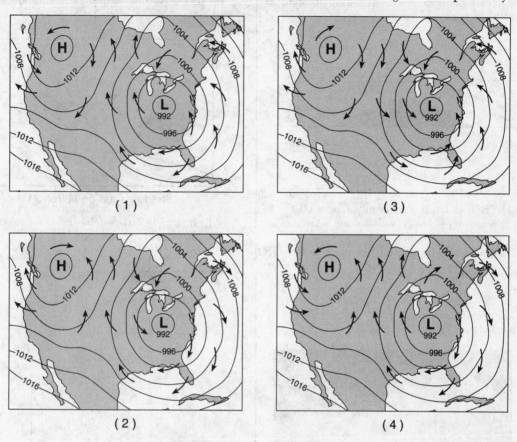

18  In each diagram below, the mass of the star is the same. In which diagram is the force of gravity greatest between the star and the planet shown?

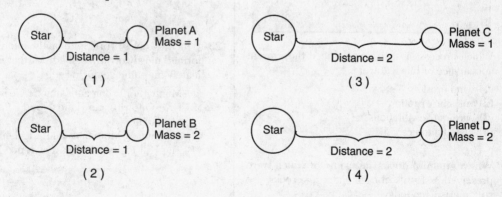

19 The cross section below shows rock layers that underwent crustal movement during an igneous intrusion in the Cretaceous Period.

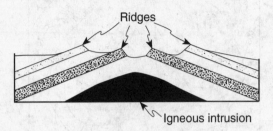

Which statement best describes the cause of the ridges shown?

(1) The rock layers were evenly weathered.
(2) Some rock layers were more resistant to weathering and erosion.
(3) The igneous intrusion flowed over the surface.
(4) More deposition occurred at the ridge sites after uplift.

20 The picture below shows a geological feature in the Kalahari Desert of southwestern Africa.

Which process most likely produced the present appearance of this feature?

(1) wind erosion
(2) volcanic eruption
(3) earthquake vibrations
(4) plate tectonics

21 Which group of organisms, some of which were preserved as fossils in early Paleozoic rocks, are still in existence today?

(1) brachiopods      (3) graptolites
(2) eurypterids      (4) trilobites

22 The diagram below shows the shadow cast by a telephone pole on March 21 at solar noon at a location in New York State.

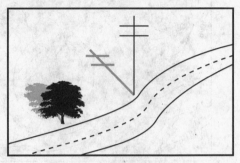

**Shadow Cast on March 21**

Which shadow was cast by the same telephone pole on June 21 at solar noon?

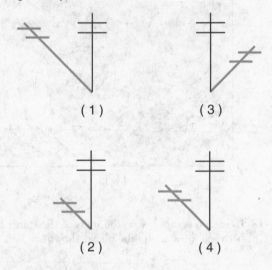

23 Which two New York State landscape regions are formed mostly of surface bedrock that is approximately the same geologic age?

(1) Manhattan Prong and Atlantic Coastal Plain
(2) Erie-Ontario Lowlands and Adirondack Mountains
(3) Adirondack Mountains and Allegheny Plateau
(4) Tug Hill Plateau and St. Lawrence Lowlands

24 The photograph below shows deformed rock structure found on Earth's surface.

Deformed rock structure like this is most often caused by

(1) crustal plate collisions    (3) extrusion of magma
(2) deposition of sediments     (4) glacial movement

25 The seismogram below shows the time that an earthquake *P*-wave arrived at a seismic station in Albany, New York.

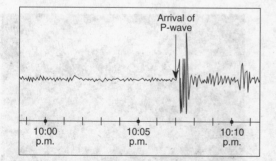

Arrival of P-wave

10:00 p.m.    10:05 p.m.    10:10 p.m.

If the earthquake occurred at exactly 10:00 p.m., approximately how far from the earthquake epicenter was Albany, New York?

(1) 1,900 km    (3) 4,000 km
(2) 3,200 km    (4) 5,200 km

26 On each topographic map below, the straight-line distance from point *A* to point *B* is 5 kilometers. Which topographic map shows the steepest gradient between *A* and *B*?

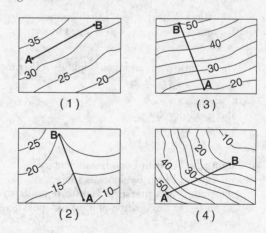

(1)

(3)

(2)

(4)

27 Which seismogram was recorded approximately 4,000 kilometers from an earthquake epicenter?

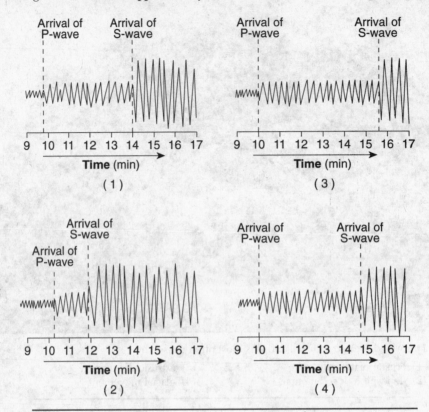

28 When the velocity of a stream suddenly *decreases,* the sediment being transported undergoes an increase in

(1) particle density     (3) deposition
(2) erosion               (4) mass movement

29 When granite melts and then solidifies, it becomes

(1) a sedimentary rock
(2) an igneous rock
(3) a metamorphic rock
(4) sediments

30 During the Permian Period, sedimentary bedrock in the Appalachian Region was subjected to high temperature and pressure. Calcite deposits that had existed in this environment would most likely have formed

(1) schist      (3) marble
(2) gabbro      (4) gneiss

31 The satellite photograph below shows a geologic feature composed of silt, sand, and clay.

The geologic feature shown in the photograph was primarily deposited by which agent of erosion?

(1) glaciers     (3) wave action
(2) wind         (4) running water

32  Which graph shows the relative duration of geologic time for the Precambrian, Paleozoic, Mesozoic, and Cenozoic time intervals?

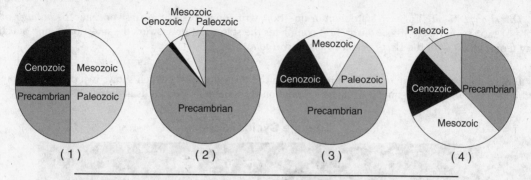

( 1 )            ( 2 )            ( 3 )            ( 4 )

33  The graph below shows the relationship between the cooling time of magma and the size of the crystals produced.

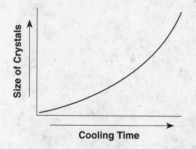

Which graph correctly shows the relative positions of the igneous rocks granite, rhyolite, and pumice?

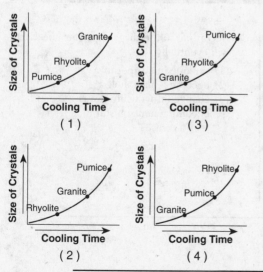

( 1 )            ( 3 )

( 2 )            ( 4 )

34  According to the Geologic History of New York State in the *Earth Science Reference Tables*, the inferred latitude of New York State 362 million years ago was closest to

(1) where it is now      (3) the Equator
(2) the North Pole       (4) 45° south

35  The diagram below shows a tectonic plate boundary.

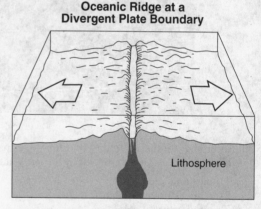

**Oceanic Ridge at a Divergent Plate Boundary**

Lithosphere

Which mantle hot spot is at a plate boundary like the one shown in this diagram?

(1) Hawaii Hot Spot
(2) Yellowstone Hot Spot
(3) Galapagos Hot Spot
(4) Canary Hot Spot

## Part B–1

### Answer all questions in this part.

*Directions* (36–50): For *each* statement or question, write on your separate answer sheet the *number* of the word or expression that, of those given, best completes the statement or answers the question. Some questions may require the use of the *Earth Science Reference Tables*.

Base your answers to questions 36 through 38 on the diagram below, which shows two possible sequences in the life cycle of stars, beginning with their formation from nebular gas clouds in space.

### The Life Cycles of Stars

36 According to the diagram, the life-cycle path followed by a star is determined by the star's initial

(1) mass and size
(2) temperature and origin
(3) luminosity and color
(4) luminosity and structure

37 Stars like Earth's Sun most likely formed directly from a

(1) nebula          (3) red giant
(2) supernova       (4) black dwarf

38 According to the diagram, a star like Earth's Sun will eventually

(1) explode in a supernova
(2) become a black hole
(3) change into a white dwarf
(4) become a neutron star

Base your answers to questions 39 and 40 on the maps below, which show changes in the distribution of land and water in the Mediterranean Sea region that scientists believe took place over a period of 6 million years.

39 Which type of rock was precipitated from seawater as the Mediterranean Sea evaporated between 8 million years ago and 5.5 million years ago?

(1) rock salt        (3) sandstone

(2) basalt          (4) metaconglomerate

40 During which geologic time period did the changes shown in the maps take place?

(1) Cambrian      (3) Permian

(2) Cretaceous    (4) Neogene

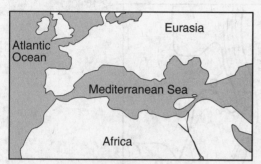

**About 10 Million Years Ago**

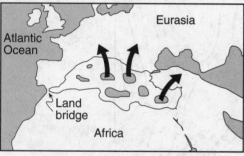

**About 8 to 5.5 Million Years Ago**
**Evaporation from Mediterranean Sea**

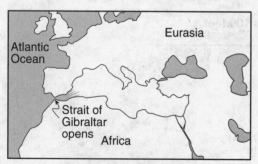

**About 4 Million Years Ago**
**Mediterranean Sea Refills**
**with Atlantic Ocean Water**

Base your answers to questions 41 through 45 on the maps below. Points A, B, C, X, and Y are locations on the topographic map. The small map identifies the New York State region shown in the topographic map.

### Topographic Map

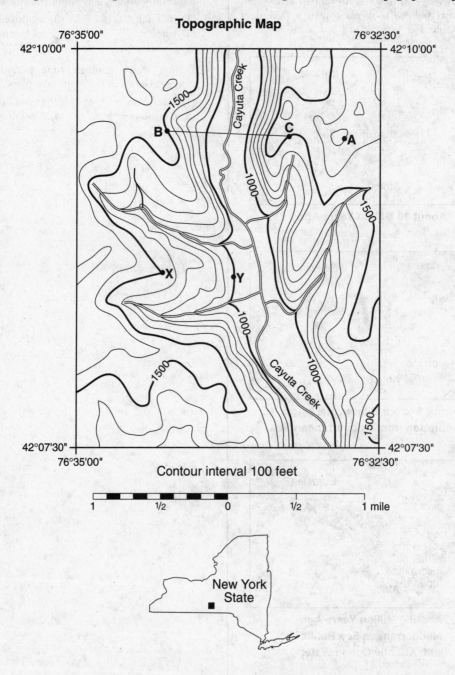

Contour interval 100 feet

New York State

41  Which graph best represents the profile from point *B* to point *C*?

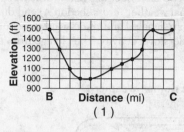

( 1 )

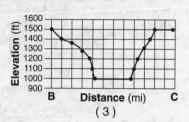

( 3 )

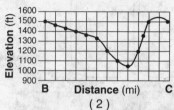

( 2 )

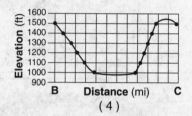

( 4 )

42  What is the elevation of point *A* on the topographic map?

(1)  1,700 ft          (3)  1,600 ft
(2)  1,650 ft          (4)  1,550 ft

43  What is the approximate gradient between point *X* and point *Y*?

(1)  100 ft/mi          (3)  500 ft/mi
(2)  250 ft/mi          (4)  1,000 ft/mi

44  At the end of the Ice Age, the valley now occupied by Cayuta Creek was a channel for southward flowing glacial meltwater. Into which present-day river valley did this meltwater most likely flow?

(1)  Hudson River
(2)  Genesee River
(3)  Delaware River
(4)  Susquehanna River

45  Which evidence best supports the inference that the meltwater river that once occupied the Cayuta Creek valley was larger than the modern Cayuta Creek?

(1)  The modern Cayuta Creek occupies a V-shaped valley.
(2)  The valley floor is wider than the modern Cayuta Creek.
(3)  The modern Cayuta Creek lacks meanders and a flood plain.
(4)  The tributary streams meet the modern Cayuta Creek at nearly right angles.

Base your answers to questions 46 through 50 on the two cross sections below, which represent the Pacific Ocean and the atmosphere near the Equator during normal weather (cross section *A*) and during El Niño conditions (cross section *B*). Sea surface temperatures (SST) are labeled and trade-wind directions are shown with arrows. Cloud buildup indicates regions of frequent thunderstorm activity. The change from normal sea level is shown at the side of each diagram.

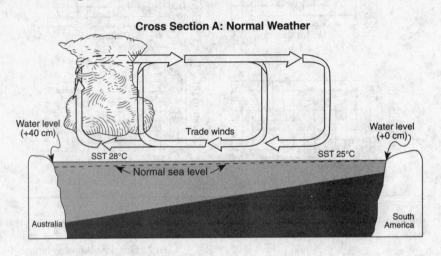

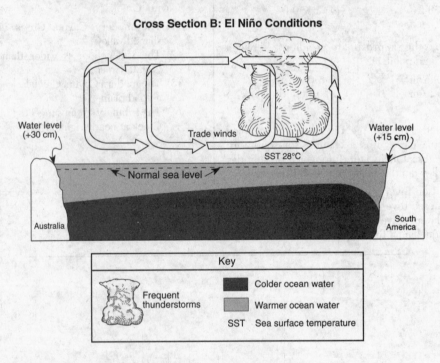

46 Which statement correctly describes sea surface temperatures along the South American coast and Pacific trade winds during El Niño conditions?

(1) The sea surface temperatures are warmer than normal, and Pacific trade winds are from the west.

(2) The sea surface temperatures are warmer than normal, and Pacific trade winds are from the east.

(3) The sea surface temperatures are cooler than normal, and Pacific trade winds are from the west.

(4) The sea surface temperatures are cooler than normal, and Pacific trade winds are from the east.

47 Compared to normal weather conditions, the shift of the trade winds caused sea levels during El Niño conditions to

(1) decrease at both Australia and South America

(2) decrease at Australia and increase at South America

(3) increase at Australia and decrease at South America

(4) increase at both Australia and South America

48 During El Niño conditions, thunderstorms increase in the eastern Pacific Ocean region because the warm, moist air is

(1) less dense, sinking, compressing, and warming

(2) less dense, rising, expanding, and cooling

(3) more dense, sinking, compressing, and warming

(4) more dense, rising, expanding, and cooling

49 The development of El Niño conditions over this region of the Pacific Ocean has caused

(1) changes in worldwide precipitation patterns

(2) the reversal of Earth's seasons

(3) increased worldwide volcanic activity

(4) decreased ozone levels in the atmosphere

50 Earth's entire equatorial climate zone is generally a belt around Earth that has

(1) high air pressure and wet weather

(2) high air pressure and dry weather

(3) low air pressure and wet weather

(4) low air pressure and dry weather

## Part B–2

### Answer all questions in this part.

*Directions* (51–64): Record your answers in the spaces provided in your answer booklet. Some questions may require the use of the *Earth Science Reference Tables*.

51 The atmospheric conditions at a given location are represented by the weather station model below.

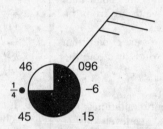

On the lines provided *in your answer booklet*, fill in the correct information for *each* variable listed, based on this weather station model.   [2]

Base your answers to questions 52 through 54 on the diagram provided *in your answer booklet*, which represents the Sun's rays striking Earth at a position in its orbit around the Sun.

52 On the diagram provided *in your answer booklet,* neatly and accurately shade the area of Earth that is in darkness.   [1]

53 On the diagram provided *in your answer booklet,* draw the line of latitude that is receiving the Sun's direct perpendicular rays on this date.   [1]

54 What month of the year is represented by the diagram?   [1]

---

55 The diagram provided *in your answer booklet* shows the Sun, the Moon, and Earth in line with one another in space. On the diagram, draw *two* dots (•) on the surface of Earth to indicate the locations where the highest ocean tides are most likely occurring.   [1]

56 Using the "Luminosity and Temperature of Stars" graph in the *Earth Science Reference Tables*, list the five stars below in order of *decreasing* relative luminosity, with letter *a* being the brightest.   [1]

*Aldebaran, Betelgeuse, Polaris, Sirius,* the Sun

Base your answers to questions 57 through 61 on the geologic cross section provided *in your answer booklet,* which represents an outcrop of various types of bedrock and bedrock features in Colorado.

57 On the cross section provided *in your answer booklet,* indicate with arrows the direction of movement on *both* sides of the fault.   [1]

58 According to this cross section, what is the amount of vertical movement of the shale along the fault? Express your answer to the *nearest tenth of a meter.*   [1]

59 Place the geologic events listed *in your answer booklet* in order by numbering them from oldest (1) to youngest (4).   [1]

60 The shale and sandstone layers both contain fossilized leaves from the *Fagopsis* tree, an index fossil for the Oligocene Epoch. State a possible age for these rock layers, in million years.   [1]

61 The vesicular basalt includes zircon crystals containing the radioactive isotope U-235, which disintegrates to the stable isotope Pb-207. The zircon crystals have 98.44% of the original U-235 remaining, and 1.56% has decayed to Pb-207. Based on the table below, how many half-lives have elapsed since the formation of these crystals?   [1]

| Percent of U-235 Remaining | Percent Decayed to Pb-207 | Half-Lives Elapsed |
|---|---|---|
| 99.22 | 0.78 | $\frac{1}{64}$ |
| 98.44 | 1.56 | $\frac{1}{32}$ |
| 96.88 | 3.12 | $\frac{1}{16}$ |
| 93.75 | 6.25 | $\frac{1}{8}$ |
| 87.50 | 12.5 | $\frac{1}{4}$ |
| 75.0 | 25.0 | $\frac{1}{2}$ |
| 50.0 | 50.0 | 1 |
| 37.5 | 62.5 | $1\frac{1}{2}$ |
| 25.0 | 75.0 | 2 |
| 12.5 | 87.5 | 3 |
| 6.25 | 93.75 | 4 |

Base your answers to questions 62 through 64 on diagram 1 below and on diagram 2 *in your answer booklet,* which show some constellations in the night sky viewed by a group of students. Diagram 1 below shows the positions of the constellations at 9:00 p.m. Diagram 2 *in your answer booklet* shows their positions two hours later.

**Diagram 1 — 9:00 p.m.**

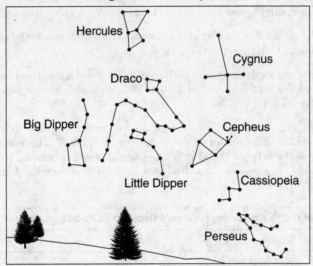

62 Circle *Polaris* on diagram 2 provided *in your answer booklet.* [1]

63 In which compass direction were the students facing? [1]

64 Describe the apparent direction of movement of the constellations Hercules and Perseus during the two hours between student observations. [1]

## Part C

### Answer all questions in this part.

*Directions* (65–81): Record your answers in the spaces provided in your answer booklet. Some questions may require the use of the *Earth Science Reference Tables*.

65 The sequence of diagrams below shows how coal is formed. Describe the material and *two* processes involved in the formation of coal.   [2]

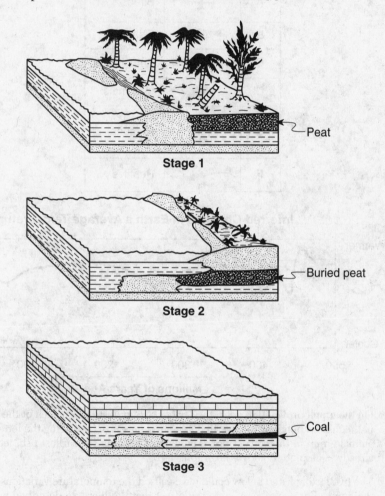

Peat

**Stage 1**

Buried peat

**Stage 2**

Coal

**Stage 3**

Base your answers to questions 66 and 67 on the table and graph below. The table labeled "Animal Key" shows symbols to represent various animal groups that exist on Earth. The graph shows inferred changes in Earth's average temperatures over the last 500 million years.

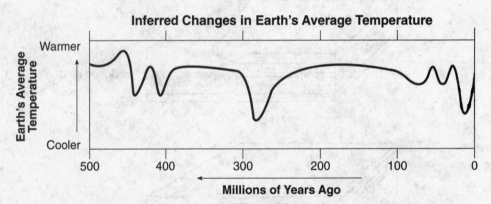

66 On the graph provided *in your answer booklet*, indicate when each of the life-forms in the table is believed to have first appeared on Earth by placing the letter for *each* animal group in the correct box. The correct location for earliest fish, letter *B*, has already been plotted above the graph.    [2]

67 The two factors listed below could have caused the temperature variations shown on the graph. For *each* factor, state the effect that the increase described would have had on Earth's temperature, and explain why that temperature change would have taken place.    [2]

### Factors

*A* Increase in carbon dioxide ($CO_2$) and water vapor ($H_2O$ gas) content of Earth's atmosphere

*B* Increase in volcanic ash in Earth's atmosphere

Base your answers to questions 68 through 71 on the data table below, which shows recorded information for a major Atlantic hurricane. Use the map provided *in your answer booklet* to answer questions 68 and 69.

**Hurricane Data**

| Date | Time | Latitude | Longitude | Maximum Winds (knots) | Air Pressure (mb) |
|------|------|----------|-----------|-----------------------|-------------------|
| Sept. 10 | 11:00 a.m. | 19° N | 59° W | 70 | 989 |
| Sept. 11 | 11:00 a.m. | 22° N | 62° W | 95 | 962 |
| Sept. 12 | 11:00 a.m. | 23° N | 67° W | 105 | 955 |
| Sept. 13 | 11:00 a.m. | 24° N | 72° W | 135 | 921 |
| Sept. 14 | 11:00 a.m. | 26° N | 77° W | 125 | 932 |
| Sept. 15 | 11:00 a.m. | 30° N | 79° W | 110 | 943 |

68 Using the latitude and longitude data in the table, place an **X** on the map provided *in your answer booklet* for *each* location of the hurricane during these 6 days. Connect all the **X**s with a solid line.    [1]

69 Label the September 15 (9/15) position of the hurricane on the map. Starting from this plotted position on September 15, draw a dashed line on the map provided *in your answer booklet* to indicate the storm's most likely path for the next 5 days.   [1]

70 Identify the weather instrument used to measure the air pressure associated with this hurricane.   [1]

71 Describe the relationship between air pressure and wind speed associated with this hurricane.   [1]

_____

Base your answers to questions 72 and 73 on the weather map provided *in your answer booklet*, which shows a large white band of clouds moving toward the southeast. The line shown in the middle of the white cloud band is the frontal boundary between a cP air mass and an mT air mass. Two large arrows show the direction the front is moving.

72 On the frontal boundary line on the weather map provided *in your answer booklet,* draw the weather front symbol to represent the front moving toward the southeast. [1]

73 On the same weather map, place an **X** centered on the geographic region that was most likely the source of the warm, moist (mT) air mass.    [1]

_____

Base your answers to questions 74 through 79 on the reading passage and maps below and on your knowledge of Earth science. The enlarged map shows the location of volcanoes in Colombia, South America.

### Fire and Ice — and Sluggish Magma

On the night of November 13, 1985, Nevado del Ruiz, a 16,200-foot (4,938 meter) snow-capped volcano in northwestern Colombia, erupted. Snow melted, sending a wall of mud and water raging through towns as far as 50 kilometers away, and killing 25,000 people.

Long before disaster struck, Nevado del Ruiz was marked as a trouble spot. Like Mexico City, where an earthquake killed at least 7,000 people in October 1985, Nevado del Ruiz is located along the Ring of Fire. This ring of islands and the coastal lands along the edge of the Pacific Ocean are prone to volcanic eruptions and crustal movements.

The ring gets its turbulent characteristics from the motion of the tectonic plates under it. The perimeter of the Pacific, unlike that of the Atlantic, is located above active tectonic plates. Nevado del Ruiz happens to be located near the junction of four plate boundaries. In this area an enormous amount of heat is created, which melts the rock 100 to 200 kilometers below Earth's surface and creates magma.

Nevado del Ruiz hadn't had a major eruption for 400 years before this tragedy. The reason: sluggish magma. Unlike the runny, mafic magma that makes up the lava flows of oceanic volcanoes such as those in Hawaii, the magma at this type of subduction plate boundary tends to be sticky and slow moving, forming the rock andesite when it cools. This andesitic magma tends to plug up the opening of the volcano. It sits in a magma chamber underground with pressure continually building up. Suddenly, tiny cracks develop in Earth's crust, causing the pressure to drop. This causes the steam and other gases dissolved in the magma to violently expand, blowing the magma plug free. Huge amounts of ash and debris are sent flying, creating what is called an explosive eruption.

Oddly enough, the actual eruption of Nevado del Ruiz didn't cause most of the destruction. It was caused not by lava but by the towering walls of sliding mud created when large chunks of hot ash and pumice mixed with melted snow.

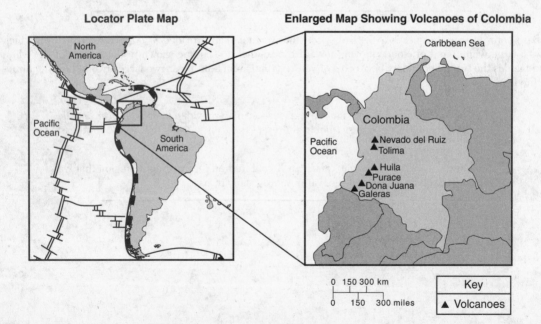

**Locator Plate Map**

**Enlarged Map Showing Volcanoes of Colombia**

74 What are the names of the *four* tectonic plates located near the Nevado del Ruiz volcano?   [1]

75 What caused most of the destruction associated with the eruption of Nevado del Ruiz?   [1]

76 What caused the magma to expand, blowing the magma plug free?   [1]

77 Vesicular texture is very common in igneous rocks formed during andesitic eruptions. Explain how this texture is formed.   [1]

78 Why are eruptions of Nevado del Ruiz generally more explosive than most Hawaiian volcanic eruptions?   [1]

79 Describe one emergency preparation that may reduce the loss of life from a future eruption of the Nevado del Ruiz volcano.   [1]

---

**GO RIGHT ON TO THE NEXT PAGE ⇨**

Base your answers to questions 80 and 81 on the cross section below. The cross section represents a part of Texas where weakly cemented sandstone is exposed at the surface. The mineral cement holding the sandstone grains together is calcite. Area $X$ is a circular depression of loose sand that has been partially removed by prevailing winds. Sand dunes have developed downwind from depression $X$.

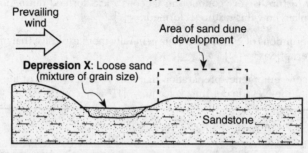

**Present Day, Dry Climate**

80 On the diagram of the area of sand dune development provided *in your answer booklet*, draw a sketch showing the general sideview of a sand dune formed by a wind blowing in the direction indicated. Your sketch should clearly show any variations in the slope of the sides of the dune.   [1]

81 The cross section below shows this same area of Texas near the end of the last ice age when this area had a much wetter climate. More infiltration of rainwater was occurring at area $X$. Scientists infer that depression $X$ was an area where slightly acidic rainwater collected and infiltrated into the sandstone.

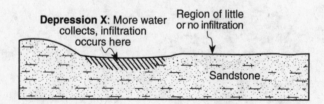

**Late Pleistocene, Wetter Climate**

Describe the effect that the slightly acidic infiltrating water had on the calcite cement holding the sandstone together.   [1]

The University of the State of New York

REGENTS HIGH SCHOOL EXAMINATION

# PHYSICAL SETTING
# EARTH SCIENCE

**Friday,** June 18, 2004 — 1:15 to 4:15 p.m., only

## ANSWER SHEET

Student ............................................. Sex: ☐ Male ☐ Female  Grade ............

Teacher ........................................... School ...................................

**Record your answers to Part A and Part B–1 on this answer sheet.**

| Part A | | | Part B–1 | |
|---|---|---|---|---|
| 1 ............ | 13 ............ | 25 ............ | 36 ............ | 44 ............ |
| 2 ............ | 14 ............ | 26 ............ | 37 ............ | 45 ............ |
| 3 ............ | 15 ............ | 27 ............ | 38 ............ | 46 ............ |
| 4 ............ | 16 ............ | 28 ............ | 39 ............ | 47 ............ |
| 5 ............ | 17 ............ | 29 ............ | 40 ............ | 48 ............ |
| 6 ............ | 18 ............ | 30 ............ | 41 ............ | 49 ............ |
| 7 ............ | 19 ............ | 31 ............ | 42 ............ | 50 ............ |
| 8 ............ | 20 ............ | 32 ............ | 43 ............ | |
| 9 ............ | 21 ............ | 33 ............ | | |
| 10 ............ | 22 ............ | 34 ............ | | |
| 11 ............ | 23 ............ | 35 ............ | | |
| 12 ............ | 24 ............ | | | |

Part B–1 Score

Part A Score

**Write your answers to Part B–2 and Part C in your answer booklet.**

**The declaration below should be signed when you have completed the examination.**

_____

Signature

Tear Here

The University of the State of New York

REGENTS HIGH SCHOOL EXAMINATION

# PHYSICAL SETTING
# EARTH SCIENCE

**Friday,** June 18, 2004 — 1:15 to 4:15 p.m., only

### ANSWER BOOKLET

Student...................................... Sex: ☐ Male / ☐ Female

Teacher ...............................................................

School..................................... Grade .........

**Answer all questions in Part B–2 and Part C. Record your answers in this booklet.**

| | Performance Test Score (Maximum Score: 23) | |
|---|---|---|
| **Part** | **Maximum Score** | **Student's Score** |
| A | 35 | |
| B–1 | 15 | |
| B–2 | 15 | |
| C | 20 | |

**Total Written Test Score (Maximum Raw Score: 85)**

**Final Score (from conversion chart)**

Raters' Initials:

Rater 1 .......... Rater 2 ..........

---

### Part B–2

**For Raters Only**

**51** Air pressure: _____ **mb**

Air temperature: _____ °F

Amount of precipitation during last six hours: _____ inch(es)        **51** ☐

Cloud cover: _____ %

Present weather: _____

**52** and **53**

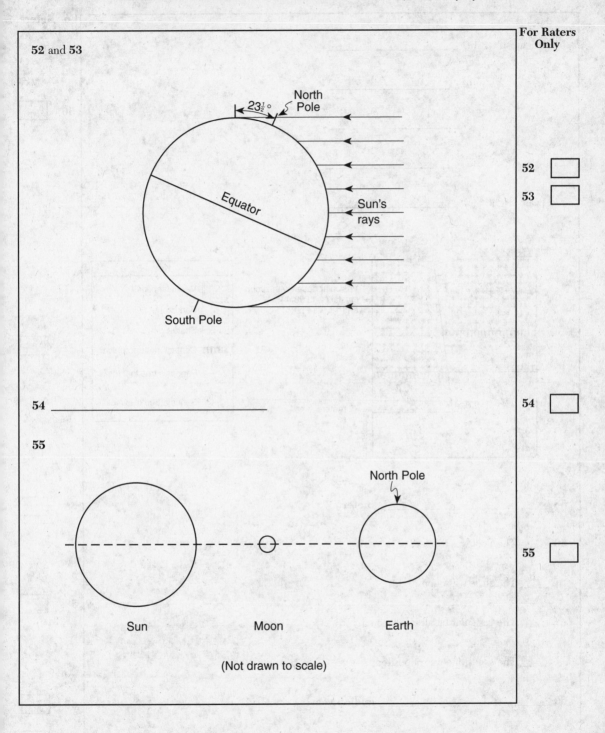

(Not drawn to scale)

54 _____

55

For Raters
Only

**56** Brightest: (a) _____

(b) _____

(c) _____

56 ☐

(d) _____

Least bright: (e) _____

**57**

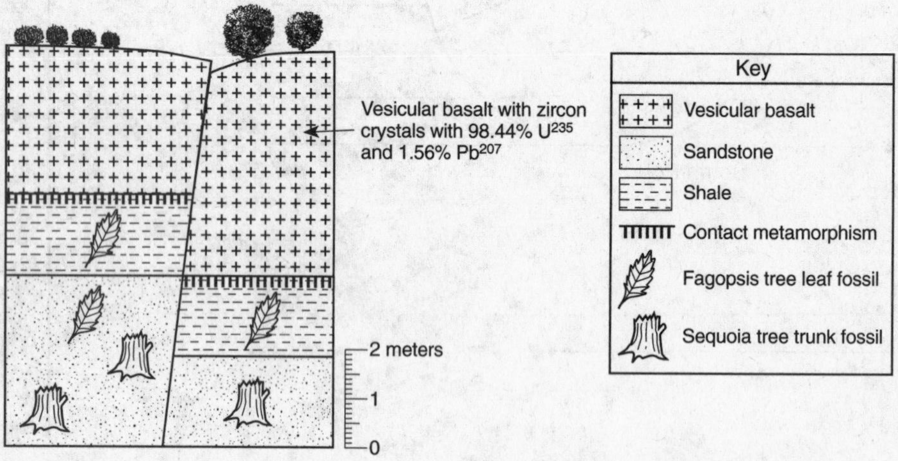

Vesicular basalt with zircon
crystals with 98.44% $U^{235}$
and 1.56% $Pb^{207}$

Key

| | |
|---|---|
| +　+　+ | Vesicular basalt |
| | Sandstone |
| - - - | Shale |
| ⊓⊓⊓⊓ | Contact metamorphism |
| 🍂 | Fagopsis tree leaf fossil |
| 🪵 | Sequoia tree trunk fossil |

57 ☐

— 2 meters
— 1
— 0

**58** _____ **meter(s)**

58 ☐

**59** _____ The fault was formed.

_____ The shale was deposited.

_____ The vesicular basalt was formed.

59 ☐

_____ The sandstone was deposited.

**60** _____ **million years**

60 ☐

**61** _____ **half-lives**

61 ☐

For Raters Only

62

**Diagram 2 — 11:00 p.m.**

Hercules
Cygnus
Draco
Cepheus
Cassiopeia
Little Dipper
Perseus
Big Dipper

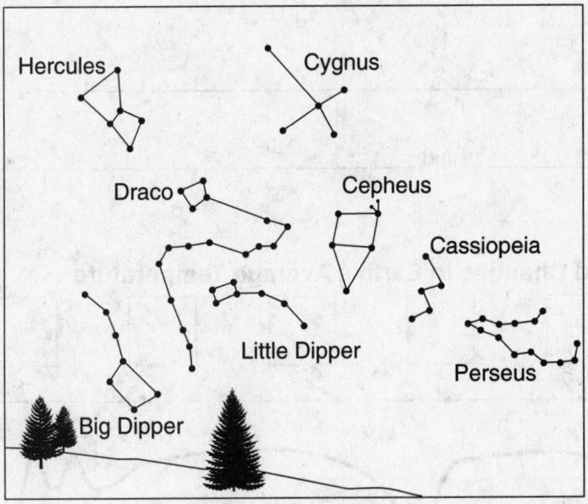

62 ☐

63 ____________________

63 ☐

64 Hercules appears to have moved: ____________________

Perseus appears to have moved: ____________________

64 ☐

**Total Score for Part B–2**

**Part C**

**65** Material: _____

Processes: _____ and _____

**66**

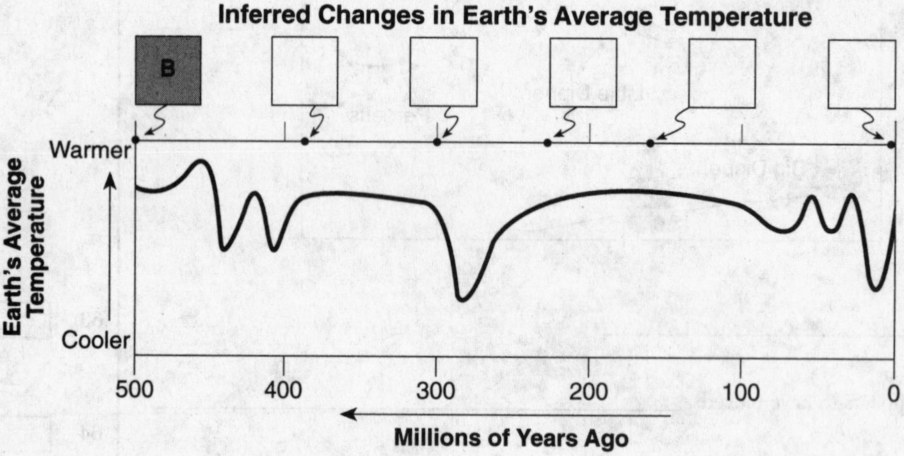

### Inferred Changes in Earth's Average Temperature

**67** Factor *A*:

Effect on Earth's temperature: _____

Why temperature changes: _____

_____

Factor *B*:

Effect on Earth's temperature: _____

Why temperature changes: _____

_____

**68** and **69**

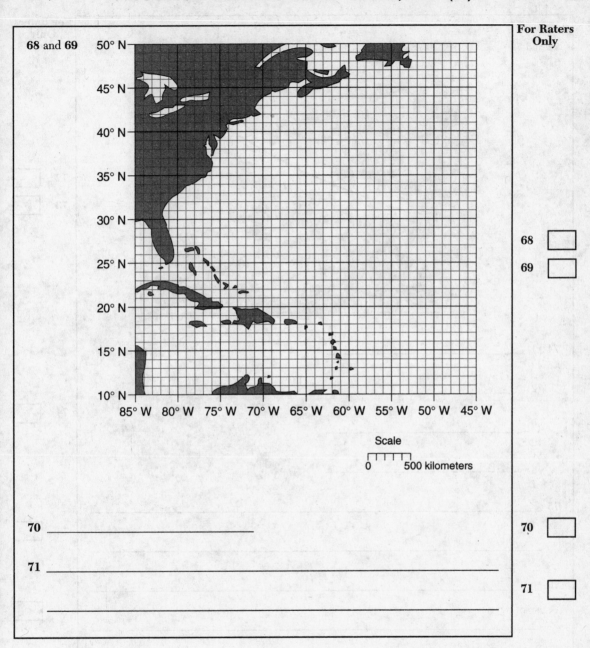

68 ☐

69 ☐

70 _____

71 _____

_____

70 ☐

71 ☐

**72** and **73**

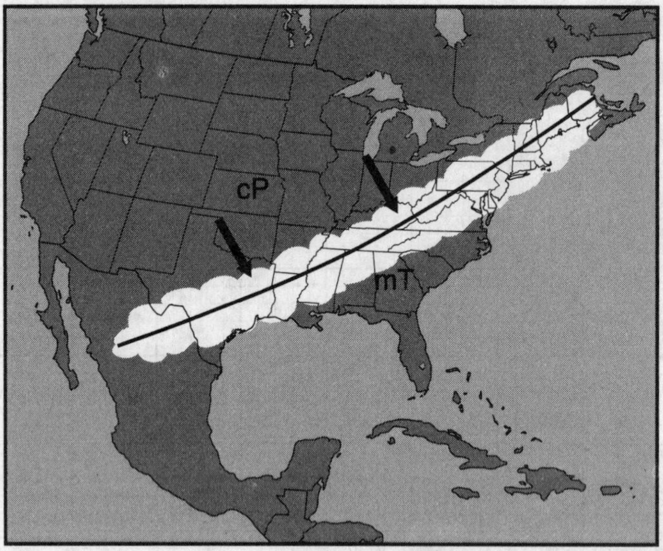

72 ▢

73 ▢

**74** (1) _____

(2) _____

(3) _____

(4) _____

74 ▢

**75** _____

_____

75 ▢

**76** _____

_____

76 ▢

**77** _____

_____

77 ▢

78 _____

_____

79 _____

80

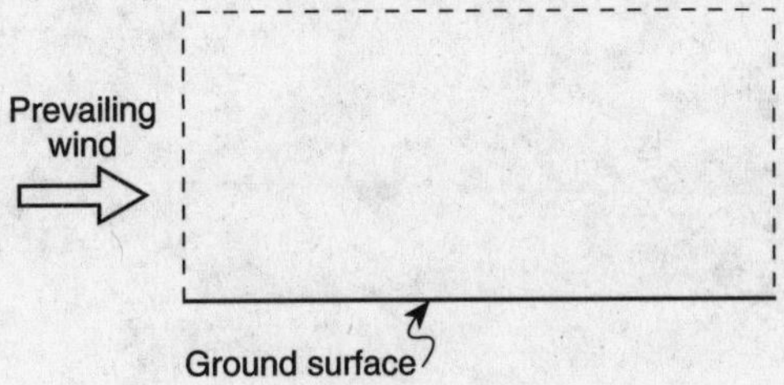

Prevailing
wind
⟹

Ground surface

81 _____

_____

78 ▭

79 ▭

80 ▭

81 ▭

▭

**Total Score for Part C**

# NOTES

# NOTES

# NOTES

# NOTES

# NOTES

# NOTES

# NOTES

# NOTES

# NOTES

# NOTES

# NOTES

# NOTES

# NOTES

# NOTES

# NOTES

NOTES

# NOTES

# NOTES

# NOTES